THE RESTAURANT GUIDE 2023

Restaurant descriptions and feature writing were contributed by Jim Barker, Jackie Bates, Mike Pedley, David Popey, Allen Stidwill and Mark Taylor.

AA Media would like to thank Tracey Freestone, Lauren Havelock, Nicky Hillenbrand, Lin Hutton, Ian Little, Jess Little, Nigel Phillips, David Popey, Julia Powers and Victoria Samways in the preparation of this guide.

Cover design by Austin Taylor and page design by Tom Whitlock.

Printed by Stamperia Artistica Nazionale – Trofarello – TORINO – ITALY.

ISBN: 978-0-7495-8311-8

A05834

Discover restaurants with Rosettes as well as AA-rated hotels, B&Bs and more at www.ratedtrips.com

Contents

Welcome to the AA Restaurant Guide 2023

We are delighted to introduce the 2023 AA Restaurant Guide. Packed full of quality independent restaurants across the UK incorporating the full spectrum of cuisine types and dining styles. From relaxed and casual lunches to the heights of fine dining, and from modern British and classic French dishes to diverse specialities from all over the world.

Although the restaurant industry has been operating as normal throughout 2022, the sector remains very much in recovery mode. Staffing challenges across the whole of the hospitality industry have meant many restaurants have yet to fully re-open, and you may find some are closed for lunch and dinner at the beginning of the week. As always, it's best to check in advance before making a journey that may result in disappointment.

There's no doubt that the ongoing pressures of Covid 19 mean many of us have come to appreciate and value even more the joy that eating out affords us. Restaurants continue to face many challenges, dealing with acute staffing shortages, significant inflation in food prices and other rising operating costs, such as the well documented huge increases in energy bills. That's why it's so important that we continue to support all these fantastic establishments, whose kitchen and front-of-house teams work so tirelessly to give us such amazing experiences.

Restaurant Awards

We are delighted to welcome back our national awards, recognising excellence across the UK and celebrating the achievements of all AA rated restaurants at our AA Hospitality Awards in September. Our award winners are chosen as best in class following our professional inspections, and verified by our Hospitality Awards Panel. The Restaurants of the Year for England, Scotland, Wales and London represent both established and up-and-coming places to eat (see page 22). Our Food Service Award recipient (page 27) represents one of the finest dining experiences in London. The AA Chefs' Chef Award is really special – this is a peer-selected award, voted for by all the establishments that hold a Rosette in this year's guide. Our Lifetime Achievement award for 2022-23 recognises an outstanding chef in John Williams MBE, Executive Chef at The Ritz.

New to the Guide

This year there are over 140 restaurants that have received their Rosettes since the 2022 edition. Most have achieved either one or two Rosettes, but a few have gone straight in at three or four Rosettes. We've spotlighted restaurants who are joining the ranks of multi-Rosette venues (those with 3, 4 or 5 Rosettes) on pages 9-13 so head to those pages to see who they are.

This year you'll also find a feature on some fabulous kitchen gardens. Growing your own fruit and veg is increasingly common among establishments with the room to do so, and there's never been a better time to eat food grown on site. Have a read and see what some of our restaurants have been up to.

Toasting the best

The Notable Wine List accolade (see page 32) singles out restaurants that our inspectors feel show a real passion for, and knowledge of wine. There are 255 notable wine lists throughout the guide – so look out for ![notable wine list].

Always changing

The transient nature of the hospitality industry means that chefs move around all the time, and restaurants may change ownership or style. Unfortunately, during the life of every edition of the guide, some will close.

As any change at the multi-Rosette (3, 4 or 5) level requires a new inspection to verify their award, some of these restaurants appear in the guide with their Rosette level suspended at the time of going to press. Check RatedTrips.com for the latest updates.

Looking ahead

Looking ahead to what the future may bring, you can expect an ever-stronger focus on the environment, as restaurants look to become even more sustainable, including further championing of local and home grown produce, more plant and vegetable-based dishes and a greater use of foraging. English wines – and not just sparkling – will become commonplace on more wine lists, reflecting the strength and depth of UK vineyards and their produce. More outdoor dining spaces will be developed, from domes and terraces to lobster huts. And as 'no shows' (uncancelled reservations) sadly become more prevalent, credit card confirmation, and in some cases deposits, will become the norm.

How we assess for Rosettes

First introduced in 1956, our Rosette award scheme was the first nationwide scheme for assessing the quality of food served by restaurants and hotels. It has been a 5-tier system since 1992.

A consistent approach

The Rosette scheme is an award, not a classification, and although there is necessarily an element of subjectivity when it comes to assessing taste, we aim for a consistent approach throughout the UK. Our awards are made solely on the basis of a meal visit or visits by one or more of our hotel and restaurant inspectors, who have an unrivalled breadth and depth of experience in assessing quality. Essentially, it's a snapshot, whereby the entire meal, including ancillary items (when served) are assessed. Of all the restaurants across the UK, approximately 10% are of a standard worthy of 1 Rosette and above.

Rosette worthiness

For our inspectors, the top and bottom line is the food. The taste of a dish is what counts, and whether it successfully delivers to the diner the promise of the menu. A restaurant is only as good as its worst meal. Although presentation and competent service should be appropriate to the style of the restaurant and the quality of the food, they cannot affect the Rosette assessment as such, either up or down. The summaries opposite indicate what our inspectors look for, but are intended only as guidelines. We are constantly reviewing its award criteria, and competition usually results in an all-round improvement in standards, so it becomes increasingly difficult for restaurants to reach an award level.

The next level

Receiving a Rosette is a huge achievement and something not to be underestimated. We are often asked by chefs and proprietors: "What is the difference between 1 and 5 Rosettes and how can I get to the next level?" We answer that it's how well a chef manages to apply advanced technique while retaining maximum flavour, and assuming an appropriate quality of source ingredients.

While we endeavour to work with the industry and promote great cooking across the UK, it is of paramount importance for chefs to always serve their market first. We recommend they don't chase awards, but see them as something to celebrate when they come along. Where, however, the winning of Rosettes is an aspiration, the simple guidelines, shown opposite, may help. Experiencing our food tastings, enhanced food tastings or signing up to one of the AA Rosette Academies can also give further insight and guidance, but these are separate from the awards process and do not influence any assessments.

Announcements of awards

One and two Rosettes are awarded at the time of inspection. Three and four Rosette awards are announced twice during the year, but never at the time of inspection. Five Rosettes are awarded just once a year and never at the time of inspection.

◉ One Rosette

These restaurants will be achieving standards that stand out in their local area, featuring:

- food prepared with care, understanding and skill
- good quality ingredients
- The same expectations apply to hotel restaurants where guests should be able to eat in with confidence and a sense of anticipation.

◉◉ Two Rosettes

The best local restaurants, which aim for and achieve:

- higher standards
- better consistency
- greater precision apparent in the cooking
- obvious attention to the selection of quality ingredients.

◉◉◉ Three Rosettes

These are outstanding restaurants that achieve standards that demand national recognition well beyond their local area. The cooking will be underpinned by:

- the selection and sympathetic treatment of the highest quality ingredients
- timing, seasoning and the judgment of flavour combinations will be consistently excellent
- these virtues will tend to be supported by other elements such as intuitive service and a well-chosen wine list.

◉◉◉◉ Four Rosettes

Among the top restaurants in the UK where the cooking demands national recognition. These restaurants will exhibit:

- intense ambition
- a passion for excellence
- superb technical skills
- remarkable consistency
- an appreciation of culinary traditions combined with a passionate desire for further exploration and improvement.

◉◉◉◉◉ Five Rosettes

The pinnacle, where the cooking compares with the best in the world. These restaurants will have:

- highly individual voices
- exhibit breathtaking culinary skills and set the standards to which others aspire, yet few achieve.

Using the guide

A few handy tips to help you get the most out of using the guide. We regularly ask restaurants to refresh their information and this is then used alongside updates from our inspection team.

1 Order: Restaurants are listed in country and county order, then by town and then alphabetically within the town. There is an index by restaurant name at the back of the guide.

2 AA Rosette Award: Restaurants can be awarded from 1 to 5 Rosettes (see pages 6–7). 'Rosettes Suspended' indicates that an award of 3 Rosettes or above was suspended shortly before going to press. 'Awaiting Inspection' means a restaurant is due to be inspected soon and Rosettes will be awarded after going to press.

3 Notable Wine List: The 🍷 symbol indicates a wine list chosen as notable by our inspectors (see page 32).

4 Open/Closed: We note if a restaurant is open all year. Otherwise, we list a period or periods when a venue is closed. Check in advance via the venue's website for daily opening times.

5 Chef: The name of the chef(s) is as up-to-date as possible at the time of going to press, but changes in personnel often occur, and may affect both the style and quality of the restaurant.

6 Food Style: A summary of the main cuisine type(s).

---

1 ── Ascot

Restaurant Coworth Park 🌹🌹🌹 **2** **3** NOTABLE WINE LIST
London Road, SL5 7SE
01344 876600
www.coworthpark.com
4 ── Open: All year

Coworth Park is an elegant Georgian mansion with an effortlessly stylishly Palladian frontage, set in 240 acres of parkland and lovely gardens in the heart of rural Berkshire. Public rooms are high-ceilinged and spacious, with thoughtful contemporary design enhancing the classic country-house feel. Work up an appetite by taking on some of the equestrian opportunities – there

Chef: Adam Smith ────── **5**
Food Style: Modern British ── **6**

are horses for riders of all abilities – or something more sedentary in the state-of-the-art spa, before heading to the restaurant. It's a serene space, calmly minimalist with views across the rose terrace. Service is formal but engaging. Executive chef Adam Smith's menus change with the seasons and he finds inspiration for his precise, dextrous and often innovative take on country-house cooking in the hotel's beautiful surroundings and in locally produced ingredients of the highest order. Dishes are picture-perfect and every element is thoughtfully considered.

The top restaurants of 2023

Restaurants with 3, 4 or 5 Rosettes represent the best in the UK. They are often internationally recognised and serve cuisine of the highest standard. The restaurants in this year's list all had 3 or more Rosettes at the time of going to press.

England

Berkshire
The Fat Duck, Bray

Cambridgeshire
Midsummer House Restaurant, Cambridge

Cumbria
L'Enclume, Cartmel

Devon
Lympstone Manor Hotel, Exmouth

Lancashire
Moor Hall Restaurant with Rooms, Ormskirk

London, by postcode
Restaurant Story, SE1
Marcus, SW1
Claude Bosi at Bibendum, SW3
Hélène Darroze at The Connaught, W1
Pollen Street Social, W1
Sketch (Lecture Room & Library), W1
Core by Clare Smyth, W11

Nottinghamshire
Restaurant Sat Bains with Rooms, Nottingham

Oxfordshire
Belmond Le Manoir aux Quat'Saisons, Great Milton

Scotland

Edinburgh
The Kitchin, Edinburgh

Wales

Eglwys Fach
Ynyshir Restaurant & Rooms, Ceredigion

England

Berkshire
Restaurant Coworth Park, Ascot

Buckinghamshire
The Hand & Flowers, Marlow

Cornwall
Paul Ainsworth at No. 6, Padstow
Outlaw's New Road, Port Isaac

Cumbria
Allium at Askham Hall, Askham
Forest Side, Grasmere
HRiSHi at Gilpin Hotel & Lake House, Windermere

Devon
Àclèaf, Plymouth

Gloucestershire
Le Champignon Sauvage, Cheltenham

Greater Manchester
Adam Reid at The French, Manchester
Mana, Manchester

Lancashire
Northcote Restaurant, Langho

Lincolnshire
Winteringham Fields, Winteringham

London, by postcode
Dinner by Heston Blumenthal, SW1
Muse, SW1
Seven Park Place by William Drabble, SW1
The Five Fields, SW3
Restaurant Gordon Ramsay, SW3
Alain Ducasse at The Dorchester, W1
Murano, W1
Ormer Mayfair, W1
The Ritz Restaurant, W1
Social Eating House, W1
The Ledbury, W11

Norfolk
Morston Hall, Blakeney

Nottinghamshire
Alchemilla, Nottingham

Oxfordshire
Orwells, Henley-on-Thames

Rutland
Hambleton Hall, Oakham

Suffolk
Upstairs at the Mill, Newmarket

Surrey
Steve Smith at Latymer,
  Bagshot
Sorrel, Dorking

Sussex, West
Gravetye Manor Hotel,
  West Hoathly

Tyne & Wear
House of Tides,
  Newcastle upon Tyne

West Midlands
Grace & Savour, Solihull
Peel's Restaurant, Solihull

Wiltshire
The Dining Room, Malmesbury

Yorkshire, North
The Angel at Hetton, Hetton
The Black Swan at Oldstead,
  Oldstead

Yorkshire, West
The Man Behind The Curtain,
  Leeds

Channel Islands

Jersey
Ocean Restaurant at
  The Atlantic Hotel,
  St Brelade
Bohemia Restaurant,
  St Helier
Tassili, St Helier

Scotland

Edinburgh
21212, Edinburgh
Number One, The Balmoral,
  Edinburgh
Restaurant Martin Wishart,
  Edinburgh

Perth & Kinross
Andrew Fairlie at Gleneagles,
  Auchterarder
The Glenturret Lalique
  Restaurant, Crieff

Scottish Islands
Edinbane Lodge, Edinbane

Wales

Isle of Anglesey
Sosban & The Old Butcher's
  Restaurant, Menai Bridge

Monmouthshire
The Whitebrook, Whitebrook

Pembrokeshire
The Fernery, Narberth

England

Bedfordshire
Paris House Restaurant,
  Woburn

Berkshire
The Hind's Head, Bray
The Waterside Inn, Bray
The Vineyard, Newbury
The Woodspeen – Restaurant
  and Cookery School, Newbury
The Loch & The Tyne by Adam
  Handling, Old Windsor
L'Ortolan, Shinfield

Buckinghamshire
The Artichoke, Amersham
The Coach, Marlow
The Cliveden Dining Room,
  Taplow

Cambridgeshire
Restaurant 22, Cambridge
The Chubby Castor,
  Peterborough
Prévost @ Haycock, Wansford

Cheshire
Arkle Restaurant, Chester

Cornwall & Isles of Scilly
Hell Bay Hotel, Bryher
New Yard Restaurant, Helston
The Seafood Restaurant,
  Padstow
Kota Restaurant with Rooms,
  Porthleven
Hotel Tresanton, St Mawes

Cumbria
Lake Road Kitchen, Ambleside
The Old Stamp House
  Restaurant, Ambleside
Rothay Manor Hotel, Ambleside
Rogan & Co Restaurant, Cartmel
Pentonbridge Inn, Pentonbridge
Henrock, Windermere
The Samling, Windermere

Derbyshire
Cavendish Hotel, Baslow
Fischer's Baslow Hall, Baslow
The Peacock at Rowsley,
  Rowsley

Devon
Gidleigh Park, Chagford
The Old Inn, Drewsteignton
Sandy Cove Hotel, Ilfracombe
Great Western,
  Moretonhampstead
The Horn of Plenty, Tavistock
The Elephant Restaurant by
  Simon Hulstone, Torquay

Dorset
Summer Lodge Country House
  Hotel, Restaurant & Spa,
  Evershot

Essex
Talbooth Restaurant, Dedham
Haywards Restaurant, Epping
The Flitch of Bacon, Little
  Dunmow

Gloucestershire
Buckland Manor, Buckland
The Greenway Hotel & Spa,
  Cheltenham
Lumière, Cheltenham
The Slaughters Manor House,
  Lower Slaughter
Wilder, Nailsworth
The Feathered Nest Inn,
  Nether Westcote
Lords of the Manor, Upper
  Slaughter

Manchester, Greater
Where the Light Gets In,
  Stockport

Hampshire
36 on the Quay, Emsworth
The Elderflower Restaurant,
  Lymington
Hartnett Holder & Co,
  Lyndhurst

The Fernery, Wales

Hertfordshire
THOMPSON St Albans,
St Albans

Kent
The West House Restaurant
with Rooms, Biddenden
ABode Canterbury, Canterbury
Fordwich Arms, Canterbury
Hide and Fox, Hythe
Thackeray's,
Royal Tunbridge Wells

Lancashire
White Swan at Fence, Burnley
Hipping Hall, Cowan Bridge
The Barn at Moor Hall, Ormskirk
The Freemasons at Wiswell,
Whalley

Leicestershire
John's House, Mountsorrel
Hammer & Pincers, Wymeswold

London, by postcode
Galvin La Chapelle, E1
Cornerstone by Chef Tom
Brown, E9
Anglo, EC1
The Clove Club, EC1

Club Gascon, EC1
City Social, EC2
The Princess of Shoreditch, EC2
La Dame de Pic London, EC3
Odette's, NW1
Trivet, SE1
Peninsula Restaurant, SE10
Amaya, SW1
A. Wong, SW1
Chutney Mary, SW1
The Goring, SW1
Ikoyi, SW1
Pétrus by Gordon Ramsay, SW1
Wild Honey St James, SW1
Elystan Street, SW3
Trinity Restaurant, SW4
Medlar Restaurant, SW10
Myrtle Restaurant, SW10
Chez Bruce, SW17
Corrigan's Mayfair, W1
CUT at 45 Park Lane, W1
Galvin at Windows Restaurant
& Bar, W1
Gauthier Soho, W1
The Grill at The Dorchester, W1
Hakkasan Mayfair, W1

Hide Above, W1
Kitchen Table, W1
KOL Restaurant, W1
Le Gavroche Restaurant, W1
Les 110 de Taillevent, W1
Little Social, W1
Locanda Locatelli, W1
Mere, W1
The Ninth, W1
Orrery, W1
Pied à Terre, W1
Portland, W1
Roka Charlotte Street, W1
Roka Mayfair, W1
Sketch (The Gallery), W1
SOLA, W1
Umu, W1
The River Café, W6
Kitchen W8, W8
Launceston Place, W8
Clos Maggiore, WC2
Frenchie Covent Garden, WC2
Frog by Adam Handling, WC2
Kerridge's Bar & Grill, WC2
The Northall, WC2

London, Greater

Chapter One Restaurant, Bromley

The Glasshouse, Kew

Bingham Riverhouse, Richmond upon Thames

The Dysart Petersham, Richmond upon Thames

Norfolk

The Neptune Restaurant with Rooms, Hunstanton

Benedicts, Norwich

Farmyard, Norwich

Roger Hickman's Restaurant, Norwich

The Dial House, Reepham

The Ingham Swan, Stalham

Titchwell Manor Hotel, Titchwell

Northamptonshire

Tresham Restaurant, Kettering

Murrays, Whittlebury

Oxfordshire

The Sir Charles Napier, Chinnor

The Wild Rabbit, Kingham

Minster Mill, Minster Lovell

The Nut Tree Inn, Murcott

Shropshire

Fishmore Hall, Ludlow

Old Downton Lodge, Ludlow

The Haughmond, Upton Magna

Somerset

The Bath Priory Hotel, Restaurant & Spa, Bath

The Dower House Restaurant, Bath

The Olive Tree at the Queensberry Hotel, Bath

Staffordshire

The Boat Inn, Lichfield

Suffolk

The Bildeston Crown, Bildeston

The Great House, Lavenham

Surrey

Stovell's, Chobham

Tony Parkin at the Tudor Room, Egham

Langshott Manor, Horley

The Victoria Oxshott, Leatherhead

The Clock House, Ripley

Sussex, East

etch. by Steven Edwards, Brighton

The Little Fish Market, Brighton

Sussex, West

Amberley Castle, Amberley

The Camellia Restaurant at South Lodge, Lower Beeding

Restaurant Interlude, Lower Beeding

AG's Restaurant at Alexander House Hotel, Turners Hill

Dean Banks at The Pompadour, Scotland

Warwickshire
The Cross at Kenilworth, Kenilworth
The Dining Room at Mallory Court Hotel, Royal Leamington Spa
Salt, Stratford-upon-Avon

West Midlands
Adam's, Birmingham
Carters of Moseley, Birmingham
Opheem, Birmingham
Purnell's, Birmingham
Restaurant 8, Birmingham
Restaurant Folium, Birmingham
Simpsons, Birmingham
The Wilderness, Birmingham

Wiltshire
Bybrook at The Manor House Hotel, Castle Combe
Restaurant Hywel Jones by Lucknam Park, Colerne
Red Lion Freehouse, Pewsey

Worcestershire
The Back Garden, Broadway
MO, Broadway
Brockencote Hall Country House Hotel, Chaddesley Corbett

Yorkshire, North
Yorebridge House, Bainbridge
The Burlington Restaurant, Bolton Abbey
Goldsborough Hall, Goldsborough
Horto Restaurant, Harrogate
Shaun Rankin at Grantley Hall, Ripon
The Hare, Scawton
The Bow Room Restaurant at Grays Court, York
Roots York, York

Yorkshire, South
JÖRO Restaurant, Sheffield
Rafters Restaurant, Sheffield

Yorkshire, West
Box Tree, Ilkley

Channel Islands

Jersey
Longueville Manor Hotel, St Saviour

Scotland

Aberdeenshire
Douneside House, Tarland

Angus
Gordon's, Inverkeilor

Argyll & Bute
Restaurant at Isle of Eriska, Eriska
Airds Hotel and Restaurant, Port Appin
Inver Restaurant, Strachur

Ayrshire, South
Glenapp Castle, Ballantrae

Dumfries & Galloway
The Auldgirth Inn, Dumfries
Knockinaam Lodge, Portpatrick

Dunbartonshire, West
Tamburrini & Wishart, Balloch

Edinburgh
Dean Banks at The Pompadour, Edinburgh
Timberyard, Edinburgh

Fife
The Cellar, Anstruther
The Peat Inn, Peat Inn
HAAR, St Andrews
Road Hole Restaurant, St Andrews

Glasgow
Cail Bruich, Glasgow
The Gannet, Glasgow
UNALOME by Graeme Cheevers, Glasgow

Highland
Station Road, Fort Augustus
The Cross, Kingussie
Kilcamb Lodge Hotel, Strontian
The Torridon 1887 Restaurant, Torridon
The Dipping Lugger, Ullapool

Lanarkshire, South
Crossbasket Castle, Blantyre

Perth & Kinross
Fonab Castle Hotel & Spa, Pitlochry

Scottish Islands
The Three Chimneys & The House Over-By, Colbost
Loch Bay Restaurant, Stein

Stirling
Roman Camp Country House Hotel, Callander
Cromlix and Chez Roux, Dunblane

Wales

Conwy
The Jackdaw, Conwy
Bodysgallen Hall and Spa, Llandudno

Gwynedd
Pale Hall Hotel & Restaurant, Bala

Monmouthshire
The Walnut Tree Inn, Abergavenny

Newport
Gem 42, Newport

Pembrokeshire
Blas Restaurant, St Davids
Coast Restaurant, Saundersfoot

Swansea
Beach House Restaurant, Oxwich Beach, Oxwich

Northern Ireland

Belfast
Deanes EIPIC, Belfast
OX, Belfast

County Antrim
Galgorm, Ballymena

County Fermanagh
Lough Erne Resort, Enniskillen

For up-to-date information on the top AA rated restaurants visit
www.ratedtrips.com/aa-rosette-restaurants

Cream of the crop

The UK's gastronomic scene is finding its feet again in the post-pandemic world. Our inspectors have been out on the road around the country to bring you the newcomers and the high flyers achieving new 3- and 4-Rosette awards for 2023.

A great new wave of 142 restaurants joined our scheme in the last 12 months. These include new openings, new finds and chefs with strong pedigrees that have gone on to open their own places.

Given the demand for the scheme, when new restaurants apply to join, they need to offer at least two lunch openings, plus a minimum of six services per week; they need to have a food hygiene rating of 4 out of 5 or above and most importantly a menu and approach to food that we feel would be worthy of achieving a Rosette standard (see full details on pages 6-7). The restaurants highlighted below have all won new three- and four-Rosette accolades in inspections carried out between 2021 and 2022.

Northern Stars
The north continues to power ahead with our inspectors experiencing some exceptional cooking from 31 newcomers to the guide. Top of the pile with four Rosettes for its contemporary country house food is Allium at Askham Hall. The dynamic northern dining scene is boosted further by a cluster of three-Rosette winners: Rafters in Sheffield, White Swan at Fence in Burnley, Windermere's Henrock, Goldsborough Hall and Arkle at Chester Grosvenor.

Heart of England

The guide is thrilled to welcome 22 new entries across the Midlands region. Life is still yum in Brum, which continues to raise the bar – in the city centre there's Opheem, Restaurant Folium and Restaurant 8, all winning three-Rosette awards. Newcomer, Grace & Savour in Solihull receives an astonishing four Rosettes in its first year of opening. Out in Leicestershire, the Hammer & Pincers trades up to three Rosettes for its dishes.

Culinary Capital

London, the surrounding counties and southeast have always attracted chefs at the cutting edge, bringing in a bag of 32 new Rosette-awarded venues. Among the A-listers, Jason Atherton's Social Eating House has raised its game to four Rosettes, joined at this rarefied level by The Ledbury, back on peak form after reopening in 2022, and Ormer Mayfair with refined cooking courtesy of Sofian Msetfi. Adam Handling's mini-empire gains another three-Rosette award courtesy of The Loch & The Tyne in Old Windsor, as does The Victoria Oxshott, The Sir Charles Napier in Chinnor, The Camellia Restaurant at South Lodge in West Sussex, and The Nut Tree Inn in Murcott.

Restaurant 8

Scotland

Food-wise, chefs in Scotland are certainly enjoying a Highland fling, dancing a reel with 12 new entries. The Glenturret Lalique Restaurant gains four Rosettes for its precise and adventurous cooking, as does Edinbane Lodge on the Isle of Skye. New three Rosette winners include Paul Tamburrini and Martin Wishart in their namesake restaurant in Balloch, along with The Auldgirth Inn in Dumfries, and The Dipping Lugger in Ullapool. Last, but far from least, Dean Banks, who scores twice with his name above the opulent Pompadour in Edinburgh, and by the seaside at HAAR in St Andrews.

East Anglia

The chefs of East Anglia and the Eastern counties (Essex, Cambridgeshire, Rutland) are on a roll this year, coming in with 17 new entries. Leading the pack with three Rosettes, we welcome new entries The Flitch of Bacon in Little Dunmow and The Chubby Castor in Peterborough. Also climbing the Rosette ladder to three-Rosette level, hats off to Restaurant 22 in Cambridge, The Great House in Lavenham, Prévost @ Haycock in Wansford, The Dial House in Reepham and The Ingham Swan in Stalham,

The Camellia Restaurant at South Lodge

Coast Restaurant

Àclèaf

Welsh Dragons, Celtic Tigers

Wales has four new entries in the 2023 guide, as well as another quartet who have risen to the heights of multi-Rosette awards. The Fernery at the boutique Grove of Narberth hotel now boasts four Rosettes – take a bow chef Douglas Balish – while Blas Restaurant in St Davids, Coast Restaurant in Saundersfoot and The Jackdaw in Conwy all get to display three-Rosette awards on their walls.

Northern Ireland

Northern Ireland also comes in with four new venues earning their place on the Rosette listings.

West Country & Channel Islands

When it comes to classy cooking, you're spoilt for choice with 27 new entries across the West Country counties of Devon, Cornwall, Dorset, Somerset, Gloucestershire and Wiltshire. Ricki Weston is flying high with four Rosettes for top-class country house cuisine at The Dining Room at Whatley Manor in Malmesbury, alongside fellow four-Rosette winners Àclèaf in Plymouth and, in Jersey, Bohemia at The Club Hotel. Raising their game to three Rosettes, congratulations to The Dower House Restaurant in Bath, Sandy Cove Hotel in Ilfracombe, The Horn of Plenty in Tavistock and New Yard in Helston.

New Yard Restaurant

Le Manoir aux Quat'Saisons

Growing their own

Whether it's a huge acreage of beds and polytunnels or a rooftop full of pots, a kitchen garden is a fantastic asset for any restaurant, allowing chefs to showcase perfectly ripe ingredients with impeccable provenance and zero food miles. We talk to restaurants around the country about their green-fingered endeavours.

Belmond Le Manoir aux Quat'Saisons

At the top end of the scale, Raymond Blanc's gardens at Le Manoir are legendary, running to 11 different gardens, plus a 2,500-strong heritage orchard. Nurtured by head gardener Anne-Marie Owens and the team, the gardens are an essential part of the extraordinary Le Manoir journey – you will spend as much time in the garden as you will at the table. The kitchen can take its pick from over 250 different organic varieties of fruit and vegetables, rustling up a garnish from the herb garden, which specialises in seasonal micro-herbs, or wander over to the earthy mushroom valley, which grows many varieties of fungus including maitake and parasol. The result: dishes such as 'Assiette Anne-Marie' in honour of Anne-Marie who has worked closely with Monsieur Blanc for over 35 years. At its heart, this recipe is all about simplicity – the purity of the very best ingredients plucked straight from the garden and treated with respect. It includes young carrots, white and green asparagus, pods of garden peas, broad beans, flower stamens and stigmas, and pea shoots.

Grace & Savour

The new kid on the block, the Grace & Savour team got to grips with resurrecting a half-acre garden that had been left to go derelict until 4 years ago. Head chef David Taylor says 'It has been a journey to bring the soil back to life and we have faced challenges but year on year we get more from the soil as it gets it health back. We even found carrots taste different in the top end and the bottom end of the garden! We get wonderful produce to include on our menu and help us on our journey to only use British grown produce. Ultimately, we only want to be 50% self sufficient because we will always want to tell the story of our growers'.

Full-time gardener Stephen manages the garden, and the chefs do all the picking and harvesting, while bees have been introduced as they are nature's pollinators and they make delicious honey.

One of Taylor's favourite produce is the blackcurrant: 'We make a milk sorbet infused with the blackcurrant wood, served with a compôte of berries, and then finished with a drizzle of blackcurrant leaf oil, all covered in oxalis leaves to give the impression of a bush.'

> 'We are passionate about the sustainability of our business, preserving the beautiful landscape around our home and lowering our environmental impact'
>
> Helen Hatton, Ferry House Inn

Ferry House Inn

Ferry House owner Alex Burden, whose family have been farming the wild wetlands beside the Swale estuary on the Isle of Sheppey since the 1960s, says 'Our hyper-local focus extends into foraging the surrounding hedgerows and shorelines, as well as using beef from our own herd of locally grass-grazed cattle, wild game from the Harty Estate, and as much produce as possible from local Kent. As well as reducing the environmental impact of our operations, our kitchen garden yields an enormous variety of high-quality produce, which is cropped daily. This ensures fantastic fresh and seasonal flavours come to our guests quite literally from 'Plot to Plate'.

The kitchen garden had humble beginnings – starting as one lettuce bed in 2013. Today the kitchen garden is over one acre, with established vegetable beds, a large fruit cage, orchard, herb garden and two poly tunnels. Burden plans to develop two more acres and plant hazelnut trees to protect the gardens from the estuary winds.

The Garden Artichoke dish from the current dinner menu features globe artichokes picked while still young, cooked sous vide in brine until tender, then pan-fried crisp and served with whipped goats' cheese, a tahini dressing with local Sheppey honey, last year's smoked chillies and gnocchi.

L'Enclume

Simon Rogan's exceptional food has always been driven by ingredients in peak condition: 'When we opened L'Enclume back in 2002, our aim was always to work towards making the restaurant operation as self-sufficient as it could be, which of course starts with sourcing our ingredients from as close to home as possible' says Rogan. 'When we found we were struggling to get all of the quality produce we required, we set about creating Our Farm. You could say that the farm is the epicentre of everything we do, it's where inspiration for all our menus comes from so it's important that myself and my

Gravetye Manor

team visit the farm regularly to see which ingredients are at their peak. Every chef who starts working within the group spends a fortnight on the farm before they enter the kitchen – this is the best way to connect them with our philosophy from the get go. At the moment, we are making the most of the British strawberry season. Malwina strawberries grown on the farm are being used in a dessert on our current menu with muscovado, sheep's yogurt, fragrant cream and herbs'.

Gravetye Manor
Head chef George Blogg and the kitchen team at Gravetye Manor are blessed with a cornucopia of prime pickings from the historic 30-acre gardens, but it took a lot of work to restore the badly neglected 1.5-acre original walled kitchen garden to a productive state. It now grows fruit, vegetables and herbs that are central to the menu; crops are organically grown and help keep food miles very low. The Gravetye Garden Salad is available on the menu as a starter year round and is composed entirely of vegetables, herbs and flowers grown at Gravetye and changes throughout the seasons.

'It's all about respecting the slowness of the process and getting closer to the produce'

Sam Buckley, Where the Light Gets In

Where The Light Gets In
A world apart from heritage-listed Victorian kitchen gardens, Sam Buckley, chef-patron of WTLGI supplies his kitchen from the rooftop of a car park, known as 'The Landing'. 'We grow a lot of what we serve on the menu at The Landing, the bulk of the produce being herbs that we use in many different ways. We grow a lot of non indigenous plants up there due to the temperatures we have access to, Korean mint, tomatillo and Thai basil to name a few. We have a polytunnel with tomatoes and cucumbers, which flourish in the warmth, we have plenty of beans growing, and flourishes of fruit coming out with wild strawberries, red- and whitecurrants. The Elephant garlic soup we have on at the moment is made all from produce grown on The Landing'.

THE PIG at Combe

'The bond between garden and kitchen is now so strong, an almost obsessional culture for all things home-grown, homemade and local runs through our DNA'

Peter Lewis, THE PIG, Brockenhurst

THE PIG hotels

Right from the start, Robin Hutson, founder of THE PIG hotels, wanted the kitchen gardens to be at their heart and soul and to play a big part in influencing the menus. The original PIG in the New Forest, THE PIG at Combe and THE PIG on the Beach in Dorset all boast highly passionate and skilled teams who manage the kitchen gardens all year round to support their 25-mile menus. Peter Harris from THE PIG at Combe says 'Every plate of food we serve is touched by the garden in some form, as are many of our cocktails, but it also gives us the opportunity to talk to and inspire our guests into trying something in their own space at home'.

Rudding Park

At first glance the garden could be an art installation with the geometric shapes of the 52 raised beds made from English oak, but this is a serious set up where over 500 different herbs, salads, edible flowers and fruits are grown by kitchen gardener, Emma Pugh. Callum Bowmer, head chef at Horto Restaurant was keen to devise a pudding with lots of flavours to excite the tastebuds and his 'Taste of the Garden' dish has become a firm favourite – the team make a lemon verbena ice cream and poach gooseberries in rose syrup using roses from the garden.

> 'Provenance is so important, and you can't beat a kitchen garden – the chefs can pick ingredients each day ensuring they are using the freshest most in-season produce'
>
> **Nicola Cook, Rudding Park**

Thornbury Castle

Thornbury has always had a small kitchen garden, however executive chef Carl Cleghorn was very keen on expanding the kitchen garden further. There's now a beautiful herb garden inside the Tudor walled garden that produces salads, fennel and a variety of herbs that are used extensively in the kitchen. Over the next 12 months the plan is to expand the garden to at least three times the size, concentrating on a smaller variety of vegetables but in larger quantities. The spring lamb dish incorporates some of the beautiful produce grown on site: baby courgettes are picked daily and the flowers are stuffed with a tomato fondue using tomatoes from the greenhouse and finished with basil and a courgette and basil purée using overgrown marrows and homegrown herbs.

To read more about the kitchen gardens featured here, and others, head to **www.ratedtrips.com/restaurants**

Rudding Park

> 'We would like not just the chefs but our guests to be inspired by what we grow and how we implement the produce on the menus'
>
> **Simone Arcucci, Thornbury Castle**

AA Restaurants of the Year 2022–23

Potential Restaurants of the Year are nominated by our team of full-time inspectors, based on their routine visits. We look for somewhere that is exceptional in its chosen area of the market. While the Rosette awards are based on the quality of the food alone, the Restaurants of the Year awards take all aspects of the dining experience into account.

AA RESTAURANT OF THE YEAR ENGLAND

Socius ☼☼
Burnham Market, Norfolk
See page 369

This is a gem of place, a stylish modern building situated in a recently developed area of Burnham Market, and opened in 2018 by Natalie Stuhler and Dan Lawrence, who created the space from scratch. The menu changes regularly and dishes are designed to share; the theme is very much modern British tapas. The open plan kitchen/dining room has a very contemporary feel, it's light and airy with a black metal staircase leading up to a mezzanine floor, and service is very attentive; the team are friendly and there is a real sense of pride as the dishes are placed in front of you and described in full.

AA RESTAURANT OF THE YEAR SCOTLAND

The Cellar ⊛⊛⊛
Anstruther, Fife

See page 580

The charming fishing harbour of Anstruther is a fitting location for chef Billy Boyter's restaurant, housed in a 17th-century former smokehouse and cooperage just off the quayside. With beamed ceilings, stone walls and wood-burning stoves, the ambience is calmly rustic, with thoughtfully chosen artworks and beautiful wooden and ceramic dishes. Boyter's inventive modern Scottish cooking sticks faithfully to the seasons, making excellent use of local and foraged produce on the nine-course tasting menu at dinner (six at lunch).

AA RESTAURANT OF THE YEAR WALES

Gem 42 ⊛⊛⊛
Newport

See page 644

The unassuming building is easy to miss, but once inside you're hardly likely to forget the exuberant Mediterranean feel, with Botticelli-style ceilings and crisply dressed tables with Murano glass ornaments. The emphasis is on Italian style and ingredients, combined with top quality Welsh seasonal produce, and you can expect a happy fusion of classical foundations and contemporary techniques. A selection of differing tasting menus is available, along with an excellent wine selection, or, for a non-alcoholic option, a matching tasting flight of Kombucha makes for an enjoyable variation.

AA RESTAURANT OF THE YEAR LONDON

Chez Bruce ⊛⊛⊛ ⌐NOTABLE WINE LIST
Wandsworth, SW17

See page 316

Chez Bruce opened in 1995 and has been a stalwart of the London dining scene ever since. It has a charming neighbourhood feel to it, set in small row of shops, and the dining room is spacious, with plenty of natural daylight and colourful, vibrant artwork. The restaurant does everything brilliantly and apparently effortlessly, producing top-notch modern food, based loosely on classical and regional French/Mediterranean cuisine. Dishes are simple, unfussy and focus on great flavours, with home-made charcuterie and slow cooked braises. Service is highly professional and there's an excellent sommelier to match the impressive wine list.

Chefs' Chef of the Year 2022–23

A popular and coveted title, this unique award was first introduced in 1996, and offers all AA Rosette-awarded chefs the chance to decide which of their peers deserves the ultimate recognition for their performance over the past twelve months.

Mark Birchall, Chef Patron, Moor Hall Restaurant with Rooms, Aughton, Ormskirk, Lancashire
Mark Birchall is, without doubt, one of Britain's most talented chefs, and given his impressive pedigree and achievements, it comes as no surprise that he is so highly regarded by his peers. Born in Chorley, Lancashire, Mark trained at Runshaw College. Previously Executive Chef of L'Enclume, Mark won the Roux Scholarship in 2011. Since opening five years ago, he has established Moor Hall as one of the UK's best restaurants, achieving five AA Rosettes, and an additional three AA Rosettes for The Barn. Every detail is carefully considered and rather special, from uniforms to waiters' stations. There's an on-site butchery, a bakery, temperature-controlled cheese and wine rooms, and a garden full of wonderful produce. Mark has created a true international foodie destination here, and his cooking offers a very modern take on British flavours, where the natural flavour and freshness of the produce is paramount.

Moor Hall Restaurant with Rooms

Previous winners

JASON ATHERTON
City Social, London EC2
Little Social, London W1
Pollen Street Social, London W1
Social Eating House, London W1

RAYMOND BLANC, OBE
Belmond Le Manoir aux Quat' Saisons,
    Great Milton, Oxfordshire

HESTON BLUMENTHAL
The Fat Duck, Bray, Berkshire
Hinds Head, Bray, Berkshire
Dinner by Heston Blumenthal, London SW1
The Crown at Bray, Berkshire

CLAUDE BOSI
Bibendum, London SW3

MICHAEL CAINES
The Coach House by Michael Caines,
    Kentisbury, Devon

DANIEL CLIFFORD
Midsummer House, Cambridge, Cambridgeshire

ANDREW FAIRLIE
Andrew Fairlie at Gleneagles,
    Auchterarder, Perth & Kinross

CHRIS AND JEFF GALVIN
Galvin La Chapelle, London E1

SHAUN HILL
Walnut Tree Inn, Abergavenny, Monmouthshire

PHILIP HOWARD
Elystan Street, London SW3

TOM KERRIDGE
The Hand and Flowers, Marlow, Buckinghamshire
The Coach, Marlow, Buckinghamshire
Kerridge's Bar & Grill, London WC2

PIERRE KOFFMANN

JEAN-CHRISTOPHE NOVELLI

NATHAN OUTLAW
Outlaw's New Road, Port Isaac, Cornwall

GORDON RAMSAY
Restaurant Gordon Ramsay, London SW3

SIMON ROGAN
L'Enclume, Cartmel, Cumbria

GERMAIN SCHWAB

RICK STEIN
The Seafood Restaurant, Padstow, Cornwall
Rick Stein at Sandbanks, Sandbanks, Dorset

KEVIN VINER

MARCUS WAREING
Marcus, The Berkeley, London SW1

MARCO PIERRE WHITE

JOHN WILLIAMS, MBE
The Ritz Restaurant, London W1

MARTIN WISHART
Restaurant Martin Wishart, Edinburgh
Tamburrini & Wishart, Balloch

Lifetime Achievement Award 2022–23

John Williams, MBE
Executive Chef, The Ritz Restaurant, London W1

A native of South Shields, John Williams began his career as an apprentice at the Percy Arms in Northumberland but set his sights on the capital from an early age. He joined The Savoy Group in 1986, spending time in the kitchens both at The Savoy and Claridge's. In 2004 he arrived at The Ritz, where he is Executive Head Chef of all culinary operations, and where he won four AA Rosettes. He was named AA Chef's Chef in 2017.

His dedication to his profession and craft has seen a host of other awards, including the Craft Guild of Chefs Award and full Liveryman of the Worshipful Company of Cooks. He has represented the UK in the prestigious Bocuse D'Or culinary competition and continues to mentor the English team.

He was the first British chef to be recognised with a CMA by the French Government and in 2008 was presented with an MBE for his services to hospitality. John is Chairman and Trustee of the Royal Academy of Culinary Arts which aligns with his passion for excellence and the promotion of his craft as one of the best professional careers.

AA Food Service Award 2022-23

This award recognises restaurants that deliver truly excellent standards of service and hospitality. The teams at these restaurants demonstrate high levels of technical service skills, and their food and drink knowledge is of the highest standard.

Hélène Darroze at The Connaught, London, W1

See page 327

Parisian designer Pierre Yovanovitch has brought a more colourful, contemporary look to this intimate dining room. The ambience is welcoming and sophisticated, with warm tones and beautiful velvet seating, as well as a pink marble chef's table overlooking the pass. The effortlessly stylish setting creates the perfect tone for the dishes here, and it's no surprise that the perfectly managed service mirrors the meticulous nature of the cuisine, with every stage striking a pleasing balance between slick professionalism and relaxed confidence. The immaculate restaurant team, including the team of sommeliers, are so engaging and fluent in their approach, it really is a joy to experience.

AA Restaurant with Rooms of the Year 2022–23

Introduced in 2017, this award recognises AA-rated guest accommodation that is also a dining destination.

AA RESTAURANT WITH ROOMS ENGLAND

The Angel at Hetton ֎֎֎֎
Hetton, North Yorkshire
See page 521

At its heart, the Angel is a roadside inn, easily recognised by generations of diners. Parts of the building date back to the 15th century. Now the recently refreshed and updated interiors are the perfect setting for the famous culinary skills of Michael Wignall. Food is obviously a highlight of any stay, and Michael's cooking is showcased through both carte and tasting menu options. There is a deftness and lightness to his dishes that demonstrate first rate cooking and produce. The large, stylish bedrooms across the road in a converted barn have magnificent views over Rylstone Fell and beyond, while the rooms in the main building are comfortably contemporary.

AA RESTAURANT WITH ROOMS SCOTLAND

The Bonnie Badger ֎֎
Gullane, East Lothian
See page 604

Located in the quiet East Lothian town of Gullane, renowned for its links golf, wonderful beaches and coastline, The Bonnie Badger is Tom Kitchin's first 'restaurant with rooms' venture. Rescued from near dereliction, it continues to evolve and develop, displaying the same high quality and attention to detail as his other restaurants. Bedrooms, in the main house and two cottages, are beautifully designed with little touches of luxury to ensure a memorable stay. The Stables Dining room offers Tom's award-winning 'nature to plate' style menus, and there's outside dining with a large fire pit to keep the chill off.

AA RESTAURANT WITH ROOMS WALES

Crug Glâs Country House ◉◉
Solva, Pembrokeshire

See page 653

A delightful, luxurious country house restaurant with rooms, set in 600 acres of rolling farmland in north Pembrokeshire, just a mile from the coast on the St David's peninsula. Deeply comfortable rooms are individual in style with contemporary bathrooms and signature baths. Flawless attention to detail throughout guarantees a wonderful stay, and the restaurant showcases the fantastic local produce (including home-reared beef) through seasonal menus. They have their own wind turbine, and heating and hot water come from eco-wood burning boilers.

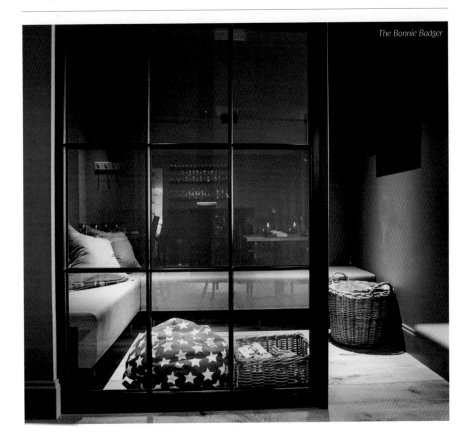

The Bonnie Badger

AA Wine Awards 2022–23

The annual AA Wine Awards, sponsored by Matthew Clark Wines, attracted a huge response from our AA recognised restaurants this year, with over 950 wine lists submitted for judging. Three national winners were chosen.

All the restaurants in this year's guide were invited to submit their wine lists. From these the panel selected a shortlist of over 250 establishments, who are highlighted in the guide with the Notable Wine List symbol ⚑NOTABLE WINE LIST. As part of the judging process, shortlisted restaurants were asked to choose wines from their list (within a budget of £80 per bottle) to accompany an 8-course menu designed by Peels Restaurant at Hampton Manor (see below).

The final judging panel included last year's winner, Max Allwood, Head of Wine at Hampton Manor, Nick Zalinski, National Account Director, Matthew Clark Wines (our sponsor) and Simon Numphud, Managing Director, AA Media. The winners and judges' comments are shown opposite.

Winning selection from The Vineyard at Stockcross chosen by Romain Bourger, Director of Wine & Beverage

Menu	Your Wine Selection
CANAPES/SNACKS Chicken liver parfait, brick pastry tart, crispy chicken skin, lemon thyme, sherry vinegar caramel & Berkswell cheese custard, celery salt lavash cracker, pickled walnut gel	2008 Schramsberg Reserve Brut, Nirth Coast California 2008 (sparkling)
STARTER Wagyu beef tartare, black truffle ketchup, beer-pickled onions, tarragon & beef fat mayonnaise, smoked bone marrow crumb	Weingut DR Heger, Spatburgunder, Mimus, Baden, Germany 2004
FISH COURSE Cornish crab, lime gel, Nam Pla jelly, tapioca crisp with brown crab mayonnaise, lemongrass and coriander consommé	Alsace Grand Cru, Pinot Gris Eichberg, Kuentz Bas, Alsace, France 2015
MEAT COURSE Devonshire farm lamb stuffed with marjoram mousse, BBQ purple sprouting broccoli, broccoli purée, malt vinegar and marjoram caramel, lamb sauce	Lismore, Syrah Greyton, South Africa, 2017
CHEESE COURSE Pevensey blue, crimson crisp apple, treacle tart, cider vinegar caramel	Blandy's 10 Year old, Bual, Madeira, Portugal, NV
PUDDING COURSE Yorkshire rhubarb, caramelised custard, YQ tart, and buttermilk sorbet	Hosmer, Rielsing Late Pick, Cayaga Lake, New York 2017

AA WINE AWARD FOR ENGLAND & OVERALL WINNER

The Vineyard ⊛⊛⊛ 🍷NOTABLE WINE LIST
Stockcross, Newbury, Berkshire

See page 46

A truly stellar list that ranks as one of the best in the country. The investment, time, love and passion that have gone into this list really stand out. Impressively for a list of such epic stature, the judges felt it successfully strikes the balance of being serious while still accessible. They loved the wine journey index, over 50 wines by the glass, the dedicated vegan wine selection and the selection of everyday drinking wines under £30. Whether a novice or expert, one can't help being inspired by this list.

AA WINE AWARD FOR SCOTLAND

UNALOME by Graeme Cheevers ⊛⊛⊛ 🍷NOTABLE WINE LIST
Glasgow

See page 594

A modern, compact list that feels very accessible, with quality selections throughout. The judges loved the format of the list; divided by drinking style categories, with mature vintages, an interesting selection by the glass and a good selection of dessert wines.

AA WINE AWARD FOR WALES

The Fernery ⊛⊛⊛ 🍷NOTABLE WINE LIST
Narberth, Pembrokeshire

See page 646

An impressive list with great presentation that was easy to read and navigate. A great selection by the glass, and the judges loved the flexibility that any bottle can be opened with a minimum of two glasses served. Head sommelier Alexios Stasinopoulos' passion for this list was palpable, offering the best range of quality wines at all price points and with a really interesting mixture of familiar classics and intriguing new wines from artisan growers.

The AA Wine Awards are sponsored by:
Matthew Clark, Whitchurch Lane, Bristol, BS14 0JZ
Tel: 01275 891400
Email: enquiries@matthewclark.co.uk
www.matthewclark.co.uk

AA Notable Wine List 2022–23

What makes a wine list notable?

Every year, we highlight restaurants with wine lists that have impressed our inspectors with the Notable Wine List symbol. These vary from small, personally selected lists with much personality to epic lists offering a simply stunning range of wines and supported by dedicated wine teams. To be one of the 255 highlighted in this year's guide, we look for a real passion for wine and service to match, which should come across to the customer.

We look for lists that feature well chosen, quality wines, and that have been curated with real care and interest. Ranging from compact to grand lists, they will be well presented, clear and easy to navigate. They will often feature diversity across grape varieties, countries and style, and the best individual growers and vintages. To reflect the demand of diners, there should be a good choice of varied wines available by the glass.

We also look for a fair pricing policy (depending on the style of the restaurant); and interesting coverage (not necessarily a large list), which might include areas of specialism, perhaps a particular wine area; sherries, dessert wines or larger formats such as magnums.

It is really encouraging to see more and more restaurants championing English wine as both the quality and depth continues to grow. Wine flights and pairings to accompany menus have become a regular feature of many restaurants, giving the opportunity for diners to experience a range of wines they may not have tasted before.

Sommelier's Table, Hélène Darroze at The Connaught

AA College Restaurant of the Year 2022–23

Now in its fifth year, the AA College Restaurant of the Year Award celebrates the very best of future talent. Open exclusively to all People 1st Accredited colleges, each holding an AA college Rosette for culinary excellence.

Senara Restaurant – Truro & Penwith College, Penzance, Cornwall

A commercial offering that has adapted to incorporate a takeaway service for the local community, the restaurant is staffed by students preparing for a career in the hospitality industry, under the watchful eye of industry professionals with years of experience between them. The exciting and varied menu sources fabulous Cornish produce, and makes excellent use of both modern and classic techniques, creating affordable, exciting and delicious dishes. Coupled with a fantastic view over the Cornish coast, this is the perfect venue to enjoy a great meal while supporting the stars of the future.

ENGLAND

Bedfordshire

Henlow

The Crown ◉
2 High Street, SG16 6BS
01462 812433
www.crownpub.co.uk
Closed: 25–26 December

Chef: Will Ingarfill
Food Style: Modern British

The busy pub on the main road through the village functions as a quintessential rural hostelry, full of enthusiastic local custom in both bar and dining room. Despite modernisation it retains its pub ethos, and boasts a young, classically trained chef.

Luton

Adam's Brasserie at Luton Hoo ◉ ⚑NOTABLE WINE LIST
Luton Hoo Hotel, Golf & Spa,
The Mansion House, LU1 3TQ
01582 734437
www.lutonhoo.co.uk
Open: All year

Chef: Chris Mouyiassi
Food Style: Modern British

The extensive Luton Hoo Estate, with its golf course and magnificent gardens, is home to this spa hotel. Adam's Brasserie is found in the former stables, where high ceilings and large windows give a sense of space, and the menu is a roster of feel-good dishes.

Wernher Restaurant at Luton Hoo Hotel, Golf & Spa ◉◉ ⚑NOTABLE WINE LIST
The Mansion House, LU1 3TQ
01582 734437
www.lutonhoo.co.uk
Closed: First 2 weeks January

Chef: Christopher Mouyiassi
Food Style: Modern British

When only the full stately-home extravaganza will do, the magnificent Wernher in Luton Hoo is hard to top, with its marble panelling, ornate chandeliers and opulent fabrics. The kitchen puts emphasis on using regional and seasonal produce throughout the year to create their well balanced and tempting menus.

Woburn

Paris House Restaurant ◉◉◉
See pages 38-39

Wyboston

The Waterfront Restaurant at Wyboston Lakes ✿
Great North Road, MK44 3BA
0333 700 7667
www.thewaterfronthotel.co.uk
Closed: 25–26 December

Chef: Lee Clarke
Food Style: Traditional British, European

The Waterfront Restaurant offers a relaxed and modern brasserie-style dining experience with views over the south lake. The breads are home made and served with tapenade as well as oil and balsamic vinegar. For dessert, tuck into tiramisù with Madagascan vanilla cream and biscotti.

Female Chefs with 3 or more Rosettes

✿✿✿✿✿
Core by Clare Smyth
Clare Smyth
Page 349

**Hélène Darroze
at The Connaught**
Hélène Darroze
Page 327

✿✿✿✿
The Five Fields
Marguerite Keogh
Page 311

Murano
Angela Hartnett,
Emily Brightman
Page 333

Northcote Restaurant
Lisa Goodwin-Allen
Page 260

✿✿✿
Cail Bruich
Lorna McNee
Page 588

Fordwich Arms
Natasha Smith
Page 245

Hartnett Holder & Co
Angela Hartnett
Page 225

Inver Restaurant
Pam Brunton
Page 561

**La Dame de Pic
London**
Anne-Sophie Pic
Page 291

Mere
Monica Galetti
Page 332

Myrtle Restaurant
Anna Haugh
Page 316

Peninsula Restaurant
Aurelie Simon
Page 299

**The Princess of
Shoreditch**
Ruth Hansom
Page 290

The River Café
Ruth Rogers,
Sian Wyn Owen
Page 347

Woburn

Paris House Restaurant

London Road, Woburn Park, MK17 9QP
01525 290692
www.parishouse.co.uk
Closed: 23 December to 5 January

Chef: Phil Fanning
Food Style: Modern British

Impeccable contemporary cooking in an idyllic setting and mock-Tudor timbered building

While the entrance and approach is every bit the showstopper, passing through a grand gateway and crossing the Duke of Bedford's 22-acre deer park at his Woburn Estate, the sight of the beautiful half-timbered Tudor-style building of the Paris House Restaurant is equally beguiling. Okay, it maybe fake, originally constructed in Paris for the 1878 International Exhibition, then dismantled, shipped across the Channel and reassembled here, but it makes a thoroughly endearing statement and raises the anticipation and expectation ante.

It's a different look inside, one of snazzy, refined contemporary styling, complete with modern chandeliers, sleek furniture (with hues of blue seating), and

a wall of seasonally changing, food-related artworks. This is the classy, unique setting for chef-patron Phil Fanning's innovative, high-impact modern British cuisine, which comes at one with the seasons, on-cue with fashion and driven by prime ingredients, while Phil's refined Japanese technique is pivotal in achieving maximum flavour. His plates come dressed to thrill, displaying craftsmanship, precision and creativity, and highlighted by those brushstrokes of flavour and texture combination, teamed with a subtle nod to Asian. It's all delivered by a seasonal tasting menu; perhaps the luxury of baked Orkney scallop to start, served with spring vegetables and a miso beurre blanc with Avruga caviar, while turbot could be teamed with Isle of Wight tomatoes, chorizo, and a mussel and black olive ragù with sea herbs. Lamb Caesar might feature as the meat course, with a fermented lettuce, wild garlic and anchovy partnership, and the final flourish, perhaps strawberries, served with white chocolate, marshmallow and pink peppercorn.

For the ultimate experience, aim for a prized Chef's Table seat (surcharged) in the heart of the kitchen overlooking the pass. Relaxed, knowledgeable and professional service aptly fits the bill wherever you sit, while wine pairings add the final touch of class to proceedings.

"...plates come dressed to thrill, displaying craftsmanship, precision and creativity..."

Berkshire

Ascot

The Barn at Coworth ❀❀
Blacknest Road, SL5 7SE
01344 876600
www.coworthpark.com
Open: All year

Set at the heart of this lavish country house hotel, The Barn at Coworth is where you can tuck into classy brasserie-style food. Housed in the original barn frame, with rustic features, the design makes it perfect for all seasons. It looks great with its open-to-view kitchen, unbuttoned vibe and cheerful service team and there's a fabulous terrace, too.

Chef: Adam Smith
Food Style: British

See advertisement opposite

Bluebells Restaurant ❀❀
London Road, SL5 0PU
01344 622722
www.bluebells-restaurant.co.uk
Closed: 25–26 December, 1–14 January

Smartly traditional and uncluttered, Bluebells Restaurant has full length windows, and a dark green interior with rose highlights. Service is upbeat and friendly, but still very professional. Staff dress in black and white with pink ties to complement the decor. Menus feature a selection of appealing European dishes with some Asian influences.

Chef: Tamas Baranyai
Food Style: Modern European

What changes have you seen over the past few years?

A wonderful response to the hardships of Covid and Brexit – the industry becoming more collegiate and collaborative. The result is a focus on what really is essential to a restaurant.

AA Inspector

A TASTE OF
COUNTRY LIVING

The scent of crushed herbs.
A sense of warmth. A rustic charm.
A moment to savour. A taste of the season.
The Barn, Coworth Park.

ASCOT +44 (0)1344 876 600
DORCHESTERCOLLECTION.COM

#DCmoments
f CoworthPark
𝕏 CoworthParkUK
CoworthPark

Ascot *continued*

Restaurant Coworth Park ⊕⊕⊕⊕ ⏶NOTABLE WINE LIST

London Road, SL5 7SE
01344 876600
www.coworthpark.com
Open: All year

Chef: Adam Smith
Food Style: Modern British

Coworth Park is an elegant Georgian mansion with an effortlessly stylishly Palladian frontage, set in 240 acres of parkland and lovely gardens in the heart of rural Berkshire. Public rooms are high-ceilinged and spacious, with thoughtful contemporary design enhancing the classic country-house feel. Work up an appetite by taking on some of the equestrian opportunities – there are horses for riders of all abilities – or something more sedentary in the state-of-the-art spa, before heading to the restaurant. It's a serene space, calmly minimalist with views across the rose terrace. Service is formal but engaging. Executive chef Adam Smith's menus change with the seasons and he finds inspiration for his precise, dextrous and often innovative take on country-house cooking in the hotel's beautiful surroundings and in locally produced ingredients of the highest order. Dishes are picture-perfect and every element is thoughtfully considered.

Bray

Caldesi in Campagna ⊕⊕

Old Mill Lane, SL6 2BG
01628 788500
www.caldesi.com
Closed: Monday, Tuesday, 25–26 December

Here, in an immaculate house on the edge of Bray, expect classic Italian stuff made with (mostly) British ingredients. Among antipasti, deep-fried courgette flowers are filled with ricotta and basil, and to finish, traditional desserts might include Sicilian lemon tart.

Chef: Gregorio Piazza
Food Style: Traditional Italian

The Crown at Bray ⊕⊕

High Street, SL6 2AH
01628 621936
www.thecrownatbray.com
Open: All year

Devotees of the British pub know The Crown is safe in Heston Blumenthal's hands. His third address in the village, this 16th-century inn offers real ales, a well-constructed wine list and a menu that owes much to pub traditions while honouring the Blumenthal name.

Chef: Shannon Pay
Food Style: Traditional British

The Fat Duck ⊚⊚⊚⊚⊚ ⧪NOTABLE WINE LIST
High Street, SL6 2AQ
01628 580333
www.thefatduck.co.uk
Closed: 25 December to 8 January

Chef: Heston Blumenthal
Food Style: Modern British

Heston Blumenthal's The Fat Duck, and its telegenic proprietor himself, have entered the modern pantheon of culinary legend. 2022 sees the restaurant's 25th anniversary, and in celebration they've switched things up a bit, offering a new menu quarterly, each featuring famous dishes from the last quarter-century. Reading through these is a history lesson in Blumenthal's development, from the comfortable French dishes of the late nineties to the beginnings of the extraordinary and unique meals of the twenties. Anyone who's been watching what's been going on over in Bray will recognise noughties signature snail porridge and thrill to the opportunity to experience the exuberant theatricality of Damping Through the Boroughgroves, A Kid in A Sweetshop or A Walk in the Woods. It's hard to predict what 2023 will bring, but rest assured you will always be able to expect a marathon of idiosyncratic and inventive eating on a bucket-list experience that will stay with you forever. A foodie pilgrimage here has never come cheap but when you appreciate the work that goes into each dish – the craft, the passion, the time – the cost seems easier to justify. It's ultimately what great cooking is about: when all the theatrical ingenuity makes sense and has purpose delivering flavour, emotion and craftsmanship; something The Fat Duck always achieves.

The Hind's Head ⊚⊚⊚ ⧪NOTABLE WINE LIST
High Street, SL6 2AB
01628 626151
www.hindsheadbray.com
Closed: 25 December

Chef: Peter Gray
Food Style: British

Heston Blumenthal may still be reinventing the gastronomic at The Fat Duck but there is plenty of culinary magic at his reimagined 15th-century pub nearby. A former royal hunting lodge, the oak panelling, heavy beams and real fires are in step with the building's heritage, as are the hearty British dishes served by unstuffy staff. A classic chicken liver parfait is paired with cherry jelly, nasturtium leaf and toasted brioche. For main course, a perfectly timed roast fillet of cod is accompanied by kale, mussels and cider butter sauce. Finish with cherry Bakewell tart topped with yogurt ice cream.

The Waterside Inn ⊚⊚⊚ ⧪NOTABLE WINE LIST
Ferry Road, SL6 2AT
01628 620691
www.waterside-inn.co.uk
Closed: 26 December to 30 January

Chef: Alain Roux
Food Style: French

The little car park is a squeeze, so accept the valet parking – an elegant and sophisticated introduction to The Waterside, a renowned destination for refined dining. Floor-to-ceiling windows give views on to the little jetty and its moored boats, and here in the peaceable upper reaches of the Thames everything really is idyllic. The cooking, too, is all you could wish for, Alain Roux maintaining the formidable standards of the legendary late Michel Roux père. Pan fried lobster medallions come with a white port sauce and ginger flavoured vegetable julienne; main course grilled rabbit fillets are served on celeriac fondant, with glazed chestnuts and Armagnac sauce.

Cookham

The White Oak ⚜⚜
The Pound, SL6 9QE
01628 523043
www.thewhiteoak.co.uk
Closed: Monday, Tuesday

The team behind the White Oak reopened it in 2008 as a modern dining pub. Set in Stanley Spencer's beloved Cookham, it has splashy contemporary artwork, bare tables and generous washes of natural light from a skylight and patio doors onto the garden.

Chef: Jason Hall
Food Style: Modern British

Hungerford

The Great Shefford ⚜⚜
Newbury Road, Great Shefford, RG17 7DS
01488 648462
www.thegreatshefford.com
Open: All year

Chef: Sam Cary
Food Style: Modern British

A large pub, set in the heart of the village, The Great Shefford is also very much at the heart of the community. The River Lambourn runs through the back of the property, and the whole place has a real country feel with wooden flooring, exposed brick, light green wooden panelling, and fishing pictures and memorabilia on the walls.

Hurley

Hurley House ⚜⚜
Henley Road, SL6 5LH
01628 568500
www.hurleyhouse.co.uk
Closed: First week January

The candlelit restaurant at Hurley House offers two main menus – Japanese (plus a takeaway version) and International, although dishes from both menus can be combined. The International lists chipotle lime cauliflower steak, whole grilled Dover sole and home-made fermented sourdough pizzas. A good wine list is expertly explained by the young team.

Chef: Emanuele Privitera
Food Style: Japanese, International

See advertisement opposite

HURLEY HOUSE
HOTEL

Maidenhead

Fredrick's Hotel and Spa ❀❀
Shoppenhangers Road, SL6 2PZ
01628 581000
www.fredricks-hotel.co.uk
Open: All year

Chef: Charlie Murray
Food Style: Modern British

On the fringes of Maidenhead, Fredrick's is a popular venue for spa pampering and weddings. The restaurant goes for a neutral, modern look involving off-white panelled walls enlivened by bright artworks and designer lighting. The kitchen team continue to produce uncomplicated, contemporary cooking with an eye to seasonal produce.

Newbury

Donnington Valley Hotel & Spa ❀❀❀ 🍾 NOTABLE WINE LIST
Old Oxford Road, Donnington, RG14 3AG
01635 551199
www.donningtonvalley.co.uk
Open: All year

The Wine Press is the atmospheric and relaxed restaurant at Donnington Valley Hotel & Spa, with its light-filled, raftered room, galleried upper level and laid-back jazz soundtrack. Menus present modern, uncomplicated combinations of conventional British fare. The expertly compiled wine list is worthy of serious attention.

Chef: Darren Booker-Wilson
Food Style: Modern British

AA WINE AWARD FOR ENGLAND & OVERALL WINNER 2022-23

The Vineyard ❀❀❀ 🍾 NOTABLE WINE LIST
Stockcross, RG20 8JU
01635 528770
www.the-vineyard.co.uk
Open: All year

Chef: Tom Scade
Food Style: Modern British

The Vineyard really is a rather unique place – the split-level dining area is full of character, with light flooding in through the ceiling cupola skylight and huge, double height floor-to-ceiling windows. An impressive setting for equally impressive dining, where the menu changes with the seasons, and you'll find excellent ingredients treated with respect; flavours are allowed to speak for themselves in a classic, straightforward approach. Nothing unnecessarily complicated, just very good food cooked very nicely – crab tortellini to begin, perhaps, and apple and caramel millefeuille for dessert. As you might guess from the name they're serious about wine here, with more than 100 by the glass.

The Woodspeen – Restaurant and Cookery School ❀❀❀

Lambourn Road, RG20 8BN
01635 265070
www.thewoodspeen.com
Open: All year

Chef: Peter Eaton
Food Style: Modern British

Occupying a tranquil location in the beautiful West Berkshire countryside, The Woodspeen is set in a lovingly restored 19th-century farmhouse. With picture windows framing idyllic countryside views, and an open kitchen for added atmosphere, the contemporary restaurant is light and airy and very much Scandi in style. Start, perhaps, with a precisely cooked pigeon breast with sweetcorn and tarragon polenta, black garlic and artichokes. A first-rate fillet of Cornish cod is paired with spiced Puy lentils, buttered cabbage, creamed potato, pickled apples and parsley. Dark chocolate delice, honeycomb and vanilla ice-cream is an elegant way to end.

Old Windsor

NEW The Loch & The Tyne by Adam Handling ❀❀❀

See page 48

Reading

Caprice Restaurant & Terrace ❀❀

Crowne Plaza Reading East, Wharfedale Road,
Winnersh Triangle, RG41 5TS
0118 944 0444
www.cpreading.co.uk
Open: All year

Located in the bustling Winnersh Triangle Business Park, Caprice Restaurant is part of Crowne Plaza Reading East, and the Terrace overlooks landscaped podium gardens. The restaurant is bright, modern and open plan, while the menu is modern British and authentic Indian. As well as offering outstanding flavours, the kitchen does a great job with its imaginative presentation.

Chef: Mahendra Rawat
Food Style: Modern British,
Authentic Indian

See advertisement on page 49

Chez Mal Brasserie ❀

Malmaison Reading, Great Western House,
18–20 Station Road, RG1 1JX
0118 956 2300
www.malmaison.com
Open: All year

Chef: Szabolcs Deli
Food Style: Modern European,
International

By all accounts the world's oldest railway hotel, the early Victorian property is a real charmer. Its historic past is recognised in some decorative touches, but this being a Mal, the overall finish is glamorous and stylish. Settle into the Malbar for a pre-dinner cocktail.

Old Windsor

NEW The Loch & The Tyne by Adam Handling

SL4 2QY
01753 851470
www.lochandtyne.com
Open: All year

Chef: Adam Handling, Steven Kerr, Jonathan McNeil
Food Style: Modern British

Despite its location in a charming village only a few miles from the Queen's Windsor residence, the name of this contemporary pub with rooms is named in honour of Scotland and Newcastle – the two places where the three chef co-owners met. Whether it's next to the real fire or outside on the covered terrace, enjoy a pre-meal drink as you scan a menu written around what's currently growing in the kitchen garden and orchard. Sustainability and hyperlocal sourcing is key at The Loch & The Tyne by Adam Handling, the style underpinned by solid technique in the kitchen. Start, perhaps, with a well balanced and beautifully presented dish of accurately timed Orkney scallop teamed with leek and horseradish foam that balances the natural sweetness of the scallop. Move on to an exquisite dish of salt-aged duck breast covered with spices and served with a potato cake and treacle onions. Simplicity at its best is displayed with a classic tart, its crisp pastry case filled with light custard.

INTRODUCING ...
CAPRICE RESTAURANT

THE BEST RESTAURANT IN TOWN

CROWNE PLAZA
AN IHG HOTEL
READING EAST

ENJOY THE FINEST BRITISH & INDIAN CUISINE

Discover the new 2 AA Rosette Caprice Restaurant, located in the exceptional new 4 Silver Star Crowne Plaza Reading East. The perfect spot to enjoy your meal in tranquil surroundings, with floor to ceiling windows and comfortable seating, all complemented by great service and fine wines.

Monty's Bar & Lounge with tranquil outdoor Terrace, offers a fresh and quality modern British menu, as well as an extensive authentic Indian menu. Why not try some creative cocktails on the landscaped lawns and gardens.

The splendid Afternoon Teas are the finest in Berkshire. Our flexible dining options, including private and corporate banqueting, as well as Christmas Parties and residential packages/ offers, are also available upon request.

T: 0118 944 0444 | E: fb@cpreading.co.uk
W: www.cpreading.co.uk
Crowne Plaza Reading East, Wharfedale Road,
Winnersh Triangle, Berks, RG41 5TS

The French Horn 🌸🌸

Sonning, RG4 6TN
0118 969 2204
www.thefrenchhorn.co.uk
Closed: 1–4 January

Chef: Josiane Diaga
Food Style: Traditional French,
British

The riverside setting is a treat, with the dining room opening on to a terrace, at the family-run French Horn, which is full of old-school charm with slick and well-managed service. The menu looks across the Channel for its inspiration, with a classically based repertoire.

Shinfield

L'Ortolan 🌸🌸🌸 🍷 NOTABLE WINE LIST

Church Lane, RG2 9BY
0118 988 8500
www.lortolan.com
Closed: 25 December to 8 January

Chef: James Greatorex
Food Style: Modern French

A country-house style restaurant set in an elegant red-brick former vicarage with Gothic-style front door and bow-fronted windows, L'Ortolan is a name synonymous with modern gastronomy since the 1980s. Now, talented young chef James Greatorex is the man in 'whites', delivering sophisticated, highly detailed, aspiring contemporary cooking via carte and tasting menus. Dishes come dressed to thrill, with flavour, texture, balance and precision to the fore; witness 'melting' citrus cured Cornish mackerel teamed with cucumber and buttermilk, or 'sparkling fresh' Cornish cod ballotine with clams, sea herbs and watercress. Fine-dining standards like canapés, bread, pre-desserts and petits fours round off a polished act, alongside professional and informed service.

Thatcham

The Bunk Inn 🌸

Curridge, RG18 9DS
01635 200400
www.thebunkinn.co.uk
Open: All year

Chef: Lewis Spreadbury
Food Style: Modern British, French

A short canter from Newbury Racecourse, this convivial inn is still very much the village hub where locals prop up the bar by the open fire with a glass of ale and a packet of crisps, but its confident modern cooking also attracts foodies.

White Waltham

The Beehive 🌹🌹
Waltham Road, SL6 3SH
01628 822877
www.thebeehivewhitewaltham.com
Closed: 25–26 December

With the cricket ground opposite, The Beehive is the epitome of the English village pub, and offers chatty and friendly service too. Driven by the seasons, its regularly changing modern British menus deliver dishes packed with flavour such as Cornish cod with cannellini beans, grapes, monks beard, caviar, wild garlic and smoked butter sauce.

Chef: Alex Parker
Food Style: British

Windsor

The Greene Oak 🌹
Oakley Green, SL4 5UW
01753 864294
www.thegreeneoak.co.uk
Open: All year

Very much a dining pub, The Greene Oak is a charming old place with bright, homely decor and cheerful staff who keep it all ticking along nicely. The kitchen makes good use of local seasonal ingredients, focusing on gently contemporary British- and European-inspired ideas.

Chef: Sergio Araujo
Food Style: Modern British

Bristol

Bristol

Berwick Lodge 🌹🌹
Berwick Drive, Henbury, BS10 7TD
0117 958 1590
www.berwicklodge.co.uk
Closed: 25–26 December, 1 January

The Victorian gent who built this manor house back in the 1890s picked a good spot, surrounded by 18 acres of gardens and woodland. The smart boutique restaurant, Hattua, is the perfect setting for creative modern dishes which look as good as they taste.

Chef: Matt Buscombe
Food Style: Modern British

Bristol *continued*

The Bird in Hand ⚜
Weston Road, Long Ashton, BS41 9LA
01275 395222
thebirdinla.co.uk
Closed: Monday

Just beyond Bristol's western limits, The Bird in Hand
offers the charm you'd expect from a village pub, while
here and there hinting at the South African origins of
one of the owners. There's the country's national flag,
of course, paintings and, on the menu, lamb Durban
curry bunny chow, alongside modern British dishes and
pub classics.

Chef: Moe Lister
Food Style: Modern British

NEW The Ethicurean Awaiting Inspection
Barley Wood Walled Garden, Long Lane,
Wrington, BS40 5SA
01934 245888
www.theethicurean.com
Closed: Monday, Tuesday, 19 September to 5 October,
19 December to 5 January

Apparently an Ethicurean is one who believes in 'eating
ethically without depriving oneself of taste'. The food
here, with many ingredients grown in their large and
beautifully-kept Victorian walled garden, is ethically
sourced, and certainly not deprived of flavour. A fine
mix of rustic and modern, with outstanding views of the Mendips.

Chef: Mark McCabe
Food Style: Modern British

Hotel du Vin Bristol ⚜ 🍷 NOTABLE WINE LIST
The Sugar House, Narrow Lewins Mead, BS1 2NU
0117 925 5577
www.hotelduvin.com
Open: All year

Chef: Marcus Lang
Food Style: French, British

In a former sugar warehouse close to the waterfront, the casual French-inspired bistro at the
Bristol HdV is a buzzy and easy-going venue. Factor in the world-class wine list, and you've got
a compelling package. The bilingual menu deals in classic stuff.

The Ox 🏵️

The Basement, 43 Corn Street, BS1 1HT
0117 922 1001
www.theoxbristol.com
Closed: 25–28 December

Head down to the basement, a one-time bank vault, and you'll find a restaurant that the old boys of yesteryear would have admired, with its oak panels, ox blood leather seats and murals. They'd have appreciated the red-blooded menu too – steaks are their thing.

Chef: Rob Crouch
Food Style: Modern British

Paco Tapas 🏵️🏵️

3A Lower Guinea Street, BS1 6SY
0117 925 7021
www.pacotapas.co.uk
Closed: Sunday, Monday, 25–26 December

Located directly on the docks at Bristol harbourside, this bustling tapas bar offers authentic dishes from the owners' Andalusian home. Much of the produce comes directly from the region while daily specials are added by way of fresh fish and seafood delivered daily from the Cornish coasts.

Chef: Joel Breakwell
Food Style: Andalusian tapas

Second Floor Restaurant 🏵️🏵️ 🍷NOTABLE WINE LIST

Harvey Nichols, 27 Philadelphia Street,
Quakers Friars, BS1 3BZ
0117 916 8898
www.harveynichols.com
Closed: Easter Sunday, 25 December, 1 January

Overlooking the old Quakers Friars Dominican friary in the heart of Cabot Circus shopping quarter, this gold and beige-hued, second-floor dining room is a supremely relaxing place. The kitchen turns out a menu of lively modern British and European food. There are interesting wines on offer too.

Chef: Lucy Lourenco
Food Style: Modern British

Bristol *continued*

The Spiny Lobster ⚜
128 Whiteladies Road, Clifton, BS8 2RS
0117 973 7384
www.thespinylobster.co.uk
Closed: Sunday, Monday

Mitch Tonks' seafood brasserie and fish market
maintains a rigorous commitment to freshness and
simplicity, using fish and shellfish mostly landed by the
Brixham boats. The dining room sports linen-clothed
tables, staff are friendly, and top-class materials slapped
onto a charcoal-burning Josper grill can't be beaten.

Chef: Charlie Hearn
Food Style: Mediterranean,
Seafood

NEW The Star and Dove ⚜⚜
75–78 St Luke's Road, Totterdown, BS3 4RY
0117 4030386
thestaranddove.com/
Closed: Monday, Tuesday, 25 December, 1 January

The Star and Dove offers pleasing modern vintage
styling in a traditional Victorian city pub. The pub
ambience is retained in one half where locals enjoy a
pint with friends, while the stylish restaurant on the
other side provides a selection of top quality dishes
utilising local and seasonal produce to its best.

Chef: Newstead Sayer
Food Style: Modern British

Tare Restaurant ⚜⚜
Unit 14, Museum Street, Wapping Wharf, BS1 6ZA
0117 929 4328
tarerestaurant.co.uk
Closed: Sunday, Monday, Tuesday,
18 December to 3 January

Operating out of a converted shipping container
in the up-and-coming Wapping Wharf harbourside
development, Tare offers intimate, relaxed and modern
dining. The carefully sourced top-quality produce
contributes to the regular and seasonal menu updates
including a five-course tasting menu. There are some
interesting bottled beers and ciders too.

Chef: Matt Hampshire
Food Style: Modern European

Buckinghamshire

The Artichoke 🏵🏵🏵 ⬥NOTABLE WINE LIST

9 Market Square, Old Amersham, HP7 0DF
01494 726611
www.artichokerestaurant.co.uk
Closed: 25 December to 8 January, 1 week Easter, 2 weeks August/September

Chef: Laurie Gear, Ben Jenkins
Food Style: Modern European

Amersham's finest continues to set a regional standard for dazzling modern cooking delivered with engaging brio in an atmosphere enlivened by views of the kitchen pass. Laurie Gear offers a variety of menus that will suit everyone. The Chiltern black ale bread with cultured butter is an unmissable intro to what's to follow. Start with Bledlow Ridge pork belly, Burrow Hill perry, roast pear purée, fennel and sourdough tuile, then move onto roast poussin, asparagus, black garlic, truffle, seasonal mushrooms and cep ketchup. For dessert, sit back for 15 minutes and wait for the passionfruit soufflé with passionfruit and dark chocolate sorbet.

Gilbey's Restaurant 🏵🏵

1 Market Square, HP7 0DF
01494 727242
www.gilbeygroup.com
Closed: 24–29 December

Housed in Old Amersham's 17th-century former grammar school, the fully renovated Gilbey's offers the style and intimacy you'd expect with low ceilings and wood flooring. Cooking is traditional and simple with modern touches – expect dishes such as roasted red pepper soup with green tomato salsa followed by confit leg of duck with tomato and olive gnocchi.

Chef: Adam Whitlock
Food Style: Modern British

Hawkyns by Atul Kochhar 🏵🏵

The Crown, 16 High Street, HP7 0DH
01494 721541
www.hawkynsrestaurant.co.uk
Open: All year

Chef: Atul Kochhar
Food Style: Modern British, Modern Indian

Set within The Crown, a Tudor-style building in the pretty town of Amersham, Hawkyns is run by the celebrated Indian chef Atul Kochhar. Set against a backdrop of original wooden beams, stripped floorboards and brick fireplaces, the scrubbed farmhouse-style tables and mismatched chairs add an informal pub feel but the food is a combination of the best British and Indian cooking.

Aylesbury

The Chequers Inn 🏵️🏵️
35 Church Lane, Weston Turville, HP22 5SJ
01296 613298
www.thechequerswt.co.uk
Closed: Monday

Dating from the 16th century, its traditional bar features old beams and polished flagstone floors, while the restaurant is more contemporary. Home to chef/owner Dritan and his maître d' wife Ranka, their 11 years here have seen them turn it into a locally renowned establishment. Although not open to the public, the prime minister's Chequers is just a few miles away.

Chef: Jamie Maserati
Food Style: Modern British

Hartwell House Hotel, Restaurant & Spa 🏵️🏵️ 🍷NOTABLE WINE LIST
Lower Hartwell, Vale of Aylesbury, HP17 8NR
01296 747444
www.hartwell-house.com
Open: All year

Set in 90 acres of landscaped parkland 40 miles north west of London, this stately home occupies a stunning location on the edge of the Chilterns in the Vale of Aylesbury. The grand dining room with its high domed ceiling is an opulent setting for the skilful, modern British cooking.

Chef: Daniel Richardson
Food Style: Modern British

Beaconsfield

The Jolly Cricketers 🏵️
24 Chalfont Road, Seer Green, HP9 2YG
01494 676308
www.thejollycricketers.co.uk
Closed: 25–26 December

A red-brick, wisteria-festooned Victorian pub, The Jolly Cricketers is the hub of village life. Inside it's a genuinely unspoilt and unreconstructed village local that has created a reputation strong enough to bring in diners from much further afield. Uncomplicated cooking shows good attention to detail and big hearty flavours from well-sourced ingredients. Pub classics as well as more contemporary ideas.

Chef: David Wilkerson
Food Style: Modern British

Buckingham

Duke's Restaurant & Bar 🌸
Buckingham Villiers Hotel, 3 Castle Street, MK18 1BS
01280 822444
www.villiers-hotel.co.uk
Open: All year

Chef: Paul Stopps
Food Style: Modern British

Overlooking a courtyard, the restaurant at the Villiers Hotel offers a range of booths and seating options. The kitchen focuses on tried-and-tested dishes, but more ambitious ideas are just as well handled, such as roasted rump of lamb, shepherd's pie, Merguez sausage, peas, samphire, courgette and lamb jus.

Burnham

Burnham Beeches Hotel 🌸🌸
Grove Road, SL1 8DP
01628 429955
corushotels.com/burnham-beeches-hotel
Open: All year

Chef: Nenad Bibic
Food Style: Modern British, European

Close to Windsor, this extended Georgian manor house is set in 10 acres of attractive grounds. The oak-panelled Gray's restaurant is a formal affair with white linen and views of the pretty garden. The gently contemporary dishes are based on classical themes and techniques.

Gerrards Cross

The Three Oaks 🌸🌸
Austenwood Lane, Chalfont St Peter, SL9 8NL
01753 899016
www.thethreeoaksgx.co.uk
Closed: Monday, Tuesday

Part of the draw at this attractive gastro pub is attentive service from a cheerful young team. There's a lovely garden for those balmy days, while inside, the place has a smartly updated look – a brick fireplace, bare wood tables and easy-on-the-eye colours. Expect to find accomplished, contemporary cooking built on top-drawer produce.

Chef: Jason Biswell
Food Style: Modern British

Great Missenden

Nags Head Inn & Restaurant ❀
London Road, HP16 0DG
01494 862200
www.nagsheadbucks.com
Closed: 25 December

Only a 15-minute stroll from the enchantments of the
Roald Dahl Museum in the High Street, the family-
run Nags Head is a 15th-century country inn by the
River Misbourne. Lightly modernised inside, it makes
a relaxed, welcoming setting for creatively fashioned
cooking, and dishes with the populist touch.

Chef: Howard Gale
Food Style: British, French

Marlow

The Coach ❀❀❀
3 West Street, SL7 2LS
www.thecoachmarlow.co.uk
Closed: 25–26 December

Chef: Tom De Keyser, Tom Kerridge
Food Style: French, British

The pint-sized Coach is a cosy, chic pub dominated by its stainless-steel, L-shaped bar,
decked out with elbow-to-elbow leather bar stalls and tables with matching banquettes,
while an open kitchen adds to the buzzy, up-tempo action. Head chef Tom De Keyser turns
out plates with the same DNA as the garlanded Hand & Flowers – big on flavour and technical
finesse. Divided between 'meat' and 'no meat' dishes, the menu reads like a roster of big-
hearted modern pub food – perhaps turbot Scotch egg with curried onion and moilee sauce,
and whole stuffed rotisserie quail with pickled chilli and satay sauce. The Coach doesn't take
bookings, so turn up early.

Danesfield House Hotel & Spa ❀❀
Henley Road, SL7 2EY
01628 891010
www.danesfieldhouse.co.uk
Closed: 25–26 December

Built in 1901, Danesfield House is set in 65 magnificent
acres, just a hop from central London and a skip from
Heathrow. As well as memorable views across the River
Thames, the Orangery restaurant also offers interesting
and innovative menus. The flavour is modern British
but there's plenty of European influence.

Chef: Massimo Principe
Food Style: Modern British

See advertisement opposite

Glaze Restaurant ◉
Crowne Plaza Marlow, Fieldhouse Lane, SL7 1GJ
01628 496800
www.cpmarlow.co.uk/dine
Open: All year

Just outside Marlow is the Crowne Plaza Marlow, and
its flagship restaurant. Glaze is a light-filled, stylish
modern space, enjoying views over the hotel's lake
in the grounds. Diners can choose from seasonally-
changing menus of brasserie cooking or Indian cuisine,
either of which always has something new and exciting
to offer.

Chef: Robert Quehan
Food Style: Modern British, Indian

See advertisement on page 60

INTRODUCING ...

GLAZE RESTAURANT

THE BEST RESTAURANT IN TOWN

CROWNE PLAZA
MARLOW

ENJOY THE FINEST BRITISH & INDIAN CUISINE

The exceptional new AA Rosette awarded Glaze Restaurant with lake views, invites you to enjoy our delicious British or authentic Indian cuisine in superb surroundings, all complemented by great service and fine wines.

Alternatively, why not treat yourself to an indulgent Sparkling Afternoon Tea or a creative cocktail or two in the Conservatory or Terrace, overlooking the stunning lake and lawns.

Enjoy a BBQ feast on our terrace, the ideal way to bring friends and family together for a special occasion.

T: 01628 496 800 | E: fb@cpmarlow.co.uk
W: www.cpmarlow.co.uk
Crowne Plaza Marlow, Fieldhouse Lane, Marlow, Bucks, SL7 1GJ

Marlow *continued*

The Hand & Flowers ◉◉◉◉◉ ⚑ NOTABLE WINE LIST

126 West Street, SL7 2BP
01628 482277
www.thehandandflowers.co.uk
Closed: 24–26 December

Chef: Tom Kerridge, Tom De Keyser
Food Style: French. British

Tom Kerridge's motivation has always been to create food that people want to eat, rather than messing about with baffling peculiarities they feel they ought to try. The nerve-centre of his empire remains the whitewashed country pub with its hanging baskets, where an atmosphere of friendly enthusiasm prevails amid the bare tables and half-boarded walls. Keen to emphasise a passion for produce that's been 'selected with care and prepared with love and respect' the menu might offer Cornish 'Tin Mine' tart with spiced date sauce, soft cheddar and crispy beef, or glazed omelette of smoked haddock and parmesan. Mains might include 30-day dry aged fillet of beef with potato buttermilk waffle, or malt roasted pork tenderloin and cheek with cod's roe. The strawberry and salted biscuit soufflé with crème fraîche ice cream is a lighter option, or try the signature chocolate and ale cake with Pedro Ximenez and Rebellion beer ice cream.

NEW The Oarsman ◉

46 Spittal Street, SL7 1DB
01628 617755
www.theoarsman.co.uk
Open: All year

Chef: Scott McNicholas Smith
Food Style: Modern British bistro

A bistro-pub and wine bar in fashionable Marlow, The Oarsman serves a bistro-style roster from an open kitchen and small plates from a larder counter. The on-vogue modern refit looks the part, decked out in leather seating, darkwood floorboards and subtle references to its name, while a rear terrace is an alfresco hot-ticket. Corking wine list too.

Taplow

The Cliveden Dining Room ◉◉◉ ⚑ NOTABLE WINE LIST

See pages 62-63 and advertisement on page 64

Waddesdon

The Five Arrows ◉◉

High Street, HP18 0JE
01296 651727
fivearrowshotel.co.uk/restaurant
Closed: Monday, Tuesday

Part of the Rothschild Estate, this small Victorian hotel stands at the gates of Waddesdon Manor but has none of the airs and graces of the grand French château-style stately home. The relaxed restaurant sports a smart, contemporary look with wine-related prints on the walls.

Chef: Matthew Butcher
Food Style: Modern British

Taplow

 **NOTABLE WINE LIST**

The Cliveden Dining Room

Cliveden Estate, SL6 0JF
01628 668561
www.clivedenhouse.co.uk
Open: All year

Chef: Paul O'Neill
Food Style: Modern British

Stunning dishes in a stately home

Boasting a 350-year history of celebrity parties and political gatherings, high society scandal and lording it over a whopping 376-acres of National Trust estate, Grade I Cliveden belongs unquestionably in the premier league of England's stately homes.

The first house was built in 1666 by George Villers, the 2nd Duke of Buckingham for his mistress, the Countess of Shrewsbury, however, the glorious building you see today is the third on the site and designed by famed architect, Sir Charles Barry.

The dining experience is very special too, in an impeccably elegant, swagged and chandeliered restaurant with shimmering south-facing views over the parterre and the National Trust gardens all the way to the Thames in the distance. Paul O'Neill's dazzling cooking is more than a match for this luxurious setting.

There are vegan and vegetarian menus as well as the standard à la carte, from which you might choose a Cornish fish stew of red mullet, Fowey mussels with a saffron bun, or a perfectly timed double-baked cheese soufflé with walnut and apple salad to start. Follow on with roasted duck, gooseberries, confit leg and sweet cicely; or 28-day aged beef fillet, pickled chanterelle, beef fat potato and BBQ tongue. A side dish of 'invisible chips' is intriguingly 0% fat and 100% donated to charity.

For non-meat eaters, there could be a starter of beef tomato tartare, confit pepper yolk and caper crackers or truffle risotto, then smoked aubergine, shiso, almond dashi and radish or a dish named 'Alliums' – caramelised onion, charred leek and spring onion broth.

Desserts certainly keep pace with the dishes presented so far – choose Valhrona chocolate mousse, salted caramel and java pepper or spiced pineapple, passionfruit,

coconut sorbet and lemongrass. For an unforgettable meal, factor in either the Classic, or the Sommelier's Cellar Selection offering premier cuvées from the world's greatest vineyards

See advertisement on page 64

"Paul O'Neill's dazzling cooking is more than a match for this luxurious setting."

CLIVEDEN

EXCEPTIONAL DINING

Steeped in history and romance, Cliveden Dining Room pairs the drama and elegance of the spectacular setting with innovative, exceptionally crafted dishes inspired by our passion for British produce.

Experience your moment in history.

RELAIS &
CHATEAUX

Taplow, Berkshire, SL6 0JF | Tel: 01628 668561 | Reservations@clivedenhouse.co.uk

BOOK NOW: CLIVEDENHOUSE.CO.UK

ICONIC
LUXURY HOTELS

Wooburn

Chequers Inn ◉◉
Kiln Lane, Wooburn Common, HP10 0JQ
01628 529575
www.chequers-inn.com
Open: All year

Chef: Pascal Lemoine
Food Style: British, French

A 17th-century former coaching inn, there's no denying that the Chequers has moved with the times. The Anglo-French cooking in its chic and spacious restaurant delivers compelling flavour combinations. Eating out on the sunny patio in summer is a delight.

Cambridgeshire

Bartlow

The Three Hills ◉◉
Dean Road, CB21 4PW
01223 890500
www.thethreehills.co.uk
Closed: Monday, Tuesday

The Three Hills is a charming 17th-century, Grade II listed pub with a lovely garden leading down to a river. The relaxed main restaurant has the feel of an 'orangery', and overlooks a heated terrace, while the kitchen offers a modern British menu based on quality local produce in dishes created with skill and flair.

Chef: Harry Ashcroft
Food Style: Modern British

Cambridge

Midsummer House Restaurant ◉◉◉◉◉ ▲ NOTABLE WINE LIST
See pages 66-67 and advertisement on page 68

Quy Mill Hotel & Spa, Cambridge ◉◉
Church Road, Stow-Cum-Quy, CB25 9AF
01223 293383
www.cambridgequymill.co.uk
Closed: Monday, Tuesday, Wednesday

Dine in the historic Waterwheel, where the Quy water literally runs through the middle of the Grade-II listed original waterwheel, featuring modern British cuisine in a unique setting. The 'Chef's Plate of Pig' will keep meat eaters very happy. There's a good wine list too.

Chef: Karl Blackmore
Food Style: Modern European, British, French

Cambridge

 NOTABLE WINE LIST

Midsummer House Restaurant

Midsummer Common, CB4 1HA
01223 369299
www.midsummerhouse.co.uk
Closed: 25 December to 8 Janaury, Last week April, 2 weeks August/September

Chef: Daniel Clifford
Food Style: Modern British

Long-established star of the Cambridge dining scene

Since Daniel Clifford bought the idyllically located Midsummer House in 1998, he has turned this former private residence into a world class dining destination. The handsome Victorian villa sits on the banks of the River Cam, looking out over the cows grazing on the common.

The chic and light-filled conservatory dining room to the rear is a tranquil space, separated from the kitchen by a window, through which Daniel and his head chef,

Mark Abbott, can be observed at close quarters. They are supported by a talented team of studious and focused chefs creating elegant, precise and inventive modern British dishes, showcased in a nine-course tasting menu and, from Wednesdays to Saturdays, a more compact set lunch menu.

The atmosphere is calmly civilised, an ideal combination of formality and informality. Menu descriptions are concise

– even terse – which contrasts with the intricacy of the food. You can be confident that each carefully sourced ingredient is treated with respect and is on the plate for a reason.

Clear flavours chime perfectly with the seasons, and an early summer meal might begin with salmon rillette tartlet and pickled cucumber followed by freshwater prawn with gazpacho mousse, sun dried tomatoes and peas. Sautéed duck liver is enlivened by verjus, Comte cheese, home-dried sultanas and walnuts, before you move on to slowly cooked Loch Duart salmon with white chocolate and caviar sauce. Another highlight is a delicate dish of braised Cornish turbot, white asparagus, razor clams and jus de caisson.

Next up, a cheese course of Tete de Moine with celeriac custard, grapefruit sorbet and truffle honey that might precede poached kumquat with buffalo yogurt sorbet. Finally, English strawberries with champagne and elderflower might carry you through to coffee and a plate of delicate petits fours.

See advertisement on page 68

"Clear flavours chime perfectly with the seasons..."

MIDSUMMER HOUSE

Midsummer House is located in the heart of historic Cambridge. This Victorian Villa encapsulates Daniel Clifford's vision for culinary perfection and is home to some fresh innovative dishes.

Daniel Clifford has taken the restaurant to another level over the past 24 years; his cooking has a modern-focus which is underpinned by classical French technique offering seriously sophisticated food.

Upstairs there is a private dining room, a welcoming lounge and terrace for after dinner drinks with river views. The private dining room is the perfect location for small weddings, lavish birthday celebrations, simple family gatherings or corporate entertaining.

Midsummer Common, Cambridge CB4 1HA

Tel: 01223 369299 **Website:** www.midsummerhouse.co.uk

Email: reservations@midsummerhouse.co.uk

Instagram: @midsummer_house **Twitter:** @Midsummerhouse

Facebook: www.facebook.com/midsummerhouserestaurant

Cambridge *continued*

Restaurant 22 🌸🌸🌸
22 Chesterton Road, CB4 3AX
01223 351880
www.restaurant22.co.uk
Closed: 4–13 September, 25 December

Chef: Sam Carter
Food Style: Modern British

Backing onto the River Cam and Jesus Green, Restaurant 22 is a converted Victorian townhouse with an elegant but unfussy dining room in shades of grey and crisp white. The late 19th-century stained-glass windows are well worth a look. Expect precise cooking with layers of flavour. Dry aged pork belly with Yorkshire rhubarb and XO sauce, simply presented on a white china plate makes for a great starter. Follow this with lightly poached halibut with thinly sliced brassicas and a dusting of seaweed, in a lovely broth. Try the unusual dessert of dark chocolate with miso gel, thyme leaves and buttermilk.

NEW Terrace Restaurant 🌸
Gonville Place, CB1 1LY
01223 366611
www.gonvillehotel.co.uk
Open: All year

Chef: Jamie De Cruz
Food Style: Modern British

Right by Parker's Piece, close to central Cambridge, Terrace Restaurant is part of the well-established boutique Gonville Hotel. There's glass to front and sides in this modern new extension, along with dark wood floors, velour covered chairs and natural wood tables. Sliding glass doors open out onto a terrace, and staff are attentive and smartly uniformed.

Fordham

The White Pheasant 🌸🌸
21 Market Street, CB7 5LQ
01638 720414
www.whitepheasant.com
Closed: Monday, Tuesday

The White Pheasant is a modern foodie pub with simply decorated interior, log fires and plain wood tables, but chef-proprietor Calvin Holland's cooking sets it a cut above the average. The kitchen sources the very best materials from local producers.

Chef: Calvin Holland
Food Style: British, European

Hinxton

The Red Lion Inn ◉
32 High Street, CB10 1QY
01799 530601
www.redlionhinxton.co.uk
Open: All year

Chef: Jiri Wolker
Food Style: British

A perfect example of timeless rustic cosiness, the bar at the Tudor, pink-painted, timbered Red Lion is a great spot for classic pub grub, but for contemporary cuisine, head for the airy, oak-raftered restaurant, where there's an eclectic carte pitched just right for the kitchen's ambitions.

Peterborough

The Chubby Castor ◉◉◉
See pages 72-73 and advertisement opposite

Stilton

The Bell Inn ◉◉
Great North Road, PE7 3RA
01733 241066
www.thebellstilton.co.uk
Closed: Bank Holidays, 25 December

Chef: Morgan de Smidt
Food Style: Modern British

Dating from 1642, this rambling village coaching inn has a contemporary outlook when it comes to cooking. The kitchen turns out bright ideas displaying a good balance of flavours. Perhaps open with chicken liver parfait, mango chutney and toasted brioche before Moroccan lamb loin, harissa-spiced couscous, bok choi and red pepper purée.

Wansford

NEW Prévost @ Haycock ◉◉◉
Great North Road, PE8 6JA
01780 72223
www.haycock.co.uk
Closed: Sunday, Monday, Tuesday

Chef: Lee Clarke, Sam Nash
Food Style: Modern British

Prévost @ Haycock is a bright space with lots of glass including large, modern chandeliers housed in metal bird cages. There are also two massive standing birdcages you can sit inside. The flooring is dark wood while chairs are brightly upholstered. Service is polished and attentive, and the chefs actually deliver the food to the table and explain each dish. Start with roasted Cornish lobster, pork jowl, Grelot onion and elderflower gel, or Lincolnshire poacher dumplings, Tokyo turnip and hen of the woods. Follow with poached Cornish brill, sea vegetables, BBQ crosnes and shrimp sauce. A sweet ending is provided by Yorkshire rhubarb, ginger and rice pudding parfait.

Civilised Dining

From the exquisite presentation, to the flavours and textures, we can ensure our dishes are plated to perfection. It's all in the detail...

TASTING MENU | À LA CARTE | SUNDAY LUNCH | SET MENUS

Peterborough

The Chubby Castor

34 Peterborough Road, Castor, PE5 7AX
01733 380801
www.thechubbycastor.com
Closed: Monday, Tuesday, 1–15 August

Chef: Cory White
Food Style: Modern British

Set within the historic Fitzwilliam Arms, a thatched Grade II listed building dating back to the 17th-century, The Chubby Castor is a charming and characterful restaurant. Its timeless chocolate box look belies a contemporary interior, with attentive staff explaining each course in detail at the table. Much of the dialogue is inevitably about the produce used as there is an unwavering commitment to sustainability and many of the raw materials are grown in the kitchen garden. Whether ordering from the à la carte, set, tasting or plant-based menus, there is plenty to choose from and it won't be easy.

Start with a moist terrine of chicken and duck liver, Sauternes jelly and light-textured onion brioche, or maybe go for the smoked eel, Charlotte potatoes, salted Exmoor caviar and sage velouté.

When it comes to the main course, there might be a correctly timed and flavoursome fillet of bass with smoked crab tortellini, leeks, salsify, asparagus and rich lobster bisque, or if sharing is

your thing, the char siu pork loin (for two people) with polenta cake, Stornoway black pudding and chargrilled lettuce is a winning combination.

The quality of the cooking and pin-sharp presentation continues right through to the pudding stage. Chocolate ganache with candied pistachios, apricot jam and whipped Chantilly cream is a dessert with plenty of finesse. The chefs can be really tested by ordering the light and airy strawberry soufflé with its refreshing mint ice cream.

Of course, an exemplary additional course of perfectly kept British cheeses – five or nine different types – with all the proper accompaniments is another way to round off a memorable meal. An extensive wine list has been carefully considered to complement the dishes, with wine flights and a strong choice is also available by the glass.

"...there is an unwavering commitment to sustainability..."

See advertisement on page 71

Wisbech

Crown Lodge Hotel ❀
Downham Road, Outwell, PE14 8SE
01945 773391
www.thecrownlodgehotel.co.uk
Closed: 25–26 December, 1 January

Chef: Jamie Symons
Food Style: Modern, Traditional

A modern hotel kitted out to host conferences and meetings, Crown Lodge is a useful local resource. The flexible approach to dining means you can go for simple things like fish and chips or a burger, but there's also a more ambitious carte.

Cheshire

Broxton

Carden Park Hotel, Golf Resort & Spa ❀
Carden Park, CH3 9DQ
01829 731000
www.cardenpark.co.uk

Chef: Graham Tinsley MBE
Food Style: Modern British

A country estate with a Jacobean core, Welsh mountain views and a three-acre vineyard. The cooking style encompasses Asian-style red mullet terrine with wakame seaweed and sesame salad; and pan-roasted chicken breast and leg crépinette with hay-smoked mash and roasted cauliflower. Chocolate mousse, salted caramel and milk ice cream is in there too.

Burwardsley

The Pheasant Inn ❀
Higher Burwardsley, CH3 9PF
01829 770434
www.thepheasantinn.co.uk
Open: All year

Midway along the Sandstone Trail in rural Cheshire, the far-reaching views from The Pheasant stretch as far as the Welsh hills. Pub classics done well rub shoulders with more contemporary ideas on their crowd-pleasing menu. Steamed Menai mussels followed by Italian-influenced pork saltimbocca then local Cheshire Farm ice cream is one way to go.

Chef: Matt Leech
Food Style: British, European

Chester

Arkle Restaurant ⚘⚘⚘ ▮NOTABLE WINE LIST
Eastgate, CH1 1LT
01244 324024
www.chestergrosvenor.com
Closed: Sunday, Tuesday

Deep within the luxurious Chester Grosvenor hotel, the
Arkle Restaurant has a club feel with its warm woods,
rich dark blues and yellows and sumptuous furnishings.
The sophisticated space is illuminated by a skylight
and large chandelier, tables elegantly dressed in crisp
double linens. Service from smartly uniformed staff is
as polished as the modern cooking which displays well

Chef: Elliot Hill , Raymond Booker
Food Style: Modern French

defined flavours and precise technical skills. A well-made ballotine of confit chicken with caviar,
hazelnut, grapes and dill emulsion could lead on to deep-flavoured loin and sweetbread of
Herdwick hogget with English asparagus, sheep's yogurt and wild garlic.

Brasserie ABode
Grosvenor Road, CH1 2DJ
01244 405820
www.brasserieabode.co.uk/chester
Open: All year

Chef: Sean Sutton
Food Style: Modern & Classic
French

The Cheshire outpost of the ABode hotel group occupies a shiny modern rotunda overlooking
Chester racecourse. Its restaurant is on the fifth floor, with stellar views over the castle and lush
countryside. There's a contemporary finish, with stylish fixtures and rather glam light fittings.

La Brasserie at The Chester Grosvenor & Spa ⚘⚘
Eastgate, CH1 1LT
01244 324024
www.chestergrosvenor.com
Closed: 25 December

La Brasserie offers commendable support to The Arkle
Restaurant at the same hotel. With all the swagger
of an authentique Parisian outfit, it has black-leather
banquettes, shimmering brass and a giant hand-painted
skylight, plus a menu that builds confidently on classic
ideas at both lunch and dinner.

Chef: Elliot Hill, Arron Tye
Food Style: Modern European

Chester *continued*

NEW hypha 🌸🌸
5 City Walls, CH1 2JG
01244 312490
www.www.hypha.uk
Closed: 25 December, 1 January

Set high on the city walls, above the canal, hypha is
something of an experimental dining venue. It has its
own fermentation lab and creative food workspace,
and aims to produce dishes unlike any other. Every
ingredient has been grown or foraged in the area, and
the end product is a constantly evolving micro-seasonal
tasting menu. Plant-based and sustainable.

Chef: László Nagy
Food Style: Sustainable, Modern

Palm Court 🌸
Grosvenor Pulford Hotel & Spa, Wrexham Road,
Pulford, CH4 9DG
01244 570560
www.grosvenorpulfordhotel.co.uk/palmcourt
Open: All year

Garden room-style with lots of palm trees and
greenery, Palm Court has an open-plan lounge and
restaurant. There's a water feature along one end, and
plenty of glass and chandeliers, a great mix of art deco
and contemporary. Expect modern brasserie food. The
Palm Court is part of the stylish Grosvenor Pulford
Hotel & Spa complex.

Chef: Richard Scutt
Food Style: British and European

Restaurant 1539 🌸
The Racecourse, CH1 2LY
01244 304611
www.restaurant1539.co.uk
Open: All year

Chef: Ian Penn
Food Style: Modern British

Part of the Chester Racecourse complex, 1539 was given a cool half-million's worth of upgrade
in 2014. The full-drop windows of the restaurant are still a major feature, and if your heart isn't
given to equestrianism, swivel round for an ambient view into the kitchen.

The Sticky Walnut ⊛⊛
11 Charles Street, CH2 3AZ
01244 400400
www.stickywalnut.net
Closed: 25–26 December

The Sticky Walnut is spread over two floors, with chunky wooden tables, blackboards and an open kitchen. With cracking desserts like a deconstructed lime cheesecake with pecan butter biscuits and chocolate sorbet, this is a kitchen that delivers real impact.

Chef: James Kiernan
Food Style: Modern European

Congleton

Pecks ⊛
Newcastle Road, Moreton, CW12 4SB
01260 275161
www.pecksrest.co.uk
Closed: 25 December, 1 January

Pecks' culinary expertise is greatly appreciated round here, especially its Dinner at Eight tasting menu, with waiting staff describing the ingredients, flavours and techniques used. Choices may include onion and thyme galantine of guinea fowl, and hot smoked salmon with sautéed samphire. On certain evenings you can bring your own wines, corkage free. Plat du Jour is popular at lunchtime.

Chef: Les Wassall
Food Style: Modern British

See advertisement on page 78

Handforth

Best Western Plus Pinewood on Wilmslow ⊛
180 Wilmslow Road, SK9 3LF
01625 529211
www.pinewood-hotel.co.uk
Open: All year

This good-looking red-brick, in part, hotel is home to the thoroughly modern One Eighty restaurant, a sleek-looking space with darkwood tables and fashionably muted tones. The menu maintains the brasserie attitude and reveals keen creativity in the kitchen. Expect honest cookery produced with very good skill levels.

Chef: Colin Starkey
Food Style: Modern, Traditional

IF IT HAS TO BE SPECIAL... THEN IT HAS TO BE PECKS

All of our dishes are freshly prepared with the best seasonal produce to deliver exciting menus that combine classic simplicity with unique originality. A blend of traditional favourites and modern culinary practices ensure that each dish is both original and exciting.

Pecks is also available for any special celebration. Weddings, birthday, baby showers, anniversary, private parties, business meetings and groups and organisations. Pecks can create a bespoke menu for any occasion.

PECKS RESTAURANT, NEWCASTLE ROAD, MORETON,
Nr CONGLETON, CHESHIRE CW12 4SB
01260 275161   info@pecksrest.co.uk   www.pecksrest.co.uk
Please advise us if you have any specific dietary requirements, including allergens when booking.
Member of the Pear Hospitality and Retail Group.

AA Rosette
For Culinary Excellence

in f 𝕏 ⦿

Cottons Hotel & Spa 🏵

Manchester Road, WA16 0SU
01565 650333
www.cottonshotel.co.uk/food-drink
Open: All year

Chef: Joe Liptrot, Adrian Sedden
Food Style: Italian

A large, modern hotel at the edge of town, Cottons' menu is an appealing Mediterranean brasserie-style package. Try the lemon and black pepper queenie scallops with chilli mayonnaise; chicken liver parfait, Armagnac prunes, baby leeks, pickled mushrooms and toasted brioche.

Mere Court Hotel & Conference Centre 🏵

Warrington Road, Mere, WA16 0RW
01565 831000
www.merecourt.co.uk
Open: All year

Chef: Mike Malbon
Food Style: Modern Mediterranean

Set at the heart of Cheshire in seven acres of lovely gardens, Mere Court Hotel was originally built in 1903 as a wedding present for author and journalist William Dunkerley and his wife, Amy. Dining is in a selection of intimate rooms overlooking the manicured gardens and lake. Up to six people can also dine in the futuristic POD.

The Mere Golf Resort & Spa 🏵🏵

Chester Road, Mere, WA16 6LJ
01565 830155
themereresort.co.uk
Open: All year

The Mere is a must for Cheshire's fairways fans, plus it's a good location for accomplished brasserie dining in the open-plan Browns. Linen tablecloths and relatively formal service are slightly at odds with the overall tone, but the food makes some good modern statements.

Chef: Simon Mason
Food Style: International

The Church Green British Grill 🏵🏵

Higher Lane, WA13 0AP
01925 752068
www.thechurchgreen.co.uk
Closed: 25 December

Chef: Aiden Byrne
Food Style: Modern British

Chef-patron Aiden Byrne will be a familiar face to *MasterChef* fans, and his focus is on traditional British grill cooking, with excellent prime materials and touches of modern technique. On the menu might be a serving of home-made black pudding with a crispy poached egg (quite a feat) and caper and rocket salad, and comfort-pud finales like Bakewell tart with black cherry and Amaretto ice cream.

Mottram St Andrew

Mottram Hall
Wilmslow Road, SK10 4QT
01625 828135
www.champneys.com/hotels/mottram-hall
Open: All year

Chef: Colin Gannon
Food Style: Modern British

Mottram Hall is an amazing 18th-century country house set in 272 acres of some of Cheshire's most beautiful parkland. The restaurant is contemporary brasserie style with herringbone parquet floor and white marble tables. The colour scheme is subdued with vintage football photos on the walls. Windows look onto the golf course and grounds.

Nantwich

NEW Churches Mansion
150 Hospital Street, CW5 5RY
01270 627 311
www.churchesmansion.co.uk
Closed: Monday, Tuesday, 26 December, 1 January

Churche's Mansion is one of the oldest buildings in Cheshire, even surviving The Great Fire of Nantwich in 1583. The restored Tudor building retains plenty of original features but the cooking is contemporary, as is the quality tableware and open-plan bar. There is an intelligently curated wine list, too.

Chef: Mark Fletcher
Food Style: Modern, British

Rookery Hall Hotel & Spa
Main Road, Worleston, CW5 6DQ
01270 610016
www.handpickedhotels.co.uk/rookeryhall
Closed: 31 December

Chef: Mark Walker
Food Style: Modern British

Rookery Hall was built in 1816 by the owner of a Jamaican sugar plantation whose wealth is evident in the sumptuous interior, and its setting in 38 acres of gardens, pasture and parkland. The restaurant is all dramatic dark wood and has views of the grounds, which can be enjoyed even more if dining on the terrace.

Warmingham

The Bear's Paw ✿
School Lane, CW11 3QN
01270 526317
www.thebearspaw.co.uk
Open: All year

A Victorian pub given a modern makeover inside, with lots of light wood, and library shelves in the dining room. Local farmers supply the kitchen with quality north-west produce, with cheeses and ice creams also sourced from within a tight radius.

Chef: Scott Cunningham
Food Style: Modern European, British

Cornwall & the Isles of Scilly

Bodmin

Trehellas House Hotel & Restaurant ✿
Washaway, PL30 3AD
01208 72700
www.trehellashouse.co.uk
Open: All year

Chef: Simon Woon
Food Style: Traditional

With a history that stretches back to the Civil War, Trehellas House is a Cornish-stone building in a beautiful part of Cornwall. The restaurant is spacious with a stone-flagged floor, low ceilings and stone walls, and feels like an independent restaurant. The atmosphere is relaxed, and the food is unpretentious and honest.

Boscastle

The Wellington ✿✿
The Harbour, PL35 0AQ
01840 250202
www.wellingtonhotelboscastle.com
Open: All year

Chef: Kit Davis
Food Style: Modern British, French

There's a traditional bar with real ales and blackboard menus and a charming restaurant with chandeliers at this 16th-century coaching inn with a castellated tower. The kitchen sources its materials from within the county and serves bright, modern ideas with their roots in the classics.

Bryher (The Isles of Scilly)

Hell Bay Hotel ◉◉◉
TR23 0PR
01720 422947
www.hellbay.co.uk
Closed: 1 November to 15 March

Chef: Richard Kearsley
Food Style: Modern British

Not nearly as alarming as it sounds, Hell Bay is actually an idyllic secluded cove embraced by gorse-laden hillocks. Reached by ferry, Bryher is small enough to get around on foot, and the unassuming Hell Bay Hotel is the perfect spot to set off from. There is much to love in its Cornish art-filled rooms and sea views, while on the food front Richard Kearsley's assured, confident cooking is a major draw. You're in the right place when it comes to fish and seafood, whether it's pan-roasted Cornish scallops, Newlyn hake with smoked haddock and mussel velouté or Bryher crab. There are meat and vegetarian options too if fish is not your thing, while for dessert maybe plump for the tangy lemon meringue pie.

Coverack

NEW Hevva ◉
North Corner, TR12 6TF
01326 280464
www.thebayhotel.co.uk
Closed: Sunday, Monday

Food Style: Modern British

The Bay Hotel dates back to 1928, and Hevva is its current dining option. It's an intimate setting, relaxed and welcoming with stunning views across the bay, plus a friendly team with plenty of smiles and positivity. The menu is short and punchy with reassuring skills underpinning the output. Expect lots of fish, landed just a short stroll from the hotel.

Falmouth

Brasserie on the Bay ◉◉
St Michaels Resort, Gyllyngvase Beach, Seafront,
TR11 4NB
01326 312707
www.stmichaelshotel.co.uk/dine/brasserie-on-the-bay
Open: All year

There's a stylishly upmarket vibe at this seaside hotel with its hip-looking bar and nautically themed restaurant. The panoramic view is inspiring, jaw dropping, even. The kitchen buys materials solely from local producers, and its passion for cooking is palpable in well-executed modern dishes with a hint of the classics.

Chef: Darren Millgate
Food Style: Modern Mediterranean, British

The Greenbank Hotel
Harbourside, TR11 2SR
01326 312440
www.greenbank-hotel.co.uk
Open: All year

The location of The Greenbank Hotel allows for really interesting and constantly changing views of Falmouth's busy estuary harbour. The stylish restaurant has a stand-alone identity, mixing blues with beige and lots of light streaming through the large windows. Food is punchy and well intentioned, paying close attention to all individual components and elements.

Chef: Nick Hodges, Bobby Southworth
Food Style: Modern British

Merchants Manor Rosettes Suspended
1 Weston Manor, TR11 4AJ
01326 312734
www.merchantsmanor.com
Open: All year

The Rosette award for this establishment has been suspended due to a change of chef and reassessment will take place in due course.
Set within sub-tropical gardens between the beach and Falmouth's bustling high street, Merchants Manor is a luxurious coastal setting for a meal. Meaning 'grill' in Cornish, the relaxed Rastella restaurant offers contemporary dining, tables appointed with vintage candles, white linen and designer crockery. A wood-fired grill called Bertha is the workhorse of the kitchen and dishes are big-flavoured.

Penmorvah Manor
Penjerrick Hill, Budock Water, TR11 5ED
01326 250277
www.penmorvah.co.uk
Open: All year

Chef: Shannon Richards
Food Style: Classic British

The stone-built manor house has stood in its six acres of wooded gardens near Falmouth since 1872. The atmosphere is white-linened gentility, the culinary style is modern brasserie, with well turned-out dishes making an impact on both eye and palate.

What is your advice for cooking great food?
Keep it simple, keep it fresh

AA Inspector

Falmouth *continued*

The Restaurant - The Royal Duchy Hotel 🏵️🏵️
The Royal Duchy Hotel, Cliff Road, TR11 4NX
01326 313042
www.royalduchy.co.uk
Closed: 23 December to 2 January

Set on Falmouth's wonderful seafront, the Royal Duchy
Hotel was built as a hotel in the early 20th century. Its
large restaurant is elegantly traditional, decorated in
dove greys and rich plums, with large windows to take
in the enviable views across the bay. Food is assured
and purposeful with a light, skilful touch.

Chef: John Mijatovic
Food Style: Modern British

See advertisement below

Helston

New Yard Restaurant ⊛⊛⊛
Trelowarren Estate, Mawgan, TR12 6AF
01326 221595
www.newyardrestaurant.co.uk
Closed: Sunday, Monday, Tuesday, Wednesday

On Cornwall's stunning Lizard peninsula, New Yard
Restaurant is at the heart of the historic Trelowarren
Estate. Occupying the former stables, the distinctive
interior sports a chequered floor, arched windows
and bare wooden tables, while the open-plan kitchen
produces punchy, seasonal cooking. Guests can
peruse the impressive walled garden prior to eating

Chef: Jeffrey Robinson
Food Style: British

produce grown there. Chefs help waiting staff serve and guide diners through the dishes, which
might include sea bass, cured tomatoes, fig leaf and yogurt, followed by kiln-roasted chicken,
courgette and creamed chard. Cheese millefeuille with apple and raisin gel is an ingenious way
to end.

Hugh Town (The Isles of Scilly)

Spirit ⊛
St Mary's Hall Hotel, Church Street, TR21 0JR
01720 422316
www.stmaryshallhotel.co.uk
Closed: 18 October to 15 March

Chef: Ben Hingston, Phil Fallows
Food Style: Modern British

Local sourcing is key at the Spirit restaurant in this handsome townhouse hotel set in charming
Mediterranean gardens. Served in a gently updated setting, rare breed meats come from the
owners' farm, while fish and seafood are hauled in daily by local boats to form the bedrock of
carefully prepared, fuss-free dishes.

Little Petherick

Old Mill Bistro ⊛
The Old Mill House, PL27 7QT
01841 540388
www.oldmillbistro.co.uk
Closed: 18–27 December, January

Set in a 16th-century, former corn mill in a postcard-
pretty hamlet, this homely family-run bistro comes
with a full complement of beamed and stone-floored
character. Service is warm and informed, while the
cooking is full of panache, with sharply defined flavours
and confident combining of impeccably local and
seasonal materials.

Chef: Adam Tomlinson
Food Style: Modern British

Lizard

Fallowfields ⚙⚙
Housel Bay Hotel, Housel Bay, TR12 7PG
01326 567500
www.houselbay.com
Closed: Sunday, Monday, Tuesday

On the spectacular Lizard peninsula, the granite-built Housel Bay Hotel dates back to Victorian times and the light and airy Fallowfields restaurant boasts stunning Atlantic views. As befits the coastal setting, local fish is a strength here, perhaps in a main of sea bass, tiger prawn, bisque, crab ravioli, cavolo nero and curry oil.

Chef: Joseph Fallowfield
Food Style: British, Seafood, Seasonal

Looe

NEW The Old Sail Loft Restaurant ⚙
Quay Street, PL13 1AP
01503 262131
www.oldsailloftlooe.co
Closed: Sunday, 25 December

Housed in one of the oldest buildings in Looe, The Old Sail Loft is an intimate, engaging restaurant with an unpretentious approach. With low beams and period charm, there's a real sense of the place's seafaring past. Seafood is a speciality here with fish literally landed in front of the restaurant, but there are also plenty of other options.

Chef: Nick Hawke
Food Style: Modern British, Seafood

Lostwithiel

Asquiths Restaurant ⚙⚙
19 North Street, PL22 0EF
01208 871714
www.asquithsrestaurant.co.uk
Closed: 25–26 December, 1st 3 weeks January

Its black and white decor, smartly set tables and elegant staff create positive impressions of this restaurant opposite the church, where food is taken seriously. Confit duck and beetroot pastilla is teamed with pomegranate molasses and couscous. Fish gets a decent showing, maybe a well-timed roast hake fillet, curried cauliflower, a courgette bhaji and potato purée.

Chef: Graham Cuthbertson
Food Style: Modern British

Lower Town (The Isles of Scilly)

Cloudesley Shovell Restaurant ◉◉
Karma St Martin's, TR25 0QW
01720 422368
www.karmastmartins.com
Closed: November to March

Food Style: Modern, Seafood

Admiral Sir Cloudesley Shovell's disastrous loss of 22 ships off the Scilly Isles in 1707 is remembered here in the Karma St Martin's Hotel. The restaurant overlooks the crystal-clear Atlantic – a source of the fresh fish, crab and lobster which feature heavily on the menu. Alternatively, simply order a Cornish pasty picnic and head for the beach.

See advertisement on page 88

Mawgan Porth

The Herring ◉◉
Bedruthan Hotel and Spa, TR8 4BU
01637 861200
www.bedruthan.com

Food Style: Modern British

The Herring is elegant, understated and contemporary, with stunning views out to sea. Unclothed tables and designer chairs give the room a real Scandi feel. The team are personable, engaging and genuinely eager to please. Dinner starts with a set of sharing plates, well-balanced and cohesive, and follows with a choice of main course. A fascinating food journey.

The Scarlet Hotel ◉◉ 🍷NOTABLE WINE LIST
Tredragon Road, TR8 4DQ
01637 861800
www.scarlethotel.co.uk
Closed: 2–27 January

Chef: Mike Francis
Food Style: Modern European

In a stunning location with expansive views out across the bay, The Scarlet Hotel is ideal for relaxation and reconnection. Light and airy, the stylish restaurant has huge floor-to-ceiling windows, showing unrivalled views. The operation has a casual efficiency, and staff express themselves and interact with diners in a natural way. The kitchen team concentrates on West Country produce.

Mawnan Smith

Meudon Hotel ◉◉
TR11 5HT
01326 250541
www.meudon.co.uk
Closed: 28 December to January

Chef: Iain McKay
Food Style: Modern British

The restaurant at the Meudon Hotel is elegant and engaging, with floor-to-ceiling windows that look out over the stunning sub-tropical gardens. Clothed tables add to the sense of occasion, while chatty and smiling staff ensure a happy and contented buzz. Cooking is nouvelle cuisine inspired, perfectly in step with the whole demeanour of the hotel.

CULINARY EXCELLENCE

Karma St. Martin's is home to the Isles of Scilly's premier dining destination, the AA acclaimed two-Rosette award-winning Sir Cloudesley Shovell restaurant. From our local fisherman's seafood platter or gourmet lobster rolls, a delicious afternoon tea, or a Cornish Pasty picnic on the beach, our Head Chef and the team plate up some of the very best food of the Isles of Scilly & Cornwall.

When it comes to potent potables, Karma St. Martin's takes the love of the grape to the next level. Guests receive a wine card upon arrival and unfettered access to our Enomatic Wine Machine. We stock an extensive wine list (by far the best on the islands) showcasing over 100+ wines for Old World traditionalists and New World boffins alike.

E : reception@karmastmartins.com | T : +44 (0)1720 422 368

WE CREATE... EXPERIENCES

Mawnan Smith *continued*

Trelawne Hotel 🏵️
Maenporth Road, TR11 5HT
01326 250226
www.trelawnehotel.co.uk
Open: All year

Chef: David Waplington
Food Style: Modern British

The light, airy dining room at the Trelawne Hotel enjoys stunning views across to Falmouth Bay. Things are informal and utterly unpretentious here and the team are very genuine. The cooking is underpinned by sound technique and results in very well dressed plates, showing an underlying sense of pride, and awareness of texture.

Mullion

Mullion Cove Hotel 🏵️🏵️
TR12 7EP
01326 240328
www.mullion-cove.co.uk
Open: All year

This solidly built white property on the Lizard Peninsula sits on the clifftop, giving uninterrupted sea and coast views. The kitchen is committed to local suppliers, with day boats providing seafood – an international element is evident in some dishes.

Chef: Paul Stephens
Food Style: Modern British

Newquay

Dune 🏵️
Esplanade Road, TR7 1PT
01637 852221
www.fistralbeachhotel.co.uk
Open: All year

Chef: Daniel Kerr
Food Style: Modern

Dune is well named, as it's all about the spectacular view of the relentless surf, with Newquay's surfers always at play amidst the foaming breakers. The elegant restaurant has a light, airy feel, with a relaxed atmosphere. The team are committed and focused, but not over attentive, allowing guests to take their time.

What are the most common misconceptions you face?

That we ask for a specific (traditional) style; that service plays a part in the award when assessing for AA Rosettes.

AA Inspector

Newquay *continued*

The Samphire Restaurant ⦿⦿
The Headland Hotel and Spa, Fistral Beach, TR7 1EW
01637 872211
www.headlandhotel.co.uk
Closed: 2 January to April 2023

The Headland Hotel and Spa stands proudly at the
cliff's edge, creating stunning views for the Samphire
Restaurant, so understandably window tables are in
high demand. The room itself is traditional in the main
but with some contemporary touches. The team are
friendly and approachable, while dishes have a simple,
uncluttered style with a clear sense of purpose.

Food Style: Modern British

Silks Bistro and Champagne Bar ⦿
Atlantic Hotel, Dane Road, TR7 1EN
01637 839048
www.atlantichotelnewquay.co.uk
Open: All year

Chef: Matt Ring
Food Style: Mediterranean,
Seafood

Although it was built in 1892 Silks Bistro and Champagne Bar is no gloomy Victorian haunt. It's
a large space, bright and chic, with zebra-patterned bar stools and sunburst-styled café chairs at
linen-swathed tables. In the evenings, candlelight softens the scene. Great sea views from the
terrace. Part of the Atlantic Hotel complex.

The Terrace ⦿
The Headland Hotel and Spa, TR7 1EW
01637 872211
www.headlandhotel.co.uk/eat/terrace-restaurant/
Open: All year

Chef: Tony Ward, Chris
Archambault
Food Style: Classic British

Located just steps from the famous sands of Fistral Beach, The Terrace restaurant has floor to
ceiling glass, wooden floors, and a laid-back beach vibe. The short bistro-style menu presents
such starters as garlic prawns and harissa dip, or Cornish mussels. Enjoy the ocean views.

Padstow

Paul Ainsworth at No. 6 ⦿⦿⦿⦿ ⬗NOTABLE WINE LIST
See pages 92-93 and advertisement opposite

Padstow

🌹 🌹 🌹 🌹 🍷 NOTABLE WINE LIST

Paul Ainsworth at No. 6

Padstow Townhouse, 6 Middle Street, PL28 8AP
01841 532093
www.paul-ainsworth.co.uk
Closed: 24–26 December, 13 January to 6 February

Chef: Paul Ainsworth,
Chris McClurg
Food Style: Modern British

Defining contemporary cooking in a pint-sized townhouse

Padstow is undeniably a shining beacon on the UK's gastronomic map, and Paul Ainsworth's townhouse restaurant, tucked down one of the narrow streets, just back from the harbour, has been a major player here since 2005. Paul has built a reputation for creating contemporary food focused on the regional produce that makes Cornwall such a culinary destination these days, while a healthy run of TV exposure via the BBC's *The Great British*

Menu and *Royal Recipes* has certainly helped boost his public profile.

The restaurant occupies a whitewashed Georgian townhouse split into three diminutive spaces on the ground floor and another upstairs, with the period charm of the spaces intact and bold artworks peppering the walls with visual entertainment. Ainsworth's cooking, interpreted here by Chris McClurg (also a winner on

The Great British Menu), has always tended towards the creatively sharp end of the modern British spectrum, with technical pizzazz galore and eye-catching presentation. Prime ingredients of the finest and freshest to be found in Cornwall's seasonal larder are helped along by global goodies in dishes that deliver muscular layers of flavour and texture. Local scallops are hard to ignore at the best of times, and here they might be served warm and raw with Camel Valley velouté and acorn-fed ham, or go for crapaudine beetroot, pommes Anna and aged Kaluga caviar.

Next to consider might be the deceptively understated dish of wild turbot, mashed potato and onion gravy or for the meat lover, tallow aged fillet of short rib savarin with a morel farcie. Ingenious desserts can be expected of course and are equally hard to overlook – expect the likes of 75% chocolate 'vol au vent' with cep caramel; the showpiece 'Fairground Tale', a true extravaganza built around a bitter chocolate soufflé; or compañero baba, manille strawberries and lapsang cremè.

See advertisement on page 91

"Paul has built a reputation for creating contemporary food focused on regional produce..."

Padstow *continued*

The Restaurant at THE PIG at Harlyn Bay ⊛⊛ 🍷NOTABLE WINE LIST
Harlyn Bay, PL28 8SQ
01841 550240
www.thepighotel.com/at-harlyn-bay/eat-padstow
Open: All year

The Restaurant at THE PIG at Harlyn Bay offers an unpretentious and engaging dining environment, with mismatched tables and chairs, designed to enhance that relaxed vibe the group champions. Service is unfussy, but underpinned by professionalism. The buzz created by guests means this is a million miles away from a whispering dining room. Meals are seasonal and often homegrown.

Chef: Adam Bristow
Food Style: Modern British

St Petroc's Bistro ⊛
4 New Street, PL28 8EA
01841 532700
www.rickstein.com/restaurants/st-petrocs-bistro
Closed: 25–26 December

Chef: Mark O'Hagan
Food Style: Mediterranean, French

The bistro is an informal and relaxing sort of place, with simple tables and chairs on worn wooden floorboards, modern paintings on plain white walls, and professional service from attentive staff. There's a cosy bar and a pleasant lounge for pre-dinner drinks.

The Seafood Restaurant ⊛⊛⊛ 🍷NOTABLE WINE LIST
Riverside, PL28 8BY
01841 532700
www.rickstein.com
Closed: 25–26 December

Chef: Stephane Delourme
Food Style: International, Seafood

Padstow may be rather different these days from the little fishing village of Rick Stein's youth, with great places to eat a dime a dozen, but this is still top of everyone's list, so book well ahead for the busy season. There's a sunny conservatory, a roof terrace and a friendly, informal air – seaside colours, comfortable seating and modern art. Once at your table you'll be keen to get cracking – literally, if you go for one of the magnificent fruits de mer platters. Otherwise, begin with crispy smoked mackerel salad before moving on to a perfectly cooked tronçon of turbot with hollandaise sauce.

Port Gaverne

Pilchards 🏵
PL29 3SQ
01208 880244
www.portgavernehotel.co.uk
Closed: January to Easter

Chef: James Lean
Food Style: Modern British

The Port Gaverne is a traditional inn, set in a tiny cove on Cornwall's dramatic north coast, just five minutes' walk from Port Isaac. Pilchards is their café, slap-bang on the beach. It's relaxed and friendly, offering excellent snacky dishes as well as larger plates.

Port Gaverne 🏵
PL29 3SQ
01208 880244
www.portgavernehotel.co.uk
Open: All year

Chef: James Lean
Food Style: Modern British, Seafood

Tucked away in a hidden cove, a hilly but short stroll from Port Isaac, this whitewashed village inn with its hanging baskets and outdoor tables is pretty as a picture, the slate-floored bar giving way to a pair of interlinked dining rooms. The traditionally-based cooking is inventive.

Port Isaac

Outlaw's New Road 🏵🏵🏵🏵 🍷 NOTABLE WINE LIST
6 New Road, PL29 3SB
01208 880896
nathan-outlaw.com
Closed: Sunday, Monday

Chef: Nathan Outlaw
Food Style: Modern British, Seafood

Perched at the top of Port Isaac, Outlaw's New Road occupies an enviable spot on the edge of the famous fishing village, overlooking the ocean. Appealingly understated with wooden floors, piscatorial-inspired artwork and unclothed tables, there are superb views of the sea and also bar seating with a view straight into the kitchen. The relaxed feel is echoed by the charming front-of-house staff who are never intrusive and genuinely friendly. The food is simple and unfussy but underpinned by solid technique and experience, as well as strong connections with local fishermen who supply the very best ingredients each day. An elegant starter of raw gilthead bream with peas, mint and yogurt might be followed by a no-frills classic of spankingly fresh whole Dover sole with potatoes, garlic and parsley butter. Blackberry cream, champagne jelly, vanilla crème fraîche and almond crumble is one of the well orchestrated desserts.

Porthallow

Talland Bay Hotel 🌸🌸
Porthallow, PL13 2JB
01503 272667
www.tallandbayhotel.co.uk
Closed: January

Talland Bay Hotel offers an elegant and stylish dining environment with sublime sea views. Passion, integrity and skill all combine to create thoroughly enjoyable and flavoursome cooking. The success of dishes is underpinned by the quality of produce, gleaned from land and sea, exemplified by the freshest of seafood from Cornish waters – a genuine taste of the locale.

Chef: Glen Merriot
Food Style: Modern International

Porthleven

Kota Kai 🌸
Celtic House, The Shipyard, TR13 9JY
01326 574411
www.kotakai.co.uk
Closed: 25–26 December

Chef: Jude Kereama
Food Style: Asian Fusion

On the upper floor of Celtic House, Kota Kai is blessed with unbeatable views over the inner harbour of Porthleven, Britain's southernmost port. The menu, with its Asian bias, also rewards close attention, listing, for example, bao bun with hoisin sauce, kimchi, spring onions and peanuts.

Kota Restaurant with Rooms 🌸🌸🌸
Harbour Head, TR13 9JA
01326 562407
www.kotarestaurant.co.uk
Closed: January

Chef: Jude Kereama
Food Style: British, Pacific Rim, Seafood

Situated on the harbour, Kota (the Maori word for shellfish) aims to bring a Pacific Rim seafood ethos to windblown Cornwall. New Zealander Jude Kereama brings an Asian-influenced approach of the southern hemisphere to bear on his menus. Typical dishes on the set menu are beetroot, goats' cheese mousse, pickled shallots, hazelnuts and honey truffled; pork belly, swede dashi, sea vegetables and pork skin furikake; panko-coated hake, katsu curry sauce, carrot and daikon pickle. For dessert – vanilla pannacotta, poached rhubarb, rhurbarb sorbet, orange jelly and chocolate brownie crumb, or blue cheese ice cream with red wine poached pear.

Portloe

The Lugger ⊚⊚
TR2 5RD
01872 501322
www.luggerhotel.com
Open: All year

Chef: Richard Lipscombe
Food Style: Modern, Classic

Dating from the 16th century, now a luxury inn, The Lugger overlooks the sea and tiny harbour of a picturesque village on the Roseland Peninsula, with a terrace outside the smart, spacious restaurant for summer dining. Local ingredients are the kitchen's linchpin, particularly seafood.

Portscatho

Driftwood Rosettes Suspended
See page 98

St Austell

Carlyon Bay Hotel ⊚
Sea Road, Carlyon Bay, PL25 3RD
01726 812304
www.carlyonbay.com
Open: All year

Perched on a clifftop, the large Carlyon Bay Hotel, spa and golf course is an imposing presence above the bay. The huge windows allow maximum exposure to the rugged Cornish coast views. The kitchen keeps things simple and relies on the quality and provenance of its ingredients.

Chef: Simon Brown
Food Style: Modern, Traditional British

St Ives

Porthminster Beach Café ⊚⊚
TR26 2EB
01736 795352
www.porthminstercafe.co.uk
Closed: 25 December

Slap bang on stunning Porthminster Beach, this landmark white building occupies an enviable position. Whether you dine in the restaurant or on the terrace, the sea views are breathtaking. Vibrant pan-Asian dishes dominate the menu, which uses the best local seafood available.

Chef: Mick Smith
Food Style: International, Seafood

Driftwood Rosettes Suspended

Rosevine, TR2 5EW
01872 580644
www.driftwoodhotel.co.uk
Closed: early December to early February (subject to change)

Food Style: Modern European

The Rosette award for this establishment has been suspended due to a change of chef and reassessment will take place in due course.

Perched on cliffs overlooking Gerrans Bay, elegant Driftwood hotel is set within seven acres of grounds leading down to a private beach. The coastal views from the open-plan dining room are stunning and the welcome is as warm as the ambience is relaxed. Clothed tables, gleaming glassware and polished cutlery add finesse to the room with its cushioned white wood chairs adding a New England edge. Attentive and friendly staff display impressive knowledge when it comes to the food and the wine list. A well balanced octopus carpaccio with Isle of Wight tomatoes, verjus and ginger dressing, watermelon and cucumber is an enjoyable way to begin and it could be followed by barbecued and glazed rib of shorthorn beef, grelot onions, radish cooked with beef fat, smoked ox tongue and curds and whey dressing. If tip-top local fish is more your thing, Cornish turbot is served with Jersey Royals, brown shrimp and whipped roe and sea herbs. Finish with burnt honey pannacotta, yogurt, Sauternes raisins, almond and chamomile.

St Mawes

Hotel Tresanton ⚜⚜⚜
27 Lower Castle Road, TR2 5BH
01326 270055
www.tresanton.com
Open: All year

Chef: Paul Wadham
Food Style: Mediterranean,
Seafood

A stunning cliffside location is the setting for this collection of cottages, transformed by Olga Polizzi into a supremely elegant and understated hotel. Superb views of the Cornish coast and laidback nautical chic contribute to an atmosphere of refined luxury. The calm, airy restaurant, with its mosaic tiled floor and shell-like lighting is classy, with simple table settings and engaging, responsive staff. If you're here in daylight it will be hard to drag yourself away from the views, so give yourself plenty of time for a long lunch. The cooking matches the environment with a pleasing simplicity; the uncluttered dishes have a refreshing Mediterranean influence. Kick off with a couple of Porthilly oysters or indulge with Exmoor Caviar. Follow with turbot with asparagus and hollandaise, a satisfying main course, and you can keep it simple at dessert with the classic Italian affogato using Tresanton's home-made ice cream.

Tresco (The Isles of Scilly)

The New Inn ⚜
TR24 0QQ
01720 422849
www.tresco.co.uk
Open: All year

The friendly and welcoming New Inn sits beside the water, right at the heart of this small community, where guests and islanders mix happily. The fine dining here is based around island produce (everything else has to be brought in by sea, don't forget).

Chef: Liam Caves
Food Style: Modern, Traditional

Truro

The Alverton Hotel ⚜⚜
Tregolls Road, TR1 1ZQ
01872 276633
www.thealverton.co.uk
Open: All year

Dating from 1830, The Alverton is an impressive building designed by the same chap as Truro Cathedral. There is plenty of period charm and a contemporary sheen to the upmarket brasserie. The menu takes a modern European path with a good representation of Cornish ingredients.

Chef: Nick Hodges, Ollie Wyatt
Food Style: Modern British,
European

Truro *continued*

Hooked! Restaurant & Bar ◉
Tabernacle Street, TR1 2EJ
01872 274700
www.hookedrestaurantandbar.co.uk
Closed: Sunday, 25–26 December, 1 January

Tucked away down a quiet street just off the city
centre, the open kitchen feeds into a lively buzz
in this smart modern brasserie, with unclothed
tables, exposed brickwork and high ceilings adding
to the jaunty seaside feel. Seafood is the leading
suit, with full-size and tapas dishes available daytime
and evening.

Chef: Robert Duncan
Food Style: Modern British,
Seafood

Mannings Hotel ◉◉
Lemon Street, TR1 2QB
01872 270345
www.manningshotels.co.uk
Closed: 25–26 December

Chef: Scott Williams
Food Style: Modern, Pacific Rim

Mannings is a classic-looking, solid-stone building – Grade II listed no less – but within it is all
slick modernity and contemporary attitude. The restaurant has its own entrance, and an interior
design spec that includes moody black-and-white photos, stainless steel, and trendy lights.

Veryan

The Dining Room Restaurant ◉
The Nare, Carne Beach, TR2 5PF
01872 501111
www.narehotel.co.uk
Closed: 25 December

The more traditional fine dining option at The Nare
hotel on the beautiful Roseland peninsula, The Dining
Room provides diners with magnificent panoramic
sea views and local fish to match. Fresh Portloe crab
rillettes could precede a grilled fillet of lemon sole, leek
purée, capers, samphire, saffron Parmentier potatoes
and champagne velouté.

Chef: Nick Lawrie
Food Style: Traditional

The Quarterdeck at The Nare ⓦⓦ 🍷NOTABLE WINE LIST
Carne Beach, TR2 5PF
01872 500 000
www.narehotel.co.uk/dining/the-quarterdeck
Closed: 25 December

The Quarterdeck is a shipshape, yachtie-themed setting
of polished teak, gingham seats and square rails. The
kitchen produces modern dishes bursting with bold
flavours and local fish and shellfish are a strong point
too; perhaps choose a luxurious duo of pan-fried turbot
and lobster medallion.

Chef: Nick Lawrie
Food Style: Traditional British

Cumbria

Ambleside

Lake Road Kitchen ⓦⓦⓦ
Susse House, Lake Road, LA22 0AD
015394 22012
www.lakeroadkitchen.co.uk
Closed: Monday, Tuesday

Chef: James Cross
Food Style: Modern British

James Cross's restaurant is deeply rooted in the concept of 'the North', and that means an all-
embracing passion for Lakeland and Scottish produce, as well as clear Nordic sensibilities, from
the stark simplicity of its sauna-like, Scandi-style pine plank walls and bare tables to a fervour
for pickling, foraging and fermenting. Daily-changing menus come in eight- and 12-course
versions, and the self-styled 'cold climate cooking' brings remarkable combinations of taste and
texture. A revelatory spring meal opens with slow-barbecued, smoky veal rib with a celeriac
'taco', yogurt, fermented cabbage, wild garlic and capers. Then pine nut stew with garlic, parsley
purée and oil accompany mussels cooked a la plancha.

The Old Stamp House Restaurant ⓦⓦⓦ
Church Street, LA22 0BU
015394 32775
www.oldstamphouse.com
Closed: Sunday, Monday, 25 December

Chef: Ryan Blackburn
Food Style: Modern British

In the heart of walker-friendly Ambleside, The Old Stamp House has become a real foodie
destination thanks to the ambitious team behind it. A low-slung basement property, the
restaurant is split into two rustic rooms with closely packed tables adding to the intimate feel.
Cumbrian produce takes the starring role in creative dishes such as a well balanced crab, caviar,
artichoke, roast chicken jus and seaweed custard. It might be followed by braised shoulder and
loin tartare of Herdwick hogget, carrot, confit potato, scrumpet, mint and anchovy. Leave room
for parsnip cake, rum caramel and rum ice cream.

Ambleside *continued*

Rothay Manor Hotel ❋❋❋ NOTABLE WINE LIST
Rothay Bridge, LA22 0EH
015394 33605
www.rothaymanor.co.uk
Closed: 2–20 January

Chef: Daniel McGeorge
Food Style: Modern British

Built by a Liverpool shipping merchant in 1823, Rothay Manor Hotel has kept many original Regency features. It's a great example of a traditional Lake District country-house hotel, standing in attractive landscaped gardens close to Ambleside. Substantial investment has raised the bar, not least in the restaurant, which has a gently contemporary look that matches the adventurous, complex modern cooking with Japanese and Scandinavian influences. A sample à la carte starts off with scallop and kohlrabi with elderflower, dashi and sorrel, then moves on to halibut with mussel, allium, burdock root and sea aster. Chocolate with rice, miso, kaffir lime and cep is the finisher.

NEW Table 22 @ The Regent ❋
Waterhead Bay, LA22 0ES
015394 32254
www.regentlakes.co.uk
Open: All year

Food Style: British, European

Situated very close to the lake and Ambleside Pier, the Regent is a smart and stylish, family-run hotel that offers a warm welcome to guests and their four-legged friends; Table 22 is the hotel's cosy restaurant. The menu features the best of Cumbrian produce, utilised to great effect.

Askham

Allium at Askham Hall ❋❋❋❋ NOTABLE WINE LIST
See page opposite

NEW Queen's Head ❋
Askham, CA10 2PF
01931 712225
www.queensheadaskham.co.uk
Closed: 25–27 December

Chef: Gareth Webster
Food Style: Modern British

Part of the Askham Hall estate, the Queen's Head has had a facelift. Now it's a charming, modern take on the gastropub. It's small inside, only 15 or so tables, with low beamed ceilings, open fires, a copper topped bar, and lots of local colour. Service is professional, yet informal and the staff demonstrate a superb knowledge of food and wine.

🌸🌸🌸🌸 🍾 NOTABLE WINE LIST

Allium at Askham Hall

Askham Hall, Askham, CA10 2PF
01931 712350
www.askhamhall.co.uk
Closed: 25 December, 4–21 January

Chef: Richard Swale
Food Style: Contemporary British

Surrounded by 40 acres of gardens along the River Lowther, Askham Hall hotel occupies a 12th-century country house less than eight miles from Ullswater. A popular wedding venue, the light and airy Allium restaurant is the only modern addition to the building, and it overlooks the magnificent gardens. Tables are not clothed, which adds an informality, but crisp linen napkins are used and locally made bespoke pottery provides a contemporary touch. The kitchen garden features heavily on the seasonal menus and other produce arrives from tenant farms on the estate. Start with Lincolnshire smoked eel, brown shrimp, garden pickles, onion and sea kelp broth before moving on to a carefully cooked salt-aged duck with melt-in-the-mouth duck liver, sour cherries, celeriac, caramelised chicory and a hint of orange. A refreshing finale of tropical fruits, sea buckthorn, passionfruit sorbet and coconut foam is one of the well balanced desserts. A notable wine list including bottles from the family's cellar features a number of vintage French stunners.

Barrow-in-Furness

Abbey House Hotel & Gardens ⚜

Abbey Road, LA13 0PA
01229 838282
www.abbeyhousehotel.com
Open: All year

Chef: Ashley Wood
Food Style: Traditional British, French

This grand red-brick house in 14 acres of countryside is home to the charming and gently contemporary Oscar's restaurant. There's nothing stuffy about the place, with a relaxed (but professional) approach all round. The kitchen turns out modern dishes based on good regional produce.

Bassenthwaite

Lake View Restaurant ⚜⚜

Armathwaite Hall Hotel and Spa, CA12 4RE
017687 76551
www.armathwaite-hall.com
Open: All year

Part of the ornate Armathwaite Hall Hotel, Lake View enjoys extraordinary views over the mature, manicured grounds to the lake and fells surrounding. Inside you'll find attractive, elegant decor and beautiful high-ceilings, along with well-spaced tables to allow dining in comfort. Menus draw inspiration from both traditional English cooking and classical French cuisine.

Chef: Noel Breaks
Food Style: British, French

Ravenstone Lodge Country House Hotel ⚜

CA12 4QG
017687 76629
www.ravenstonelodge.co.uk
Closed: 15–26 December

Chef: Anthony Wilson
Food Style: Modern British

Enjoying an enviable position near Bassenthwaite Lake, this country-house hotel has plenty going on, including a bar and bistro in the former stables. The Coach House restaurant is smartly turned out and the team in the kitchen uses quality regional ingredients.

Borrowdale

Borrowdale Gates Hotel ⊛⊛
CA12 5UQ
017687 77204
www.borrowdale-gates.com
Closed: 25 December, 1 January

Revered Lakeland Fells guidebook author Alfred Wainwright especially loved the Borrowdale Valley, where this classic country house turns out skilfully cooked modern dishes. Extensive use is made of locally sourced meat, including the world famous Herdwick Lamb which can be seen grazing here. Panoramic windows in the restaurant offer captivating fell views.

Chef: Christopher Standhaven
Food Style: British, French

Borrowdale Hotel ⊛
CA12 5UY
017687 77224
www.lakedistricthotels.net/borrowdalehotel
Closed: 4 January to 4 March

Tucked away in the beautiful Borrowdale Valley overlooking Derwentwater, Borrowdale Hotel has a traditionally-styled restaurant offering great quality and a friendly welcome. One feature here is the gueridon trolley, rather 'old hat' in many places, but here it's so well done that it's well worth a try; excellent roasts and skilled carving, with a full-on silver cloche trolley.

Chef: Kristine Moodie
Food Style: Modern British

Hazel Bank Country House ⊛⊛
Rosthwaite, CA12 5XB
017687 77248
hazelbankhotel.co.uk
Closed: December to January

Chef: Donna MacRae
Food Style: British

Set amid four acres in the gorgeous Borrowdale Valley, this classic stone-built Lakeland hotel offers a daily-changing set menu, with a cheeseboard as an optional extra. High-end ingredients are given the modern British treatment with occasional Asian influences in dishes like a starter of teriyaki mackerel and roasted watermelon.

Borrowdale *continued*

Lodore Falls Hotel 🏵🏵

CA12 5UX
017687 77285
www.lakedistricthotels.net/lodorefalls
Open: All year

Chef: Shane Hamilton
Food Style: Modern British

With an enviable location overlooking Derwentwater, Lodore Falls Hotels had been part of this incredible landscape for more than two centuries. Its spa offering is extensive and very popular. The Lake View Restaurant is stylishly turned out, with some outstanding paintings on display. Menus offer a global range of dishes cooked with precision.

Mizu 🏵

Lodore Falls Hotel, CA12 5UX
017687 77285
www.lakedistricthotels.net/lodorefalls
Open: All year

Food Style: Pan-Asian

A megabucks refurb of this luxe spa hotel overlooking Derwentwater brought the opening in 2018 of Mizu, a sleek, contemporary pan-Asian restaurant done out in cool, cosmopolitan style, with floor-to-ceiling windows and lake views. The chefs at work in the open kitchen provide culinary theatre, and there's also a heated riverside terrace.

Bowness-on-Windermere

Belsfield Restaurant 🏵🏵

Laura Ashley The Belsfield Hotel, Kendal Road, LA23 3EL
015394 42448
www.lauraashleyhotels.com/thebelsfield
Open: All year

Chef: Chris Lee
Food Style: Modern, International

This lovingly restored Windermere hotel is set in six acres of landscaped gardens. As you might expect from a hotel owned by the Laura Ashley brand, it's tastefully furnished, forming an elegant setting for a menu that fuses British dishes with inspiration from further afield.

Braithwaite

The Cottage in the Wood Rosettes Suspended

Whinlatter Pass, CA12 5TW
017687 78409
www.thecottageinthewood.co.uk
Closed: January

Food Style: Modern British

The Rosette award for this establishment has been suspended due to a change of chef and reassessment will take place in due course.
One thousand feet up, in England's only mountain forest, The Cottage in the Wood has wonderful views of Skiddaw and the fells; a great place for mountain biking and hiking. Interiors feature thick plank oak floors, solid wood tables and tidy plastering. Cooking has a real clarity, with a confident, impressive approach to seasoning and flavours.

Brampton

The Cedar Tree Restaurant ◉◉
Hallbankgate, CA8 2NG
016977 46234
www.farlamhall.co.uk
Open: All year

Farlam Hall Hotel's fine dining option is the Cedar Tree. The Hall dates back to 1428, although most of what you see today was created in the mid-19th century. The restaurant is central in the building – a large space, high ceilings, intricate plasterwork, silver and glass. Menus offer a modern twist on some classic dishes.

Chef: Stephen Pott
Food Style: Modern British

Carlisle

Crown Hotel ◉
Station Road, Wetheral, CA4 8ES
01228 561888
www.crownhotelwetheral.co.uk
Closed: 2 weeks in January

The Georgian hotel is in a picturesque village a few miles out of Carlisle, close to Hadrian's Wall. Its Conservatory Restaurant overlooks the landscaped gardens, and has a striking raftered ceiling and red quarry floor tiles. The kitchen favours a largely modern British approach.

Food Style: Modern British

NEW Fleece at Ruleholme ◉
Ruleholme, CA6 4NF
01228 832030
www.thefleeceruleholme.com
Open: All year

Chef: Ben Parker
Food Style: British

Built on the site of a guest house of the same name, the brand new Fleece is a modern luxury hotel that's spared no expense. The fine dining option is quite intimate, benefiting from natural daylight, with rustic wooden tables and very comfortable seating. Open fires, wooden beams and exposed dressed stone all add to the charming country feel.

How do you keep yourself under the radar?

By adopting plenty of aliases, have 'reasons' to be in the area – perhaps looking at a property or undertaking consultancy work down the road.

AA Inspector

Carlisle *continued*

NEW Lounge on the Green 🌼🌼
27 The Green, Houghton, CA3 0NF
01228 739452
www.loungeonthegreen.co.uk
Closed: Sunday, Monday, Tuesday, 23–30 December,
1–9 January

In a quiet village suburb of Carlisle, Lounge on the
Green is a cut above the usual neighbourhood
restaurant. Looking like a corner shop from outside, it's
about the same size inside, with only seven tables and
around 20 covers. The colour palette is green and grey,
giving it a clean, fresh organic look.

Chef: James Hill
Food Style: Modern British

Cartmel

Aynsome Manor Hotel 🌼
LA11 6HH
015395 36653
www.aynsomemanorhotel.co.uk
Closed: 22–31 December, 1–29 January

A few miles from Cartmel, lovely Aynsome Manor Hotel
is a 16th-century house that's home to an intimate
Georgian dining room with just eleven tables. On the
walls, charming old paintings; in your ears, no intrusive
music. The views across to the priory are stunning, and
the welcome is relaxed but still professional. Cuisine is
classic country house.

Chef: Gordon Topp
Food Style: Modern, Traditional
British

Inspector Insight

What it means to be an inspector?

- A privilege, sense of pride
- A brand ambassador
- Hospitality knowledge for the industry
- A critical eye, especially when it comes to food
- Dedication, as often away from home
- Love for the industry

L'Enclume

Cavendish Street, LA11 6PZ
015395 36362
www.lenclume.co.uk
Closed: 25–26 December

Chef: Simon Rogan, Paul
Burgalieres
Food Style: Modern British

One of the UK's best-known sites of culinary pilgrimage, L'Enclume ('anvil' in French – as it's housed in the former blacksmith's) is a true destination restaurant set in the rather idyllic medieval village of Cartmel. The restaurant interior is plain – with beams, stone floors, unclothed tables, whitewashed walls, and windows overlooking a small but perfectly manicured garden. Table appointments are bespoke, with an array of stunning dishes and serving vessels designed to highlight the ultra-local produce, some from Simon Rogan's own organic farm while others are foraged from the surrounding fields, hedgerows and woods. The wine list is superb and recommendations come with real depth of knowledge, while the daily and seasonally changing menus are complex productions that you'll be guided through by the polished, switched-on staff. Here, you'll experience triumphant levels of skill and invention, very refined, dazzlingly contemporary cooking, every perfect miniature dish bursting with dynamism and creativity and allowing the tremendous quality of the ingredients to speak for themselves. A must-try opening dish is the fritter of Duroc pig and smoked eel, lovage and fermented sweetcorn, which packs a big hit of flavour. For mains, the Passandra cucumbers compressed in calamint, raw Orkney scallop and pickled elderflower is amazing, while the signature 'Anvil' dessert is a caramel mousse with miso, apple and spruce.

Rogan & Co Restaurant

The Square, LA11 6QD
015395 35917
www.roganandco.co.uk
Closed: Tuesday, First week January

Chef: Simon Rogan, Tom Barnes
Food Style: Modern British

The more accessible sibling to Cartmel's celebrated L'Enclume, Rogan & Co occupies the ground floor of a riverside cottage, close to the village's stunning mediaeval priory. The restaurant is modern, clean and uncluttered. Rough stone walls, polished floors, local art and a low beamed ceiling add plenty of character with an open kitchen bringing a touch of theatre. Highly trained staff deliver creative dishes like a terrine of Old Spots pork, crumpet, apple and caper, which might be followed by perfectly timed parmesan crusted cod, caramelised artichoke and shrimp sauce. Finish with rhubarb and almond rice pudding with blood orange sorbet.

Clifton

George and Dragon, Clifton ⚜
Clifton, CA10 2ER
01768 865381
www.georgeanddragonclifton.co.uk
Closed: 26 December

Chef: Gareth Webster
Food Style: British pub food

Comfy sofas and little alcoves all characterise this popular inn, meticulously renovated by owner Charles Lowther, on his historic family estate. His ancestor, Lord Lonsdale helped found the AA, which adopted yellow, his favourite colour, as its trademark. British cooking relies on the estate for pedigree Shorthorn beef, and pork from rare-breed stock, while game and most fish is also pretty local.

Crosthwaite

The Punchbowl Inn at Crosthwaite ⚜⚜
Lyth Valley, LA8 8HR
015395 68237
www.the-punchbowl.co.uk
Open: All year

A small country house in the Lyth Valley, The Punchbowl is one of Lakeland's homelier places, run with great civility by the hands-on team. A slate-topped bar and modern rustic furniture give the place a fresh look, and the menu shows plenty of fashion-conscious technique.

Chef: Kamil Aszyk-Siwek
Food Style: Modern British

Glenridding

Inn on the Lake ⚜⚜
Lake Ullswater, CA11 0PE
017684 82444
www.lakedistricthotels.net
Open: All year

On the edge of Ullswater in a quiet village, the Inn on the Lake is a Victorian mansion with a number of major expansions. Views are wonderful, and the restaurant has many window tables that benefit. Decor is all silvers, creams and greys with splashes of colour. Service is professional, even formal to a point, but still friendly.

Chef: James Watt
Food Style: Modern European

Clare House ⊛
Park Road, LA11 7HQ
015395 33026
www.clarehousehotel.co.uk
Closed: mid December to mid January

Chef: Andrew Read, Mark
Johnston, Adrian Fenton
Food Style: Modern British

The Read family has owned this traditional hotel with secluded gardens overlooking Morecambe Bay since the 1960s, and their passionate care is evident wherever you look. In the two-roomed dining area, well-spaced tables dressed in crisp linen are attended by smartly turned-out, loyally long-serving staff.

Forest Side ⊛⊛⊛⊛ ▲NOTABLE WINE LIST
Keswick Road, LA22 9RN
015394 35250
www.theforestside.com
Open: All year

Chef: Paul Leonard
Food Style: Modern British

In the heart of the Lake District, Grasmere destination restaurant Forest Side certainly lives up to its verdant name. The views of the forest and hotel garden are breathtaking and there is an elegant rusticity to the airy dining room with tables made from upcycled floorboards and locally made crockery. The tasting menus roll with the seasons and what ends up in the kitchen on the day, whether it's from suppliers or foragers. Although rooted in classic technique, this is modern cooking of a high order, with in-your-face flavours. Beetroot, slow-cooked for several hours, is paired with whipped cod's roe and cultured sheep's yogurt. Super-fresh John Dory is roasted in butter with caramelised Roscoff onions and whey is as visually stunning as it is well executed. Chocolate with sea buckthorn, sweet cheese ice cream and lemon curd is a delicious way to finish a meal.

Inspector Insight

Why is the scheme so important?

- Objective benchmarks
- Reliable consumer advice
- Professional inspections
- Respected and trusted
- Heritage - 60+ years of publication
- Aspirational
- Assures potential guests of quality levels

Grasmere *continued*

The Wordsworth Hotel
Stock Lane, LA22 9SW
015394 35592
www.thewordsworthhotel.co.uk
Open: All year

Just upriver from Grasmere, and once the Earl of
Cadogan's hunting lodge, the Wordsworth Hotel is
set in two acres of riverside gardens, with some great
views of the lake. The Signature Restaurant is an
airy conservatory, offering excellent, well-balanced
dishes. Not just a hotel dining room, it's now quite a
destination in itself.

Chef: Alan Doughty, Jaid Smallman
Food Style: Modern British

See advertisement below

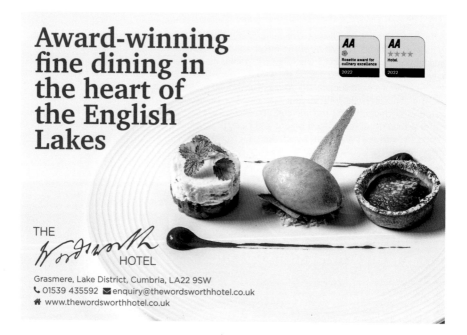

Keswick

Brasserie 31
Main Street, CA12 5BN
017687 72071
www.lakedistricthotels.net/skiddawhotel
Closed: 24-26 December, 30 December to 1 January

Part of the popular Skiddaw Hotel on Keswick's busy
Main Street, Brasserie 31 has been refurbished and
looks pretty smart. There's a conservatory to the front,
and an all-day bar. The colour scheme is neutral, stylish
and comfortable, with upholstered banquettes and
chairs. The table d'hôte menu offers imaginative and
well-executed dishes.

Chef: Robert Fillingham
Food Style: Modern British

Brossen Steakhouse
Inn on the Square, Main Street, CA12 5JF
017687 73333
www.innonthesquare.co.uk/brossen
Open: All year

Chef: Daniel Lansley
Food Style: Modern British

The Inn on the Square is a revamped hotel with a contemporary edge and a restaurant that is all
about prime protein cooked over coals. The dining room is a light, bright and casual space, with
a view into the kitchen.

Kirkby Lonsdale

Pheasant Inn
Casterton, LA6 2RX
015242 71230
www.pheasantinn.co.uk
Closed: Monday, Tuesday, 25 December

An 18th-century coaching inn with a proper bar
complete with real ales and snug. Grab a table by the
fire in the bar, or head on through to the slightly more
refined restaurant – the menu is the same throughout.
Expect dishes that reflect the easy-going pub setting
but don't lack ambition and flair.

Chef: Duncan Wilson
Food Style: Modern British

Kirkby Lonsdale *continued*

Sun Inn Restaurant ◉◉
6 Market Street, LA6 2AU
015242 71965
www.sun-inn.info
Closed: Tuesday, Wednesday, 25 December

The Sun is a 17th-century inn situated in the
destination market town of Kirkby Lonsdale. Its
tastefully decorated restaurant has good table spacing
to provide some privacy for diners. It's an ideal
destination for those with 'foodie' inclinations. Reliable
hands in the kitchen conjure up full-flavoured dishes
using the best local and seasonal ingredients.

Chef: Joe Robinson
Food Style: Modern British

Levens

The Villa Levens ◉◉
Brettargh Holt, LA8 8EA
01539 980980
www.thevillalevens.co.uk
Open: All year

The nuns are long gone from this former Victorian
convent, now the imposing Villa Levens hotel. Much
survives from its early days, including wood panelling
and a fireplace in the intimate dining room, where a
contemporary British menu offers the likes of pan-
seared scallops, and dry-aged fillet steak. The hotel also
offers a brasserie menu.

Chef: Luckasz Branas
Food Style: Modern, Traditional

See advertisement opposite

Lupton

The Plough Inn ◉
Cow Brow, LA6 1PJ
015395 67700
www.theploughatlupton.co.uk
Open: All year

The Plough sports a clean-lined contemporary look
without sacrificing the best of its pubby character. It's
a classy act with leather sofas, and a Brathay slate-
topped bar set against the cosiness of wooden floors,
beams, real fires and the like. Comforting modern takes
on classic dishes prevail.

Chef: Richard Hall
Food Style: Modern British

Near Sawrey

Ees Wyke Country House
LA22 0JZ
015394 36393
www.eeswyke.co.uk
Closed: 23–30 December

Beatrix Potter spent her holidays in this white Georgian house. These days, on a scale small enough to unite guests, a four-course dinner menu is served at a single start time. A pair of choices is offered at most stages.

Chef: Richard Lee
Food Style: Traditional British

Penrith

FYR 🏵

North Lakes Hotel & Spa, Ullswater Road, CA11 8QT
01768 868111
www.fyrgrill.co.uk
Open: All year

Food Style: Modern British

Next to Wetheriggs Country Park, this Thwaites-owned hotel occupies an enviable position in Penrith at the edge of the Lake District. FYR restaurant features an impressive bespoke open-fire grill at the heart of the restaurant where guests can experience the theatre of their dishes being cooked in front of them.

Pentonbridge

Pentonbridge Inn 🏵🏵🏵

See pages 118-119 and advertisement opposite

Pooley Bridge

1863 Restaurant with Rooms 🏵🏵

High Street, CA10 2NH
017684 86334
www.1863ullswater.co.uk
Closed: 25 July to 3 August, 24–27 December, 2–9 January

Built in 1863 for the village blacksmith, this contemporary dining room is a small operation with a small bar area that gives as much space to dining as possible. The decor is fun, with clocks, mirrors, art and different kinds of seating. Cooking is skilful, using prime ingredients from Britain and beyond to underpin the modern British menu.

Chef: Phil Corrie
Food Style: Modern British

Ravenstonedale

The Black Swan 🏵🏵

CA17 4NG
015396 23204
www.blackswanhotel.com
Open: All year

Set in the heart of the conservation village of Ravenstonedale, The Black Swan is popular with visitors and locals alike and offers very friendly hospitality. There are two restaurants, both cosy and welcoming, and offering the same seasonally-changing menus of modern dishes and pub classics. The team work closely with many local suppliers.

Chef: Scott Fairweather
Food Style: Modern British

PENTONBRIDGE INN

Relaxed Fine Dining In The Debatable Lands

01228 586 636 I pentonbridgeinn.co.uk
Penton Cumbria Carlisle CA6 5QB

Pentonbridge

Pentonbridge Inn

CA6 5QB
01228 586636
www.pentonbridgeinn.co.uk
Open: All year

Chef: Christopher Archer
Food Style: British, International

A culinary gem on the border

Located close to the Scottish border but within easy reach of Carlisle and major road networks, Pentonbridge Inn is an old coaching inn that has been transformed into a stylish restaurant-with-rooms. In the small Cumbrian hamlet of Penton, it has been extensively refurbished from its previous incarnation, The Bridge Inn. Modern yet traditional inside, log-burning stoves create a warm and welcoming ambience to enjoy assured cooking of local produce, including seasonal ingredients from the nearby walled kitchen garden at Netherby Hall.

The food is as visually stunning as it is flavoursome and a meal could open with beef tartare, Montgomery Cheddar and lovage mayonnaise – the lean beef accurately served near to room temperature and dressed with creamy horseradish and generously indulgent shavings of the full strength cheese.

For something a little lighter to begin, how about slices of raw, hand-dived Orkney scallop with diced and raw Jerusalem artichoke, winter truffle and a drizzle of garlicky vinaigrette. The precise cooking and carousel of flavours continues with main courses like a perfectly timed and super-fresh piece of halibut served with a generous portion of mussels, leeks and well-balanced saffron sauce. Game is a strong point here so you could also find yourself ordering pink and tender loin of roe deer with offal croquette, hen of the woods mushrooms, celeriac and cavolo nero.

When it comes to dessert, there are some tough decisions to be made. A tartlet filed with a layers of poached Yorkshire rhubarb and moist frangipane is served with a well made 'ripple' ice cream with rhubarb and gingery notes. Or there's a light and airy Valrhona Manjari chocolate mousse with Piedmont hazelnuts and Frangelico. A small but well-defined wine list offers some interesting drinking, and plenty are also available by the glass.

See advertisement on page 117

"The food is as visually stunning as it is flavoursome..."

Rosthwaite

Scafell Hotel ⬡
CA12 5XB
017687 77208
www.scafell.co.uk
Open: All year

Chef: Chris Dougan
Food Style: Modern British

Surrounded by peaks and the lush greenery of the Borrowdale Valley, the Scafell Hotel is ideal for those seeking time in the great outdoors. The Riverside Bar and lounge bar offer informal dining, with the main restaurant has a more formal option. Salmon is cured in-house.

Sedbergh

The Black Bull Inn ⬡⬡
44 Main Street, LA10 5BL
01539 620264
www.theblackbullsedbergh.co.uk
Closed: 25 December

Not far from historic Moulton Hall, The Black Bull Inn has wood-cladded walls, wood floors and simple black wooden furniture in a simple, understated restaurant. Elegant glassware and linen napkins sit alongside moss and stone table decorations, while sea urchins, driftwood and moss adorn the walls and windowsills. Much of the produce is taken from the inn's nearby kitchen garden.

Chef: Nina Matsunaga
Food Style: British, European, Pan-Asian

Skelton

The Dog and Gun Inn ⬡⬡
CA11 9SE
017684 84301
www.dogandgunskelton.co.uk
Closed: Monday, Tuesday, Wednesday, Bank Holidays, 25 December

You can be sure a meal at this atmospheric little dining pub will feature local produce cooked with skill. There's an emphasis on generous portions and big flavours, and menus might feature a perfectly timed, twice-baked Lancashire cheese and chive soufflé and glazed shoulder, braised leg and hot pot of Pringle House lamb with roasted cauliflower purée and salsa verde. Opening hours are limited, so booking is advised.

Chef: Ben Queen-Fryer
Food Style: British, European

Ulverstone

NEW Base Restaurant Awaiting Inspection
The Coach House, Ford Park, LA12 7JP
07825 785735
www.baserestaurant.co.uk
Closed: Sunday, Bank Holidays, 25–30 Decemberr

The current team created Base during 2020, at a very difficult time for the restaurant business, but they've certainly succeeded in turning things around with their fine cooking and the support of the local community. Using the best of local produce, the kitchen offers a daytime of light lunches and interesting sides, with fine dining in the evening.

Chef: Mark Satterthwaite
Food Style: British, Global influences

Windermere

Briery Wood Country House Hotel ◉◉
Ambleside Road, Ecclerigg, LA23 1ES
015394 33316
www.lakedistrictcountryhotels.co.uk
Open: All year

Set in seven acres of grounds, Briery Wood is a charming, white-painted property, dating to the late 19th century. It's a cosy, relaxing place with an informal atmosphere. In the dining room you'll find attentive staff serving modern country-house style cooking.

Chef: Jamie Hopkins
Food Style: Modern, Traditional

Cragwood Country House Hotel ◉◉
Ambleside Road, LA23 1LQ
015394 88177
www.lakedistrictcountryhotels.co.uk
Open: All year

Built in 1910 from stone quarried in its own 21 acres of grounds, Cragwood has bags of country-house charm, as well as marvellous views across the gardens to Lake Windermere. The two dining rooms have lovely views and smart furnishings. Cooking is modern country-house style, and plenty of attention is paid to flavour contrasts and balance.

Chef: Calvin Harrison
Food Style: British, French

Windermere *continued*

Gilpin Spice ◉◉

Gilpin Hotel & Lake House, Crook Road, LA23 3NE
015394 88818
www.thegilpin.co.uk/eat-and-drink/gilpinspice
Closed: 25 December

Adjacent to the main Gilpin Hotel building with its
own entrance, this restaurant is a stunner – divided
into three sections, each decorated differently in
bright colours. There is an open kitchen with high,
comfortable bar-stool seating directly facing the chefs
at work. The pan-Asian menu is designed to offer lots
of taster dishes.

Chef: Hrishikesh Desai
Food Style: Pan-Asian

Henrock ◉◉◉

Crook Road, LA23 3JA
015394 88600
www.leeucollection.com/UK/linthwaite-house
Open: All year

Chef: Simon Rogan, Sam Fry
Food Style: International

Henrock is set in the stunning Linthwaite House Hotel and enjoys lovely views of the National
Park and Windermere. Simon Rogan's team operates here so expect lots of produce from his
farm in Cartmel. The restaurant is understated – three rooms in muted, natural tones with a few
splashes of colour – very comfortable and thoroughly designed. Beef tartare with light truffle
and soy cream, puffed quinoa and farm brassicas is an ideal starter, followed by white Peking
duck with Gochujang (Korean red chilli paste) and date croquette, celeriac and bitter chocolate.
Chocolate raspberry and peanut tart with Dulcey ice cream is the perfect finisher.

Holbeck Ghyll Country House Hotel ◉◉

Holbeck Lane, LA23 1LU
015394 32375
www.holbeckghyll.com
Closed: Tuesday, Wednesday

Holbeck Ghyll began life as a Victorian hunting
lodge, when its eminent position overlooking Lake
Windermere must have suggested itself as a suitable
bolthole for country pursuits. Dining goes on in an
austerely panelled room, where the window seats are
literally that, rather than freestanding chairs, for those
with their backs to the view. Additionally, there's a
chef's table for up to 10 diners.

Chef: Ross Marshall
Food Style: Modern British

HRiSHi at Gilpin Hotel & Lake House ◉◉◉◉
See pages 124-125 and advertisement opposite

Windermere

HRiSHi at Gilpin Hotel & Lake House

Gilpin Hotel & Lake House, Crook Road, LA23 3NE
015394 88818
www.thegilpin.co.uk/eat-and-drink/hrishi
Open: All year

Chef: Hrishikesh Desai
Food Style: Modern British,
Asian influences

Refined European cooking with Asian flourish

A luxurious country house set in beautiful countryside in the heart of the Lakes on the edge of Windermere, HRiSHi at Gilpin Hotel & Lake House is very much a culinary destination. Three charming, individual dining rooms in the main house form this high-end dining option where immaculately set tables and highly polished service add to the overarching warmth and genuine hospitality. A tasting menu, together with plant-based alternative,

offers plenty of flexibility for diners and the modern European cooking has an innovative Indian influence, with high quality ingredients used at every stage. First-rate bread follows a selection of delicious amuse bouches including truffle arancini with truffle mayonnaise and cod cured with soya, honey, carrot and cumin. A starter of cured, marinated and slow-poached parfait of duck liver is beautifully executed, the velvety liver accompanied

by toasted hazlenuts, jalapeño and pickled cherry chutney gel with warm toasted brioche. Another way to kick off is a plate of English tomatoes in various forms – tartare, pickled, dehydrated, sorbet and spiced velouté – with an aged Gran Pandano custard.

These could precede a superb piece of Gigha halibut fillet with a rich potato 'risotto', smoked butter emulsion and herb garnish. If it's meat you're craving, look no further than an impressively tender fillet and braised cheek of Cumbrian beef with crispy onion and buttered green Tenderstem broccoli. The pin-sharp techniques continue through to the desserts, which include a light and refreshing coconut bavarois with marinated pineapple, passionfruit and lemon granita. Alternatively, a rich and elegantly presented Valrhona dark chocolate delice is served with a spiced pannacotta dipped in orange jelly with caramelised hazelnuts and milk ice cream. It's all complemented

by a wine list with a large selection by the glass and a knowledgeable sommelier available for advice.

See advertisement on page 123

"...the modern European cooking has an innovative Indian influence..."

Windermere *continued*

Lindeth Howe Country House Hotel & Restaurant ◉◉

Lindeth Drive, Longtail Hill, LA23 3JF
015394 45759
www.lindeth-howe.co.uk
Open: All year

Chef: Chris Davies
Food Style: Classic French

Once the property of Beatrix Potter, Lindeth Howe is a classic country house on a hillside, overlooking Windermere and the mountains beyond. The restaurant has large windows that reward the diner with views of the large, sweeping gardens. Decor is strikingly contemporary with a bold flora and fauna theme. Service is low key and efficient.

Merewood Country House Hotel ◉◉

Ambleside Road, Ecclerigg, LA23 1LH
015394 46484
www.lakedistrictcountryhotels.co.uk/merewood-hotel
Open: All year

Built in 1812 from stone quarried in the hotel's grounds, Merewood is perfectly positioned to make the best of the views over Lake Windermere. There are 20 acres of woodland and gardens, and this Lakeland country house is equally on the money on the inside.

Chef: Carl Semple
Food Style: Modern British

Porto ◉

3 Ash Street, Bowness, LA23 3EB
015394 48242
www.porto-restaurant.co.uk
Open: All year

The cool greys, blues and greens of Porto's comfortable dining room pick up those of the surrounding lakes, fells and mountains; tables are natural oak and framed retro prints line the walls. Modern and classic British food prevails, but you'll notice European and Asian influences too. Eating on the heated roof terrace or in the garden is also an option.

Chef: Slav Miskiewicz
Food Style: Modern British, European

The Samling 🏵️🏵️🏵️ 📖 NOTABLE WINE LIST
Ambleside Road, LA23 1LR
015394 31922
www.thesamlinghotel.co.uk
Open: All year

Chef: Robby Jenks
Food Style: Modern British

The Samling's contemporary dining room of Lakeland slate and floor-to-ceiling glass offers spectacular views of the hotel gardens and Lake Windermere. The colour palette of greys and neutrals is understated, and there's a hint of formality with tables covered in crisp white linen. Head chef Robby Jenks has created several menus, all featuring modern British cooking, such as the five-course tasting menu that might include turbot and mussels with watercress pesto, sea vegetables and radish, or duck with beetroot, turnip and apple. The impressive wine list is clearly curated by someone in the know, and the very knowledgeable sommelier has excellent recommendations.

Storrs Hall Hotel 🏵️🏵️
Storrs Park, LA23 3LG
015394 47111
www.storrshall.com
Closed: 25 December, 1 January

In an enviable location – Lake Windermere is literally at the bottom of the garden – Storrs Hall Hotel has a classic style perfectly in keeping with its 18th-century origins. The restaurant has heavy gilt mirrors and well spaced tables dressed with fine linen. Cooking here is seasonal, contemporary and skilled, delivered by a small, dedicated brigade.

Food Style: Modern British

The Wild Boar Inn, Grill & Smokehouse 🏵️
Crook, LA23 3NF
015394 45225
www.englishlakes.co.uk/the-wild-boar
Open: All year

Close to Windermere, the white-painted Wild Boar Inn is in a peaceful rural location. Inside, the low beams, dark wood, polished stone floor and open fires make for a very cosy, welcoming retreat. The Grill & Smokehouse features quality local and seasonal ingredients on its menus. As the name implies, plenty of comfort food from the grill and the smokehouse is offered.

Chef: Dylan Evans
Food Style: Traditional British

Derbyshire

Ashbourne

NEW The Garden Room ◎◎
Mappleton Road, DE6 2AA
01335 300900
www.wildhive.uk
Open: All year

Once a private residence, Callow Hall has been
a hotel since the 80s and has recently reopened
under new ownership and after a multimillion pound
refurbishment. Expect natural, calming colours, bespoke
wallpaper and an array of details and amenities. Dining
is in the new Garden Room and Bar, supplied by only
the best of local farms and suppliers.

Chef: David Bukowicki
Food Style: Modern British

Bakewell

NEW Lovage by Lee Smith ◎◎
Bath Street, DE45 1DS
01629 815 613
www.restaurantlovage.co.uk
Closed: Sunday, Monday, Tuesday, 21–24 September,
23 December to 1 February

Lovage by Lee Smith is reached by either of two
unassuming shop-front entrances in Bakewell's bustling
centre. One entrance leads directly into the main
restaurant, while the other puts you into a large bar
area where a tapas-style menu is served. The main
restaurant has some beautiful panelling, which came
from a nearby country house.

Chef: Lee Smith
Food Style: English

NEW Rafters at Riverside House ◎◎ ⌑NOTABLE WINE LIST
Fennel Street, Ashford in the Water, DE45 1QF
0114 2304819
www.riversidehousehotel.co.uk
Closed: Monday, Tuesday, 25 December

Located within the Peak District and in the picturesque
village of Ashford in the Water, Rafters is a lovingly
restored restaurant with rooms. Food is a highlight
of any stay with creative cooking and noteworthy
breakfasts. At the rear is a walled garden where alfresco
eating and drinking is possible when the weather
permits. Look out for the Rafters signature snacks.

Chef: Scot Philliskirk
Food Style: Modern British

Baslow

Cavendish Hotel ⊚⊚⊚
Church Lane, DE45 1SP
01246 582311
www.devonshirehotels.co.uk/cavendish-hotel-baslow
Open: All year

Chef: Adam Harper
Food Style: Modern British

Part of the Duke of Devonshire's hospitality empire, this stylish hotel dates back to the 18th century, and the comfortable public areas are adorned with paintings from the Duke's extensive collection. The Gallery restaurant is traditionally decorated with a smart modern twist, and in season, menus feature produce from the estate. This is excellent modern British cooking, with tip-top technical skills and presentation to match. An accomplished starter of mackerel comes with fennel, orange, ras el hanout, crème fraîche and wild rice, while rare breed pork (belly and tenderloin) is a classic dish with interesting contemporary overtones.

Fischer's Baslow Hall ⊚⊚⊚
See pages 130-131

The Prince of Wales, Baslow ⊚
Church Lane, DE45 1RY
01246 583880
www.princeofwalesbaslow.co.uk
Closed: Monday, Tuesday, 25 December

With its real fire, locally-brewed ales and live music, the Prince of Wales is very much the village hub, but the seasonal food draws diners from afar. There's a working fireplace and a very welcoming, convivial atmosphere. An ideal place to stop if you've been for a visit to nearby Chatsworth House.

Chef: Matt Booth
Food Style: Modern British

See advertisement on page 132

Beeley

The Devonshire Arms at Beeley ⊚ 🍾NOTABLE WINE LIST
Devonshire Square, DE4 2NR
01629 733259
www.devonshirebeeley.co.uk
Open: All year

Chef: Lewis Thornhill
Food Style: Modern British

The Devonshire Arms is on the magnificent Chatsworth Estate, in a picture postcard English village. Dining is traditional pub style, with dark wooden tables, low ceilings and beams at one end, and lighter wood and a more contemporary feel at the other, overlooking the stream. Food is modern British gastropub with many international influences and adapted local recipes.

Baslow

Fischer's Baslow Hall

Calver Road, DE45 1RR
01246 583259
www.fischers-baslowhall.co.uk
Closed: 25–26 December

Chef: Nathan Wall
Food Style: Modern European

Modern cooking in elegant country house hotel

Set in an Edwardian manor house accessed via a tree-lined drive, Fischer's Baslow Hall is set in extensive gardens and woodland close to Chatsworth House and Bakewell. Once a family home, the handsome building is a popular base for visitors to the glorious Peak District countryside. The grounds include an abundant kitchen garden supplying a steady flow of produce for the restaurant. With a palette of soft greys and blues, floral wallpaper and subtle lighting, the dining room is traditional and sophisticated with well-spaced tables, crisp linen tablecloths and soft music.

Formal yet still intimate, the dining room is flanked by views of the well-tended gardens on two sides and service from immaculately attired staff is attentive but not overly stuffy. The food is a fine example of modern cooking with contemporary techniques and classical flavour combinations but always an

emphasis on quality raw materials and flavour. A lot of produce is grown on site and most of the other ingredients are sourced from the surrounding area.

A starter of mackerel, apple and dill is simple and effective, the noticeably fresh fish lightly cured, torched and served with a salad of diced cucumber, apple, capers, chives dressed in dill oil and garnished with monk's beard. An apple caramel provides a sweet counterpoint to a well-balanced dish.

To follow, a roasted loin and confit leg of deep-flavoured Derbyshire lamb is served with softly cooked Roscoff onions topped with a light herb crumb; Boulangère potatoes cooked with lamb stock together with a rich jus complete the dish. End with a white chocolate mousse filled with strawberry compôte and topped with yuzu gel. There's a comprehensive wine list with an excellent choice by the glass and wine flights are available to accompany tasting menus.

"The food is a fine example of modern cooking with contemporary techniques and classical flavour combinations..."

Chesterfield

Casa Hotel ◉◉
Lockoford Lane, S41 7JB
01246 245990
www.casahotels.co.uk
Open: All year

Casa's Cocina restaurant is an über-chic space with darkwood, white chairs and floor-to-ceiling windows. The menu has a selection of salads and tapas running from a board of Spanish charcuterie to a croquette of hake, cheese and chives with tartare dressing.

Chef: Tom Marr
Food Style: Modern British, Mediterranean

NEW The Coaching House Restaurant ⊛
Brimington, S43 1DQ
01246 280077
www.ringwoodhallhotel.com
Closed: 25 December

The Coaching House restaurant is at the heart of
the Ringwood Hall Hotel and Spa, a beautifully
presented Georgian manor house, set in 29 acres of
peaceful gardens. The menu is proudly seasonal and
presents a wide variety of locally sourced meats and
fish, as well as plenty of just-picked herbs and veg from
the kitchen gardens.

Chef: Dan Fincher
Food Style: British

Peak Edge Hotel at the Red Lion ⊛⊛
Darley Road, Stone Edge, S45 0LW
01246 566142
www.peakedgehotel.co.uk
Open: All year

A new-build stone edifice on the border of the Peak
District National Park, the family-owned hotel is handy
for Chatsworth and Haddon Hall. Next door is the
Red Lion, a Georgian coaching inn that is home to the
hotel's bar and bistro, where all-day eating from wide
ranging options is offered.

Chef: Ben Peverall
Food Style: Modern British

Orangery Restaurant ⊛
Worksop Road, S43 4TD
01246 387386
www.vandykbywildes.co.uk
Open: All year

Chef: Marc Wildes
Food Style: Modern British

A brand new, very modern dining room with a light and airy feel, that's the Orangery
at the elegant Hotel van Dyk. There's a wall of glass to one side as well as an indoor
pagoda-style section overlooking the front of the hotel. Very much a brasserie-style
operation with a variety of comfortable seating. Relaxed service, informal yet
still professional.

Darley Abbey

Darleys Restaurant ◉◉
Waterfront, Darley Abbey Mills, DE22 1DZ
01332 364987
www.darleys.com
Closed: 25–26 December, 1 January

This converted silk mill by the River Derwent is the setting for some bright, modern cooking making really excellent use of regional produce. The shady terrace makes the most of the riverside location, a great backdrop for the thoroughly contemporary menus. Desserts demonstrate real creativity.

Chef: Thomas Burton
Food Style: Modern British

Froggatt

The Chequers Inn ◉
S32 3ZJ
01433 630231
www.chequers-froggatt.com
Closed: 25 December

Chef: Richard Spencer
Food Style: Modern, Traditional

The 16th-century Chequers Inn is very much a country inn, with log fires in the winter months. When you walk in, you'll find wooden tables and chairs and a large bar area. The service at dinner is very attentive but also really relaxed. The cooking deftly steers between stalwarts and more modern offerings.

Hartington

Biggin Hall Hotel ◉
Biggin-by-Hartington, SK17 0DH
01298 84451
www.bigginhall.co.uk
Open: All year

Dating back to around 1620, Biggin Hall is a Grade II* listed building, surrounded by open countryside in the heart of the Peak District. Ideal for exploring the Tissington Trail. The restaurant is a rustic low-beamed room with flagstone flooring. Its conservatory extension is more contemporary, with bamboo Chiavari chairs and stunning panoramic views over the garden.

Chef: Ziggy Baran
Food Style: Modern British

NEW Bank House Hathersage 🌸
Main Road, S32 1BB
01433 449060
www.bankhousehathersage.co.uk
Closed: 25 December

A magnificent building boasting Neo-Jacobean style architecture, Bank House is a multi-purpose space split across three levels including a stylish cocktail bar on the ground floor. In the restaurant with its modern look, Mediterranean-themed decor and vintage twist, enjoy European-influenced fusion cooking that's rustic and seasonal.

Chef: Andrew Wornes
Food Style: Modern British, Mediterranean influences

The Plough Inn 🌸
Leadmill Bridge, S32 1BA
01433 650319
www.theploughinn-hathersage.co.uk
Closed: 25 December

Chef: Mark Rowan
Food Style: Modern European

Set in nine acres of grounds that slope gently to the River Derwent, the stone-built 16th-century Plough Inn is welcoming and friendly. The courtyard's the place to be in summer, and the dining room is always smartly turned out, as is the cooking. Fresh flowers and linen napkins are placed on each table.

Santo's Higham Farm Hotel 🌸
Main Road, DE55 6EH
01773 833812
www.santoshighamfarm.co.uk
Open: All year

Chef: Raymond Moody
Food Style: Modern, International

Santo Cusimano has retired, but the name remains, and Santo's Higham Farm Hotel is a unique rural retreat. With the rolling Amber Valley all around, it's in prime Derbyshire walking country, and was fashioned from an old farmstead. Menus mobilise plenty of pedigree local produce and Italian influences are never distant.

Matlock

Stones Restaurant ⟨⟩⟨⟩
1 Dale Road, DE4 3LT
01629 56061
www.stones-restaurant.co.uk
Closed: 25 December to 3 January

Stones may be an intimate basement venue,
but it has the best of both worlds on fine days,
thanks to a stylish conservatory and tiled sun terrace
perched above the Derwent. The decor is a mix
of subtle earthy tones, to match a Mediterranean-
inflected menu.

Chef: Kevin Stone, Chris Higham
Food Style: Modern British

Melbourne

Amalfi White ⟨⟩⟨⟩
50 Derby Road, DE73 8FE
01332 694890
www.amalfiwhite.com
Closed: Monday, Tuesday, 25–26 December,
1 January

With a terraced garden plus a children's play area, this
stylish brasserie has all the attributes needed to make
a family-friendly venue all year round. Inside, there's a
contemporary space in greys and silvers with a mixture
of artwork in the softly-lit dining room.

Chef: Alex McNeil
Food Style: Modern British,
European

Morley

The Morley Hayes Hotel ⟨⟩⟨⟩
Main Road, DE7 6DG
01332 780480
www.morleyhayes.com
Closed: 27 December, 1 January

Chef: Nigel Stuart
Food Style: Modern British

Morley Hayes has been a dynamic hotel since the 1980s, and with its golf complex,
conference facilities and popular wedding venue, it has most bases covered. The kitchen
offers a roster of unpretentious modern dishes, with influences from around the globe adding
vibrancy and colour.

Repton

The Boot Inn ◎◎

12 Boot Hill, DE65 6FT
01283 346047
www.thebootatrepton.co.uk
Open: All year

Five miles from the National Brewery Centre, you
would expect beer to be a strong draw, especially in a
stylishly-appointed 17th-century coaching inn. A range
of evocatively named ales from its microbrewery is a
plank of The Boot's huge popularity. There's something
on the menus to suit everyone.

Chef: Matt Allsopp
Food Style: Modern British

Rowsley

The Peacock at Rowsley ◎◎◎

See pages 138-139 and advertisement on page 140

Sandiacre

La Rock ◎◎

4 Bridge Street, NG10 5QT
0115 939 9833
www.larockrestaurant.co.uk
Closed: Monday, Tuesday, Wednesday, 24 December
to 7 Janaury

Hidden away down a side street in Sandiacre, La Rock's
sophisticated and contemporary interior has exposed
brick walls, wooden floors, solid oak tables with granite
centres and sparkling glassware, and there's a glass-
roofed lounge area with inviting comfy sofas; soft music
plays in the background.

Chef: Nick Gillespie
Food Style: Modern British

Thorpe

The Izaak Walton Hotel ◎◎

Dovedale, DE6 2AY
01335 350981
www.izaakwaltonhotel.com
Open: All year

Chef: Andy Davies
Food Style: Modern, Traditional

This creeper-clad country house has glorious views over the Dovedale Valley and
the Derbyshire peaks. Decorated in rich hues of red and gold, the elegant Haddon
Restaurant favours a traditional candlelight-and-linen look, in contrast to the up-to-date
and creative menu.

Rowsley

The Peacock at Rowsley

Bakewell Road, DE4 2EB
01629 733518
www.thepeacockatrowsley.com
Open: All year

Chef: Dan Smith
Food Style: Modern British

Chic country house dining

Originally a manor house, built in 1652, The Peacock at Rowsley has been a hotel since the 1830s. It's part of the Haddon Hall Estate (make sure you visit Haddon while you're in the area, a truly fabulous Tudor building) and is the perfect size – just 15 bedrooms and a properly cosy, comfortable place. It's ideally situated on the A6 between Matlock and Bakewell, handy for 1,000-acre Chatsworth Park and the Peak District National Park with its multitude of stunning walks and trails. Interiors are comfortable, with plenty of polished wood and stone walls, period features, an inviting bar and an intimate dining room.

Here you'll find traditional portraits in oil, and walls in dark plum and lime green for a slightly contemporary twist on the country-house look, with chunky, unclothed tables, crisp linen napkins, and quite a formal atmosphere, the setting

for chef Dan Smith's inventive modern British menus. These change seasonally, and are creative and technically nimble, the multi-layered dishes making excellent use of produce from the kitchen gardens as well as locally reared organic meats from nearby estates. The à la carte might offer starters of mackerel, radish, turnip and horseradish velouté, Oscietra caviar bagel or buttermilk fried quail, pea, pickled mushroom, BLT. An English asparagus salad, almond, lemon, seaweed and herbs makes a good vegetarian alternative.

Mains could take in an accurately cooked Derbyshire beef fillet, cheek and tail ragout, potato mousseline, caramelise onion, celeriac, herb and watercress emulsion, bordelaise sauce, or monkfish, grilled mussels, fennel, beans, kohlrabi, spring onions and sea vegetables. When it comes to dessert you might choose the Casa Luker chocolate soufflé, malted milk sorbet, mocha sauce or maybe the strawberry cheesecake, kalamansi lime,

meringue, beignets, pistachio. The concise wine list is well chosen, with a good selection by the glass.

See advertisement on page 140

"...the multi-layered dishes making excellent use of produce from the kitchen gardens..."

THE PEACOCK AT ROWSLEY

The Peacock at Rowsley is a cosy, chic boutique hotel, originally a manor house in the heart of the Peak District National Park and very close to Haddon Hall and Chatsworth House. Perfect for a countryside break with comfortable bedrooms including four posters and one of the best hotel suites in the region. Our award winning restaurant serves a delicious fine dining menu, crafted by Head Chef Dan Smith. Dan worked with notable chefs such as Tom Aikens before joining The Peacock. The atmospheric bar with open fire is a very convivial place to meet for lunch, dinner or just a drink – with its own menu of freshly cooked seasonal food. Treat yourself to a drink from the extensive cocktail menu. Sunday lunch at The Peacock is a local favourite. The hotel is famed for is excellent fly fishing on the Derbyshire Wye and River Derwent.

For further information or to make a booking please call **01629 733518** or email **reception@thepeacockatrowsley.com**. The Peacock at Rowsley, Derbyshire DE4 2EB

Tideswell

The Merchant's Yard ◉◉
St John's Road, SK17 8NY
01298 872442
www.themerchantsyard.com
Closed: Monday, Tuesday, 25–26 December, 1 January

Once an actual merchant's yard, the property is full
of references to its past, and has a strong industrial
feel. This is softened by teal velvet bench seating,
and technical drawings of many household items.
The young and enthusiastic staff are passionate and
knowledgeable, while the menus are always evolving,
offering precise cookery and showing a high level
of skill.

Chef: Daniel Box
Food Style: Contemporary, Classic

Woolley Moor

The White Horse & The View @ Woolley Moor ◉
Badger Lane, DE55 6FG
01246 590319
www.thewhitehorsewoolleymoor.co.uk
Closed: 25–26 December, First 3 weeks January

Chef: Jack Cabourn
Food Style: Modern British

In the hamlet of Woolley Moor on the outskirts of Ashover, this stone-built country inn sits
on the eastern edge of the Peak District National Park. It's a glorious setting to enjoy modern
British dishes like blue cheese and walnut soufflé, followed by crispy belly pork, spring onion
mash and smoked bacon sauce.

Devon

Axminster

Tytherleigh Arms ◉◉
Tytherleigh, EX13 7BE
01460 220214
www.tytherleigharms.com
Closed: 25–26 December, First 2 weeks January

A family-run, 16th-century coaching inn on the borders
of Devon, Dorset and Somerset, The Tytherleigh Arms
offers relaxed dining. The restaurant has beamed
ceilings, wooden floors and a warming wood-burner
in the winter. The menu has attitude, and the food
deserves respect, but it's not too pompous. There's
honesty and integrity there.

Chef: Jack Cannell
Food Style: Modern British

Bampton

The Swan ◉◉
Station Road, EX16 9NG
01398 332248
www.theswan.co
Closed: 25-26 December

Chef: Paul & Donna Berry
Food Style: Modern British

The Swan is a smart, centuries old country pub – warm colours, lots of oak, a few sofas, soft lighting, an original bread oven and with a convivial atmosphere. The bar is the heart of the operation, but it's easy to see why the whole place can be full of diners.

Barnstaple

The Arlington Restaurant ◉
The Imperial Hotel, Taw Vale Parade, EX32 8NB
01271 345861
www.brend-imperial.co.uk
Closed: 23 December to 1 January

Set in the Edwardian grandeur of the riverside Imperial Hotel, this elegant old-school restaurant offers plenty of period character with its chandeliers, paintings and fancy plasterwork. It's a fitting setting for gently modern, classically-based cooking that achieves satisfying results thanks to skilful technique and quality ingredients rather than outlandish ideas.

Chef: Shaun Brayley
Food Style: British

Seasons Brasserie ◉
The Park Hotel, Taw Vale, EX32 9AE
01271 372166
www.parkhotel.co.uk
Open: All year

Warm oak, gleaming marble, soft lighting and cheery service all combine to create a soothing ambience in this smart, contemporary restaurant overlooking Rock Park. The buzzy hub of the hotel, Seasons Brasserie fits the bill whether you're here for coffee and cakes, cocktails or a please-all roster of straightforward modern and traditional cooking.

Chef: Pete Woolacott
Food Style: Modern British

Beaworthy

The Blackriver Inn
Broad Street, Black Torrington, EX21 5PT
01409 231888
www.blackriverinn.co.uk
Closed: Monday, 1–27 January

Apparently, The Blackriver Inn has been around since the early 1820s, and describes itself as a 'proper village pub'. In addition to options such as hearty home-made burgers there are a wide variety of 'small plates', many classic dishes presented in smaller form. This means you can experience more of the kitchen's diverse output.

Chef: Alex Pallatt
Food Style: Traditional

Beesands

The Cricket Inn
TQ7 2EN
01548 580215
www.thecricketinn.com
Closed: 25 December

Chef: Jamie Smith
Food Style: Modern, Seafood

Smack on the seafront overlooking the shingle beach, with stunning views across Start Bay, The Cricket enjoys an unrivalled location and retains every ounce of its identity as a former fisherman's pub. Blackboard menus advertise what has been freshly drawn from the bay.

Bideford

The Royal George
Irsha Street, Appledore, EX39 1RY
01237 424138
www.trgpub.co.uk
Closed: 25 December, 2 weeks January

Right on the water, complete with an ancient slipway that runs into the sea, The Royal George overlooks the Taw and Torridge Estuary. Inside the cosy dining room, the food is as fine as the view, drawing heavily on fresh fish and local venison and lamb. The roast venison loin with breaded shoulder is a real treat.

Chef: John Cairns
Food Style: Modern British

Brixham

The Bonaparte Restaurant ⊕
Berry Head Hotel, Berry Head Road, TQ5 9AJ
01803 853225
www.berryheadhotel.com
Open: All year

Chef: Luvo Mafani
Food Style: Modern British

Views of the bay are very much the feature here at the Berry Head Hotel's formal dining option. The daily-changing menu offers quality ingredients and traditional cookery. The cuisine is enjoyable and clearly popular with the locals.

Burrington

Northcote Manor and Spa ⊕⊕
EX37 9LZ
01769 560501
www.northcotemanor.co.uk
Open: All year

Northcote Manor and Spa is a gorgeous 18th-century country house that sits happily in 20 acres of beautiful Devon countryside. As you'd expect, its restaurant is reassuringly traditional, and makes the best use of locally sourced West Country ingredients. Service is as efficient and discreet as you'd expect at a red star hotel.

Chef: Richie Herkes
Food Style: Modern British

See advertisement opposite

Chagford

Gidleigh Park ⊕⊕⊕ ☙NOTABLE WINE LIST
TQ13 8HH
01647 432367
www.gidleigh.co.uk
Open: All year

Chef: Chris Eden
Food Style: Modern, Classic

Gidleigh Park is nothing if not impressive. Set in over a hundred acres of mature grounds, it's a wide Tudor-style building that takes you back in time. One gets a sense of privilege arriving here, but you'll also feel like you're home. The whole team contribute to an engaging and absorbing guest experience. The dining room's split into three, all relatively understated, with impeccably clothed tables and a simple, refined elegance. Chris Eden's menus deal in precision and big flavours, and you can also take a tour of the kitchen garden or go on a 'Fungi Foray', both followed by lunch.

Northcote Manor

Northcote Manor
Burrington
Umberleigh
Devon
EX37 9LZ

Tel: 01769 560501

Fax: 01769 560770

E: rest@northcotemanor.co.uk

www.northcotemanor.co.uk

Chagford *continued*

Mill End Hotel ⊛⊛
Dartmoor National Park, TQ13 8JN
01647 432282
www.millendhotel.com
Closed: 7 January to 2 February

The River Teign flows past this pretty white-painted
hotel, where a Devon cream tea is just the ticket, with
a lush pastoral backdrop. There's an air of genteel
formality in the restaurant with its linen-clad tables,
while the kitchen's output is modern, seasonal, and
well-presented.

Chef: Laszlo Heygi
Food Style: Modern British

Chittlehamholt

Highbullen Hotel, Golf & Country Club ⊛⊛
EX37 9HD
01769 540561
www.highbullen.co.uk
Open: All year

Chef: Stephen Walker
Food Style: Modern British

The Devon View Restaurant at the Highbullen Hotel doesn't disappoint when it comes to the
promised vista, and that is indeed the rolling Devon countryside you can see through the bank
of windows. The restaurant makes this golfing and spa hotel a useful stopover.

Crediton

The Lamb Inn ⊛
The Square, Sandford, EX17 4LW
01363 773676
www.lambinnsandford.co.uk
Closed: 25 December

A 16th-century former coaching house with open
fires, low ceilings and a pretty, sheltered garden on
three levels, this lovely village pub is unpretentious and
welcoming. The accomplished cooking makes good use
of quality, local produce, the seasonal menu changing
daily. Leave room for comforting desserts.

Chef: Tomasz Buwaj
Food Style: Chargrill

Paschoe House Awaiting Inspection
Bow, EX17 6JT
01363 84244
www.paschoehouse.co.uk
Closed: Monday, Tuesday, 5 January to 7 February

With an elegant boutique country house feel, Paschoe House offers an intimate dining room, alongside some very good cooking. The kitchen team takes a lot of produce from their kitchen garden and focuses upon the inherent quality of the produce to highlight the flavours therein. There's a lovely front-of-house team, adding to the charming and engaging atmosphere.

Chef: James Checkley
Food Style: French, British, Pan-Asian

Dartmouth

The Angel Restaurant – Taste of Devon ⚜⚜
2 South Embankment, TQ6 9BH
01803 833488
www.theangeldartmouth.co.uk
Closed: Sunday, Monday, Tuesday, 23 June to 6 July, 25–26 December, 1 January, 2 weeks January

There has been a notable restaurant on this site since 1974 when Joyce Molyneux opened it as the legendary Carved Angel. Elly Wentworth continues the tradition of a female head chef at the stoves with elegant, seasonal dishes such as braised halibut, seaweed and crab ravioli, charred gem, smoked caviar and lettuce cream.

Chef: Elly Wentworth
Food Style: Contemporary

The Dart Marina Hotel ⚜⚜
Sandquay Road, TQ6 9PH
01803 832580
www.dartmarina.com
Open: All year

With a split-level dining room, elegantly clothed tables, a mix of seating with banquettes at one end, and great views over the river, The Dart Marina is the place for watching all the waterborne activities which make Dartmouth so beguiling. Food has a strong sense of identity here, serious cooking which wants to be taken seriously.

Chef: Peter Alcroft
Food Style: Modern British

Doddiscombsleigh

The NoBody Inn ⊛
EX6 7PS
01647 252394
www.nobodyinn.co.uk
Closed: 1 January

Chef: Mike Pooley
Food Style: Modern British

This characterful 17th-century inn has a good local reputation, built upon its stylish food, excellent local cheeses, hefty wine list and a 240-long list of whiskies. Reached via winding lanes, inside it has blackened beams, mismatched tables, and walls adorned with plenty of visual interest.

Drewsteignton

The Old Inn ⊛⊛⊛
EX6 6QR
01647 281276
www.old-inn.co.uk
Closed: Sunday, Monday, Tuesday, 3 weeks January

Chef: Duncan Walker
Food Style: International

Despite the narrow roads that lead into it on either side, Drewsteignton was once a major staging-post on the coach route from Exeter to Okehampton. A slip of a Dartmoor village to the modern eye, it boasts Duncan Walker's stylish 17th-century inn. The ambience is homely, with striking modern artworks, and a menu of assured, classically based cooking that offers a wealth of enticement. Start with grilled fillet of red mullet bourride, or sautéed calves' sweetbreads with onion and thyme tart. Then, grilled fillet of turbot with crab and roast shellfish velouté, or roast squab pigeon with artichoke and port. A compact wine list is impeccably chosen.

Ermington

Plantation House ⊛⊛
Totnes Road, PL21 9NS
01548 831100
www.plantationhousehotel.co.uk
Open: All year

Chef: Richard Hendey, John Raines
Food Style: Modern British

A boutique restaurant in a restored Georgian rectory, with great garden views. The dinner deal here is simple – three courses or five. The five-course option maybe starts with an appetiser, then lentil, leek and Yarg cheese terrine; fillet of turbot with mussels; medallion of fillet steak with smoked lardons; and hand-carved Serrano ham with cave-aged cheddar.

NEW The Five Bells Inn ◉
Clyst Hydon, near Cullompton, EX15 2NT
01884 277288
www.fivebells.uk.com
Closed: Monday

Food Style: Gastropub

Originally an 18th-century farmhouse, the thatched Five Bells Inn occupies a peaceful spot in the heart of the village. Enjoy a pint of local ale next to the crackling fire or, if the sun shines, in the large beer garden before trying the skilful cooking of locally sourced ingredients.

Lympstone Manor Hotel ◉◉◉◉◉ ⬩NOTABLE WINE LIST
Courtlands Lane, EX8 3NZ
01395 202040
www.lympstonemanor.co.uk
Open: All year

Chef: Michael Caines MBE,
Dan Gambles
Food Style: Modern British

With breathtaking views of the Exe Estuary and the stunning Jurassic Coast, this contemporary country house hotel is surrounded by 28 acres of grounds and its own vineyard. It makes for an elegant and refined setting for the food, which can be enjoyed in three sumptuous dining rooms, each named after an area of Devon. Rather than austere and buttoned-up, the food and environment are designed to be enjoyed rather than revered for the sake of it and it's a relaxed and engaging experience. The food is reassuring in its classical underpinnings, not feeling any necessity to re-invent a wheel which already turns smoothly and cohesively. There are no illusions or trickery, just beautifully crafted dishes with clarity and distinction, the success enhanced by quality produce. The kitchen has its roots in the French classics but it's utterly contemporary and ingredient-driven, starting with a finely-tuned pan-fried duck liver with braised chicory, confit orange purée, anise and orange-scented jus. It might be followed by a subtle and restrained dish of butter-poached Brixham turbot, braised leeks, poached scallops, truffle and chive butter. Pistachio soufflé with pistachio ice cream is a classic way to finish.

Saveur ◉◉
9 Tower Street, EX8 1NT
01395 269459
www.saveursrestaurant.com
Closed: Sunday, Monday

Hidden down a quiet pedestrianised street behind the church, this neighbourhood restaurant ticks all the right boxes when it comes to cosiness, informality and fine cooking. Meaning 'flavour', Saveur celebrates local seafood from Lyme Bay and Brixham as well as other, equally local produce.

Chef: Nigel Wright
Food Style: Modern European

Haytor Vale

Conservatory Restaurant ⊛
The Moorland Hotel, TQ13 9XT
01364 661142
www.moorlandhoteldartmoor.co.uk
Open: All year

At the foot of Haytor in the heart of Dartmoor National
Park, the spacious Conservatory Restaurant is set
within The Moorland Hotel and offers far-reaching
views. Locally sourced ingredients dominate the
modern British menu, with typical offerings including
a duo of smoked duck and liver parfait, followed by
lemon sole, wilted spinach, samphire, crab bisque, crab
croquette and lemon oil.

Chef: Grace Taylor
Food Style: Modern British

Rock Inn ⊛⊛
TQ13 9XP
01364 661305
www.rock-inn.co.uk
Closed: Monday, Tuesday, 25–26 December

As you might expect, The Rock Inn has thick granite
walls, and stone flagged floors. You'll also find
low beams, a crackling fire, bonhomie at the bar
and motivated staff who deliver unobtrusive and
attentive service. There's no formal dining area, rather
some appealing areas in the bar lounge. Food is
contemporary with good seasonality.

Chef: Josh Porter
Food Style: Modern British, Classic

Honiton

THE PIG at Combe ⊛⊛ 🍷 NOTABLE WINE LIST
Giltisham, EX14 3AD
01404 540400
www.thepighotel.com/at-combe
Open: All year

At THE PIG at Combe, an Elizabethan mansion of
honeyed stone in 3,500 acres, any hint of starchy
country-house formality is banished. Dining is an
informal affair in a rustic-chic setting, and the '25 Mile'
menu means the kitchen is serious on sustainability and
localism, with an abundant kitchen garden for seasonal
supplies and minimal food miles.

Chef: Daniel Gavriilidis
Food Style: Seasonal British

Ilfracombe

Sandy Cove Hotel ◉◉◉
See pages 152-153 and advertisement on page 155

Ilsington

Ilsington Country House Hotel ◉◉
Ilsington Village, TQ13 9RR
01364 661452
www.ilsington.co.uk
Open: All year

Surrounded by the majesty of Dartmoor, Ilsington
Country House Hotel is the perfect place for a relaxing
break. Its dining room offers lovely views of Devon
countryside from a light and airy, uncluttered room,
with bold artwork and no pretensions. The kitchen
team delivers impressive dishes with poise and
elegance. Somewhere really special.

Chef: Mike O'Donnell
Food Style: Modern European

Kingsbridge

NEW Twenty Seven ◉◉
TQ7 1ED
01548 288847
www.27devon.co.uk
Open: Sunday, Monday, last 2 weeks November,
25–26 December

A loft-like restaurant, Twenty-Seven's simple lines and
soothing artwork provide a relaxed and informal setting
for the enjoyable and skilfully prepared cooking. Set in
the popular food quarter of this charming harbourside
town, the approachable wine list includes some notable
English bottles. There's a stylish cocktail bar downstairs.

Chef: Jamie Rogers
Food Style: Modern British

What changes have you seen over the past few years?

A wonderful response to the hardships of Covid and Brexit –
the industry becoming more collegiate and collaborative.
The result is a focus on what really is essential to a restaurant.

AA Inspector

Ilfracombe

Sandy Cove Hotel

Old Coast Road, Combe Martin Bay,
Berrynarbor, EX34 9SR
01271 882243
www.sandycove-hotel.co.uk
Closed: Tuesday–Saturday, 24–26 December, 30–31 December, 1 January

Chef: Ciro Beales
Food Style: Modern British

Local seafood a specialty here

Perched on a clifftop with uninterrupted views across the Bristol Channel and Exmoor, Sandy Cove Hotel enjoys a truly spectacular position. After a swim in the hotel pool, a trip to the beach or one of the many excellent walks, a drink on the spacious terrace makes for the perfect setting before a meal in The Cove restaurant, where local fish and shellfish have a starring role on the menu. Perfectly cooked Lundy lobster paired with a Devon crab cake, lobster mayonnaise, braised fennel and bouillabaisse is an intelligent combination of flavours and textures.

Or maybe you are tempted by a precisely timed piece of cod with fennel velouté, roasted cauliflower and brown shrimp beurre blanc. If a more traditional meal is what you're looking for, start with the pork and beef meatballs in

tomato sauce with mozzarella and toasted sourdough and then move on to steaks cooked on the grill or one of the wood-fired pizzas. End with an intensely chocolatey rocky road with a full-flavoured cherry sorbet or a light and fragrant mango and passionfruit Eton mess.

As a popular family-friendly hotel, the restaurant offers something for everyone throughout the day. Until 4pm, there are freshly made sandwiches including Devon crab with apple, crème fraîche, lemon and dill or minute steaks with caramelised onion chutney and garlic mayo.

There are also hotel restaurant staples, from Devon beef burgers and fries to fish and chips. Of course, like any Devon hotel worth its salt, there are cream teas served until 5pm and these include the standard version and the full afternoon tea comprising scones with clotted cream and jam, home-made cakes, sandwiches and a choice of tea and coffee. For those guests

really pushing the boat out, there are additional Champagne or Prosecco options available.

See advertisement on page 155

"...local fish and shellfish have a starring role on the menu."

Moretonhampstead

Great Western ⊛⊛⊛ ⁂NOTABLE WINE LIST

Bovey Castle, Dartmoor National Park, North Bovey,
TQ13 8RE
01647 445000
www.boveycastle.com
Open: All year

Chef: Mark Budd
Food Style: Modern British

Built in 1890 by stationery supremo WH Smith, Bovey Castle was reinvented as a 'golfing hotel' by the Great Western Railway back in 1930, an association acknowledged in its top dining venue, the Great Western restaurant. Local lad Mark Budd leads the kitchen team, and his fondness for regional and seasonal ingredients from land and sea looms large in good-looking contemporary dishes that reveal well-honed technical skills and sound classical roots – from starters like roasted veal sweetbreads, new season girolles, broad beans and summer truffle to mains such as Devonshire duck with roasted peach and white carrots. Aerated white chocolate, almond milk pannacotta is one way to round things off.

Smith's Brasserie ⊛

Bovey Castle, Dartmoor National Park, North Bovey,
TQ13 8RE
01647 445000
www.boveycastle.com/eat/smiths-brasserie
Open: All year

Built in 1890 by retailer W H Smith, Bovey Castle has two restaurants, of which Smith's Brasserie is the more informal – but smart all the same. With some dishes clearly Mediterranean inspired, choices include tapas-style snacks, Dover sole with poached oyster, and garden vegetable and rocket risotto. The terrace overlooks the River Bovey.

Chef: Mark Budd
Food Style: British

Okehampton

Lewtrenchard Manor ⊛⊛

Lewdown, EX20 4PN
01566 783222
www.lewtrenchard.co.uk
Open: All year

Lewtrenchard Manor is a Grade II listed Jacobean manor house with a fascinating history. There's a sense of grandeur with wood panelling, ornate plasterwork and old portraits, yet the restaurant is still intimate and not at all pompous. An emphasis on local meat and fish, including fruit and veg from the manor garden, drives the modern menu.

Chef: David Brown
Food Style: Modern British

Seacliff
DINING

The Seacliff Restaurant at Sandy Cove Hotel

Berrynarbor, Ilfracombe,

Devon, EX34 9SR

www.sandycove-hotel.co.uk/dinc/seacliff

01271 882243

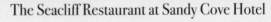

SANDY COVE
HOTEL

Plymouth

Àclèaf ⊚⊚⊚⊚
See pages 158-159 and advertisement opposite

Barbican Kitchen ⊚
Plymouth Gin Distillery, 60 Southside Street, PL1 2LQ
01752 604448
www.barbicankitchen.com
Closed: 24–27 December, 1 week from 31 December

The British, European and vegetarian-friendly dishes clearly appeal to the young evening crowd in Chris and James Tanner's colourful, loft-conversion-style restaurant. At lunchtime, though, the age range is wider. The brothers' place has stood the test of time in an area that survived wartime bombing to remind one of a much older Plymouth.

Chef: Martyn Compton
Food Style: Modern, International

The Fig Tree @ 36 ⊚
36 Admiralty Street, PL1 3RU
01752 253247
www.thefigtreeat36.co.uk
Closed: Monday, Tuesday

In an area on the up, menus here change frequently, with fish and meat given equal billing. The fish, locally caught of course, appears on the specials board soon after landing. The comfortable dining area contains a happy collection of mis-matched tables and chairs, while in a courtyard is the small fig tree after which the restaurant is named.

Chef: Ryan Marsland
Food Style: Modern British

See advertisement on page 161

What excites you most in your work?

Being surprised by something or someone.
The simple pleasure of tasting something truly delicious.

AA Inspector

Plymouth

Àclèaf

Boringdon Hill, Plympton, PL7 4DP
01752 344455
www.boringdonhall.co.uk
Closed: Monday, Tuesday

Chef: Scott Paton
Food Style: Modern French

Refined cooking in historic Tudor house

Five miles from Plymouth and close to Dartmoor National Park, 16th-century manor house Boringdon Hall was once given to the Earl of Southampton by none other than Henry VIII. Nowadays, it's a luxurious country house hotel, full of charm and elegance although it doesn't take much for you to imagine the doors swinging open and Henry VIII striding in, accompanied by the sound of buglers. Intimate and elegant Àclèaf is the ultimate fine dining restaurant, with tables looking out over the Great Hall. It's all aged beams and period features, with an atmosphere that gives a sense of occasion without being overly formal.

There's an unstuffy elegance about the setting, but it has a nicely balanced ambience that's enough to make a dining occasion feel special with plenty of chat at the tables. Attention to detail starts as soon as the bread arrives –

excellent pain de campaign and oat-crusted rolls served with Normandy butter and whipped Wagyu beef fat butter. Before the main events, snacks of fennel salami, bouillabaisse studded with red mullet and shiitake mushroom and game doughnuts prepare the tastebuds for what's to come.

The seasonally led menus showcase the stylishly inventive cuisine, where creative yet simple combinations can be seen in dishes such as starter of sole, velouté and fermented grape – a great re-working of a classic pairing, updated for the 21st century – or perhaps beetroot paired with rosehip and elder.

It could be followed by a precisely cooked piece of turbot with yuzu and langoustine, or confidently prepared Highland Wagyu beef with beetroot and pepper. Raspberry with pistachio and white chocolate makes for a stunning finish. The vegetarian and vegan options are equally enticing and might include such innovative flavour pairings as celeriac, walnut and caviar or Jerusalem artichoke, celery and goats' curd.

See advertisement on page 157

"...with an atmosphere that gives a sense of occasion without being overly formal."

Plymouth *continued*

NEW Fletcher's Restaurant ⚜
27 Princess Street, PL1 2EX
01752201523
www.fletchersrestaurant.co.uk
Closed: Sunday, Monday

Chef: Fletcher
Food Style: Modern British

In a quiet city centre position close to the Theatre Royal, the eponymously named Fletcher's Restaurant has a relaxed and engaging atmosphere from the outset. Set across two levels with a conservatory-style terraced area and showpiece bar, the accomplished cooking is ambitious, elegant and demonstrates a strong skill set.

See advertisement below

The Fig Tree @ 36

Admiralty Street
Plymouth, Devon
PL1 3RU

01752 253247

info@thefigtreeat36.co.uk

OPEN

Wednesday – Saturday
12 – 2:30pm & from 5:30pm

Sunday Lunch
12 – 3pm
Last Sunday of every month

Home of the Trust the Chef!
(Wed & Thurs evenings)

Plymouth *continued*

Salumi Bar & Eatery
18 Millbay Road, PL1 3LH
01752 267538
www.rocksaltcafe.co.uk
Closed: 24–26 December

Tucked away on a back street, Salumi Bar & Eatery is spread over two floors and has a refreshing look with turquoise painted features pared with bare wood and exposed brick. There is a heated dining space outside where food is cooked over coals in an open kitchen. Expect dishes such as whole roasted fish and steaks to share.

Chef: David Jenkins
Food Style: Modern British

See advertisement below

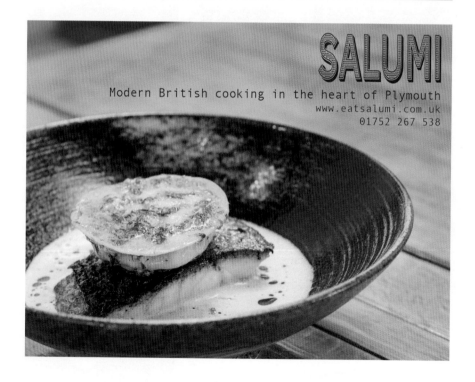

SALUMI

Modern British cooking in the heart of Plymouth
www.eatsalumi.com.uk
01752 267 538

The Jack In The Green Inn ⊛⊛

EX5 2EE
01404 822240
www.jackinthegreen.uk.com
Closed: Tuesday, 25 December to early January

This family-friendly roadside pub has gained a well-deserved reputation for its upmarket, modern British food. With its low-beamed rooms, soft brown leather chairs and a wood-burning stove, the smart interior creates a contemporary atmosphere and innovative menus offer smart, thoughtful dishes with punchy flavours.

Chef: Craig Griffin
Food Style: Modern British

The Jetty ⊛

Salcombe Harbour Hotel & Spa, Cliff Road, TQ8 8JH
01548 844444
www.harbourhotels.co.uk/hotels/salcombe
Open: All year

Part of Salcombe Harbour Hotel, The Jetty enjoys views across Salcombe estuary and beyond. Decor is modern open plan and there's a real buzz. Big windows afford great views, or you could always grab a terrace table for an even better look. Food is simple in construction, light and uncluttered, and as you'd expect includes a lot of seafood.

Chef: Jamie Gulliford
Food Style: Modern, International

Soar Mill Cove Hotel ⊛⊛

Soar Mill Cove, Marlborough, TQ7 3DS
01548 561566
www.soarmillcove.co.uk
Closed: 1 January to 10 February

With the stunning cove below, this family-run hotel occupies a fabulous position with sweeping sea views. Needless to say, local fish and seafood get a strong showing in a kitchen that combines classical techniques with modern ideas. Thus, monkfish with boulangère potatoes, mussel and clam provençale with basil purée.

Chef: Ian Macdonald
Food Style: Modern British

Saunton

Saunton Sands Hotel ◉◉
EX33 1LQ
01271 890212
www.sauntonsands.com
Closed: 23 December to 2 January

The location alone is a draw at Saunton Sands, a
long white art deco hotel overlooking three miles of
unspoiled sandy beach. At the heart of the hotel is
The Dining Room, bright, elegant and glamorous with
its original 1930s chandeliers, overlooking dunes, beach
and sea. In summer there's also the Beachside Grill
which offers a more informal alternative.

Chef: Mathias Oberg
Food Style: Traditional,
Modern British

Sidmouth

Hotel Riviera ◉◉
The Esplanade, EX10 8AY
01395 515201
www.hotelriviera.co.uk
Open: All year

The spotless bow-fronted Riviera is a prime example
of Devon's own seaside grandeur. Terrace tables make
the most of the summer weather and the traditional,
elegant dining room overlooks the bay. A seasonal
menu of gently modernised British cooking, with an
emphasis on fresh fish dishes, caters for most tastes.

Chef: Patrice Bouffaut
Food Style: Modern British

The Salty Monk ◉◉ ◆NOTABLE WINE LIST
Church Street, Sidford, EX10 9QP
01395 513174
www.saltymonk.com
Closed: Sunday, Monday, 25–27 December

The name is not a reference to a seafaring friar,
but rather to the building's 16th-century role as
a store for the salt that the monks traded at Exeter
Cathedral. The Garden Room restaurant makes
a smart yet understated backdrop for the
unpretentious cooking.

Chef: Annette and
Andy Witheridge
Food Style: Modern British

The Victoria Hotel
The Esplanade, EX10 8RY
01395 512651
www.victoriahotel.co.uk
Open: All year

Chef: Stuart White
Food Style: Traditional

The setting at the end of the town's impressive esplanade is alluring, with the expansive bay offered up in all its shimmering glory. From the doorman to the pianist, The Victoria oozes old-world charm and what appears on the plate is generally classically minded.

South Zeal

Oxenham Arms
EX20 2JT
01837 840244
www.oxdevon.com
Closed: Monday, 25 December

Set in deepest Dartmoor country, the historic Oxenham Arms is still the hub of village life. The place began in the 12th century as a monastery but today contemporary touches blend seamlessly with an ambience of gnarled beams, whitewashed stone walls and stone mullioned windows. A comfort-oriented menu of unfussy country inn food scores many hits.

Chef: Lyn Powell
Food Style: Modern British

Tavistock

Bedford Hotel
1 Plymouth Road, PL19 8BB
01822 613221
www.bedford-hotel.co.uk
Open: All year

With its grand castellations, Tavistock's Bedford Hotel is an impressive Gothic building that's been offering hospitality since at least 1719. The elegant dining room carries on the theme and grandeur of the building, with historic artefacts helping to create the atmosphere. Staff are pleasant and engaging, while the menu mixes classics with Asian influenced dishes.

Chef: Raoul Ketelaars
Food Style: British

Tavistock *continued*

The Horn of Plenty ⊛⊛⊛
See page opposite

Thurlestone

Trevilder Restaurant ⊛⊛
TQ7 3NN
01548 560382
www.thurlestone.co.uk
Closed: January

Family-owned and run since 1896, Thurlestone
Hotel is located in the peaceful and unspoilt South
Devon countryside, with stunning views of the
English Channel. The art deco-style Trevilder restaurant
boasts floor-to-ceiling windows with stunning sea
views, which makes for a stylish backdrop to the
contemporary cooking.

Food Style: British

The Village Inn ⊛
Thurlestone Hotel, TQ7 3NN
01548 563525
www.thurlestone.co.uk
Open: All year

Among the original building materials of the
16th-century Village Inn are timbers from ships of the
Spanish Armada wrecked off the Devon coast. It's all
been sensitively spruced up, with plenty of light wood
and a log burner.

Food Style: Modern British

Torquay

NEW Brasserie at the Bay ⊛⊛
Meadfoot Sea Road, TQ1 2LQ
01803 228998
www.brasserieatthebay.com
Open: All year

Chef: Callum Tasker
Food Style:

Tucked away in a quiet residential area, Brasserie at the Bay is a short stroll from Meadfoot
Beach, and has a genuine sense of welcome, making it very popular with locals. Dishes impress
with their clarity and sense of purpose; good produce treated with care and reverence is
allowed to shine in simply crafted and well-balanced dishes.

Tavistock

The Horn of Plenty

Gulworthy, PL19 8JD
01822 832528
www.thehornofplenty.co.uk
Open: All year

Chef: Ashley Lewis
Food Style: Modern British

On the border of Devon and Cornwall, overlooking the famous Tamar Valley towards Bodmin Moor, The Horn of Plenty enjoys a long reputation as a luxurious bolt-hole going back more than 60 years. An elegant Regency mansion house converted into a privately owned country house hotel, its location close to the Dartmoor National Park makes it a popular spot for locals and visitors. The panoramic and uninterrupted views from the restaurant make for a stunning backdrop to enjoy the French-influenced British food, the majority of raw materials sourced within the county. Start with fresh and flavourful hand-picked crab teamed with lemon, gel cucumber, celery and robust crab bisque. It might be followed by perfectly cooked roast venison loin, pumpkin, salsify and a well-balanced red win jus. A correctly made pistachio crème brûlée is accompanied by vanilla ice cream and mixed berries with enough acidity to counter the richness. Enjoy pre-meal drinks on the terrace overlooking the well-manicured gardens.

Torquay *continued*

Cary Arms
Babbacombe Beach, TQ1 3LX
01803 327110
www.caryarms.co.uk
Open: All year

On a glorious summer's day, the terraced gardens
leading to the water's edge are an unforgettable place
to eat, but the whitewashed Cary Arms does have more
than its fair share of good things: a beamed bar with
stone walls and dreamy views.

Chef: Steve Poyner
Food Style: British, Seafood

NEW The Dining Room
Meadfoot Road, TQ1 2JX
01803 213361
www.lincombehallhotel.co.uk
Closed: 3–13 January

The Dining Room is part of Lincombe Hall Hotel and
Spa, close to the town centre and harbour. It's an
intimate space, with just enough of a 'stand-alone'
feel. Decor is understated elegance, while the food is
purposeful with a reassuring lack of over-elaboration.
The hotel is for adults only, but children may dine in
the restaurant.

Chef: Phil Sampson, Jon Pearce
Food Style: Modern British

The Elephant Restaurant by Simon Hulstone
3–4 Beacon Terrace, TQ1 2BH
01803 200044
www.elephantrestaurant.co.uk
Closed: First 2 weeks January

Chef: Simon Hulstone
Food Style: Modern British

Torquay can think itself very fortunate that Simon Hulstone has made his base here for
over 15 years. A relaxed brasserie-style vibe permeates The Elephant, a split-level room
overlooking the harbour with elegant period features combined with contemporary touches.
The cooking has a maturity and confidence, so expect precise dishes with elegant presentation,
starting with Orkney scallops, seared foie gras, pumpkin and date with sherry vinegar jus. It
could precede an impressively tender Crediton duckling with brown butter hispi, pickled walnut,
shallot purée and Granny Smith. Strawberry and camomile tart, strawberry sorbet and pistachio
is a typical dessert.

The Imperial Hotel
Park Hill Road, TQ1 2DG
01803 294301
www.theimperialtorquay.co.uk
Open: All year

Chef: Mark Brankin
Food Style: Modern British

The Imperial's Victorian founders couldn't have chosen a better spot for their hotel, whose clifftop position has wide-ranging views over the bay and Channel. The kitchen chooses its ingredients diligently, making good use of fish and local produce, and turns out well-considered, carefully-timed dishes.

Orestone Manor
Rockhouse Lane, Maidencombe, TQ1 4SX
01803 897511
www.orestonemanor.com
Closed: Tuesday, January

This handsome Georgian manor house occupies landscaped grounds overlooking Lyme Bay. The main restaurant is a relaxing space with wooden table tops and tartan accents – a suitable setting for the kitchen's ambitious à la carte menus. Classic French-accented technique delivers refined dishes with affordable set price menus.

Chef: Neil D'Allen
Food Style: Modern, European

Seasons
Belgrave Sands Hotel & Spa, Belgrave Road, TQ2 5HF
01803 226366
www.belgravesands.com
Open: All year

Chef: Stephen Sanders
Food Style: Modern British

Part of the seafront Belgrave Sands Hotel, Seasons is a modern dining room with a feature entertainment area for live music and dancing. Tables are dark wood, while seating is fully upholstered, and bold artwork hangs on the walls. Cooking is articulate and polished with a very competent and skilled brigade underpinning its success.

Totnes

Gather
50 Fore Street, TQ9 5RP
01803 866666
www.gathertotnes.com
Closed: Monday, 25 December

The young, enthusiastic team trained together in the Michael Caines Academy and it's great to see them doing so well. The dining room is inviting, with big plate glass windows and an open kitchen, and the approach is genuine, with a particular interest in foraged and less well-known produce, making for light, elegant and flavour-driven dishes.

Chef: Harrison Brockington
Food Style: Modern British

Two Bridges

Two Bridges Hotel ◉◉
PL20 6SW
01822 892300
www.twobridges.co.uk
Open: All year

Deep in the Dartmoor National Park, the Tors
restaurant in this character riverside hotel was
refurbished in 2019. Local farmers and fishermen
supply the kitchen with top notch produce for modern
British dishes like Devon crab ravioli, bisque, brown
shrimp and crayfish or Creedy Carver duck, red
cabbage, pink peppercorn and pistachio praline.

Chef: Mike Palmer
Food Style: Modern British

Woolacombe

Bay Brasserie ◉◉
The Woolacombe Bay Hotel, South Street, EX34 7BN
01271 870388
www.woolacombe-bay-hotel.co.uk
Closed: 3 January to 16 February

Part of The Woolacombe Bay Hotel, a fine Tudor-Gothic
hotel overlooking the beach, Bay Brasserie is a relaxed
and informal venue with a great atmosphere, and a long
bar providing its focal point. The dapper young team
add a sense of theatre and occasion. Food is punchy
and well conceived, with great clarity of flavour and
attention to detail.

Chef: Eduard Grecu
Food Style: Modern British

Watersmeet Hotel ◉◉
Mortehoe, EX34 7EB
01271 870333
www.watersmeethotel.co.uk
Closed: January to February

Surfers hang loose in the Atlantic below as diners enjoy
the attentive, uniformed service of the hotel's clifftop
Pavilion Restaurant. A frequently-changing menu of
British cooking might suggest a three-course meal of
wild mushroom and egg-yolk ravioli; halibut fillet with
oyster emulsion and bacon; and vanilla pannacotta,
cherry compôte and meringues.

Chef: Sebastian Davidson
Food Style: Traditional British,
European

Dorset

The Connaught Brasserie ⊛
Best Western Plus The Connaught Hotel,
30 West Hill Road, West Cliff, BH2 5PH
01202 298020
www.theconnaught.co.uk
Open: All year

Chef: Peter Tofis
Food Style: Modern British

With sandy beaches stretching below, the grand old Connaught rules the roost on Bournemouth's West Cliff. The Connaught Brasserie overlooks the hotel's gardens, where candlelit outdoor tables are popular on summer evenings. Inside, the lightly formal tone makes an agreeable ambience for traditionally-based, modern British dishes.

The Crab at Bournemouth ⊛⊛
Park Central Hotel, Exeter Road, BH2 5AJ
01202 203601
www.crabatbournemouth.com
Open: All year

The epitome of a seafront venue, The Crab is part of the white-fronted Park Central Hotel, but functions as a restaurant in its own right, smartly done out in sandy hues. An array of fresh fish and shellfish is on the menu.

Chef: Marcin
Food Style: Modern British

Cumberland Hotel ⊛⊛
27 East Overcliffe Drive, BH1 3AF
01202 290722
www.cumberlandbournemouth.co.uk
Open: All year

Chef: Yessica Gorin
Food Style: Modern British

High up on Bournemouth's East Cliff, this art deco hotel boasts all the monochrome touches of that decadent period. Not that the cooking in the hotel's elegant Ventana Grand Café restaurant is stuck in the 1930s – the food is modern British to the core. As befits a hotel with panoramic sea views, fish gets a strong showing.

Bournemouth *continued*

The Green House 🏵🏵
4 Grove Road, BH1 3AX
01202 498900
www.thegreenhousehotel.co.uk
Open: All year

The Green House is a striking-looking, centrally located property converted and run on sustainable principles. There are beehives on the roof, and the Arbor (Latin for 'tree' to further underline its green credentials) Restaurant deals in only organic, Fairtrade and farm-assured, mostly local produce.

Chef: Andrew Hilton
Food Style: Modern British

Roots 🏵🏵
141 Belle Vue Road, BH6 3EN
01202 430005
www.restaurantroots.co.uk
Closed: Sunday, Monday, Tuesday, 2 weeks August, 25–26 December

The food at Roots is simple, confident and effective. Service is charming, passionate and knowledgeable, and a key part of the experience. Monthly changing tasting menus, either 5- or 7-course, feature well-executed dishes with punchy flavours.

Chef: Jan Bretschneider
Food Style: Modern European

Bridport

NEW The Station Kitchen 🏵🏵
Old West Bay Railway Station, Station Road, West Bay, DT6 4EW
01308 422845
www.thestationkitchen.co.uk/
Closed: Sunday, Monday, Tuesday

In an old railway station, the Station Kitchen offers two refurbished and repurposed railway carriages, and a bar in the old waiting room. The popularity of the place means that many diners come for the novelty and stay for the outstanding cuisine. The style is modern British with emphasis on local fish and seafood dishes. Very friendly team.

Chef: Chris Chatfield
Food Style: Modern British with International influences

Christchurch

Captain's Club Hotel & Spa ⚜⚜
Wick Ferry, Wick Lane, BH23 1HU
01202 475111
www.captainsclubhotel.com
Open: All year

A glass-fronted boutique hotel by the River Stour, where the kitchen serves up modern brasserie fare, fully in keeping with the attractive surroundings. Veggie possibilities include an Indian-spiced cauliflower risotto with coconut and coriander, and the desserts include some crowd-pleasing choices.

Chef: Richard Allsopp
Food Style: Modern European

The Jetty ⚜⚜ 🍷 NOTABLE WINE LIST
Christchurch Harbour Hotel & Spa, 95 Mudeford, BH23 3NT
01202 400950
www.thejetty.co.uk
Open: All year

A dashing contemporary construction of glass and wood, The Jetty's culinary output is headed up by Alex Aitken. Provenance is everything here. In fine weather, grab a table on the terrace if you can, although floor-to-ceiling windows provide glorious views over Mudeford Quay. The kitchen turns out contemporary dishes taking inspiration from far and wide.

Chef: Alex Aitken, Karl Barrett
Food Style: Modern British

The Lord Bute & Restaurant ⚜⚜
179–181 Lymington Road,
Highcliffe-on-Sea, BH23 4JS
01425 278884
www.lordbute.com
Open: All year

Chef: Kevin Brown
Food Style: British, Mediterranean

In the grounds of 18th-century Prime Minister Lord Bute's Highcliffe Castle, this hotel is just next door to east Dorset's golden beaches. The place is very elegant and commands a fierce loyalty among local 'ladies who lunch'. Cuisine is charmingly traditional, and the excellent team are never complacent about their standards of service or cooking.

Christchurch *continued*

NEW The Noisy Lobster ◎
Avon Beach, Mudeford, BH23 4AN
01425 272162
avon-beach.noisylobster.co.uk
Closed: 25 December

Located on the seafront, enjoying great views of
Christchurch Bay and the Isle of Wight, the Noisy
Lobster is a relaxing place to enjoy locally-sourced
seafood and a cocktail. It's very modern inside with
clean lines and key colours, and there's also a takeaway
and a terrace. Although fresh seafood is the focus,
there are plenty of other options.

Chef: Steven Hall
Food Style: Seafood

Upper Deck Bar & Restaurant ◎
Christchurch Harbour Hotel & Spa,
95 Mudeford, BH23 3NT
01202 400954
www.christchurch-harbour-hotel.co.uk/upper-deck
Open: All year

Chef: Alex Aitken
Food Style: Modern British

Good views over the water are guaranteed, as is a fine showing of regional produce. The Upper
Deck is pretty swanky, featuring a sleek, contemporary bar and an upmarket seasidey vibe, plus
there's a terrace. The cooking takes a modern British route through contemporary tastes and,
given the setting, plenty of locally-landed fish.

Corfe Castle

Mortons Manor ◎◎
45 East Street, BH20 5EE
01929 480988
www.mortonsmanor.com
Open: All year

Chef: Ed Firth
Food Style: Modern British

Mortons Manor is a family-owned Grade II listed Elizabethan manor house, sitting at the base
of Corfe Castle. The manor building was built in the shape of an 'E' to honour Queen Elizabeth I
who stayed there. The traditional restaurant is elegant without being over elaborate, and offers
assured cooking with quality produce very much at its heart.

Evershot

The Acorn Inn 🌸
28 Fore Street, DT2 0JW
01935 83228
www.acorn-inn.co.uk
Open: All year

Chef: Robert Ndungu
Food Style: British

Plumb in the middle of Thomas Hardy's favourite stretch of England, the 16th-century coaching inn makes an appearance in *Tess of the d'Urbervilles* as the Sow and Acorn. The country-style restaurant is a friendly spot to linger and enjoy the seasonal dishes.

Summer Lodge Country House Hotel, Restaurant & Spa 🌸🌸🌸 🍷NOTABLE WINE LIST
Fore Street, DT2 0JR
01935 482000
www.summerlodgehotel.com
Open: All year

Chef: Steven Titman
Food Style: Modern British

A Grade II listed Georgian manor house, Summer Lodge Country House Hotel, Restaurant & Spa is surrounded by lovely countryside in the heart of the Dorset Downs. An elegant conservatory makes for a light and airy setting for diners, although the terrace is a draw in summer. Local fish is a particular strength of the kitchen, which showcases regional produce but doesn't shy away from global influences. Start, perhaps, with a flavour-packed dish of warm chalk stream trout, pickled kohlrabi, wasabi ice cream and coconut and lemongrass velouté, before tandoori-dusted hake fillet with sag aloo and lobster curry sauce.

Lyme Regis

NEW The Millside Restaurant 🌸🌸
1 Mill Lane, DT7 3PU
01297 445999
www.themillside.co.uk
Closed: 25 December, Easter Sunday

Set close to the Town Mill, the Millside Restaurant sees itself as easy-going, offering a predominantly seafood and fish based menu. The room is nicely atmospheric with intimate tables and lots of wood, relaxing and very welcoming. In nice weather you can enjoy a drink on the terrace before going inside.

Chef: Georgina Baker
Food Style: Seafood

Lyme Regis *continued*

NEW Tom's Lyme Regis ⊕

Marine Parade, DT7 3JQ
01297 816018
www.tomslymeregis.com
Closed: 25–26 December

A relaxed bistro on Marine Parade, slap bang on
the front at Lyme Regis, Tom's offers delightful views
of the sea where much of the fish and seafood on the
modern British menu is sourced. Not that carnivores
are forgotten, with local meat also served by the
friendly young staff.

Chef: Tom Robinson
Food Style: British, Seafood

Poole

Hotel du Vin Poole ⊕ ⚑NOTABLE WINE LIST

Mansion House, Thames Street, BH15 1JN
01202 785578
www.hotelduvin.com/locations/poole
Open: All year

Chef: Lee Coote
Food Style: Modern British, French

Hotel du Vin's Poole outpost is a bit of a landmark just off the quayside, a creeper-covered
Georgian mansion. As expected, the kitchen deals in crowd-pleasing brasserie staples from
over the Channel, all cooked just so. Start perhaps with escargots in garlic and herb butter.

Rick Stein Sandbanks ⊕ ⚑NOTABLE WINE LIST

10-14 Banks Road, BH13 7QB
01202 283280
www.rickstein.com
Closed: 25 December

The globetrotting Mr Stein needs no introduction and
he's picked a promising spot in well-heeled Sandbanks
for another outpost of the ever-expanding empire. The
food bears the Stein imprint, nothing too elaborate, just
light-touch treatment to let the quality of the produce
strut its stuff.

Chef: Pete Murt
Food Style: Seafood

NEW The Clockspire ◉◉
Gainsborough, Milborne Port, DT9 5BW
01963 251458
www.theclockspire.com
Closed: Monday, Tuesday, 26 December, 1 January

Originally built in 1864 as a school, The Clockspire is a truly impressive dining venue. The striking exterior is easily matched by a stunning new modern interior with bare stone walls, exposed oak roof beams and a polished concrete floor. Enjoy a drink in the chic bar before sampling fine dishes from a strong seasonal menu.

Chef: Luke Sutton
Food Style: Modern British

The Kings Arms ◉
Charlton Herethorne, DT9 4NL
01963 220281
www.thekingsarms.co.uk
Closed: 25 December

The Kings Arms is a beautiful early 19th-century inn that now serves as a chic and charming boutique hotel. The restaurant comes complete with large wooden tables and high-back chairs, and the kitchen is gallery-style so you can watch your dinner being created. The chicken and wild mushroom pie is a real treat.

Chef: Sarah Lethbridge
Food Style: Modern British

Seasons Restaurant at The Eastbury ◉◉
Long Street, DT9 3BY
01935 813131
www.theeastburyhotel.co.uk
Open: All year

Seasons Restaurant at The Eastbury overlooks the delightful walled garden, which has a dining pod for outdoor eating. However, the garden's not just for show, it's where the kitchen team grows much of the excellent produce they use. Despite the local focus of the ingredients, the menu is a bit of a globe-trotter, pulling influences and flavours from all over.

Chef: Matthew Street
Food Style: Modern British

See advertisement on page 179

Studland

THE PIG on the Beach ⦿⦿ ♦NOTABLE WINE LIST

The Manor House, Manor Road, BH19 3AU
01929 450288
www.thepighotel.com
Open: All year

Chef: James Shadbolt
Food Style: Modern British

Part of THE PIG hotel group, this particular porker has a kitchen garden, and raises its own chickens and quails, while fish and seafood are locally landed. The location is wonderful, looking out over Studland Bay, with some good walking down to Old Harry Rocks. One of those places that makes you feel like one of the family.

West Bexington

The Club House ⦿

Beach Road, DT2 9DF
01308 898302
www.theclubhousewestbexington.co.uk
Closed: Monday (excluding Bank Holidays),
25–26 December

Built in 1932, and previously a 'seaside cafe', The Club House has turned into a smart, relaxed venue that looks out onto Chesil Beach. Menus feature plenty of local seafood, along with an eclectic mix of other choices. Dishes change daily depending on the local catch, but many favourites endure. If you've got a helicopter, you can land it here.

Chef: Steve Mesher
Food Style: Modern, Seafood

Wyke Regis

Crab House Café ⦿

Ferrymans Way, Portland Road, DT4 9YU
01305 788867
www.crabhousecafe.co.uk
Closed: mid December to early February

Situated in a spruced up wooden hut overlooking Chesil Beach, the Crab House Café has natural charms aplenty. Simplicity and freshness is the name of the game, with oysters coming from their own beds and everything sourced from within a 40-mile radius. Rustic benches outside are a treat in the warmer months.

Chef: George Brace
Food Style: British, Seafood

SEASONS RESTAURANT
SHERBORNE, DORSET

Spa

FINE DINING | TASTING MENU | GREAT WINES | ALFRESCO DINING
AWARD WINNING GARDEN | COCKTAIL BAR | BOUTIQUE SPA | LIVE MUSICIAN

County Durham

The Morritt Country House Hotel & Spa ⊛
Greta Bridge, DL12 9SE
01833 627232
www.themorritt.co.uk
Open: All year

Chef: Alex Wood
Food Style: Modern French

The arrival of transport by mail coach in the 18th century saw this former farm develop into an overnight stop for travellers between London and Carlisle. Charles Dickens probably stayed here in 1839, hence the fine-dining restaurant is named after him.

NEW Nu-Sana ⊛
Rockliffe Park, Hurworth-on-Tees, DL2 2DU
01325 729999
www.rockliffehall.com
Open: All year

Rockliffe Hall is in the same complex as Middlesborough FC's training grounds, so you may find players in Nu-Sana, the hotel's health-conscious dining option, right above the spa. The menu's main focus is East Asian, although plenty of other regions are represented. Decor is bright and open, with a long terrace ideal for alfresco dining.

Chef: Martin Horsley
Food Style: East Asian

The Orangery ⁂ NOTABLE WINE LIST Rosettes Suspended
Rockliffe Hall, Rockliffe Park, Hurworth-on-Tees, DL2 2DU
01325 729999
www.rockliffehall.com
Open: All year

Food Style: Modern British

The Rosette award for this establishment has been suspended due to a change of chef and reassessment will take place in due course.
The fine dining option at luxurious Rockliffe Hall, The Orangery is filled with daylight and well-spaced tables. The modern British dishes show off the best regional ingredients and fish is a particular strength of the kitchen. A well-presented wine list has broad appeal and plenty by the glass.

Durham

Fusion Restaurant ◉
Ramside Hall Hotel Golf & Spa, Carrville, DH1 1TD
0191 386 5282
www.ramsidehallhotel.co.uk
Open: All year

Chef: Watcharin Dechbamrung
Food Style: Pan-Asian, Thai

Surrounded by 350 acres of grounds including two 18-hole championship golf courses at Ramside Hall, the restaurant at the hotel's spa serves south-east Asian-inspired food throughout the day. Overlooking the spa's thermal suite, the Oriental-styled restaurant combines the dishes of Thailand, Japan and China including 'Make Your Own Bento Box'.

The Rib Room ◉
Ramside Hall Hotel Golf & Spa, Carrville, DH1 1TD
0191 386 5282
www.ramsidehallhotel.co.uk
Open: All year

Chef: Jim Hall
Food Style: International

Sprawling outwards from a largely Victorian house, is Ramside's glossy spa and health club. Culinary options run from straightforward carvery dishes to the menu in the brasserie-style Rib Room, a temple to slabs of locally-reared 28-day aged beef.

Seaham

Seaham Hall – The Dining Room ◉◉ NOTABLE WINE LIST
Seaham Hall, Lord Byron's Walk, SR7 7AG
0191 516 1400
www.seaham-hall.co.uk
Closed: 31 December

Lord Byron was a former guest at Seaham Hall, an imposing building close to the cliffs. The interior design is stunning, displaying a commitment to the best of old and new. The restaurant has a similar ethic, with a mixture of semi-circular booths and individual tables. The menu is big on meaty, modern British dishes.

Chef: Damian Broom
Food Style: Modern British

Sedgefield

The Impeccable Pig
Front Street, TS21 3AT
01740 582 580
www.impeccablepig.co.uk/the-restaurant
Open: All year

With a mix of banquette seating, booths and deep, comfortable dining chairs you'll always be comfy eating at The Impeccable Pig, a Grade II listed building that's been transformed into an operation delivering great brasserie-style dining. Tables in the bar area have a view of the kitchen, where the chefs can be seen plying their trade. Josper grill cooking features heavily.

Chef: David Gill
Food Style: Bistro

Essex

Braintree

NEW Caesar @ Dolphin
Coggeshall Road, CM77 8EU
01376 321143
www.caesarsatthedolphin.co.uk
Closed: Monday, 25 December

A traditional pub complete with low ceilings, beams, real fires and a cosy bar still frequented by the locals, it's the pride of place pizza oven that makes Caesar @ Dolphin stand out from many village inns. That and the seasonal menu of big-flavoured dishes underpinned by strong technical skill.

Chef: Daniel Araritei
Food Style: Modern European

The House by Hilly Gant
34 New Street, CM7 1ES
01376 345615
www.thehousebyhillygant.co.uk
Closed: Monday

Choose between bistro-style dining and a more formal experience here at The House by Hilly Grant. Service is just the right mix of relaxed and attentive, and the modern British menu offers simple, unfussy cookery, using ingredients sourced within a 30-mile radius where possible.

Chef: Sam McGee
Food Style: Modern, Classic British

Brentwood

Marygreen Manor Hotel 🌸🌸
London Road, CM14 4NR
01277 225252
www.marygreenmanor.co.uk
Open: All year

Chef: Majid Bourote
Food Style: Modern European

Although the house is older than the 17th century, it was then that its owner named it 'Manor of Mary Green', after his young bride. Its many original features include exposed beams, carved panelling and the impressive Tudors Restaurant, where classically based cooking holds sway, typically pork fillet and belly; and bouillabaisse.

Chelmsford

Samphire Restaurant 🌸
County Hotel, 29 Rainsford Road, CM1 2PZ
01245 455700
countyhotelchelmsford.co.uk/food-drink/
samphire-restaurant
Closed: 24 and 26 December

The County Hotel has a cheery modern style, as typified in the smart Samphire Restaurant, where the brightly coloured, upholstered chairs brighten up the neutral, contemporary decor of sage green panelling, oak flooring and subtle lighting. Uncomplicated, modern British and European cooking is the kitchen's stock-in-trade.

Chef: Roy Ortega
Food Style: British, Mediterranean

Coggeshall

Ranfield's Brasserie 🌸🌸
4-6 Stoneham Street, CO6 1TT
01376 561453
www.ranfieldsbrasserie.co.uk
Open: All year

Chef: John Ranfield
Food Style: Modern British

A fixture of the local dining scene for almost 30 years, its setting may be a 16th-century timbered house but there's nothing old about the approach. The mood is laid-back and cosmopolitan, and the decor akin to an eclectic art gallery with antique linen-clothed tables.

Colchester

Church Street Tavern ◉◉ ⬤NOTABLE WINE LIST

3 Church Street, CO1 1NF
01206 564325
www.churchstreettavern.co.uk
Closed: Monday, Tuesday, 25 December to 1 January

Just off the main shopping mayhem, the handsome
Victorian former bank building has been repurposed as
a trendy bar and first-floor restaurant full of light and
artwork. Bare tables, banquettes and wood floors fit
the smart-casual mood, and the seasonal menu is brim
full of up-to-date ideas.

Chef: Ewan Naylon
Food Style: Modern British

Cloisters ◉◉

GreyFriars, High Street, CO1 1UG
01206 575913
www.greyfriarscolchester.co.uk
Open: All year

Chef: Liam Keating
Food Style: Modern British

Cloisters restaurant is in the modern part of GreyFriars Hotel, which was once a Franciscan
monastery. Parquet floored with an art deco feel, it's known for modern European dishes with a
British touch. Local produce is a big feature, including oysters from Mersea Island, which is only
nine miles away.

NEW Rubino Kitchen ◉

Kelvedon Road, Inworth, CO5 9SP
01621 855579
www.rubinokitchen.co.uk
Closed: Monday, Tuesday, 26 December to 11 January

Rubino Kitchen is s et in a solid Grade II listed
red-brick building with lots of period features. Tables
are traditionally dressed with white tablecloths, and
interesting artworks can be seen and purchased, if the
fancy takes you. The front terrace is great for dining
and proves very popular in warm weather. Menus
showcase local produce with Italian flair.

Chef: Rob Horton
Food Style: Modern English, Italian
influences

What is your advice for cooking great food?

Keep it simple, keep it fresh

AA Inspector

Dedham

milsoms
Stratford Road, CO7 6HN
01206 322795
www.milsomhotels.com
Open: All year

Set in a pretty Essex village, milsoms is a contemporary brasserie in a creeper-covered house, with a menu offering everything from posh lunchtime sandwiches to grilled steaks. It has a very informal and relaxed brasserie-style dining room with open-plan kitchen, rustic tables and a variety of leather chairs. Informal but attentive service.

Chef: Sarah Norman
Food Style: Modern British

The Sun Inn NOTABLE WINE LIST
High Street, CO7 6DF
01206 323351
www.thesuninndedham.com
Closed: 25–26 December

Chef: Jack Levine
Food Style: Modern British, Mediterranean

Close to the River Stour, the Sun is a 15th-century village inn with open fires, exposed timbers and old panelling. Its culinary leanings are distinctly Italian, with the kitchen turning fresh produce and quality ingredients such as cured meats, cheeses and oils into uncomplicated, well-executed dishes.

Talbooth Restaurant NOTABLE WINE LIST
Gun Hill, CO7 6HP
01206 323150
www.milsomhotels.com/letalbooth
Open: All year

Chef: Andrew Hirst, Jamie Jackson
Food Style: Modern British

This former toll house by the River Stour dates from Tudor times and the look is smartly formal with neutral, contemporary shades against the period character of leaded mullioned windows and bare beams. The kitchen sends out modern dishes full of precision and inspiration. Mersea crab tartlet with preserved lemon, avocado, dill and pickled radish is an intelligent combination of textures and flavours. It might precede chicken breast and miso-glazed leg with wilted gem lettuce, confit purple potatoes and cep sauce. Strawberry and lime Pavlova with vanilla Chantilly and mint sorbet is a light and fragrant way to finish.

Epping

Haywards Restaurant
See page 186

Haywards Restaurant

111 Bell Common, CM16 4DZ
01992 577350
www.haywardsrestaurant.co.uk
Closed: Monday, Tuesday, Wednesday, 26 December to 12 January

Chef: Jahdre Hayward
Food Style: Modern European

Occupying a converted coach house on the fringes of Epping Forest, this smart, family-run, air-conditioned restaurant looks the rustic-chic part with its high vaulted ceiling, polished wooden tables and floors and tasteful, local photographs of Epping Forest. Service is attentive, and the focus here is high quality food that is imaginatively composed and isn't afraid to doff its cap to places further afield. The kitchen draws on regional ingredients to deliver a repertoire of sprightly ideas, kicking off with roasted mackerel, potato and apple salad, pickled cucumber and relish, or roasted breast and confit leg of quail, fricassée of peas and broad beans and goats' cheese. Follow on with pan-roasted duck, duck leg croquette, roasted beetroots and raspberry, but if fish is your thing, then go for roasted fillet of halibut, roasted fennel and purée with verjus sauce. Finish with buttermilk and stem ginger mousse, poached rhubarb and orange gel, or go tropical with coconut parfait, mango sorbet and purée with lime gel. The restaurant opens on just four days a week.

Feering

The Blue Anchor ✿
132 Feering Hill, CO5 9PY
01376 571783
www.theblueanchorfeering.co.uk
Closed: Monday, Tuesday

The Blue Anchor is a converted 16th-century coaching inn that offers a warm welcome, complete with plenty of traditional features, including exposed brick and beautiful ancient beams. Like the rest of the public areas, the restaurant is nicely appointed without compromising comfort and ease of use. A seasonally changing modern British menu is the style here.

Chef: Andrew Wright
Food Style: Modern British

Great Dunmow

NEW Square 1 Restaurant ✿✿
15 High Street Dunmow, CM6 1AB
01371 859922
www.square1restaurant.co.uk
Closed: Monday, Tuesday, 25–26 December, 1 January

Set on the high street, the building housing Square 1 has been many things over the years yet has retained its beautiful period façade, much like the rest of the town. Over two levels, with low ceilings, the room has some striking portraits on the walls. There's a large fireplace, a small service bar and an open kitchen.

Chef: Ritchie Ewer
Food Style: Modern British

Great Yeldham

The White Hart ✿✿
Poole Street, CO9 4HJ
01787 237250
www.whitehartweddingvenue.co.uk
Closed: 26 December, 2–16 January

Dating back to the Tudor era, The White Hart is a classic timbered country inn set in extensive grounds. Crisp, white napery and quality tableware confer distinctive class on the dining room. In the main house restaurant, the intricate modern British menus are popular with local residents and guests alike.

Chef: Kevin White
Food Style: British, European

Harwich

The Pier at Harwich 🏵️🏵️
The Quay, CO12 3HH
01255 241212
www.milsomhotels.com
Open: All year

Built in 1860 and set right on the quayside,
The Pier at Harwich provides super-fresh seafood,
and some wonderful views of the water. You can dine
in the first-floor brasserie and take the sea air from
the outdoor balcony seating. The same menu is served
all day and offers a wide range including vegan and
vegetarian options.

Chef: John Goff
Food Style: Modern British,
Seafood

Howe Street

Galvin Green Man 🏵️🏵️
Main Road, CM3 1BG
01245 408820
www.galvingreenman.com
Closed: 1 January

Pulling in foodies from all over, Galvin Green Man is
operated by Essex-born brothers, Chris and Jeff, and
offers an outstanding modern British menu. It dates
back to the 14th century, and has kept plenty of
original features. The dining room is very smart, with
a feature timber ceiling and glass roof, and the River
Chelmer runs through the garden.

Chef: Chris Ball
Food Style: Modern British

Little Dunmow

NEW The Flitch of Bacon 🏵️🏵️🏵️
See page opposite

Orsett

The Garden Brasserie 🏵️
Orsett Hall Hotel, Restaurant & Spa,
Prince Charles Avenue, RM16 3HS
01375 891402
www.orsetthall.co.uk
Open: All year

Chef: Robert Pearce
Food Style: Modern British

Located in the Essex countryside, Orsett Hall is a large house with an inviting boutique
approach. The whole building is a faithful reproduction of the original 17th-century structure
that was sadly destroyed by fire in 2007. Its floral-inspired Garden Brasserie is beautiful, with
super views of the landscaped grounds.

NEW The Flitch of Bacon

The High Street, CM6 3HT
01371 821660
www.flitchofbacon.co.uk
Closed: Monday, Tuesday

Chef: Paul Croasdale
Food Style: Modern British

Close to the River Chelmer, The Flitch of Bacon might date back to the 16th century but it's thoroughly contemporary inside with a cosy bar and rear terrace for alfresco dining. The cooking is as modern and confident as the interior, with dishes presented with finesse. Seasonal produce is always the driving force behind the menu and this unwavering commitment to local suppliers extends to specials based on what's available at the farmers' market. Vibrant, just-picked wild garlic and Wiltshire truffle may sound like an obvious pairing with freshwater prawns and a slice of 'yesterday's bread' but it's a memorable starter full of textural and flavour contrast. English rose veal sirloin, artichoke, spring vegetables, cheek 'cannelloni' and sherry vinegar is a winning main course. Or, perhaps, go for the miso glazed flitch of bacon with native lobster, sand carrots, ranch dressing and lightly spiced broth. A delicate dish of strawberries and cream with relish, lemon and crisp sugar tuile is one of the striking desserts on offer.

Saffron Walden

The Cricketers Arms ⊛
Rickling Green, CB11 3YG
01799 619260
www.thecricketersarmspub.co.uk
Open: All year

The Cricketers Arms is exactly as you'd imagine. A pub overlooking the green, with relaxed dining throughout. There's a mixture of dining areas and seating, while service is informal, yet still attentive. The menu features plenty of top-quality, beautifully presented options, but the rump of lamb is really something special.

Chef: Harry Kodagoda
Food Style: Modern British

See advertisement opposite

Southend-on-Sea

Holiday Inn Southend ⊛
77 Eastwoodbury Crescent, SS2 6XG
01702 543001
www.hisouthend.com
Closed: 25 December

Calling all plane spotting foodies: both of your interests can be indulged in one fell swoop at the fifth-floor 1935 Restaurant overlooking the aviation action at Southend Airport. Naturally enough, soundproofing is of the highest order, and there's a real sense of occasion.

Chef: Denny George
Food Style: Traditional British

The Roslin Beach Hotel ⊛⊛
Thorpe Esplanade, Thorpe Bay, SS1 3BG
01702 586375
www.roslinhotel.com
Open: All year

If you do like to be beside the seaside, The Roslin Beach Hotel has a sea-facing terrace, a new garden terrace, and indoor space shielded by glass, so it's beach ready whatever the weather. The tables are dressed up in white linen and there's a buzzy ambience. The menu is modern British with some favourites always present.

Chef: Dabulis Marek
Food Style: British

THE Cricketers Arms

RICKLING GREEN

Award-winning gastropub with rooms,
in the beautiful Essex countryside

RICKLING GREEN,
NR SAFFRON WALDEN,
ESSEX, CB11 3YG
TEL: 01799 619260
WWW.THECRICKETERSARMSPUB.CO.UK
INFO@THECRICKETERSARMSPUB.CO.UK

Stock

Ellis's Restaurant ⚜
Greenwoods Hotel & Spa, Stock Road, CM4 9BE
01277 829990
www.greenwoodshotel.co.uk
Closed: 26 December, 1 January

Greenwoods Hotel is an appealing 17th-century, Grade
II listed building set in expansive landscaped gardens,
just a few minutes from Billericay town centre. Named
after a previous owner of the manor house, the hotel's
contemporary Ellis's Restaurant offers a pleasing array
of innovative, fuss-free dishes.

Chef: Daniel Holland Robinson
Food Style: Modern British

The Hoop ⍟
High Street, CM4 9BD
01277 841137
www.thehoop.co.uk
Closed: Monday

The Hoop is an atmospheric, weatherboarded pub
between Basildon and Chelmsford, and the restaurant
is upstairs. Lots of exposed rafters that were apparently
salvaged from redundant warships, and a menu of
well-executed pub classics with global influences that
lean mostly toward the French and Italian. Service is
relatively formal but still very friendly.

See advertisement opposite

Chef: Phil Utz
Food Style: Modern British

Thorpe-le-Soken

Bell Inn Bistro ⍟⍟
High Street, CO16 0DY
01255 861199
www.bellinnbistro.com
Open: All year

Food Style: British

The Bell Inn Bistro is a refurbed high street pub with an interesting history, and plenty of
original features. It's popular with the locals, but is also something of a destination for foodies.
A small but committed team produces hearty and well-executed meals. Almost everything on
the seasonal menu is gluten-free or has a gluten-free option.

Gloucestershire

Almondsbury

The Curious Kitchen at Aztec Hotel & Spa ⍟⍟
Aztec West, BS32 4TS
01454 201090
www.aztechotelbristol.co.uk/food-drink
Open: All year

Offering a full package of spa activities and
business facilities, the Aztec also has a restaurant
and bar which is worth a visit. It's a contemporary
alpine chalet-style space, with a high-vaulted ceiling,
leather seating and a terrace for alfresco dining.
The menu takes a broad sweep through comfort-
oriented modern ideas.

Chef: Marc Payne
Food Style: Modern British

Bibury

The Brasserie
Swan Hotel, GL7 5NW
01285 740695
www.cotswold-inns-hotels.co.uk
Open: All year

If you're already liking the sound of a former coaching inn beside the River Coln, then throw in the proposition of welcoming service and British cooking with a European accent, and the brasserie of the Swan Hotel is a shoo-in. Hearty, no-nonsense cooking is the deal; especially hard to resist is local Bibury trout fresh from the river.

Chef: Constatin Chitriuc
Food Style: Modern British

Buckland

Buckland Manor ⊛⊛⊛ ♠NOTABLE WINE LIST
WR12 7LY
01386 852626
www.bucklandmanor.co.uk
Open: All year

Chef: Will Guthrie
Food Style: Modern, Classic British

Buckland Manor is a grand 13th-century manor house in 10 acres of beautiful, well-kept gardens with a stream and a waterfall. Public areas are furnished with fine antiques and rich fabrics, and log fires warm the lounges. The elegant dining room, with views over the Vale of Evesham, is where to enjoy cooking that's English at its core, maybe roast fillet of Longhorn beef with sweetcorn, girolles and Madeira, or Cornish sea bass with crab and garden verbena sauce. Fresh herbs are grown in the Manor's grounds and – only to be expected in such a house – there's a magnificent wine cellar.

Cheltenham

NEW Bao + BBQ ⊛
3 Regent Street, GL50 1HE
01242 806199
www.baobbq.co.uk
Closed: Monday, 25–26 December

Near the Everyman Theatre, Bao + BBQ is an unusual mix of Taiwanese bao buns, and Texan BBQ cooking. All meat is smoked in-house and prepared in the open kitchen. All the beef comes from free-roaming long-horn Gloucestershire cattle, which is unique to its geographic area. Fish, pork, chicken and vegetarian options are also on the menu.

Chef: Cheikh Faye
Food Style: East Asian, Texan BBQ

The Curry Corner Est.1977 @@
133 Fairview Road, GL52 2EX
01242 528449
www.thecurrycorner.com
Closed: 25–26 December

Chef: Shamsul and Monrusha Krori
Food Style: Bangladeshi, Indian

Occupying a white Georgian townhouse on the edge of Cheltenham's main shopping area, the oldest Bangladeshi curry house in the UK has a chic, contemporary look, featuring ruby-red wall coverings as well as furniture designed by the chef and co-owner. Bangladeshi home cooking is the theme, with spices flown in from India, Morocco and Turkey.

The Greenway Hotel & Spa @@@
Shurdington, GL51 4UG
01242 862352
www.thegreenwayhotelandspa.com
Open: All year

Chef: Marcus McGuinness
Food Style: Modern British, French

Set in Shurdington, on the verdant outskirts of leafy Cheltenham, The Greenway is an Elizabethan manor house of Cotswold stone, its façade half-hidden in clambering ivy. The Garden Restaurant is named after its soothing view, with a majestic stone fireplace and venerable oak panelling adding lustre. Marcus McGuinness is a model modern-day practitioner, overseeing a thriving kitchen garden, foraging and sourcing thoroughbred prime materials, before turning it all into elegant, eye-catching dishes. Start with gratin of Cornish crab and white port, with sea buckthorn and 'piggy cake', before moving on to poached and roast Cornish brill with pumpkin, hazelnuts, mussels and sage. Soufflés often feature at dessert – witness a fine dark chocolate version with coffee sorbet and whisky custard.

Hotel du Vin Cheltenham @ NOTABLE WINE LIST
Parabola Road, GL50 3AQ
01242 588450
www.hotelduvin.com
Open: All year

Chef: Paul Mottram
Food Style: French, European

The restaurant at the Cheltenham branch of this popular hotel chain follows the usual bistro look of wooden floor, unclothed tables, banquettes and a wine-related theme of empty bottles, prints and memorabilia. The menu goes along the expected bistro route.

What are the most common misconceptions you face?

That we ask for a specific (traditional) style; that service plays a part in the award when assessing for AA Rosettes.

AA Inspector

Cheltenham *continued*

Le Champignon Sauvage ⊛⊛⊛⊛

24–28 Suffolk Road, GL50 2AQ
01242 573449
www.lechampignonsauvage.co.uk
Closed: 10 days at Christmas, 3 weeks in June

Chef: David Everitt-Matthias
Food Style: Modern French

In its fourth decade of operations, Le Champignon Sauvage is a remarkable testament to the tenacity and dedication of David and Helen Everitt-Matthias. It has remained in the upper echelons of British gastronomy throughout, achieving its longevity without any attention-grabbing culinary stunts. The interior is prospect of blond wood and dove-grey, with striking artworks and trimly linened table, creates a civilised, discreet feel. The cooking, for all its modern ingredients and techniques, retains an underlying sense of classical French cuisine. You might begin with fillet of Cornish mackerel, kohlrabi, avocado purée and caviar, or Dexter beef tartare with corned beef, wasabi mayonnaise and pickled shimeji; perhaps followed by Brecon venison with parsnip purée, baby parsnips, black pudding and bitter chocolate, or red legged partridge with turnip choucroute, walnuts and quince. Delightfully creative desserts might include frozen bergamot parfait, orange jelly, liquorice cream, or blueberry cannelloni with wood sorrel cream and yogurt sorbet. A highly distinguished wine list completes the picture.

Lumière ⊛⊛⊛ NOTABLE WINE LIST

See pages 198-199

NEW The Mahal ⊛⊛

1 Montpellier Drive, GL50 1TY
01242 226300
www.themahalrestaurant.com
Closed: Sunday

Close to Cheltenham town centre, The Mahal lives up to its palatial name with an opulent interior and refined cooking. Across two levels in a choice of rooms, service is friendly and well-judged spicing is the cornerstone of the kitchen with a menu combining old favourites and modern interpretations.

Chef: Anuj Thakur
Food Style: Indian

NEW Purslane ⊛⊛

16 Rodney Road, GL50 1JJ
01242 321639
www.purslane-restaurant.co.uk
Closed: 2 weeks August, 24–26 December,
1 January, 2 weeks January

At Purslane, an independent, family-run restaurant at the heart of Cheltenham, sustainable British seafood is the focus, in combination with the best local produce from the Cotswolds. With an exterior that forms part of a very stylish terrace, the interior is as chic as you'd expect; grey walls covered with unusual art objects, and bright blue chairs.

Chef: Gareth Fulford
Food Style: Modern British, Seafood

The Restaurant at Ellenborough Park ⧗ NOTABLE WINE LIST Rosettes Suspended

Southam Road, GL52 3NH
01242 545454
www.ellenboroughpark.com
Closed: Monday, Tuesday

Food Style: Modern British

The Rosette award for this establishment has been suspended due to a change of chef and reassessment will take place in due course.
Although the original house had been pottering along unexceptionably since the 1530s, Ellenborough really hit its stride when the first Earl of that ilk, erstwhile governor general of British India, moved himself and his wife into it 300 years later. The place itself is a sumptuous beauty in Cotswold honey, looking a little like an Oxford college, with a high-glitz panelled dining room at the centre of operations.

Cirencester

The Potager ⊛⊛

Barnsley House, near Cirencester, GL7 5EE
01285 740000
www.barnsleyhouse.com
Closed: November

The restaurant at 17th-century Barnsley House is named The Potager, after the ornamental and vegetable garden designed in the 1950s by Rosemary Verey, which it overlooks. Typical of the dishes is perfectly cooked lamb sweetbreads in a noteworthy jus served with no more than morels and garden chard.

Chef: John Jewell
Food Style: Modern European

Cheltenham

Lumière

Clarence Parade, GL50 3PA
01242 222200
www.lumiere.cc
Closed: 2 weeks Winter, 2 weeks Summer

Chef: Jon Howe
Food Style: Modern British

Enjoy modern British cuisine with plenty of bold flavours

The elegant Lumière, owned and run by the Howes, lies a little way off the leafy promenade for which Cheltenham is famous. The building may be an unassuming terrace, but indoors looks the very image of a modern dining room. It's an understated classy affair decorated in a soothing combination of cream and aubergine tones, statement mirrors and abstract artworks all adding up to a setting that says this is an operation of serious culinary intent.

The capable hand of Helen Howe on the front-of-house tiller makes for a relaxing experience so nothing is too stiff or formal. Jon Howe's inventive British cooking delivers vibrant modern flavours, deploying plenty of technical wizardry showcased in tasting menus of six or eight courses (with or without a wine flight).

Another way to appreciate Lumière and see what it has to offer is to come for lunch on Friday or Saturday and try the four-course tasting menu. Jon is proud to

use daily-harvested, organic ingredients from their own smallholding. So, if you're coming for the full tasting menus, then things begin with a volley of snacks such as Wye Vale asparagus, Severn and Wye smoked eel, Sharpes express, lemon and Avruga caviar. The palate suitably primed, a further dish might be the intriguing flavour combination of Sladesdown Farm Peking duck, lime, maple, coffee and white chocolate. A mid-meal tequila slammer with salt and lime clears the way for the meaty satisfaction of Mount Grace Farm Texel lamb, pea, baby gem, carrot and mint. Dessert creations are equally notable, such as Oakchurch raspberry soufflé, toasted sushi rice ice cream, almond and lemon. Vegetarians are not forgotten, with a tasting menu that's no mere afterthought and shows the same level of creativity in dishes such as British cauliflower, broad beans, truffle, lemon and cauliflower fungus.

"...delivers vibrant modern flavours, deploying plenty of technical wizardry..."

Cirencester *continued*

NEW Tierra & Mar Restaurant ◉◉
29 Sheep Street, GL7 1QW
01285 642777
www.tierraandmar.co.uk
Closed: Sunday, Monday, 26 December

Translated from Spanish, 'Tierra & Mar' means 'Land &
Sea', which is as good a way as any to describe a tapas
restaurant at the heart of Cirencester. The menus are
fed by nearby suppliers as well as the family smallholding on the edge of this charming market town. As
well as tapas, diners can also enjoy larger mains.

Chef: Brett Russell
Food Style: Spanish

Clearwell

Tudor Farmhouse Hotel & Restaurant ◉◉ ♦NOTABLE WINE LIST
High Street, GL16 8JS
01594 833046
www.tudorfarmhousehotel.co.uk
Open: All year

Chef: Gavin Roberts
Food Style: Modern British

The charm-laden grey stone building looks the rustic part but, once inside, its stone walls, beams, wood panelling and inglenooks are overlaid with lashings of boutique bolt-hole style. Nor is the kitchen stuck in the past – its 20-mile menus are full of fresh, up-to-date ideas.

See advertisement opposite

Coleford

Verderers ◉◉
The Speech House Hotel, Speech House Road, GL16 7EL
01594 822607
www.thespeechhouse.co.uk
Open: All year

Part of The Speech House Hotel, Verderers is set within a 17th century, former hunting lodge in the heart of the idyllic Royal Forest of Dean. In the beamed restaurant, modern British cooking sticks to the seasons with a starter of scorched mackerel, chive and cucumber salsa followed by rack of lamb, hazelnut rösti, asparagus and watercress.

Chef: Gareth Jenkins
Food Style: Modern British

Daylesford

Daylesford Farm Café ◉
GL56 0YG
01608 731700
www.daylesford.com/locations/kingham/
the-trough-cafe
Closed: 25–26 December, 1 January

On the Gloucestershire farmland that spawned a mini-empire, the Daylesford Farmshop and Café occupies a smartly converted barn with a New England finish and an open-to-view kitchen. The food makes a virtue of simplicity, with quality ingredients allowed to shine.

Chef: Gaven Fuller and Darron Bunn
Food Style: Modern British

Gloucester

Hatherley Manor Hotel & Spa 🌸
Down Hatherley Lane, GL2 9QA
01452 730217
www.hatherleymanor.com
Open: All year

A stylish brick and stone-built 17th-century house,
Hatherley Manor is popular as a wedding venue.
The Dewinton Restaurant is a relaxed setting for
contemporary dining, with rich gold drapes and
upholstery and linen-clad tables.

Chef: Richard Whittle
Food Style: Traditional British

Hatton Court 🌸
Upton Hill, Upton St Leonards, GL4 8DE
01452 617412
www.hatton-court.co.uk
Open: All year

Chef: Jeff Lewis
Food Style: Modern International

A country-house hotel not far from the M5, Hatton Court is smothered with climbing foliage,
its little windows barely peeping through the green. The formal dining room is kitted out with
linen-clad tables, wood panelling and full-drop windows at one end.

Lower Slaughter

The Slaughters Country Inn 🌸🌸
GL54 2HS
01451 822143
www.theslaughtersinn.co.uk
Closed: 24–26 December, 31 December to 1 January

This artfully modernised, 17th-century Cotswold-
stone inn makes good use of its riverside terrace in
this peaceful village. In the 1920s the building was
a crammer school for Eton College, thus it now has
Eton's Restaurant. The modern British menu also covers
the bar.

Chef: Matt Williams
Food Style: Modern British

The Slaughters Manor House ⊛⊛⊛ 🍷NOTABLE WINE LIST
GL54 2HP
01451 820456
www.slaughtersmanor.co.uk
Closed: Sunday, Monday, 24–26 December,
31 December to 1 January

Chef: Nik Chappell
Food Style: Modern British

Built from golden Cotswold stone, the comfortable Slaughters Manor House dates from the 17th century, and offers a stylish 21st-century interpretation of country living. You'll find the elegant dining room is an airy, light-filled space with nicely spaced, linen-clad tables. Dishes are often picture-perfect explorations of flavour and texture, maybe starting with a simple dish of cured monkfish with an intense basil sorbet and dashi adding flavour. The perhaps move on to Woolley Park duck with a delicious confit-filled onion and a blackcurrant ketchup. Finish with a light and refreshing raspberry, pistachio and white peach sorbet.

Moreton-in-Marsh

Manor House Hotel ⊛⊛
High Street, GL56 0LJ
01608 650501
www.cotswold-inns-hotels.co.uk/manor
Closed: 25 December (except residents)

Chef: Nick Orr
Food Style: Modern British

The Cotswold-stone Manor Hotel might date from the reign of Henry VIII, but careful renovation and updating have brought it squarely into the 21st century. The bright and airy Mulberry Restaurant has generously spaced tables, comfortable chairs and on-the-ball staff, while the kitchen produces appealing dishes without over-complicating things.

Redesdale Arms ⊛
High Street, GL56 0AW
01608 650308
www.redesdalearms.com
Open: All year

Dating from the 17th century, this inn has been sympathetically updated to give a contemporary edge. There are two dining rooms, one in a rear conservatory, the other overlooking the high street. A glance at the menu shows a kitchen seaming the modern British vein.

Chef: Craig Malins
Food Style: Modern British

Wilder ⚜⚜⚜

Market Street, GL6 0BX
01453 835483
www.dinewilder.co.uk
Open: All year

Chef: Matthew Beardshall
Food Style: Modern British

The arty market town of Nailsworth is as quintessentially Cotswolds English as you could ask for. Wilder offers a neutral, decluttered and modern space where diners all settle in at 7pm for an imaginative, daily-changing, eight-course tasting menu. The kitchen hauls in whatever's best from the local larder as the basis for sharply seasonal cooking that applies careful attention to detail and well-thought-out flavour combinations. Global influences come thick and fast, as in white miso aubergine with baba ganoush, labneh, shimeji mushrooms and a salty-sweet miso and soy dresssing. Another idea sees perfectly pink duck breast and a crispy bonbon matched with roasted and puréed artichoke, caramelised onions and red wine sauce, while sweet courses include chocolate porter cake with chocolate ganache, ale jelly and malted milk ice cream.

Nether Westcote

The Feathered Nest Inn ⚜⚜⚜

See pages 206-207

North Cerney

Bathurst Arms ⚜⚜

GL7 7BZ
01285 832150
www.bathurstarms.co.uk
Open: All year

Food Style: British

The Bathurst Arms is a beautiful old country pub with a menu that does all it can to spotlight local produce, and help organic farmers reach a larger audience. Wherever possible, everything is homemade, and obviously, organic. The serving approach is a kind of tapas style, so it's recommended that everyone order two small plates, then share it around.

Painswick

The Painswick ⚜⚜

Kemps Lane, GL6 6YB
01452 813688
www.thepainswick.co.uk
Open: All year

Chef: Jamie McCallum
Food Style: Modern European

Located in a village every bit as grand as itself, The Painswick is a grand Palladian mansion that comes with a touch of contemporary boutique chic to go with its original Arts and Crafts features. The result exudes relaxed luxury embedded into the beautiful Cotswold countryside. There's a delicious six-course tasting menu of fine modern cooking.

Selsley

The Bell Inn ⑳⑳
Bell Lane, GL5 5JY
01453 753801
www.thebellinnselsley.com
Open: All year

Dating from the 16th century, The Bell Inn is a Cotswold pub through and through, with menus offering a range of classic and contemporary dishes, typically rich local game, rolled pork belly and beer-battered fish and chips. Ales from nearby Uley brewery keep drinkers happy, as does the choice of 70 gins.

Chef: Mark Payne
Food Style: Modern British

See advertisement on page 209

Stow-on-the-Wold

The Kings Head Inn ⑳
The Green, Bledington, OX7 6XQ
01608 658365
www.kingsheadinn.net
Closed: 25–26 December

This mellow stone Cotswolds pub comes with a classic bar with wobbly floors, log fires and head-skimming beams. It's a textbook example of a switched-on village pub with cooking that's a definite notch or two up.

Chef: Piotr Skoczen
Food Style: British

Number Four at Stow ⑳⑳
Fosse Way, GL54 1JX
01451 830297
www.hotelnumberfour.com
Open: All year

Situated on the edge of this picturesque Cotswold town, Number Four at Stow is very well placed for visiting other charming villages in the area. Country style but with elements of modernity, the split-level restaurant, complete with exposed brick, wood-burning stove, muted tones and comfortable seating serves freshly prepared dishes using locally sourced produce wherever possible.

Food Style: Modern British

Nether Westcote

The Feathered Nest Inn

OX7 6SD
01993 833030
www.thefeatherednestinn.co.uk
Open: All year

Chef: Matthew Weedon
Food Style: Modern British

High quality cooking in rebooted country inn

The Feathered Nest is a born-again country hostelry that's seriously worth a detour. The views over the Evenlode Valley from this old malthouse in picturesque Nether Westcote on the Gloucestershire-Oxfordshire border are glorious.

There's pretty accommodation including a cottage in the grounds if you fancy staying the night after a memorable meal. The Cotswold-stone building looks good both inside and out, with a contemporary country-chic interior – stone walls, flagged floors and antique, stacked logs and leather sofas – the feelgood factor is ramped up by inviting real fires in winter and bucolic views from the terrace and garden in the warmer months.

Expect a genuine welcome and a modern British menu that fizzes with good ideas and appealing combinations. Local produce forms the backbone of the menus, with herbs and vegetables grown

in the kitchen garden.

There's à la carte, a six-course tasting menu and a plant-based menu to choose from. So, maybe start with sea bream, lime, avocado, rose harissa, coriander, mango and smoked mayonnaise, or ravioli of Cackleberry Farm egg yolk and truffled potato with mushrooms and spring white truffle.

Then enjoy fillet of Belted Galloway beef, sticky blade, wild garlic, beef croquettes, tomato mushrooms, watercress and red wine jus; or roasted hake, white asparagus, caramelised onion, sautéed potatoes with white wine and caviar sauce.

If no meat and no fish is your thing, then the four-course menu dishes might be white gazpacho with green olive focaccia, Wye Valley asparagus, celeriac and toasted hazelnuts; chargrilled fennel, kohlrabi, Granny Smith apple, grapes and endive; finishing with avocado with cocoa, blood orange and passionfruit. Traditional, English afternoon teas, Sunday lunches and live music in the bar are extra temptations to consider.

"...a modern British menu that fizzes with good ideas and appealing combinations."

Stow-on-the-Wold *continued*

Old Stocks Inn ⚜⚜
The Square, GL54 1AP
01451 830666
www.oldstocksinn.com
Closed: 24–26 December

An appealing package of bright and funky modern
decor, a fun ambience, an array of regionally-brewed
craft beers and an inventive take on contemporary pub
grub makes this revamped 17th-century Cotswolds inn
worth checking out.

Chef: Ian Percival
Food Style: Modern British

The Bear of Rodborough ⚜
Rodborough Common, GL5 5DE
01453 878522
www.cotswold-inns-hotels.co.uk
Open: All year

Chef: Felix Prem
Food Style: British, International

Set on Rodborough Common, the Bear of Rodborough is a 17th-century coaching inn turned
hotel that offers a real escape. Dining is in the Library and there's a good choice of solid
favourites with a modern British twist. On the Common you may bump into a few Belted
Galloway cattle with their distinctive white stripe round the middle.

Burleigh Court Hotel ⚜⚜
Burleigh, Minchinhampton, GL5 2PF
01453 883804
www.burleighcourtcotswolds.co.uk
Closed: 23-27 December

Built of Cotswold stone early in the 19th century, this
imposing, ivy-clad manor house overlooks Golden
Valley and the River Frome. Its Georgian-style interior
incorporates an oak-panelled lounge and a dining room
decorated with scenes of the house's history, where
large windows reveal a beautiful garden.

Chef: Shaun Jones
Food Style: British, Mediterranean

the
bell
at selsley

drink | food | beds

THE BELL AT SELSLEY

Set in the picturesque village of Selsley, The Bell Inn is a 16th century
Grade II listed Cotswold Inn. Your friendly country pub with rooms.
We are here to give you a true taste of the Cotswolds and all that it has
to offer, serving real ales, locally-sourced food and seasonal game.

Whether catching up with friends in our bar, settling down for a
traditional Sunday lunch or enjoying a delicious country escape –
come and soak up some country life with us.

AA

Rosette award for
culinary excellence

2022

The Bell at Selsley

Bell Lane
Selsley
Stroud
Gloucestershire
GL5 5JY

01453 753801

info@thebellinnselsley.com

thebellinnselsley.com

Tetbury

The Close Hotel 🏵🏵
8 Long Street, GL8 8AQ
01666 502272
www.theclose-hotel.com
Open: All year

The Close Hotel is a seriously handsome 16th-century
house, with perfectly balancing period details and
contemporary elegance. Fine dining is through the
doors to the Garden Restaurant, which enjoys views
over the charming garden. The modern British menu
strikes the right balance in this setting, with creative
combinations proving very tempting.

Chef: Tonko Rusev
Food Style: Modern British

The Conservatory at Calcot 🏵🏵
Calcot, GL8 8YJ
01666 890391
www.calcot.co
Open: All year

Chef: Richard Davies
Food Style: Modern British

Calcot is a boutique-style hotel of Cotswold stone with a health spa and a light-filled restaurant
called The Conservatory. The kitchen works around a repertoire of imaginative modern dishes,
and flavours have real punch. Expect modern twists to classic dishes.

Thornbury

Ronnie's of Thornbury 🏵🏵
11 St Mary Street, BS35 2AB
01454 411137
www.ronnies-restaurant.co.uk
Closed: 25–28 December, 1–5 January

Ronnie's occupies a 17th-century building done out
with a smart contemporary look that seamlessly blends
stone walls, beamed ceilings, wooden floors, and
neutral hues pointed up by paintings and photos by
West Country artists. A menu of satisfyingly unfussy
and hearty modern cooking satisfies all comers, with a
keenly priced set lunch for bargain hunters.

Chef: Ron Faulkner
Food Style: Modern British

NEW Thornbury Castle Hotel ⊛⊛
Castle Street, BS35 1HH
www.thornburycastle.co.uk
Open: All year

No messing about, Thornbury Castle is a proper castle, or at least a Tudor country house with a 'licence to crenellate'. The restaurant is all wonderful wood panelling and historic elegance, while much of the produce on the imaginative menu comes from the castle's own extensive kitchen gardens. Also, wine may come from the castle's own vineyard.

Chef: Carl Cleghorn
Food Style: Modern British

Upper Slaughter

Lords of the Manor ⊛⊛⊛ ▮NOTABLE WINE LIST
See pages 212-213

How we assess for Rosettes

⊛
One Rosette
These restaurants will be achieving standards that stand out in their local area, featuring:

■ food prepared with care, understanding and skill

■ good quality ingredients

■ The same expectations apply to hotel restaurants where guests should be able to eat in with confidence and a sense of anticipation.

⊛⊛
Two Rosettes
The best local restaurants, which aim for and achieve:

■ higher standards

■ better consistency

■ greater precision apparent in the cooking

■ obvious attention to the selection of quality ingredients.

⊛⊛⊛
Three Rosettes
These are outstanding restaurants that achieve standards that demand national recognition well beyond their local area. The cooking will be underpinned by:

■ the selection and sympathetic treatment of the highest quality ingredients

■ timing, seasoning and the judgment of flavour combinations will be consistently excellent

■ these virtues will tend to be supported by other elements such as intuitive service and a well-chosen wine list.

⊛⊛⊛⊛
Four Rosettes
Among the top restaurants in the UK where the cooking demands national recognition. These restaurants will exhibit:

■ intense ambition

■ a passion for excellence

■ superb technical skills

■ remarkable consistency

■ an appreciation of culinary traditions combined with a passionate desire for further exploration and improvement.

⊛⊛⊛⊛⊛
Five Rosettes
The pinnacle, where the cooking compares with the best in the world. These restaurants will have:

■ highly individual voices

■ exhibit breathtaking culinary skills and set the standards to which others aspire, yet few achieve.

Upper Slaughter

❀ ❀ ❀ 🍷 NOTABLE WINE LIST

Lords of the Manor

GL54 2JD
01451 820243
www.lordsofthemanor.com
Open: All year

Chef: Charles Smith
Food Style: Modern British

Decadent dining in the heart of the Cotswolds

Surrounded by eight acres of landscaped parkland in a Cotswold stone rectory, Lords of the Manor is very much the classic country house hotel. Less than three miles from the popular tourist hotspot of Bourton-on-the-Water, it's a luxurious base to explore the beautiful Cotswold countryside – the walk between the hamlets of Upper and Lower Slaughter is the best short walk in the area.

A relaxed atmosphere, underpinned by professional and attentive service, is the hallmark at the former manor house, which dates back to 1649, with guests often reluctant to leave. The hotel has elegant public rooms that overlook the immaculate lawns, and the restaurant is the venue for consistently impressive cuisine. An impressive use of top quality local and seasonal produce permeates the menu in the sumptuous dining room with its golden and silver decor.

The food is complemented by a strong selection of wines by the glass and bottle. A wine flight is available with the tasting menu and the introduction of a half-measure wine flight has proven popular. Whether it's the tasting menu or à la carte, dinner might begin with a deep-flavoured Scottish langoustine soup, scallop dumplings and black winter truffle or perhaps a fresh and vibrant plate of Isle of Wight heritage tomatoes, burrata and pickled celery.

For main course, it might be a delicate piece of steamed Cornish turbot with Wye Valley asparagus and a well-matched seaweed butter sauce. Carnivores might plump for melt-in-the-mouth Belted Galloway beef, hen of the wood mushroom and artichoke.

After a palate-cleansing verbena tea jelly, lime granita and caramelised honey, dessert could be a simple but effective dish of summer berries and vanilla cream followed by aged Cornish gouda served with a slice of cured pork collar and pickled green tomatoes.

"A relaxed atmosphere, underpinned by professional and attentive service..."

Greater Manchester

Delph

The Old Bell Inn ⚜
5 Huddersfield Road, OL3 5EG
01457 870130
www.theoldbellinn.co.uk
Open: All year

A traditional 18th-century coaching inn with a
thoroughly contemporary attitude to dining, this
pub holds a world record for its collection of 1,100
gins, displayed in the Gin Emporium. In the modern
restaurant, hearty, innovative food is created using an
abundance of local raw materials.

Chef: Stuart Brown
Food Style: Modern British

Didsbury

HISPI ⚜⚜
1C School Lane, M20 6RD
0161 445 3996
www.hispi.net
Closed: 25–26 December

Named after what has been called 'the trendiest
cabbage variety in British catering', this is serial
restaurateur Gary Usher's third crowd-funded venture.
What he gives Didsbury is minimalist decor, an open
kitchen and inviting, contemporary food, exemplified by
roast duck with braised turnip, plum sauce and duck leg
pastilla. Gary clearly trains and inspires his people well.

Food Style: Contemporary,
Brasserie

How do you keep yourself under the radar?

By adopting plenty of aliases, have 'reasons' to be in the area –
perhaps looking at a property or undertaking
consultancy work down the road.

AA Inspector

Manchester

Adam Reid at The French ✿✿✿✿ 🍷 NOTABLE WINE LIST
The Midland, Peter Street, M60 2DS
0161 235 4780
www.the-french-manchester.co.uk
Closed: 25 December

Chef: Adam Reid
Food Style: Modern British

The Midland Hotel is a very grand building, in a city not short on municipal grandeur. Opened in 1903, it was designed to lure discerning travellers to Manchester – something it's been doing efficiently for decades. Most recently some of that attraction is down to Adam Reid and a kitchen firing on all culinary cylinders. Reid makes his presence felt with a smartly contemporary operation that embraces small-plate dining while sitting at the kitchen counter, as well as grand tasting processions served in the opulent French restaurant, a handsome Grade II listed room, all moody blue and grey beneath giant crystal globes. From the witty set menu expect energetic, precise combinations – 'little bits of something fancy' – maybe surf and turf sausage roll with raw horseradish, or a cracker sandwich with Kirkham's cheese, chives and hazelnuts. Cold cuts and pickles are described as 'yesterday's dinner', while 'today's tea' offers Cumbrian Shorthorn loin cooked in its own fat, with swede, seaweed and fish eggs, or Cornish catch of the day with curry squash sauce and mussels.

Brasserie ABode ✿✿
ABode Manchester, 107 Piccadilly, M1 2DB
0161 247 7744
www.abodemanchester.co.uk
Open: All year

Chef: Jamie Smith
Food Style: European Brasserie

Relaxed, all-day dining with a menu that features plats du jour with a comfortingly, nostalgic nod and time-honoured classics. Generosity and value are at the heart of the Brasserie whether it's Sunday lunch, classic dishes with plentiful sides or cocktails with a side serving of nibbles.

Chez Mal Brasserie ✿
Malmaison Manchester, Piccadilly, M1 3AQ
0161 278 1000
www.malmaison.com/locations/manchester
Open: All year

This prime piece of heritage industrial architecture is plumb in the city centre. The interior is boutiqued to the max, while cocktails and upscale brasserie food draw in the crowds. In The Smoak Bar & Grill, the open-to-view kitchen produces surprising versions of modern comfort food.

Chef: Paul Wilde
Food Style: Modern British, International

Manchester *continued*

El Gato Negro Tapas 🏵
52 King Street, M2 4LY
0161 694 8585
www.elgatonegrotapas.com
Closed: 25 December, 1 January

Set over three floors of a stripped-back, industrial-themed building in Manchester's busy city centre, this buzzy tapas bar has a charcuterie station and restaurant with an open kitchen. Chargrilled octopus with capers, shallots and aïoli; and pork belly, celeriac purée, straw potatoes and raisins marinated in PX sherry are among the menu highlights.

Chef: Milan Sojka
Food Style: Spanish

George's Dining Room & Bar 🏵
17–21 Barton Road, Worsley, M28 2PD
0161 794 5444
www.georgesworsley.co.uk
Open: All year

Chef: Gabe Lea
Food Style: Modern British

The name of this gastro pub pays homage to Victorian architect Sir George Gilbert Scott, but this place does not look backwards. The setting is stylish, with tan leather banquettes and neutral creamy hues, and the food is very much what you'd expect of a 21st-century kitchen.

Hotel Gotham 🏵🏵
100 King Street, M2 4WU
0161 413 0000
www.hotelgotham.co.uk
Open: All year

Located in an old bank in the heart of Manchester, Hotel Gotham is a sleek art deco boutique hotel with a hip restaurant named Honey. Parquet floors, metal-topped tables and great city views from semi-circular windows all feed into the retro styling, while the menus are all about modern British and European combinations.

Chef: Rob Taylor
Food Style: Modern European

Kala Bistro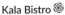
King Street, M2 4LQ
0800 160 1811
www.kalabistro.co.uk
Closed: 25–26 December

Kala Bistro is a stripped back, stylish space bang in the
city centre. The trademark open kitchen stretches the
length of the back wall, and the plate glass frontage
ensures a light, airy setting for bold, simple, seasonal
flavours. Maybe start with gazpacho followed by
smoked duck breast, confit tomatoes, lovage and duck
fat croûtons with a side of truffle and parmesan chips.

Chef: Jack Huxley
Food Style: British

The Lowry Hotel
50 Dearmans Place, Chapel Wharf, Salford, M3 5LH
0161 827 4000
www.thelowryhotel.com
Open: All year

With floor-to-ceiling windows commanding
spectacular views over the canal and the Lowry
Bridge, The River Restaurant enjoys plenty of
natural light, with glass and leather decor giving it
a contemporary feel. The elegant surroundings are
juxtaposed with informal, chatty service.

Chef: Dominic Grundy
Food Style: Classic, Traditional

Mana
42 Blossom Street, M4 6BF
0161 392 7294
www.manarestaurant.co.uk
Closed: Sunday, Monday, Tuesday

Chef: Simon Martin
Food Style: Modern,
Nordic influences

Situated on a cobbled street in Manchester, Mana has a minimalist look with high ceilings and
picture windows. Dramatic darkwood tables are unclothed and an open island-style kitchen is
populated by chefs sending out some highly accomplished Nordic-influenced cooking. Multi-
course menus deliver dishes that are highly technical, intelligent and masterfully constructed to
balance flavours and textures, with fermentation and fire contributing to the skillset. There's no
formal starter/main/dessert format so expect to find the finest raw materials underpinning the
numbered dishes of around 17 courses of varying sizes that change according to the seasons.
It's a blind tasting menu, but you might get to the experience (at the time of writing) cod roe
on ice, duck liver and smoked eel, truffle and sunchoke crisp, langoustine and nori tart, roast
quail with broad beans and mole, and barbecued Wagyu. The sweet end of the menu brings
strawberries with brown butter, woodruff and 'inoculated' grains, and cheesecake.

Manchester *continued*

NEW Podium ⬤

303 Deansgate, M3 4LQ
0161 870 1600
www.hilton.com
Open: All year

Chef: Dave Ashton
Food Style: Modern British
Brasserie

Set in one of Manchester's glass dominated skyscrapers, Podium is one dining option in Hilton Manchester Deansgate. It's on the ground floor off the high street, and has a modern timber design with neutral colours. On offer is modern dining with an international flavour

WOOD Manchester ⬤⬤

Jack Rosenthal Street, First Street, M15 4RA
0161 236 5211
woodrestaurantgroup.com
Closed: Sunday, Monday, Tuesday, 24–26 December

WOOD is the flagship restaurant of Simon Wood in the heart of Manchester City Centre. It's got a real buzz and has a local following of foodies eager to find a relaxed but sophisticated environment in which to enjoy some imaginative and innovative cooking. Expect a range of techniques to feature, including smoking, curing, preserving and fermentation.

Chef: Simon Wood
Food Style: Modern British, Nordic & Japanese influences

Stockport

Where the Light Gets In ⬤⬤⬤

7 Rostron Brow, SK1 1JY
0161 477 5744
www.wtlgi.co/restaurant
Closed: Sunday, Monday, Tuesday

Chef: Sam Buckley
Food Style: Modern British

Where the Light Gets In occupies a industrial-chic former warehouse that's fully in tune with contemporary sensibilities and the industrial heritage of Manchester. The music is loud, the vibe is casual and chefs deliver dishes hot-foot to tables. Expect a procession of small dishes – around 10 courses-worth – that takes in current trends for fermenting, pickling and sustainability. There is a truly convivial, relaxed feel to proceedings and menu sequencing is very well thought through. Among the many picks, try the flavoursome buttermilk and corn-battered oyster, wildflower sourdough and cultured butter, mackerel and fermented turnip. Finish with the lovely clean flavours of the elderflower custard tart, rhubarb molasses and berries.

Hampshire

Esseborne Manor ⊛⊛
Hurstbourne Tarrant, SP11 0ER
01264 736444
www.esseborne-manor.co.uk
Closed: Monday, Tuesday

Esseborne Manor is a Victorian country house in an Area of Outstanding Natural Beauty. The ambience is traditional with white clothed, formally set tables and candlelight. A relaxed and enjoyable dining experience with formal but friendly service. Cooking is unfussy and straightforward, but packed with flavour. Good use is made of herbs from the Manor's own herb garden.

Chef: Mateusz Krzyminski
Food Style: Modern British

Pebble Beach ⊛
Marine Drive, BH25 7DZ
01425 627777
www.pebblebeach-uk.com
Open: All year

Chef: Karl Wiggins
Food Style: British, French, Mediterranean, Seafood

A clifftop perch gives this modern bar-brasserie a sweeping vista across Christchurch Bay to the Needles and the Isle of Wight. Inside is a buzzy split-level venue where high stools at the oyster bar allow views of the open-plan kitchen. The alfresco terrace is irresistible.

Audleys Wood Hotel ⊛⊛
Alton Road, RG25 2JT
01256 817555
www.handpickedhotels.co.uk/audleyswood
Closed: 24–24 December, 31 December

This striking Victorian property stands in seven acres of grounds and woodland and has all the trappings of a luxury country-house hotel. The Conservatory Restaurant with its high vaulted ceiling and small minstrels' gallery serves a seasonally-changing menu.

Chef: Leon Sharp
Food Style: Modern British

Basingstoke *continued*

Glasshouse Restaurant ⍟⍟
Oakley Hall Hotel, Rectory Road, Oakley, RG23 7EL
01256 783350
www.oakleyhall-park.com
Closed: 24–26 December

18th-century Oakley Hall is set in its own expansive
grounds and was often visited by Jane Austen who
lived nearby. The Glasshouse Restaurant is a modern
addition to this historic house. It has a very bright,
contemporary style with a colour scheme of gold and
teal as well as plenty of art on the walls.

Chef: Jacob Rowley
Food Style: Modern International

Baughurst

The Wellington Arms ⍟⍟
Baughurst Road, RG26 5LP
0118 982 0110
www.thewellingtonarms.com
Closed: Sunday, Monday

Much of your meal in this long-standing, two-Rosette
holder will come from its garden, polytunnel or local
allotment; a flock of Jacob sheep graze in the field
behind. Understandably some items, such as Lyme Bay
king scallops, do have to travel. The pub sign displays
the coat of arms of the Dukes of Wellington, whose
estate is at Stratfield Saye.

Chef: Jason King, Helen Slater
Food Style: Modern British

Beaulieu

The Master Builder's at Buckler's Hard ⍟
Buckler's Hard, SO42 7XB
01590 616253
www.themasterbuilders.co.uk
Open: All year

Chef: Michele Mirabile
Food Style: Modern British

Named after the man who built ships for Nelson's fleet on the grassy areas running down to the
Beaulieu River, the restaurant in this rustic 18th-century hotel offers tranquil river views. The
straightforward modern British cooking is underpinned by well-sourced local ingredients. Try
the fillet of venison, pommes Anna, romanesco and glazed figs.

Monty's Inn
The Montagu Arms Hotel, Palace Lane, SO42 7ZL
01590 614986
www.montaguarmshotel.co.uk
Open: All year

Food Style: Traditional British

Specialising in hearty, unpretentious food that doesn't try to punch above its weight, Monty's Inn goes for a clubby look involving wood-panelled walls, wooden floors and unclothed tables in a posh country pub setting. Kick things off perfectly with a home-made local pork Scotch egg.

The Terrace Restaurant
at The Montagu Arms Hotel Rosettes Suspended
The Montagu Arms Hotel, Palace Lane, SO42 7ZL
01590 612324
www.montaguarmshotel.co.uk/terrace_restaurant
Closed: Monday, Tuesday

Food Style: Modern European

The Rosette award for this establishment has been suspended due to a change of chef and reassessment will take place in due course.
In a delightful New Forest setting, the ivy-clad Montagu Arms dates back to the 17th century. The Terrace Restaurant is spacious and rather splendidly decorated, with wood panelling and a country house feel of comfortable luxury, overlooking a charming sun-trap courtyard and manicured gardens. The menus champion seasonality and hyperlocal Hampshire ingredients.

Bransgore

The Three Tuns
Ringwood Road, BH23 8JH
01425 672232
www.threetunsinn.com
Closed: 25–26 December

The picture-postcard 17th-century thatched inn deep in the New Forest is a delight in summer, festooned with flowers, and cosy in winter as blazing log fires warm the low beamed bar. The welcoming scene draws foodies and forest visitors for its charm and character.

Chef: Colin Nash
Food Style: British, European

Brockenhurst

The Balmer Lawn Hotel ◉◉
Lyndhurst Road, SO42 7ZB
01590 623116
www.balmerlawnhotel.com
Open: All year

Chef: Chris Wheeldon
Food Style: Modern British

The Balmer Lawn Hotel is an imposing pavilion-style Victorian hunting lodge in a charming New Forest setting. It's a friendly, family-run operation with excellent spa, and sports and conference facilities. In the elegant, semi-formal Beresfords Restaurant, you can expect thoughtful modern cooking with a healthy showing of prime-quality, often local, materials.

Cambium ◉◉ NOTABLE WINE LIST
Careys Manor Hotel & SenSpa,
Lyndhurst Road, SO42 7RH
01590 623551
www.careysmanor.com/restaurants/cambium
Open: All year

Chef: Alistair Craig
Food Style: Modern British

The Careys Manor Hotel is to be found in the New Forest, an environment its restaurant celebrates (Cambium is a technical botanical term for the inner tissue of plants or trees). The decor incorporates leafy screens and a central bare-twigged tree with purple flowers. Alastair Craig's cooking plays its part too, with plates that look pretty and deliver convincing natural flavours.

THE PIG ◉◉ NOTABLE WINE LIST
Beaulieu Road, SO42 7QL
01590 622354
www.thepighotel.com
Open: All year

Chef: James Golding
Food Style: British

This is a restaurant for our times, with cocktails served in jam jars and massages available in the old potting shed. Here, in the wilds of the New Forest, the passion is for home-grown and foraged ingredients. It's a buzzy place with a retro interior.

Rhinefield House Hotel ◉◉
Rhinefield Road, SO42 7QB
01590 622922
www.handpickedhotels.co.uk/rhinefieldhouse
Open: All year

Chef: James Verity
Food Style: Classic,
Traditional British

Dating back in part to the 12th century, Rhinefield House is a remarkable example of Tudor-Gothic architecture at the heart of the New Forest. Interiors are awash with finely crafted mouldings, copperwork, and elegant wood panelling. The Armada restaurant offers a fine mix of classic and modern cuisine, and the private dining room is modelled on the Alhambra Palace in Granada.

Dogmersfield

Wild Carrot at Four Seasons Hotel Hampshire ✸✸
Dogmersfield Park, Chalky Lane, RG27 8TD
01252 853100
www.fourseasons.com/hampshire/dining/restaurants/
wild-carrot
Open: All year

Chef: Paolo Belloni
Food Style: Contemporary British

Named after the elegant white wildflower that defines the fields of Dogmersfield Park, Wild Carrot offers a light-filled dining space with French windows and an upscale, gently contemporary sheen. Focus is on seasonal, natural, locally sourced ingredients from Hampshire markets and further afield.

Emsworth

36 on the Quay ✸✸✸
47 South Street, PO10 7EG
01243 375592
www.36onthequay.com
Closed: First 2/3 weeks January, 1 week May, 1 week
October, 25–26 December

Chef: Gary Pearce
Food Style: Modern British,
European

A walk down though the village to the harbour will bring you to this 17th-century building, the perfect setting for a charming and long-running restaurant-with-rooms. It's a great place to watch the sun go down – have a drink outside in the courtyard before heading in to the bright, airy dining room. The menu delivers contemporary interpretations of classic dishes and flavour combinations, and tasting menus are available at both lunch and dinner. Tandoori veal sweetbreads make an interesting starter, followed by turbot with artichokes, perhaps, or Iberico pork loin with black pudding.

Fareham

Solent Hotel & Spa ✸
Rookery Avenue, Whiteley, PO15 7AJ
01489 880000
www.solenthotel.co.uk/food-drink
Open: All year

Chef: Jon Marsden-Jones
Food Style: Modern British,
European, International

A modern hotel with spa facilities among woodland, yet close by the M27, The Solent's Terrace Restaurant is a cheery contemporary space. Separated from the bar by an open fireplace, it offers cosy nooks and booths and an easygoing ambience. The wide-ranging menu aims to please all-comers with a roster of modern dishes.

Hordle

The Old Mill
Silver Street, SO41 6DJ
01590 682219
www.gordletonmill.co.uk
Open: All year

Chef: Ian Gibbs
Food Style: Modern British

Whether you settle in the cosseting bar, the contemporary river-view restaurant or the orangery, this creeper-clad inn serves properly satisfying modern British food. From bread to soups, sauces, ice cream and puddings, it's all made in-house from scratch using local and organic ingredients from producers in the nearby New Forest.

Lymington

The Elderflower Restaurant
4A Quay Street, SO41 3AS
01590 676908
www.elderflowerrestaurant.co.uk
Open: All year

Chef: Andrew Du Bourg
Food Style: Modern British, French

Andrew and Marjolaine Du Bourg's welcoming restaurant occupies a Grade II listed building close to the quayside. Low black beams and bay windows add to the old-world charm but the interior is as contemporary as the modern European cooking. Whether it's the à la carte or tasting menus, expect well-balanced dishes with a real depth of flavour. Pork consommé, smoked bacon, greengage, coco beans and sun-dried tomato could precede roast crab cannelloni, crab foam, sweetcorn and pickled black mooli. End with a perfectly risen lemon meringue soufflé with lemon sauce, bouquet garni ice cream and organic pollen.

Lyndhurst

The Crown Manor House Hotel
High Street, SO43 7NF
023 8028 2922
www.crownhotel-lyndhurst.co.uk
Open: All year

Chef: Oli Richings
Food Style: Modern British

The fireplace just inside the entrance once provided instant defrosting for travellers who had braved the horse-drawn carriage transfer from the railway station. Such is the Crown's history, which extends from 15th-century beginnings to a late Victorian makeover, its panelled dining room a refreshing space today for contemporary brasserie cooking.

Hartnett Holder & Co ⊛⊛⊛ ₰NOTABLE WINE LIST

Lime Wood, Beaulieu Road, SO43 7FZ
023 8028 7177
www.limewoodhotel.co.uk/food/hh-and-co
Open: All year

Lime Wood looks out over the peaceable expanses of
the New Forest. The kitchen here is in the hands of
Luke Holder, and overseen by Italian food superstar
Angela Hartnett. The seasonal menus work indeed
to an Italian template, with antipasti and primi before
the main course, and a wealth of respectfully treated
natural ingredients running through them. A serving

Chef: Angela Hartnett, Luke Holder
Food Style: Italian

of Cornish crab with smoked eel, radish and apple is the perfect palate-primer for a pasta dish
such as guinea fowl agnolotti with lardo di Colonnata, onion and sage. At main, there could be
one of the locally reared meats, perhaps Saddleback pork fillet with king cabbage and roasted
Cox's apple. To close, a fragrant dessert such as saffron pannacotta with rosewater
and pistachios.

New Milton

The Dining Room ⊛⊛ ₰NOTABLE WINE LIST

Chewton Glen, Christchurch Road, BH25 6QS
01425 282212
www.chewtonglen.com
Open: All year

The cuisine at Chewton Glen is one of its highly
regarded features. In the light, subtly hued Dining
Room, modern British classics include pressed duck
liver with almond, plum sake and toasted brioche;
Isle of Gigha halibut with sticky chicken wings,
aubergine, miso and lotus root; and Valrhona chocolate
and orange mousse.

Chef: Simon Addison
Food Style: Modern British

The Kitchen ⊛

Chewton Glen, Christchurch Road, BH25 6QS
01425 282212
www.chewtonglen.com/thekitchen
Open: All year

Staff are friendly and service is polished at this modern
venue, purpose-built as a restaurant and cookery
school. Take a seat in one of the deep burgundy leather
chairs or banquettes at copper-topped tables and
peruse the menu of crowd-pleasing dishes cooked up
by chefs James Martin and Adam Hart.

Chef: Luke Phillips
Food Style: Italian, American

Otterbourne

The White Horse ✿
Main Road, SO21 2EQ
01962 712830
www.whitehorseotterbourne.co.uk
Open: All year

Chef: Kunal Nadkarni
Food Style: Modern,
Traditional British

Seasonal menus list British-influenced food at this traditional village pub just south of Winchester. Friendly and welcoming staff serve dishes such as braised pork belly with bubble and squeak, and ale-battered fish and chips, but also Moroccan-style chickpea and kale stew, and Goan fish curry. Antique furnishings fill the interior, while the two large gardens incorporate a children's play area.

Portsmouth

NEW The Briny ✿
Clarence Esplanade, Southsea, PO5 3PG
023 9282 6676
www.thebriny.co.uk
Closed: 25–26 December

By the South Parade Pier, and practically on Portsmouth's stony beach, The Briny is a single-storey building with a casual vibe that offers up excellent dining. As you'd expect, most tables offer a great view of the ocean, and the menu is heavy with seafood of all kinds. It's very much a family-run and family-friendly venture.

Chef: Cameron Bradshaw
Food Style: Seafood

Restaurant 27 ✿✿
27a South Parade, PO5 2JF
023 9287 6272
www.restaurant27.com
Closed: Monday, Tuesday

Family-run with a heartfelt passion for local materials, chef-proprietor Kevin Bingham's stylish restaurant is a high-ceilinged, modern space dressed up in grey, with unclothed tables, and walls hung with eclectic artworks. Two six-course tasting menus with veggie alternatives showcase the kitchen's modern European sensibilities. Expect ambitious, thoughtfully composed dishes delivering on-trend ingredients and well-defined flavours.

Chef: Kevin Bingham
Food Style: Modern European

The Purefoy 🌸🌸
Alresford Road, RG25 2EJ
01256 389514
www.thepurefoyarms.co.uk
Open: All year

This classic red-brick Victorian pub opposite the village church proves a switched-on affair, from its country-modern interior and sunny-natured service to drawcard garden and adept cooking, it certainly ticks all the relevant 'destination' and 'local' boxes. Crowd-pleasing modern British cooking is the raison d'être, delivered via pub classics, carte and tasting menu dishes.

Chef: Gordon Stott
Food Style: British

See advertisement below

The pretty village of Preston Candover holds The Purefoy Arms; it lies in rural countryside between the Hampshire towns of Alresford, Basingstoke, and Winchester further to the south. Our multi-award-winning chef, Gordon Stott, is passionate about pubs. Here you will find a relaxed atmosphere, fine dining food and friendly staff. Tasting menu, à la carte and pub classics available in this country pub.

The PUREFOY

Preston Candover,
Hampshire RG25 2EJ

01256 389514

info@thepurefoyarms.co.uk

Rotherwick

The Oak Room Restaurant ◉◉
Tylney Hall Hotel, Ridge Lane, RG27 9AZ
01256 764881
www.tylneyhall.co.uk
Open: All year

The Oak Room at Tylney Hall remains one of
Hampshire's exemplary country-house restaurants.
What arrives in front of you will be a gently updated
take on a traditional English or European classic, thus
pan-seared scallops come with artichoke and miso
caramel, and Herefordshire lamb loin with a harissa-
spiced lamb cigar and roasted San Marzano tomatoes.

Chef: Mike Lloyd
Food Style: Modern British

Southampton

Blue Jasmine ◉◉
Unit 3-4 Alexandra Wharf, Maritime Walk,
Ocean Way, SO14 3QS
023 8063 6387
www.bluejasmine.co.uk
Closed: Monday, 25–26 December

Blue Jasmine is a show-stopping, hotspot venue on
the quayside at Ocean Village, with a smart terrace
and super-stylish interiors to match its contemporary
south-east Asian cooking. Every bit as well-dressed, the
innovative cuisine comes, flavour-packed and perfect
for sharing. The finest produce from the south of
England meets spices and more from Malaysia, China and Thailand.

Chef: Chris Tan
Food Style: South-east Asian

The Jetty ◉◉
Southampton Harbour Hotel & Spa, 5 Maritime Walk,
Ocean Village, SO14 3QT
023 8110 3456
www.southampton-harbour-hotel.co.uk
Open: All year

The Jetty is part of the rather spectacular Southampton
Harbour Hotel and enjoys panoramic views across
Ocean Village Marina. There's a terrace for outdoor
dining, surrounded by sunshine and yachts. It's chic and
elegant, with a bright airy feel and cheery turquoise and
yellow highlights.

Chef: Alex Aitken, Neil Arkley
Food Style: Modern

The Greyhound on the Test
31 High Street, SO20 6EY
01264 810833
www.thegreyhoundonthetest.co.uk
Closed: 25–27 December

The Greyhound has no shortage of appeal, from upmarket, sumptuous bedrooms to a restaurant with that opened-up, country-chic vibe. The menu is a thoroughly up-to-date affair with regional produce at its heart. You're sure to go home happy after dark chocolate brownie with chocolate mousse.

Chef: Phill Bishop
Food Style: Modern British

The Peat Spade Inn
Village Street, Longstock, SO20 6DR
01264 810612
www.peatspadeinn.co.uk
Open: All year

Chef: Paul Dive
Food Style: Modern British

A stolid-looking red-brick country inn where close-set tables add to the dining-room buzz. Rustic cooking with more than a soupçon of French influence proves abidingly popular, seen in the form of fried chicken livers on sourdough toast with charred sweetcorn in peppercorn sauce.

The Three Cups Inn
High Street, SO20 6HB
01264 810527
www.the3cups.co.uk
Closed: 25–26 December

Chef: Sebastian Edwards Smith
Food Style: Modern & Traditional British

This 16th-century coaching inn is still very much a pub offering local ales, but it's also a dining destination with low-ceilinged dining room and an orangery extension opening up to the garden. The kitchen makes good use of local foodstuffs.

Avenue Restaurant at Lainston House Hotel 🍷NOTABLE WINE LIST Rosettes Suspended

Woodman Lane, Sparsholt, SO21 2LT
01962 776088
www.exclusive.co.uk/lainston-house
Closed: 25–26 December

Food Style: Modern British

The Rosette award for this establishment has been suspended due to a change of chef and reassessment will take place in due course.

The imposing red-brick manor house is of 17th-century vintage, with an avenue of mature lime trees leading to it. It's that arboreal feature that is referenced in the name of the dignified dining room, where varnished oak panels set with contemporary wall lights, a marble fireplace and simple modern table settings establish the mood. Open-air dining on the terrace will coax the sun-lovers out.

Marwell Hotel ⚜

Thompsons Lane, Colden Common,
Marwell, SO21 1JY
01962 777681
www.marwellhotel.co.uk
Closed: 24–26 December

Chef: Phil Yeomans
Food Style: Modern European

A pastoral retreat in the manner of an African safari lodge, Marwell Hotel is set in wooded grounds next door to a wildlife park, so the odd screech of a monkey is to be expected. The kitchen applies modern styling to mostly traditional dishes.

Running Horse Inn ⚜

88 Main Road, Littleton, SO22 6QS
01962 880218
www.runninghorseinn.co.uk
Open: All year

Chef: Simon James Lawrence
Food Style: Classic British

The Running Horse is a revitalised village inn with a relaxed and informal dining environment: a wood-burning stove in a brick fireplace, some banquette seating, wooden tables and a mixture of artwork adorning the walls. The kitchen delivers stimulating full-flavoured dishes.

The Wykeham Arms ⚜⚜

75 Kingsgate Street, SO23 9PE
01962 853834
www.wykehamarmswinchester.co.uk
Open: All year

Chef: Allen Sorrell
Food Style: Modern British

Down a narrow Winchester side street sits The Wykeham Arms; historic, charming, full of character. Built in the 18th century it has plenty of old memorabilia on the walls, and cosy open fires. On offer are simple options, 'Home Comforts' on the menu, but the kitchen can and does turn out food of a higher and more refined style.

Herefordshire

The Riverside at Aymestrey ◉◉
The Riverside Inn, HR6 9ST
01568 708440
www.riversideaymestrey.co.uk
Open: All year

Close to Ludlow and Hereford on the edge of
Mortimer Forest, this 16th-century black and
white timber-framed inn features a kitchen that is
serious about its food, with produce from their own
garden. The menu changes daily and dishes are simple
and honest.

Chef: Andy Link
Food Style: Classic British

NEW The New Inn ◉◉
St Owens Cross, HR2 8LQ
01989 553387
thenewinnherefordshire.co.uk
Closed: Monday, Tuesday, 25 December

Experience Herefordshire hospitality in a contemporary,
yet rustic, setting. Expect a strong emphasis on local
produce – diners can choose from dishes which follow
the seasons with vibrant colours, textures, and flavours.
Plenty of character is retained in the main inn and
dining room where top quality dishes with carefully
sourced ingredients are offered at both dinner and

Chef: Michael Fowler
Food Style: British Modern

breakfast. In addition to a good selection of local ales and ciders at the bar, an extensive wine
list is a welcome feature including an interesting selection by the glass.

Feathers ◉
High Street, HR8 1DS
01531 635266
www.feathersledbury.co.uk
Open: All year

The heavily timbered Feathers is a wonderful slice
of Tudor England, its oak-panelled venerability
thrown into relief by a modern brasserie named
after the hop variety Fuggles, and an upmarket
dining room, Quills. Sirloins and fillets of local beef
are a big draw.

Chef: Suzie Isaacs
Food Style: Modern British

Ross-on-Wye

Conservatory Restaurant ◉
King's Head Hotel, 8 High Street, HR9 5HL
01989 763174
www.kingshead.co.uk
Open: All year

Chef: Ricky Barlow, Antony
Humble, Ashley Kibble
Food Style: British

Dating back to the 14th century, the Kings Head Hotel is full of charm and character. The Conservatory Restaurant has a very welcoming atmosphere, something like a stylish lounge, with books, artwork and plants. The cooking takes a modern tack, letting prime local materials do the talking in flavour-led dishes.

Glewstone Court Country House ◉◉
Glewstone, HR9 6AW
01989 770367
www.glewstonecourt.com
Closed: Sunday, Monday, 23–27 December, 1 January

With pleasant views over the surrounding countryside and Ross-on-Wye, Georgian Glewstone Court is a great place to stay and dine. The Cedar Tree restaurant is bright and spacious with large floor-to-ceiling windows, and on offer is seasonal fare with regularly changing tasting menus. The taster menu with wine flight is a very popular choice here.

Chef: Richard Kaye
Food Style: Traditional British, European

Symonds Yat [East]

Saracens Head Inn ◉
HR9 6JL
01600 890435
www.saracensheadinn.co.uk
Closed: 25 December

In a stunning location on the River Wye, The Saracens Head can be reached by its own ferry, operated by hand, just as it has for the past 200 years. There's a relaxed atmosphere throughout this 16th-century inn, from the dining room to two terraces.

Chef: Chris Lane
Food Style: British

Hertfordshire

The Gatsby ✤
97 High Street, HP4 2DG
01442 870403
www.thegatsby.net
Closed: 25–26 December

In what locals call Berko, the art deco, former Rex cinema is now a modern brasserie providing not just modern French cuisine but also piano accompaniment. Honey-roast ham hock rillettes and celeriac remoulade is one way to start, with pavé of Loch Duart salmon, tiger prawns and squid ink risotto to follow.

Chef: Matthew Salt
Food Style: Modern French

Down Hall Hotel & Spa ✤
Hatfield Heath, CM22 7AS
01279 731441
www.downhall.co.uk
Closed: 31 December

The house originally dates from the 1300s, but its impressively grand Italianate exterior shows the mark of a Victorian makeover. With period details such as ornate cornices and white-painted columns, the dining room has a vibe reminiscent of an upmarket French brasserie.

Chef: Robert Pearce
Food Style: Contemporary British

The Stables Restaurant at The Grove ✤
WD3 4TG
01923 807807
www.thegrove.co.uk/dining/the-stables
Open: All year

Chef: Andrew Parkinson
Food Style: Modern British

The stable block of the Georgian mansion is now an informal eatery with pared-back and sleek decor reaching to the rafters. The open-to-view kitchen is equipped with a wood-fired oven and chargrill, but the menu has more going for it than pizzas and steaks.

Datchworth

The Tilbury ⚜⚜ 🍷 NOTABLE WINE LIST
Watton Road, SG3 6TB
01438 815550
www.thetilbury.co.uk
Closed: Early August

A good local watering hole and a place to eat seriously good food, The Tilbury's kitchen is driven by quality, starting with carefully-sourced produce. A pub menu lists the likes of cottage pie or fish and chips with mushy peas and tartare sauce. Alternatively, move up a gear with pan-fried turbot paired with girolles, baby onions, kale and mash.

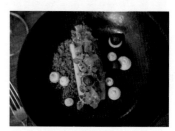

Chef: Thomas Bainbridge
Food Style: Modern British

See advertisement opposite

Flaunden

Bricklayers Arms ⚜
Black Robin Lane, Hogpits Bottom, HP3 0PH
01442 833322
www.bricklayersarms.com
Closed: 25 December

Chef: Miro Schelling
Food Style: British, French

The Bricklayers is a cheery Georgian pub with a cosy atmosphere, rustic oak beams, log fire and brick bar, with a garden and terrace. Food is a serious commitment, the kitchen sourcing locally and seasonally, supplementing the main menus with daily fish and vegetarian specials.

Hemel Hempstead

Aubrey Park Hotel ⚜
Hemel Hempstead Road, Redbourn, AL3 7AF
01582 792105
www.aubreypark.co.uk
Open: All year

Chef: Stuart Gauld
Food Style: Modern European

It stands in nine acres of rolling countryside, dates back to 1287 and has an Iron Age hillfort in the grounds. Old in parts indeed, but Aubrey Park's interiors are contemporary, particularly the light, bright Brasserie, where friendly staff serve bistro classics.

Hitchin

The Orangery ⚜⚜

The Farmhouse at Redcoats, Redcoats Green, SG4 7JR
01438 729500
www.farmhouseatredcoats.co.uk
Open: All year

Located within the original farmhouse and with lovely
garden views, there is a homely feel to this newly
added, modern kitchen garden style restaurant and
wraparound garden terrace, that can be enjoyed in the
warmer months. The modern British cooking has strong
local provenance with produce grown in the garden.
Knebworth Estate Venison or Creedy Carver Duck
feature as a typical main course.

Chef: Sherwin Jacobs
Food Style: Modern British,
Seafood

St Albans

Chez Mumtaj ⚜⚜

Centurian House, 136–142 London Road, AL1 1PQ
01727 800033
www.chezmumtaj.com
Closed: Monday, 25–26 December

Maybe it's the subtle lighting, leather banquettes and
wood panelling, but there's a touch of the gentlemen's
club about this spacious restaurant, where pan-Asian
and French cooking sometimes get quite neighbourly.
Concise lunch, dinner and Asian tapas menus list
Malaysian-style buttered black tiger prawns; corn-fed
tandoori chicken with curly kale, saffron basmati; and
sweet potato-stuffed beignets.

Chef: Chad Rahman
Food Style: French, Asian

NEW The Plough, Sleapshyde ⚜⚜

Sleapshyde Lane, Smallford, AL4 0SE
01727 823 720
www.ploughstalbans.com
Closed: Monday, Tuesday

The Plough is an independent gastro pub that prides
itself on its delicious seasonal menu, amazing Sunday
roast and friendly service. It's a rustic, thatched roof
country pub, serving carefully sourced local and
seasonal ingredients with modern British twists.
There's also an eclectic selection of wine and beer
on offer, including craft beers from their very own
Gorgeous Brewery.

Chef: Paul Cooke
Food Style: Modern British

THOMPSON St Albans ⚜⚜⚜
See pages 238-239 and advertisement on page 240

Tring

NEW Crockers Tring Awaiting Inspection
74 High Street, HP23 4AF
01442 828971
www.tring.crockersuk.com
Closed: Sunday, Monday, 25–27 December,
1–3 January

Located on Tring's charmingly historic High Street,
Crockers is a bustling modern restaurant offering
food that is both beautifully cooked and presented,
but also free of the pomp that's often associated with
fine dining. The Chef's Table is a real experience as
you watch the team prepare your meal only a few
feet away from you.

Chef: Scott Barnard
Food Style: Modern British

Welwyn

Auberge du Lac ⚜⚜
Brocket Hall Estate, Brocket Road, AL8 7XG
01707 368888
www.aubergedulac.co.uk
Closed: Monday, Tuesday

In Brocket Hall's former hunting lodge, the Auberge
takes its name from its lakeside setting overlooking
the neoclassical Hall itself. The view alone might well
prompt a daytime visit for a modern British lunch,
maybe with ingredients foraged by the kitchen team
on the magnificent 543-acre estate. A seven-course
tasting menu is offered with optional paired wines.

Chef: John Barber
Food Style: Modern British

The Wellington ⚜
High Street, AL6 9LZ
01438 714036
www.wellingtonatwelwyn.co.uk
Open: All year

Chef: John Beardsworth
Food Style: Modern British

The Wellington, on Welwyn's pretty high street, is an old coaching inn with rustic-chic exposed
brick walls, real fires and a bar stocked with proper beers. The focus is firmly on the gastro
side of the pub spectrum, with a simple, unpretentious menu. Popular with locals, and busy
throughout the day.

St Albans

❀ ❀ ❀

THOMPSON St Albans

2 Hatfield Road, AL1 3RP
01727 730777
www.thompsonstalbans.co.uk
Closed: Monday

Chef: Phil Thompson
Food Style: Modern British

Fine dining, contemporary cooking with interesting combinations

Phil Thompson's eponymous restaurant, neatly set in a row of four weatherboarded cottages in the town centre, has continued to fly St Albans's flag on the gastronomic map. Inside's good looks echo its pedigree, with a smart lounge bar for pre-meal drinks and three contemporary dining areas, taking in a cosy front room, light-and-airy conservatory (with its quaint courtyard and terrace for alfresco) and the main upstairs room. Subtle shades of grey merge with white linen and bold splashes of colour from local artworks (for sale, if anything catches your eye).

Thompson's kitchen output catches the mood and is as switched on as the attentive but relaxed service and atmosphere, intelligently playing to the local audience as well as destination diners, with his fixed-price tasting repertoire; from a 5, 7 or 9 course 'midweek and lunchtimes' menu to the

7 or 9 courser for 'weekend evening' dining, which also moves with the times to include full vegetarian or vegan options. Driven by the seasons, Thompson's contemporary cooking is underpinned by sound classical technique and driven by quality produce, including ingredients from his father-in-law's allotment. Careful, well-considered combinations deliver brushstrokes of flavour with flare and panache and dressed-to-thrill presentation.

Witness Wye Valley white asparagus teamed with a buttermilk beurre blanc, smoked roe and nettles, while Cornish plaice, served with poached Fowey mussels and grape and sea aster brings memories of the south-west's coastline to land-locked St Albans. Crapaudine beetroot, fermented garlic and mustard seed could provide the accompaniment to black treacle Lake District farmer's beef, while a summer finish might see a peach and vanilla parfait teamed with peach sorbet, fermented honey and crème fraîche. Optional wine pairings ramp up the experience factor, alongside a list of interesting global wines, with good by-glass options (including Coravin fine wines by glass too), and there are seasonal cocktails to round off a class local act.

See advertisement on page 240

"...contemporary cooking is underpinned by sound classical technique..."

Midweek & Lunchtime Dining
Tuesday to Thursday evening
Friday & Saturday lunchtime
5/7/9 courses, £59/£79/£110
Optional wine pairing, £55/£75/£99

Weekend Evening Dining
Friday & Saturday evening
7/9 courses, £79/£110
Optional wine pairing, £75/£99

Conservatory & Terrace Dining

thompsondining
@thompsondining
thompsondining
www.thompsonstalbans.co.uk

Welwyn *continued*

The White Hart ◉
2 Prospect Place, AL6 9EN
01438 715353
www.whitehartwelwyn.co.uk
Open: All year

Chef: Dan Defusto
Food Style: Modern British

Beside the river in the village of Welwyn, this 17th-century coaching inn is owned and run by brothers James and Tom Bainbridge, it's an inn that oozes charm, from the cosy bar to the flagstoned restaurant with its inglenook fireplace. The thoroughly modern brasserie-style menu has something for everyone.

Welwyn Garden City

CowShed ◉◉
Hertford Road (B1000), AL6 0JB
01438 717793
www.tewinbury.co.uk
Open: All year

Chef: Tommy McArthur
Food Style: Modern British

CowShed is part of Tewin Bury Farm, a skilful conversion of a complex of barns on a working farm, into a characterful modern hotel. The restaurant is an uncluttered space with an oak beamed ceiling, pale-blue banquettes, a boarded floor and a covered heated terrace. Many of the kitchen's raw materials are produced on site.

Willian

The Fox ◉◉
SG6 2AE
01462 480233
www.foxatwillian.co.uk
Open: All year

If you lived in a village with only one pub, you'd hope for somewhere like The Fox. This is a stylish gastro pub, with a wide range of real ales on offer in its busy bar, an open-plan dining room and 25-seat conservatory, plus a kitchen whose ambition goes beyond pub grub.

Chef: Piran Dewey
Food Style: Modern British, Seafood

Isle of Wight

Niton

NEW White Lion ⚜
High Street, PO38 2AT
01983 719402
www.whitelioniow.co.uk
Closed: 25 December

On the southern side of the island, the White Lion is a
recently renovated traditional village inn with a kind-of
contemporary farmhouse ambience. Inside are stone or
tongue and groove clad walls in pale greens and cream,
and a choice of dining areas. Modern British menus are
well balanced and use seasonal ingredients sourced
from the local area.

Chef: Nick Gerring
Food Style: Modern British

Seaview

Seaview Hotel ⚜⚜
High Street, PO34 5EX
01983 612711
www.seaviewhotel.co.uk
Closed: 22–26 December

In the picturesque fishing village of Seaview, on the
island's north-east coast, this long-established hotel is
just 50 metres from the sea that supplies much of the
fish on the menu. The cooking is refined with classic
techniques letting tip-top ingredients speak
for themselves.

Chef: Mark Wyatt
Food Style: Modern British

Shanklin

NEW The Horizon Restaurant ⚜
5 Queens Road, PO37 6AN
01983 863245
www.brunswick-hotel.co.uk
Open: All year

The Brunswick Hotel and its restaurant, the Horizon,
sit above Shanklin Beach, enjoying lovely views over
the gardens to the sea. Guests can dine in the garden
to enjoy the sunshine, or the sunset. The kitchen offers
imaginative modern British cuisine that demonstrates
very strong technical skills. Also local island produce is
very much to the fore.

Chef: Robert Green
Food Style: Contemporary British

Ventnor

NEW The Hambrough Restaurant ❀❀
Hambrough Road, PO38 1SQ
01983 856333
www.thehambrough.com
Closed: January

The Hambrough is set on a hillside near Ventnor's
seafront which means the restaurant enjoys great views
out to sea. The restaurant interior is nicely traditional
and quite intimate, while dishes are thoughtfully
adventurous. Service is friendly and attentive, and the
place is a real hit with locals as well as island tourists.

Chef: Matthew Tomkinson
Food Style: British

The Royal Hotel ❀❀
Belgrave Road, PO38 1JJ
01983 852186
www.royalhoteliow.co.uk
Closed: First 2 weeks January

The Royal is a handsome slice of Regency grandeur on
the Isle of Wight's south-east coast. Inside, is a classic
English tableau fully loaded with crystal chandeliers,
parquet floors and decorative ironwork. The island's
own Gallybagger cheese opens proceedings in a
soaring soufflé.

Chef: Matt Egan
Food Style: Modern British

Smoking Lobster ❀
Esplanade, PO38 1JT
01983 855938
www.smokinglobster.co.uk
Closed: Sunday, Monday, January

As its name suggests, fish and seafood are king in
this easygoing eatery. Bleached wooden floorboards,
unclothed tables and a minimal white decor jazzed up
with monochrome images of fish set a suitably maritime
mood and the pocket-sized galley kitchen sends out
a nice line in Asian-accented dishes to go with the
glorious sea views.

Chef: Giancarlo Giancovich
Food Style: British, Pan-Asian

Yarmouth

NEW Salty's Restaurant & Bar ⚛
Quay Street, PO41 0PB
01983 761550
www.saltysrestaurant.co.uk
Closed: 25–26 December, first 2 weeks January

On the vibrant quay at Yarmouth is Salty's, a charming
blue building, once an old sail loft, with a real seaside,
laid-back vibe. Inside is the friendly, lively bar, while
upstairs is the more formal restaurant, both with
wooden tables and refreshing coastal blue decor.
The menu's big on seafood, but there's something
for everyone.

Chef: Tom Axford
Food Style: Modern British

Kent

Biddenden

The West House Restaurant with Rooms ⚛⚛⚛ ⚑NOTABLE WINE LIST
28 High Street, TN27 8AH
01580 291341
www.thewesthouserestaurant.co.uk
Closed: 24–26 December, 1 January

Chef: Graham Garrett
Food Style: Modern European

This charming, tile-hung, 16th-century weaver's cottage in the picture-perfect village of
Biddenden, The West House has all the twisty beams and interesting nooks and crannies
you could possibly wish for. It's a family business, with husband and wife team Graham and
Jackie Garrett running the kitchen and front-of-house respectively. There's a relaxed, friendly
atmosphere in the dining room, with unclothed tables and fantastically seasonal dishes on the
menu. Graham is a passionate and enthusiastic advocate of using the best possible produce
in the most interesting ways, with an emphasis on simplicity and depth of flavour. A beautiful
piece of main-course Longhorn beef brisket is matched with potato and horseradish foam,
beef fat-cooked carrot, and pickled shiitake mushroom to cut the richness. Finish with Kentish
strawberries, accompanied by a divine sorbet, elderflower gel and heavenly olive oil custard.

What excites you most in your work?

Being surprised by something or someone.
The simple pleasure of tasting something truly delicious.

AA Inspector

Canterbury

ABode Canterbury ⚜⚜⚜
High Street, CT1 2RX
01227 766266
www.abodecanterbury.co.uk
Open: All year

Chef: Catalin Jauca
Food Style: Modern European

An ornate arched portico announces ABode Canterbury, which offers an expansive dining room with varnished floor, white walls and an appealing modern brasserie feel. There's also a chef's table, where up to a dozen diners can observe the busy kitchen. The name of the game is well-balanced, technically accomplished cooking with much use of Kentish produce, and a tasting menu if you fancy it. Start with a meaty, rich, marinated pork cheek with heritage carrots. Then a main course of fillet of Kentish beef, with braised ox cheek, celeriac, pickled walnut and black garlic purée, while dessert could be Manjari chocolate mousse with yogurt sorbet.

The Corner House ⚜⚜
1 Dover Street, CT1 3HD
01227 780793
www.cornerhouserestaurants.co.uk
Open: All year

A 16th-century former coach house overlooking Canterbury's city walls, this stylish restaurant deals in no-nonsense modern favourites. Mains include chicken supreme, wild garlic, gnocchi, asparagus, leeks and wild mushrooms, or confit pork belly, black pudding, purple sprouting broccoli, mash and cider jus. Leave room for stout cake and coffee ice cream.

Chef: Matt Swordor
Food Style: British

Fordwich Arms ⚜⚜⚜ ♦NOTABLE WINE LIST
1647 King Street, Sturry, CT2 0DB
01227 710444
www.fordwicharms.co.uk
Closed: 25 December

Chef: Daniel and Natasha Smith
Food Style: British

Under the helm of high-flying chef-patron Dan Smith since 2018, this 1930s country boozer with terrace and garden overlooking the River Stour remains a foodie hotspot. The updated stripped-back style sits comfortably alongside the period charm of its oak-panelled dining room, cosy open fires and 1930s-vintage bar. Smith's cooking is firmly in the new-wave modern British camp, allying sharp technique with intriguing combinations of first-class materials. Lunch starts with a bang – a virtuoso array of snacks before a highly technical and detailed workout involving south coast squid, smoked pork fat, apple and onion in several variations. Main-course turbot is glazed in a parsley emulsion and supported by crisp potato, unctuous Madeira sauce and Perigord truffle.

Canterbury *continued*

THE PIG at Bridge Place 🏵️🏵️ 🍾 NOTABLE WINE LIST
Bourne Park Road, Bridge, CT4 5LF
01227 830208
www.thepighotel.com/at-bridge-place
Open: All year

This elegant 16th-century manor house has a notable
rock 'n' roll history, as Pink Floyd and Led Zeppelin
were among bands who performed here in the 1970s.
Now part of THE PIG litter of fashionable, boutique
hotels, seasonal produce stars in dishes like beetroot
and bacon soup followed by fillet of day-boat cod, salad
onions and cockles.

Chef: Andrew Feasby, Will Parkes
Food Style: Classic British

Dartford

Rowhill Grange Hotel & Utopia Spa 🏵️🏵️
Wilmington, DA2 7QH
01322 615136
www.alexanderhotels.co.uk
Open: All year

Set in acres of beautiful grounds, Rowhill Grange is a
substantial 18th-century manor in acres of grounds.
It's also a boutique hotel with a fantastic Romanesque
spa. RG's is the restaurant, a symphony in grey with
windows all around, conservatory style. The kitchen
offers its famous grills and steaks, along with other
more exotic and creative dishes.

Chef: Andres Garcia
Food Style: Modern European

Deal

Dunkerleys Hotel & Restaurant 🏵️🏵️
19 Beach Street, CT14 7AH
01304 375016
www.dunkerleys.co.uk
Open: All year

Chef: Ben Dunkerley
Food Style: Modern British

Considering this is a seafront restaurant with a maritime theme, it's no surprise that Dunkerleys
Hotel & Restaurant has a strong focus on local seafood, delivered in fuss-free dishes by the
friendly down-to-earth chef owner. It's practically on Deal Beach and the pier's just a short walk
away, if you fancy catching some of your own seafood.

Dover

NEW Marquis of Granby
Alkham Valley Road, Alkham, CT15 7DF
01304 873410
www.marquisofgranby.co.uk
Closed: 2–6 January

Set in the peaceful Alkham Valley, the Marquis of Granby
is a relaxed, atmospheric old pub with quarry-tiled floors,
simple bare tables, fresh flowers, logs piled up, and some
bare brick and timber walls, all lit by pendant lights and
spots. The vibe is busy and buzzy, a very popular venue
with locals. Food is both hearty and imaginative.

Chef: Steve Piddock
Food Style: Modern British

See advertisement on page 249

Folkestone

Rocksalt
4–5 Fishmarket, CT19 6AA
01303 212070
www.rocksaltfolkestone.co.uk
Closed: Monday, Tuesday

Rocksalt is a bright, spacious restaurant in a unique
and memorable setting, a landmark building perched
above the harbour, which means lovely views through
a wall of curved glass. Inside, herringbone parquet
and olive-green leather banquettes and seats, create a
subtle and minimal vibe. The imaginative and tempting
menu is seasonal and designed to showcase the
freshest 'catch-of-the-day' seafood.

Chef: Marcin Zselag
Food Style: Modern British

Grafty Green

Who'd A Thought It
Headcorn Road, ME17 2AR
01622 858951
www.whodathoughtit.com
Closed: 25 December

Chef: David Kirby
Food Style: British

A champagne and oyster bar with rooms in a Kentish village not far from the M20 designed
with racy opulence. As well as a menu of modern classics, shellfish platters and thermidor will
please seafood purists, as will sticky toffee pudding with butterscotch sauce for those with a
sweet tooth.

Hawkhurst

The Queen's Inn 🌸
Rye Road, TN18 4EY
01580 754233
www.thequeensinnhawkhurst.co.uk
Closed: 25 December

Chef: Simon Found
Food Style: Modern British

Rejuvenated by its dynamic owners, this inviting pub offers an appealing line in hearty food. Inside, there is rustic-chic charm, pleasingly fuss-free service and a menu of unpretentious cooking that supports local producers. A separate dining room serves charcoal-grilled meat and fish dishes, plus pizzas from a wood-burning oven.

Hythe

Hide and Fox 🌸🌸🌸 ⚑NOTABLE WINE LIST
The Green, Saltwood, CT21 4PS
01303 260915
www.hideandfox.co.uk
Open: All year

A collaboration between a Kentish chef with an impressive CV and an Italian sommelier, it's easy to see the appeal of Hide and Fox. Housed in the old village shop, it's a stylish place with oak tables, colourful artwork and laidback jazz in the background. The modern European food is restrained and inventive, with a perfectly timed Orkney scallop popping up in a starter

Chef: Allister Barsby
Food Style: Modern British

with silky parsnip purée, beurre noisette, vanilla-scented chicken jus and lime gel. To follow, poached salted cod is paired with dulse, broad beans, basil and gnocchi. Finish with chocolate mousse, miso, sesame, vanilla and balsamic.

Hythe Imperial 🌸
Princes Parade, CT21 6AE
01303 267441
www.hytheimperial.co.uk
Closed: 2–3, 9–10, 16–17 December

This elegant, well established hotel stands looking out across the Channel from its prominent position on the seafront. Dishes are served on the finest tableware, in keeping with the grandeur of the setting, and menus include tried and tested favourites with an eye on seasonal produce.

Food Style: Modern, Traditional

DRINK · EAT · SLEEP
SINCE 1810
THE MARQUIS OF GRANBY
ALKHAM · KENT

A: The Marquis of Granby, Alkham Valley Road, Alkham, Dover, Kent CT15 7DF

T: 01304873410

E: info@marquisofgranby.co.uk

W: www.marquisofgranby.co.uk

Facebook: https://marquisofgranby.co.uk

Instagram: https://instagram.com/themarquisofgranby

Award Winning Pub

Drink, Eat, Sleep

AA

Rosette award for culinary excellence

2022

Kilndown

The Small Holding
Ranters Lane, TN17 2SG
01892 890105
thesmallholding.restaurant
Closed: Monday, Tuesday, 25 December

In a sleepy village in the backwoods of Kent, The
Small Holding benefits from its productive one-acre
namesake. The feel is relaxing and rustic, with a terrace
that's just lovely in nice weather. The tables and floor
are of chunky wood with mismatched seats and farm
implements on the walls. Food is all about seasonality
and honest flavours.

Chef: Will Devlin
Food Style: British

Lenham

Chilston Park Hotel
Sandway, ME17 2BE
01622 859803
www.handpickedhotels.co.uk/chilstonpark
Open: All year

Chef: Ross Pilcher
Food Style: Modern British

Surrounded by acres of immaculately landscaped gardens and parkland, Chilston Park Hotel
brims with period authenticity, antiques and oil paintings. The decor in Culpeper's Restaurant is
similar, with sash windows, ornate plasterwork and dark wood chairs. The food is right
up-to-date though, offering a range of seasonal dishes inspired by local ingredients.

Leysdown-on-Sea

The Ferry House Inn
Harty Ferry Road, ME12 4BQ
01795 510214
www.theferryhouse.co.uk
Closed: 24–30 December

Chef: James Pilcher
Food Style: Modern British

The Ferry House, a country inn alongside the Swale Estuary, has put the Isle of Sheppey on the
culinary map. It's possible to eat in the bar, but the majority of diners book into the raftered
Barn Restaurant. The kitchen's style is modern British.

Maidstone

Fish on the Green 🏵🏵

Church Lane, Bearsted Green, ME14 4EJ
01622 738300
www.fishonthegreen.com
Closed: 25 December

The pretty village green setting can be described as quintessentially English, and Fish on the Green has netted a strong local fan base with its fresh, unpretentious interior, clued-up staff, and excellent fish and seafood from a kitchen that treats super-fresh materials with intelligent simplicity. If you don't fancy fish, there are always appealing meat and veggie dishes in the mix.

Chef: Peter Baldwin
Food Style: British, French

NEW The Ringlestone 🏵🏵

Ringlestone Road, Harrietsham, ME171NX
01622 290 300
www.theringlestone.co.uk
Closed: Monday, Tuesday, first 2 weeks January

A lovely 16th-century country inn lost among the backroads of the North Kent Downs, The Ringlestone goes for a classic look with quarry tiled floors, rustic pine tables, bare flint and brick walls, and an open wood fire in an inglenook. The kitchen goes in for big, hearty flavours and has its own smokery.

Chef: Paolo Rigolli
Food Style: Modern British

Margate

Buoy and Oyster - Margate 🏵🏵

44 High Street, CT9 1DS
01843 446631
www.buoyandoyster.com
Closed: 25–26 December

The trump card at this easygoing fish and seafood-oriented restaurant is its covered first-floor terrace overlooking Margate's sandy beach. Bare brickwork, an open kitchen and piscine artworks reinforce the maritime look to go with well-tuned modern British food whose focus is clearly, as the name suggests, on fish and seafood.

Chef: Craig Edgell
Food Style: Modern British, Seafood

Minster

The Corner House ◉◉
42 Station Road, CT12 4BZ
01843 823000
www.cornerhouserestaurants.co.uk
Open: All year

Chef: Matt Sworder
Food Style: British

Opposite the church in the tranquil village of Minster, The Corner House restaurant-with-rooms makes good use of its rural location by showcasing locally sourced ingredients. Expect the likes of garden pea pannacotta, Broadstairs crab mayo and Granny Smith apple followed by roasted duck breast, confit carrot, braised cavolo nero, mash and orange sauce.

Royal Tunbridge Wells

Hotel du Vin Tunbridge Wells ◉ 🍾NOTABLE WINE LIST
Crescent Road, TN1 2LY
01892 526455
www.hotelduvin.com
Open: All year

Chef: Jimmy Worrall
Food Style: British, French

A Grade II listed Georgian mansion is home to HdV's operation in Tunbridge Wells and the enormous wine lists remain an integral part of the attraction of this hotel chain. The cooking continues on a solid French bistro basis, as well as more Anglo comfort-food.

The Kentish Hare ◉◉
95 Bidborough Ridge, Bidborough, TN3 0XB
01892 525709
www.thekentishhare.com
Closed: Monday, Tuesday

The Kentish Hare is a stylish weatherboarded village inn that offers a real welcome. Chunky oak tables, fresh flowers, bare bricks, wood floors, and lots of hares scattered around in the fabrics and decor. There's also a large terrace area out back. The cuisine is modern British using excellent produce, and demonstrating real cooking skills that shine through.

Chef: C and J Tanner,
David Boswell
Food Style: Modern British

The Orangery 🏵️🏵️
The Spa Hotel, Mount Ephraim, TN4 8XJ
01892 520331
www.spahotel.co.uk
Closed: 25 December

This grande dame of the elegant Georgian hotels in Tunbridge Wells continues to capitalise on the spa business. The Orangery presents a rather more contemporary face, with crowd-pleasing modern cooking to boot, while the sumptuous Chandelier Restaurant provides something rather more refined for a special occasion.

Food Style: Modern, Traditional British

Thackeray's 🏵️🏵️🏵️ 🍷NOTABLE WINE LIST
85 London Road, TN1 1EA
01892 511921
www.thackerays-restaurant.co.uk
Open: All year

Chef: Pat Hill
Food Style: Modern European

Just off the town's main drag, this lovely, white-weatherboarded building dates back more than 300 years. Inside, Thackeray's delightful period details – sloping ceilings, odd little corners – add up to a charming setting, blending ancient and modern with stylishly up-to-date touches and a switched-on service team. Intelligently constructed, with precise presentation and accurate execution, the food delivers intricate re-workings of classic combinations. Slow-cooked ham hock with Coronation emulsion, quail Scotch egg and soused raisins starts the show, before moving on to roast Suffolk chicken alongside blue cheese and chicken leg macaroni, braised chicory and Madeira cream. Bring things to a close with a take on lemon meringue, involving preserved Amalfi lemon and Madagascan vanilla meringue and ice cream.

Sandwich

NEW Blazing Donkey Country Hotel 🏵️
Hay Hill, Ham, Eastry, CT14 0ED
01304 617362
www.blazingdonkey.co.uk
Open: All year

A converted farmhouse that dates back in part to 1763, the Blazing Donkey Country Hotel's restaurant has all the features of a country dining room; high ceiling, beams and low windows. Some contemporary touches have been added but nothing that threatens the place's character. The kitchen puts out a fine seasonal menu using only the best of Kent produce.

Chef: Luke Bacon
Food Style: British

Stalisfield Green

The Plough Inn
ME13 0HY
01795 890256
www.theploughinnstalisfield.co.uk
Closed: 2–9 January

In a truly tranquil setting on the Kent Downs, The Plough offers a genuinely warm welcome and award-winning, adventurous food created by a classically trained chef patron. There's home-made bread and brioche, traditional pub fare and a surprising repertoire of special dishes that celebrate seasonal Kentish country and coastal produce.

Chef: Richard Baker
Food Style: Modern British

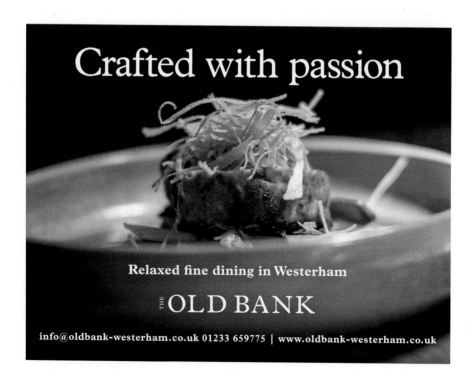

The Swan Wine Kitchen
Chapel Down Winery, Small Hythe Road, TN30 7NG
01580 761616
www.swanchapeldown.co.uk
Closed: 25 December

What better way to become acquainted with Chapel Down wines than to pair them with a meal in the striking contemporary rustic restaurant overlooking the vineyards of one of England's leading winemakers. Soak up heavenly countryside views from the bar and terrace, while the skilled kitchen sends out an appealing array of modern dishes.

Chef: Charlie Whitton, Jon Woodward
Food Style: European

See advertisement below

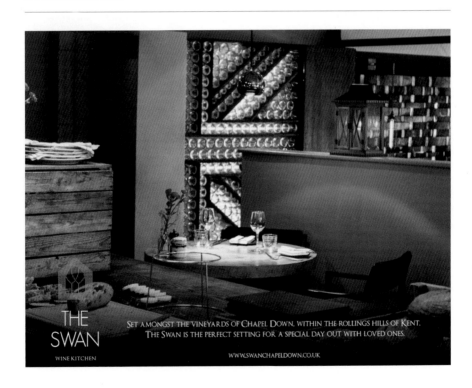

THE SWAN
WINE KITCHEN

SET AMONGST THE VINEYARDS OF CHAPEL DOWN, WITHIN THE ROLLINGS HILLS OF KENT.
THE SWAN IS THE PERFECT SETTING FOR A SPECIAL DAY OUT WITH LOVED ONES.

WWW.SWANCHAPELDOWN.CO.UK

Trottiscliffe

NEW Bowleys at The Plough ®®
Taylors Lane, ME19 5DR
01732 822233
www.theploughkent.com
Closed: Monday, 3–10 January

The Plough is a charming sage green village pub with a modern dining venue called Bowleys. Inside, it's bright and stylish, with low grey painted beams, bare wood tables, turquoise fabric seats, and old photos and other pictures on the walls. The bar side has a similar feel but more casual. Friendly, chatty and well informed service.

Chef: Alex Yates
Food Style: Modern English

Westerham

NEW The Old Bank ®®
8 Market Square, TN16 1AW
01233 659890
www.oldbank-westerham.co.uk
Closed: 27 July to 7 August, 25 December to 12 January

Set on Westerham's high street, The Old Bank generates an upmarket, clubby atmosphere. Decor is as you'd expect from an old bank; darkwood tables and floors, racing-green leather banquettes and sage green walls with framed fivers and photos. The open kitchen at the rear adds a buzz, while service is professional, relaxed and chatty.

Chef: Adam Turley
Food Style: Contemporary British

See advertisement on page 254

Wingham

The Dog at Wingham ®®
Canterbury Road, CT3 1BB
01227 720339
www.thedog.co.uk
Open: All year

Close to Canterbury, this lovely village pub once formed part of a former monastery dating from the 13th century. A boutique makeover has lent the place a sympathetic 21st-century sheen, with mismatched furniture adding a rustic-chic edge to the cosy wood-panelled restaurant. Seasonal British ingredients drive the inventive cooking.

Chef: Roberto Mantegna
Food Style: Modern British

Lancashire

Blackburn

The Millstone, Mellor
Church Lane, Mellor, BB2 7JR
01254 813333
www.millstonehotel.co.uk
Open: All year

Chef: Adam Edwards
Food Style: Modern British

Owned by Thwaites Brewery, whose ales are at the pumps, it's not all about beer at this old coaching inn. It also deals in feel-good menus that offer up pub classics, lunchtime sandwiches, locally sourced steaks cooked on the grill, and a few global flavours.

Burnley

Bertram's Restaurant
Crow Wood, Royle Lane, BB12 0RT
01282 471913
bertramsrestaurant.com/
Open: All year

Crow Wood, a modern hotel with extensive spa and leisure facilities, is set in 100 acres of woodland. Bertram's Restaurant, a stylish space with unclothed dark wood tables and smartly upholstered chairs, is popular with locals and guests alike. Prosecco cocktails get a meal of wide-ranging options off to a good start.

Chef: Gary Entwistle
Food Style: British

Fence Gate - Brasserie
Wheatly Lane Road, Fence, BB12 9EP
01282 509555
www.fencegate.co.uk
Open: All year

Food Style: Modern British

Booking is strongly advised for a table at the popular Fence Gate - Brasserie. Notable are the small gin bar, and the meat ageing room, that specialises in 35-day dry aged beef ribs. Expect friendly and attentive service, hearty portions and a convivial atmosphere. Menus display a confident combination of quality pub dishes alongside more refined modern British offerings.

Burnley *continued*

White Swan at Fence ◉◉◉
300 Wheatley Lane Road, Fence, BB12 9QA
01282 611773
www.whiteswanatfence.co.uk
Closed: 24–31 October, 26 December, 1–9 January

Chef: Tom Parker
Food Style: Modern British

The White Swan at Fence is a proper village pub in all respects and rather unassuming from the exterior. Inside, the decor is traditional with small dining areas and a bar where the locals sup pints. The food, however, is far from average pub grub and there is a real passion in the kitchen, with strong technical skills evident in boldly flavoured dishes. Start with a delicate broth – made with early tomatoes from the chef's grandfather's garden – topped with basil and wild garlic foam and diced Iberico bellota. Move on to Morecambe Bay sea bass, peas, tarragon and sweet cicely.

Wilfreds ◉
Royle Lane, BB12 0RT
01282 471913
www.wilfredsrestaurant.com
Open: All year

Food Style: Modern British,
International

Although it's set in a brand new, modern building, Wilfred's has a rich, plush, sophisticated appeal, almost like 1940s New York. Seating is comfortable, staff are friendly and attentive, and the whole place has a real buzz. The cooking claims an Italian theme, but the reality is more eclectic, offering a modern twist on many ethnic flavours.

Clitheroe

Coach and Horses ◉◉
Main Street, Bolton by Bowland, BB7 4NW
01200 447331
www.coachandhorsesribblevalley.co.uk
Closed: Monday, Tuesday

Set in a picture perfect country village, the Coach and Horses is a boutique hotel with quirky fairytale motifs. The restaurant has flagged floors and dark wood but is otherwise brightly decorated. One striking feature is the glassed wall that looks into the on-site micro-brewery. Dishes range from pub classics to contemporary British cuisine.

Chef: Ian Moss
Food Style: Modern British

Cowan Bridge

Hipping Hall 🏵🏵🏵 🍷 NOTABLE WINE LIST
LA6 2JJ
015242 71187
www.hippinghall.com
Closed: Monday, Tuesday

Chef: Peter Howarth
Food Style: Modern British

Just off the A65 in the picturesque Lune Valley, Hipping Hall is surrounded by lovely grounds and the name refers to the 'stepping stones' over the beck flowing through the gardens with its lawns and lake. Accessed via a small orangery, the restaurant has a rustic look of roaring fires, stone floors and open kitchen. A Japanese influence permeates the modern cooking and a meal could kick off with crisp-skinned Yorkshire duck teamed with nasturtium, watercress, black garlic purée and truffled ricotta. Accurately timed Loch Fyne scallop with Cornish crab, caviar and sea vegetables is another delightful dish.

Great Eccleston

The Cartford Inn 🏵🏵
Cartford Lane, PR3 0YP
01995 670166
www.thecartfordinn.co.uk
Closed: 25 December

On the banks of the River Fylde, this ever-evolving 17th-century coaching inn is enlivened by the owners' own artwork and creative eye. The menu revels in Lancashire's fine produce, bringing it together in imaginative ideas that aim to comfort rather than challenge.

Chef: Chris Bury
Food Style: Modern British

Lancaster

Wagon & Horses 🏵🏵
27 St Georges Quay, LA1 1RD
01524 846094
www.wagonandhorseslancaster.co.uk
Open: All year

Set on St George's Quay, overlooking the River Lune, the Wagon and Horses is a pub that presents an excellent modern British dining menu alongside some upgraded pub favourites. Service is very friendly, knowledgeable and attentive, and food flavours are both considered and balanced. Look out for their pork fillet or Scottish loch trout with mussels.

Food Style: Modern British

Langho

 **NOTABLE WINE LIST**

Northcote Restaurant

Northcote Road, BB6 8BE
01254 240555
www.northcote.com

Chef: Lisa Goodwin-Allen
Food Style: Modern British

Closed: Late January to early February (Obsession Food & Wine Festival)

Sophisticated modern cooking at a long-established northern gem

Northcote is justly famous as one of the best places to eat in the North, with fantastic, often local, produce used to very good effect. Enjoying a beautiful setting in the Ribble Valley, with fabulous views of the Forest of Bowland from the terrace – an ideal place for pre-dinner drinks – the original much-extended red-brick Victorian manor is comfortably decorated in a relaxed modern style, with contemporary art works and elegant furnishings.

It's a lovely place to stay and the highlight, of course, is the food. Lisa Goodwin-Allen is a staple of *The Great British Menu* and as executive chef she oversees a kitchen that takes its inspiration from the best of local ingredients – including some from Northcote's own kitchen garden.

Her years of experience and technical know-how are evident in stylish, contemporary interpretations of classic

dishes with a definite Lancashire accent.

At lunch there's a very reasonably priced seasonal three-course offering, while dinner presents a five-course tasting option, along with a vegetarian version. An early summer lunch might feature chalk stream trout tartare with horseradish buttermilk, lemon and seaweed, or chilled tomato consommé with cheese dumplings. Follow that with risotto of cauliflower with confit shallot, yogurt and frozen cheese, or Yorkshire chicken, with Spilman's asparagus, smoked bacon and tarragon.

Stick in the north for Manchester Tart with banana and raspberry, or Yorkshire rhubarb honeycomb semi freddo with fennel pollen. Accompanying it all is one of the region's outstanding wine lists, its glories dispensed with engaging knowledgeability by a fine sommelier. There's plenty to do while you're visiting – the Ribble Valley is a paradise for anyone who likes to get out and about in nature, with stunning landscapes, heritage sites and a thriving food culture.

"...stylish, contemporary interpretations of classic dishes with a definite Lancashire accent."

Langho

Northcote Restaurant ◉◉◉◉ ♨NOTABLE WINE LIST
See pages 260-261

Lower Bartle

Bartle Hall Hotel ◉
Lea Lane, PR4 0HA
01772 690506
www.bartlehall.co.uk
Open: All year

Chef: Natasha Craven
Food Style: Modern British

Between Blackpool and Preston, Bartle Hall is conveniently positioned for the M6 and the Lake District. Set within extensive gardens, this former private residence can be traced back to the 16th century although these days it's a comfortable modern hotel and wedding venue.

Lytham St Annes

Bedford Hotel ◉
307–313 Clifton Drive South, FY8 1HN
01253 724636
www.bedford-hotel.com
Open: All year

Chef: Paul Curran
Food Style: Modern British

The Bedford is a welcoming, family-run Victorian hotel with lots going on. Its Cartland Restaurant has plenty of period charm, with decorative plasterwork, warm pastel tones, black-and-white prints of film stars and neatly laid tables. The cooking steers sensibly clear of left-field flavours.

Clifton Arms Hotel ◉
West Beach, Lytham, FY8 5QJ
01253 739898
www.cliftonarmslytham.com
Open: All year

Chef: Paul Howard
Food Style: British

The present red-brick building dates from early Victorian times and is on the site of what was a small inn. Chic table settings with good napery and floral adornments look the part against the neutral hues of the main dining room, where bay windows give wide sea views. The kitchen delivers contemporary cooking that moves with the seasons.

Best Western Lothersdale Hotel

320–323 Marine Road, LA4 5AA
01524 416404
www.bfhotels.com
Closed: 22–27 December

Chef: Darren Tattersall
Food Style: Modern British

Run by the same family for more than 50 years, the seafront Lothersdale Hotel on the promenade in Morecambe has a separate bar and tapas area with an outside terrace area providing wonderful views across the bay to the Lakeland fells.

The Barn at Moor Hall

See page 264

Moor Hall Restaurant with Rooms NOTABLE WINE LIST

See pages 266–267

263

10 Camden Place, PR1 3JL
0800 246 5555
www.winckleysquarehotel.co.uk
Closed: Sunday, Monday, Tuesday, 28 August to 14 September, 25–26 December, 1–17 January

The modern 263 restaurant at the charming Winckley Square Hotel offers an unpretentious and relaxed setting in which to enjoy simple, modern British dishes that concentrate on good flavours. At dinner, expect seasonal fare with an à la carte or seven-course tasting menu with wine pairings.

Chef: Rikki Hughes, Oli Martin
Food Style: Modern British

Ormskirk

The Barn at Moor Hall

Prescot Road, Aughton, L39 6RT
01695 572511
www.moorhall.com
Closed: Monday, Tuesday, 2–26 January

Chef: Mark Birchall,
Nathan Cornwell
Food Style: Modern British

The Barn is sister to Moor Hall, but don't be fooled by the little sibling's ability to impress. As you approach there's a patio area with some seating which overlooks the lake, which can also be seen from the first-floor restaurant. Once inside The Barn, pass several small rooms before walking up the grand wooden stairs where you'll be met with a blend of original beams, new wood bar and open red brick work. To the far end is a state-of-the-art open kitchen complete with temperature-controlled cheese and wine rooms. A regularly changing menu offers contemporary cooking and features much home-grown produce and home-made ingredients. Start with accurately seasoned tartare of high quality '60-day aged' Shorthorn beef with charcoal grilled and pickled Jerusalem artichoke, nasturtium and a shallot brioche. Move on to juicy guinea fowl leg, grilled asparagus, morels, spelt grains and wild garlic. Wye Valley rhubarb with woodruff mousse, rhubarb sorbet and meringue displays an impressive contrast in flavours and textures.

Twelve Restaurant and Lounge Bar ◉◉

Marsh Mill Village, Fleetwood Road North, FY5 4JZ
01253 821212
www.twelve-restaurant.co.uk
Closed: First 2 weeks January

Twelve Restaurant's edgy design ethic embraces stripped-back bare bricks, exposed air ducts and roof beams, alongside sleek designer furniture and graffiti portraits of 20th-century cultural icons. The feel is definitely 'art space'. Staff are skilled, knowledgeable and well drilled, but still spontaneous and friendly. Food's in the modern city neighbourhood restaurant style. Simple things done well, with bold flavours.

Chef: Graham Floyd
Food Style: Modern British

See advertisement below

Ormskirk

NOTABLE WINE LIST

Moor Hall Restaurant with Rooms

Prescot Road, Aughton, L39 6RT
01695 572511
www.moorhall.com
Closed: Monday, Tuesday, 31 July to 17 August, 25–26 December, 2–26 January

Chef: Mark Birchall
Food Style: Modern British

Dynamic cooking in stunning location

Set in five acres of stunning gardens just outside Ormskirk, Grade II* listed Moor Hall dates back to the mid-16th century. Andy and Tracey Bell took over in 2015, overseeing a multi-million pound renovation, and, along with head chef Mark Birchall, they've created a stunning destination restaurant with rooms. The house itself is warmly traditional, with oak beams and floorboards and open fires, beautifully decorated and furnished with wonderful attention to detail. This focus can also be seen in the modern, glass-walled extension that houses the restaurant and state-of-the art open kitchen. Everything, from staff uniforms to light fittings, chairs and table settings, has been carefully chosen. Many of the vegetables in summer dishes are grown in the impressive kitchen gardens and feature on the constantly evolving menus.

The eight-course taster, served at

both lunch and dinner, and a four-course lunch option are dynamically modern with pin-sharp contemporary interpretations, influenced by Birchall's time at Simon Rogan's highly acclaimed Cumbrian restaurant L'Enclume.

You can expect extremely thoughtful, often virtuoso cooking, running from Crown Prince squash, chorizo, egg yolk, cod roe, chicken, chervil and caviar through to smoked eel, potato, fermented garlic and flowers before taking in Scottish langoustine, raspberry, radish and nasturtium. A meal might continue with turnip and crab, anise hyssop and sunflower seeds before tartare of Moorfields Jersey beef, BBQ celeriac, mustard and shallot. Main courses could take in a beautiful piece of turbot cooked on the bone and teamed with artichoke, mussel and roe sauce or Berkshire sika deer, kale and blackberry ragout, liver parfait and truffled honey. Gingerbread roots and pine is a delightful dessert of

caramelised ginger topped with a carefully judged gingerbread ice cream and pine powder. Or you can end with forced rhubarb, peach leaf, yogurt and blood orange.

"...expect extremely thoughtful, often virtuoso cooking..."

Whalley

Breda Murphy Restaurant ⚽
41 Station Road, BB7 9RH
01254 823446
www.bredamurphy.co.uk
Closed: Monday, 23–28 December, 1–3 January

After a top-to-toe makeover a few years ago, this
vibrant enterprise now comprises a contemporary
restaurant, a gin bar and a casual daytime deli/café.
Sitting cheek by jowl with the landmark Whalley
Viaduct, it's ideally placed for friendly get-togethers
accompanied by unfussy bistro dishes with hearty
Irish and British accents.

Food Style: Modern British
and Irish

The Freemasons at Wiswell ⚽⚽⚽ 🍷NOTABLE WINE LIST
8 Vicarage Fold, Wiswell, BB7 9DF
01254 822218
www.freemasonsatwiswell.com
Closed: Monday, Tuesday, 2–16 January

Chef: Steven Smith, Matthew Smith
Food Style: Modern British

A cream-painted inn in well-heeled Wiswell, The Freemasons has a pleasantly bucolic air, with
small carpets thrown over the flagstone floor, old paintings and prints on the walls, bare tables,
and rolled-up kitchen cloths for napkins. Head chef Steven Smith and his team have given their
all to create a diverse menu of adventurous and impeccably presented dishes. Dive in with a
pleasant and well-balanced starter of chicken liver parfait with jelly of Tomlinson's rhubarb,
chicken crackling and grilled sourdough. Follow with two succulent lamb cutlets, beautifully
timed and tender, with Turkish stuffed aubergines, BBQ gem lettuce, mint and anchovy.

Wrea Green

The Spa Hotel at Ribby Hall Village ⚽⚽
Ribby Hall Village, Ribby Road, PR4 2PR
01772 674484
www.ribbyhall.co.uk/the-spa-hotel
Closed: 24–25 December

As its name makes clear, there are some pretty
swanky spa facilities at this classy adult-only
retreat in 100 acres of Lancashire countryside.
The Brasserie and its Orangery extension are
another string to its bow, done out with orange
and lime leather seats.

Chef: Michael Noonan
Food Style: Modern, Traditional

The Villa Country House Hotel ⚜⚜
Moss Side Lane, PR4 2PE
01772 804040
www.thevilla.co.uk
Open: All year

Chef: Matthew Johnson
Food Style: Classic British

The Villa restaurant's oak panelling is but one original feature of this Victorian gentleman's carefully restored and decorated former mansion, near Lytham St Anne's. No doubt he would be pleasantly surprised by its light, relaxed atmosphere and the simple, British food with classic flavours, such as duck breast, and wild sea bass, served by the friendly staff.

See advertisement below

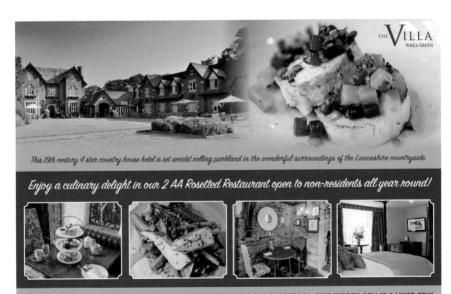

THE VILLA
WREA GREEN

This 19th century 4 star country house hotel is set amidst rolling parkland in the wonderful surroundings of the Lancashire countryside.

Enjoy a culinary delight in our 2 AA Rosetted Restaurant open to non-residents all year round!

IDEALLY LOCATED OFF THE M55 CLOSE TO THE LYTHAM ST ANNES AND BLACKPOOL, THIS HIDDEN GEM IS A MUST-TRY!

THE VILLA WREA GREEN, MOSS SIDE LANE, PRESTON, LANCASHIRE, PR4 2PE
T: 01772 80 40 40 E: RECEPTION@THEVILLA.CO.UK W: WWW.THEVILLAWREAGREEN.CO.UK

Leicestershire

Anstey

Sapori Restaurant & Bar ◉◉
40 Stadon Road, LE7 7AY
0116 236 8900
www.sapori-restaurant.co.uk
Closed: Sunday, Monday, 26 December to 9 January

Sapori Restaurant is a classy, understated place, with its own cocktail bar. Set on the edge of Leicester, it has a clean-cut modern interior with cream and grey tones, and low-lighting for a nicely intimate ambience. The kitchen offers menus dedicated to presenting the best in Italian cuisine, from classics to dishes with an imaginative, contemporary spin.

Chef: Andrea Scarpati
Food Style: Italian

Long Whatton

The Royal Oak ◉
26 The Green, LE12 5DB
01509 843694
www.theroyaloaklongwhatton.co.uk
Open: All year

The 21st-century incarnation of this thriving gastro pub is seen in a smart interior, some natty bedrooms and a focus on food. That said, real ale is part of the plan, and a few pub classics remain. The kitchen turns out some lively stuff.

Chef: James Upton
Food Style: Modern British

Market Harborough

Three Swans ◉
21 High Street, LE16 7NJ
01858 466644
www.threeswans.co.uk
Closed: 1 January

Chef: Marek Jani
Food Style: Modern, International

Dating from the reign of Henry VIII, the Three Swans is on the High Street and has played host to various crowned heads over the generations. The interior has a clean modern look that respects the original features, and smartly attired, tuned-in staff run the dining room with inspiring confidence.

Melton Mowbray

Stapleford Park
Stapleford, LE14 2EF
01572 787000
www.staplefordpark.com
Closed: exclusive use days

Chef: Tony Fitt
Food Style: Modern International, British

Stapleford's lineage can be traced back to medieval times, the estate being owned by successive generations of the Earls of Harborough for nearly 500 years. Impeccable staff keep the elevated tone buoyant, and the cooking aims high too.

Mountsorrel

John's House
139–141 Loughborough Road, LE12 7AR
01509 415569
www.johnshouse.co.uk
Closed: 25 December, 2 weeks August

Chef: John Duffin
Food Style: Modern British

John Duffin has food in his DNA: after working up an impressive CV in some of London's stellar kitchens, he returned to his roots by opening his own restaurant on the family farm where he grew up. Bare beams and brick walls, wooden floors and tables all add up to a rustic feel but think again if you're expecting food in a similar vein. Sure, Duffin is committed to a 'farm to plate' philosophy – much of the produce comes from his family's land, after all – but the cooking is ambitious, precise and full of contemporary verve.

North Kilworth

Kilworth House Hotel & Theatre
Lutterworth Road, LE17 6JE
01858 880058
www.kilworthhouse.co.uk
Open: All year

A top-to-toe restoration overseen by the eagle eyes of English Heritage means period authenticity runs seamlessly through this Italianate 19th-century mansion. The Wordsworth Restaurant is the fine-dining option: a posh setting indeed, but the kitchen team certainly rises to the occasion.

Chef: Max Faulkener
Food Style: Modern British

Shawell

The White Swan
LE17 6AG
01788 860357
www.whiteswanshawell.com
Closed: Monday, Tuesday, Wednesday,
25–26 December, 31 December, 1 January

The White Swan is an old pub that's been transformed
into a modern minimalist restaurant, which is lovely
and bright during the day, thanks to the conservatory-
style ceiling. There's a seven-course tasting menu for
carnivores, as well as one for vegetarians. The food
is modern European but with a sense of theatrical
delivery.

Chef: Rory McClean
Food Style: Modern European

Wymeswold

Hammer & Pincers
5 East Road, LE12 6ST
01509 880735
www.hammerandpincers.co.uk
Closed: Sunday, Monday, 25–26 December

Once the local forge, Hammer & Pincers is now a
charming restaurant-with-rooms with exposed beams,
midnight blue walls, comfortable brown leather seats
and marble and wood tables. Colourful artwork on
the walls keep things contemporary as the service is
switched on and knowledgeable. There is an Asian
twist to the modern British dishes, which are precisely
executed with well-defined flavours and textures. Start with a vibrant dish of koji-cured sea
trout, oyster emulsion, keta roe and coastal herbs, and move on to juicy roasted monkfish given
the Thai treatment with lemongrass, crisp squid, kaffir lime and shrimp.

Chef: Daniel Jimminson
Food Style: British, European

What changes have you seen over the past few years?

A wonderful response to the hardships of Covid and Brexit –
the industry becoming more collegiate and collaborative.
The result is a focus on what really is essential to a restaurant.

AA Inspector

Lincolnshire

Pig & Whistle ☺☺
Healing Manor Hotel, Stallingborough Road,
Healing, DN41 7QF
01472 884544
www.healingmanorhotel.co.uk
Closed: 26 December

A traditional pub, the Pig & Whistle adjoins the
picturesque, ivy-clad Healing Manor Hotel and offers
poshed-up pub grub with carefully-considered dishes
made from ingredients such as plump, juicy scallops
and excellent quality duck breasts, sitting alongside
the more conventional sausage and mash and fish and
chips. Justifying their dog-friendly claim, there's even a menu just for your canine companions.

Chef: Steven Bennett
Food Style: Modern British

Magpies Restaurant with Rooms ☺☺
73 East Street, LN9 6AA
01507 527004
www.magpiesrestaurant.co.uk/
Closed: Monday, Tuesday

In a terrace of 200-year-old cottages, Magpies has
decor of duck-egg blue, with mirrors, candlelight
and drapes over the bay windows. After enjoyable
savoury courses, if you've got room, finish with a trio of
desserts: chocolate mousse, espresso crème brûlée and
dark chocolate fondant.

Chef: Andrew Gilbert
Food Style: British, European

The Brownlow Arms ☺☺
High Road, NG32 2AZ
01400 250234
www.thebrownlowarms.com
Closed: 25–26 December, 1 January

The Brownlow Arms is an elegant restaurant with an air
of country house grandeur about it, set in the middle of
the Lincolnshire countryside. Interiors are impressive,
with tapestry-backed chairs and gilt-framed mirrors in
a panelled dining room. Meanwhile, attentive, friendly
service and a seasonal modern British menu puts
everyone at their ease.

Chef: Matt Kerekes
Food Style: British

Lincoln

The Lincoln Hotel 🏵
Eastgate, LN2 1PN
01522 520348
www.thelincolnhotel.com
Open: All year

Chef: Dale Gill
Food Style: Modern British

Just a stone's throw away from Lincoln's 12th-century cathedral, The Lincoln Hotel has a restaurant known as The Green Room. It has a striking, design-led interior, with candles and fresh flowers that add a nice, homely touch. The atmosphere is relaxed but the small restaurant retains an air of formality.

Washingborough Hall Hotel 🏵🏵
Church Hill, Washingborough, LN4 1BE
01522 790340
www.washingboroughhall.com
Open: All year

Chef: Mark Cheseldine,
Anthony Smith
Food Style: Modern British

Washingborough Hall is a Georgian country house with a small dining room at the front, overlooking the lovely garden. Small in this case means around 15-20 covers. Decor is all modern elegance with greys, silvers and a touch of duck egg blue in the fabrics and coloured water bottles. Excellent modern dining from the ambitious, talented kitchen team.

The White Hart 🏵
Bailgate, LN1 3AR
01522 563290
www.whitehart-lincoln.co.uk
Open: All year

A real feature of the historic quarter of Lincoln, The White Hart has splendid views of the cathedral, and the castle nearby. Inside, a suave contemporary theme brings wood flooring, dark wood tables and large mirrors to the Grille restaurant and bar. The menu is seasonal with an emphasis on the grill, naturally.

Food Style: Modern British

Market Rasen

The Advocate Arms 🏵🏵
2 Queen Street, LN8 3EH
01673 842364
www.advocatearms.co.uk
Open: All year

Chef: Josh Kelly
Food Style: Modern European,
British

The 18th-century restaurant with rooms in the centre of town has a contemporary finish and aims to impress with boutique styling and an open-plan interior. In the main restaurant, the output is broadly modern British, with some inventive combinations and plenty to satisfy any traditionalists.

San Pietro Restaurant Rooms 🏅🏅
11 High Street East, DN15 6UH
01724 277774
www.sanpietro.uk.com
Closed: 25–26 December

Pietro Catalano, who hails from Sicily, has created
a restaurant with rooms in a former windmill that
combines the best of Italian hospitality with a touch
of boutique swagger. A first course dish of ballotine of
rabbit and foie gras shows the style ambition.

Chef: Chris Grist
Food Style: Modern Mediterranean

The Bustard Inn & Restaurant 🏅
44 Main Street, South Rauceby, NG34 8QG
01529 488250
www.thebustardinn.co.uk
Closed: Monday, Tuesday

Set in a peaceful just a couple of miles from Sleaford,
The Bustard Inn is a beautiful Grade II listed Victorian
building offering a warm and friendly environment
in which to enjoy fine dining in the spacious, well-
ventilated restaurant or to simply relax with a beer and
sandwich in the bar or garden.

Food Style: Modern British

The Hope and Anchor Pub 🏅🏅
Sluice Road, DN18 6JQ
01652 635334
www.thehopeandanchorpub.co.uk
Closed: 25 December, 31 December, 1 January

Tucked amidst creeks and moorings, the panoramic
views from the patio and restaurant encompass the
waterways and nearby Humber Bridge. An appealingly,
updated 19th-century inn, with exposed brickwork and
a log-burning stove, this is a popular stop not only for
birdwatchers and dog-walkers but those seeking good
bistro-style food.

Chef: Slawomir Mikolajczyk
Food Style: Modern British

Stamford

The Bull & Swan at Burghley 🏵️
High Street, St Martins, PE9 2LJ
01780 766412
www.thebullandswan.co.uk
Open: All year

Chef: Phil Kent
Food Style: Traditional British

The Bull and Swan is an old stone inn once used as a staging post for coaches on the Great North Road, but nowadays it's an informal dining pub. Inside, are original beams, stone walls, rugs on dark wood floors and caramel-coloured leather dining chairs. Regional produce is the backbone, along with home-grown vegetables where possible.

The Oak Room 🏵️🏵️ 🍷 NOTABLE WINE LIST
The George of Stamford, 71 St Martins, PE9 2LB
01780 750750
www.georgehotelofstamford.com
Open: All year

History seeps from the pores of every mellow stone of this venerable coaching inn, which once fed and watered passengers on the Great North Road. The oak-panelled restaurant is a magnificent room with an old-world feel, and its menus are steadfastly traditional too.

Chef: Gareth Thorpe
Food Style: Traditional British

NEW Orbis Stamford 🏵️🏵️
11 All Saints Place, PE9 2AR
01780 669950
www.tastetheworld.uk
Open: All year

Right by the town's market square, Orbis Stamford serves up an eclectic mix of sharing plates from around the world, and all completely gluten-free. Tapas, sushi, Indian, traditional British are all on offer. High ceilings, stone, exposed beams and a friendly, attentive team all add to the mix and there's an outside terrace too.

Chef: Joshua Hames
Food Style: Global

The William Cecil ⊛⊛
High Street, St Martins, PE9 2LJ
01780 750070
www.thewilliamcecil.co.uk
Open: All year

The William Cecil is an intriguing combination of three houses built at different times during the Georgian era and named after Elizabeth I's chief advisor. It's a clever blend of old and new, with light panelling and booth seating in the restaurant. The kitchen team sources locally and has plenty of creative flair at its disposal.

Chef: Liam Goodwill
Food Style: Modern British

Winteringham

Winteringham Fields ⊛⊛⊛⊛ ⌀NOTABLE WINE LIST
See page 278

Woodhall Spa

Petwood ⊛
Stixwould Road, LN10 6QG
01526 352411
www.petwood.co.uk
Open: All year

The Petwood is a lovely Edwardian building that was once home to the famous 617 Squadron of the RAF, known as 'The Dambusters'. The original Squadron Bar still exists in this Tudor-style hotel, surrounded by delightful gardens. The menu offers classic cuisine from a kitchen team that works closely with local suppliers to promote the best of Lincolnshire's produce.

Chef: Philip Long
Food Style: Modern British

Winteringham

 NOTABLE WINE LIST

Winteringham Fields

1 Silver Street, DN15 9ND
01724 733096
www.winteringhamfields.co.uk
Closed: Sunday, Monday, 25 December to 8 January

Chef: Colin McGurran
Food Style: Modern British, European

Deep in the Lincolnshire countryside, six miles west of the Humber Bridge, Winteringham Fields is the hub of this well-heeled village. Chef Colin McGurran has created something quite magical here with farm outbuildings converted into accommodation and a high-class restaurant. A rabbit warren of rooms and private dining areas with a mix of slate tiles and wood makes a rustic setting for the contemporary ingredient-driven cooking. An eight-course tasting menu in the evening changes most days depending on what arrives in the kitchen, but a typical meal might kick off with chicken, herb emulsion, white cabbage and XO, to be followed by shoulder of Yorkshire lamb, bhuna purée, coriander curds and rice crumb, then chalk stream trout, pickled celery, grape dashi, celery broth and anchovy. There's a wine pairing for each course should you choose to amp up the dining experience. So, after savouring seven memorable courses end with a lemon tart, yogurt sorbet and marigold, a dessert that teams up superbly with a late harvest Tokaji from Hungary.

LONDON

London Locations

Index of London Restaurants

This index shows restaurants in numerical name and alphabetical order, followed by their postal district or Greater London location and page number in the guide.

London

London E1

The Buxton ⚜

42 Osbourn Street, E1 6TD
0207 392 2219
www.thebuxton.co.uk
Open: All year

Food Style: British

Located in the heart of London's Brick Lane, this compact pub-with-rooms serves a concise menu of produce-driven British and European dishes. The menu changes frequently but you might catch the gnocchi, wild mushroom and rosemary cream sauce or the fish of the day teamed with mussels and fregola. Leave a space for frangipane tart with clotted cream.

The Culpeper ⚜

40 Commercial Street, E1 6LP
020 7247 5371
www.theculpeper.com
Closed: 24–28 December

Chef: Sandy Jarvis
Food Style: British

This lively gastro pub occupies a handsome Victorian boozer rejuvenated in hipster-friendly, post-industrial style with bare-brick walls and a healthy dollop of period detail. The jam-packed ground-floor bar does an appealing line in switched-on modern food, while the first-floor Kitchen restaurant offers home-grown and European flavours on a thoroughly modern menu.

Galvin Bistrot & Bar ⚜⚜

35 Spital Square, E1 6DY
020 7299 0404
www.galvinrestaurants.com
Closed: 1 January, 24–26 December

In trendy Spitalfields, Galvin Bistrot & Bar takes a modern bistro approach. The buzzy venue has burnished copper tanks above the bar brimming with Czech Pilsner whilst the decor and table settings reflect that of a French bistro. The traditional three-course lunch format segues to a repertoire of small and larger sharing plates.

Chef: Joe Albina
Food Style: Modern French

Galvin La Chapelle ⚜⚜⚜ 🍷NOTABLE WINE LIST
35 Spital Square, E1 6DY
020 7299 0400
www.galvinrestaurants.com
Closed: 1 January, 24–26 December

Chef: Arturo Granato
Food Style: French, European

Sweeping stone archways, marble pillars and arched windows soaring to the roof rafters of the converted red-brick Victorian St Botolph's girls' school provide a suitably memorable setting for the Galvin brothers' high-flying City venue. The cooking conforms to the Galvin signature: polished classical French cuisine buffed up with a light, modern gloss. Uncluttered, fine-tuned and pretty on the plate it is too – an open 'lasagne' of luxurious crab and scallop mousse slathered in luscious beurre nantais being a case in point. Main course is another winner, heavenly Gigha halibut with charlotte potatoes, fennel, squid ink aïoli and lobster bisque. To finish, a masterclass tarte Tatin comes simply with Normandy crème fraîche.

London E9

Cornerstone by Chef Tom Brown ⚜⚜⚜
3 Prince Edward Road, E9 5LX
020 8986 3922
www.cornerstonehackney.com
Closed: Sunday, Monday

Chef: Tom Brown, Christian Sharp
Food Style: Modern British, Seafood

In a very modern grey-brick building in edgy Hackney Wick you'll find Cornerstone, a solo venture from Tom Brown, previously head chef at Outlaws at the Capital. The focus is on seafood, and making big waves. The vibe is super cool, light and relaxed; handsome industrial monochrome, with retro bow-back chairs, black tabletops and a dominant central-hub kitchen. Take a sensational opener of raw oyster with green tomato hot sauce, followed perhaps by a technically accomplished hake kiev, with cep and chanterelle butter. Round-off proceedings with well-balanced chocolate mousse cake with salted caramel, pecan, and banana ice cream. Bubbly, informed service hits a high note too.

London E14

NEW Bōkan 37 ⚜⚜
40 Marsh Wall, Isle of Dogs, E14 9TP
020 3530 0500
www.bokanlondon.co.uk
Closed: Monday, Tuesday

Bōkan 37 is a fantastic new restaurant on the 37th floor of the Novotel London Canary Wharf. Decor uses a lot of wood, steel, leather, and as you'd expect, no end of glass. Obviously, there are incredible views out across London, and the room generates a real buzzy modern vibe, aided by the busy open-plan kitchen.

Chef: Robert Manea
Food Style: Modern European

London E14 *continued*

Quadrato ◉
Canary Riverside Plaza, 46 Westferry Circus,
Canary Wharf, E14 8RS
020 7510 1999
www.canaryriversideplaza.com
Open: All year

Chef: Fabio Pellegrino
Food Style: Italian

Ensconced in a glossy white riverside hotel among the high-rise buildings of Canary Wharf, contemporary chic reigns in the Quadrato restaurant, while a terrace is a welcome bonus for fine weather dining. Simplicity is the watchword in an eclectic modern menu.

London EC1

Anglo ◉◉◉
30 St Cross Street, EC1N 8UH
020 7430 1503
www.anglorestaurant.com
Closed: 20 December to 3 January

Chef: Anthony Raffo
Food Style: Modern British

Anglo's rather unglamorous side-street setting off Leather Lane Market and equally anonymous frontage is all part of the unpretentious vibe at this personally run, pint-size highflier. The stripped-back interior of bare boards, pendant lights and concrete floor is wholly on vogue too, while the kitchen's approach – via a single tasting menu – celebrates seasonal British ingredients responsibly farmed and foraged – so expect simple, yet refined, high-skilled cooking driven by creativity and on-trend elements like fermentation alongside high-impact flavour and look. Think punchy, aspiring dishes like spelt with kale, cheddar and pear, or perhaps venison teamed with Jerusalem artichoke, broad bean miso, turnip, rosehip, elderberry and wild mushroom.

Chez Mal Brasserie ◉
Malmaison Charterhouse Square,
18–21 Charterhouse Square, Clerkenwell, EC1M 6AH
020 3750 9402
www.malmaison.com/locations/london

Chef: John Woodward
Food Style: Modern British

Like other hotels in the group, this branch is done out in best boutique fashion, with dramatic crimson and purple interiors, a sultrily lit bar and a brasserie in deep brown tones. The order of the day is lively modern British cooking with interesting variations.

The Clove Club ⊛⊛⊛
Shoreditch Town Hall, 380 Old Street, EC1V 9LT
020 7729 6496
www.thecloveclub.com
Closed: 25 December to 8 January

Chef: Isaac McHale, Oli Williamson
Food Style: Modern British

Reinvented as an arts venue, the Victorian pomp of old Shoreditch Town Hall is also home to the high-flying Clove Club, a smart but relaxed, trend-conscious destination outfit. In step with its hipster-central postcode, there's an understated look, with a pale blue and cream palette setting the tone against a backdrop of high ceilings, big-drop windows, wooden floors and white linen to complement the buildings elegance. But, it's the blue-tiled open kitchen that really ramps up the energy and excitement here, with its cutting-edge output. On-vogue multi-course taster is the style, while there's also a short tasting version and four-course lunch, all bursting with innovative ideas and presentation. Highlighting the best of British produce, elegance, precision and vibrancy feature in a beguiling myriad of small plates and snacks to make the heart sing; perhaps hot smoked Wiltshire trout teamed with almond milk and watercress and slow-roast Lincolnshire chicken with chanterelles and toasted hay hollandaise. Wine pairings and an adjacent bar round off a class act.

Club Gascon ⊛⊛⊛ ♦NOTABLE WINE LIST
57 West Smithfields, EC1A 9DS
020 7600 6144
www.clubgascon.com
Closed: Bank Holidays, 1 January, 25 December

Chef: Pascal Aussignac
Food Style: French

Open since 1998, Club Gascon is something of a grande dame of London's contemporary French restaurant scene. Located just off the historic Smithfield Market, there is a timeless feel with marble walls inset with mirrors, mustard yellow and blue upholstery and subdued lighting. Calm and formal right down to the white linen and efficient service, it's a sedate setting to enjoy imaginative plates of modern food inspired by the classic cuisine of south-west France. A typical meal might start with aromatic, umami-rich mushroom consommé, chestnut and scallop 'pearls' and continue with roast pheasant with silky Guinness and oyster sauce.

The Montcalm London City at The Brewery ⊛
52 Chiswell Street, EC1Y 4SB
020 7614 0100
www.themontcalmlondoncity.co.uk
Closed: Bank Holidays, 1 January, 25 December

Chef: Aarik Persaud
Food Style: Traditional British

Samuel Whitbread built up one of the UK's foremost beer brands on this spot, and part of his one-time Georgian brewery has been converted into this swanky hotel. There are a couple of dining options in situ, all entirely in keeping with the Georgian setting.

London EC1 *continued*

Smiths of Smithfield, The Rooftop Bar ⊛⊛
67–77 Charterhouse Street, EC1M 6HJ
020 7251 7950
www.smithsofsmithfield.co.uk/no3
Closed: 1 January, 25–26 December

Smack opposite Smithfield Market, Smith's top-floor
venue offers rooftop views of the City skyscrapers from
its long, light-filled room through full-drop sliding glass
doors and dream-ticket, fine-weather terrace. White
linen, designer chairs, semi-circular leather banquettes
and unstuffy service are spot on, while the kitchen
produces light, modern, dishes of flair and flavour.

Chef: Thomas Boland
Food Style: European

London EC2

Aviary Restaurant ⊛
Montcalm Royal London House,
22–25 Finsbury Square, EC2A 1DX
020 3873 4000
www.montcalmroyallondoncity.co.uk
Open: All year

Chef: Dan Hodson
Food Style: Modern British

Ten floors above Finsbury Square in the heart of the City, this ultra-modern restaurant
with a centralised bar and excellent roof terrace features two stuffed peacocks and sundry
birdcages, which explain the restaurant's name. The main draw, of course, is the British
brasserie-style food.

City Social ⊛⊛⊛ ▲NOTABLE WINE LIST
Tower 42, EC2N 1HQ
020 7877 7703
www.citysociallondon.com
Closed: Bank Holidays, 1 January, 25 December

Chef: Jason Atherton, Dan Page
Food Style: Modern European

With dream-ticket wraparound views of the ever-changing cityscape (think the Gerkin, the
Cheesegrater and the Shard), Jason Atherton's City Social is a high-end choice. A dedicated
lift whizzes to Tower 42's 24th floor, where the modern, darkly moody space comes with
art deco undertones; think rosewood panelling, horseshoe booths, leather banquettes and
mirrored ceiling. The food is every bit a match for those drawcard views; inventive, refined and
detailed classically founded modern European cooking, bursting with balanced flavours. Take a
typically inspired mains; Isle of Gigha halibut served with brassica, sea herbs and caviar velouté,
while a finale ruby peach and lemon parfait with peach sorbet comes as dressed-to-thrill as
everything else.

Coq d'Argent ⚜⚜
1 Poultry, EC2R 8EJ
020 7395 5000
www.coqdargent.co.uk
Closed: 1 January, 25–26 December

Chef: Damien Rigollet
Food Style: French

A stylish, modern, sharp-suit confection that comes properly dressed for the accomplished, big-flavoured French cooking and City skyscraper views. Menus boast bags of luxury for City high rollers; from oysters, lobster or caviar to deep-wallet mains like slabs of prime beef.

Miyako ⚜
Andaz London Liverpool Street,
40 Liverpool Street, EC2M 7QN
020 7618 7100
**www.hyattrestaurants.com/en/dining/uk/london/
japanese-restaurant-in-city-of-london-miyako**
Closed: 1 January, 25 December

Chef: Kosei Sakamoto
Food Style: Japanese

Miyako is within the Andaz London hotel, although it has its own entrance where queues form at lunchtime for takeaway boxes. The restaurant itself has a cool, uncluttered look, thanks to large windows, walls veneered in pale wood and bamboo, and black-lacquered tables and chairs.

Popolo Shoreditch ⚜⚜
26 Rivington Street, EC2A 3DU
020 7729 4299
www.popoloshoreditch.com
Closed: 24 December to 2 January

A fashionable and young crowd are drawn to this small, modern restaurant that's spread over two levels. The service is informal but the staff are very knowledgeable, and you can sit at the bar to view the chefs producing excellent regional Italian tapas-style dishes.

Chef: Jonathan Lawson
Food Style: Italian, Mediterranean

The Princess of Shoreditch ⚜⚜⚜
See page 290

London EC2

The Princess of Shoreditch

76–78 Paul Street, EC2A 4NE
020 7729 9270
theprincessofshoreditch.com
Closed: Monday, Tuesday

Chef: Ruth Hansom
Food Style: Modern British

Close to Old Street station on the border of the City and Shoreditch, this bustling 18th-century pub is tucked away from the main drag. The Princess of Shoreditch is stripped back with exposed floorboards and various shades of blue, with a lively bar downstairs and a more sedate dining room on the first floor. The cooking sticks to the original gastropub template, with high quality ingredients treated with respect in unfussy dishes high on flavour. A piece of firm and correctly timed South Coast gurnard is served with heritage carrot 'chips', fennel and celeriac 'risotto' and lovage. For meat fans, braised breast and loin of Swaledale lamb appears with red pepper, courgette flower and broad beans. Round things off with a well risen caramelised banana soufflé and Kraken rum and golden raisin ice cream. Service is relaxed and friendly, with staff easy to spot in their long green aprons. As well as draught beers from the downstairs bar, there's a noteworthy wine list with plenty offered by the glass.

Caravaggio
107–112 Leadenhall Street, EC3A 4AF
020 7626 6206
caravaggiorestaurant.co.uk
Closed: Saturday, Sunday, Bank Holidays, 24 December to 2 January

Chef: Alban Gura
Food Style: Modern Italian

Ornate ceilings, art deco light fittings and an imposing staircase leading to a mezzanine gallery lend a 1930s sense of vitality and glamour to this Italian restaurant in a former banking hall. The pace is full-on at lunch, while evenings are more chilled. This is food of simplicity and flavour.

Fenchurch Restaurant
Sky Garden, 1 Sky Garden Walk, EC3M 8AF
0333 772 0020
skygarden.london/fenchurch-restaurant
Closed: Monday, Tuesday, Wednesday

Chef: Daniel Fletcher
Food Style: Modern European

Up on the 37th floor of the Walkie Talkie tower, wraparound city views are a real draw at this sleek contemporary restaurant cantilevered over the tourist-magnet Sky Garden. Happily, the food is no mere afterthought, thanks to the high-level craft and creativity that goes into an appealing menu of modern European cooking.

La Dame de Pic London
Four Seasons Hotel London at Ten Trinity Square,
10 Trinity Square, EC3N 4AJ
020 3297 3799
www.ladamedepiclondon.co.uk
Open: All year

Chef: Anne-Sophie Pic,
Marc Mantovani
Food Style: French

Anne-Sophie Pic's base in London is a sleek space done out with leather, wood and mirrors in this swanky Four Seasons Hotel, and her fine-tuned culinary imagination produces some powerful and unexpected flavour combinations. The cooking is really on song in a starter of Cornish crab, steamed with sobacha and dill pannacotta, with a fab Corsican clementine jelly. John Dory meunière with a purée of coco de paimpol haricot beans, sage and coffee-infused dashi is a beautifully constructed main course, and it is followed by an impressive and elaborate dessert of smooth blackberry coulis, sorbet and fresh blackberry.

" What is your advice for cooking great food?
Keep it simple, keep it fresh

AA Inspector

London EC3 *continued*

Mei Ume
Four Seasons Hotel London at Trinity Square,
10 Trinity Square, EC3N 4AJ
020 3297 3799
www.meiume.com
Open: All year

Mei Ume is an impossibly chic Asian restaurant,
showcasing dishes from China and Japan. Part of the
incredibly impressive Ten Trinity Square hotel, the
high-ceilinged dining room, with its pillars and curved
banquettes, is a suitable venue for authentic dishes
with a modern slant.

Chef: Tong Truong
Food Style: Japanese, Chinese

NEW Straits Kitchen
80 Houndsditch, EC3A 7AB
020 7118 6888
www.panpacific.com/en/hotels-and-resorts/
pp-london/dining/straits-kitchen.html
Open: All year

Chef: Lorraine Sinclair
Food Style: South-east Asian

Offering all-day Singaporean cuisine, Straits Kitchen is part of Pan Pacific London, an impressive
43-storey bronze tower located in the heart of the City of London. Using purely Asian
ingredients grown locally for environmental reasons, the kitchen works to respectfully reflect
the many cuisines of Singapore.

London N1

12:51
107 Upper Street, Islington, N1 1QN
07934 202269
www.1251.co.uk
Closed: 25–30 December

James Cochran was voted 'Champion of Champions'
on BBC's *Great British Menu* and his restaurant, 12:51,
can be found not far from Islington Green. It may look
unassuming, spread across two floors with pale tables
and white walls, with candy-pink banquettes upstairs,
but it's loud and buzzy, and the small-plate menus,
divided into snacks, garden, sea and land sections, are
driven by seasonal produce with some fixed signature dishes.
The name 12:51, by the way, is a song by The Strokes.

Chef: James Cochran
Food Style: British

hicce ⚜⚜
102 Stable Street, Coal Drops Yard,
King's Cross, N1C 4DQ
020 3869 8200
www.hicce.co.uk
Closed: Monday, 1 January, 25–27 December

Part of the Coal Drops Yard development in King's
Cross, this second-floor restaurant occupies a
reinvented Victorian warehouse with bare brick walls
and high-beamed roof. From the vast open kitchen
with its BBQ grills, modern European dishes emerge –
perhaps cured salmon, wasabi and apple, followed by
octopus, peperonata, cured egg yolk and almonds.

Chef: Pip Lacey
Food Style: British, Scandinavian,
Mediterranean

London NW1

Odette's ⚜⚜⚜
130 Regent's Park Road, NW1 8XL
020 7586 8569
www.odettesprimrosehill.com
Closed: 24 December to 7 January

Chef: Bryn Williams, Tom Dixon
Food Style: Modern British,
European

The quintessential neighbourhood restaurant, Odette's has been a Primrose Hill stalwart
since the late 1970s. With its open-air terrace and cosy dining room, this is a restaurant for
all seasons and its surrounding greenery creates a decidedly rural feel. For the past 15 years,
Odette's has been under the stewardship of Bryn Williams whose seasonal bistro food is
simple, ingredient-driven and immaculately presented. Roast Scottish scallop, Welsh lamb belly,
cauliflower and raisin is a perfectly poised starter and might lead on to Goosnargh chicken,
Morteau sausage, sweetcorn and girolles. End with jaffa cake, milk sorbet and nibbed cocoa.

Pullman London St Pancras ⚜
100–110 Euston Road, NW1 2AJ
020 7666 9000
www.pullmanlondonstpancras.com
Open: All year

Chef: Carmelo Carnevale
Food Style: Modern European

This sleek hotel restaurant continues the cross-Channel link by refuelling Eurostar travellers at
St Pancras International, five minutes away. This is a clean-cut 21st-century space constantly
thrumming with activity. An open kitchen and Josper grill turn out an eclectic repertoire of
uncomplicated modern European dishes.

London NW1 *continued*

The Winter Garden ◉◉

The Landmark London,
222 Marylebone Road, NW1 6JQ
020 7631 8000
www.landmarklondon.co.uk/dining/winter-garden
Open: All year

Chef: Gary Klaner
Food Style: Modern European

The Winter Garden is open all day, and the mood changes with the hour (and the weather), for it is in the heart of the eight-storey atrium that forms the nucleus of The Landmark London. It's an impressive spot for classically minded modern food drawing ideas from the Continent.

London NW8

Soutine ◉

60 St John's Wood High Street, NW8 7SH
020 3926 8448
www.soutine.co.uk
Closed: 25 December

Set on a corner, a brief stroll from Regent's Park, Soutine is as Parisian as Toulouse Lautrec. There's bags of art nouveau styling, banquette seating, a glitzy bar and skylit rear dining room, so inévitablement, the menu is French bistro, with an all-day, all-in-one carte menu, alongside a range of croques and sandwiches to cover all bases.

Chef: Maciej Banas
Food Style: French

London NW10

Parlour ◉

5 Regent Street, Kensal Green, NW10 5LG
020 8969 2184
parlourkensal.com
Closed: Monday, 25 December

The former Grey Horse has been reinvented as an on-trend, food-oriented pub for a switched-on young crowd. Open for business from brunch to lunch and dinner, the place sports a shabby-chic look with white-tiled walls, painted panelling and banquette seating. Food-wise, expect a mix of heartily reworked British classics and creative dishes with a European accent.

Chef: Jesse Dunford Wood
Food Style: Modern British

London SE1

Brasserie Joël ⚫⚫
Park Plaza Westminster Bridge London, SE1 7UT
020 7620 7200
www.brasseriejoel.co.uk
Open: All year

Chef: Franck Katemesha
Food Style: Modern French

Park Plaza's dining options centre on a French venue called Brasserie Joël, a monochrome space with a large tree in the middle and funky music filling the air. A mix of traditional and lightly modernised French dishes brings plenty of lustre to the brasserie-style menu.

Chino Latino London ⚫⚫
Park Plaza London Riverbank,
18 Albert Embankment, SE1 7TJ
020 7769 2500
www.chinolatino.eu/london
Open: All year

Chef: Werner Seebach
Food Style: Modern Pan-Asian,
Peruvian

Part of an international chain, Chino Latino London is located in Park Plaza London, south of Lambeth Bridge. The design is like a high-tech movie set, but the menu is all about pan-Asian food with Latin inflections, as the name implies. Check out the sushi and sashimi, the tempura dishes and the marinated blow-torched salmon.

See advertisement on page 297

Florentine Restaurant ⚫
Park Plaza London Waterloo, 6 Hercules Road, SE1 7DP
0845 450 2145
florentinerestaurant.co.uk
Closed: Sunday, Monday

Chef: Darren Thomas
Food Style: British, Italian

A short walk from the South Bank's attractions and London Waterloo, this all-day contemporary restaurant and bar is a buzzy and informal setting for crowd-pleasing Mediterranean brasserie-style food. Flatbreads come freshly baked from the wood-fired oven, while the open kitchen deals in straight-up steaks and an appealing roster of uncomplicated, fresh and vibrant dishes.

Le Pont de la Tour ⚫⚫
The Butlers Wharf Building, 36d Shad Thames, SE1 2YE
020 7403 8403
www.lepontdelatour.co.uk
Open: All year

Chef: Orson Vergnaud
Food Style: Modern French

The name translates as Tower Bridge, and that's what lies before you, a blue-chip view framed by the City skyscrapers, whether you're sitting out on the riverside terrace or indoors soaking up the vista through floor-to-ceiling windows in the sleek art deco-style dining room. The well-executed food is rooted in the French classics and doesn't stint on luxury ingredients.

London SE1 *continued*

The Oxo Tower Restaurant ◉◉ ♦NOTABLE WINE LIST
8th Floor, Oxo Tower Wharf,
Barge House Street, SE1 9PH
020 7803 3888
www.oxotowerrestaurant.com
Closed: 25 December

On the eighth floor of the old Oxo building, this bar,
brasserie and restaurant overlooks the river and
St Paul's Cathedral, a world-class vista which never fails
to impress. The cooking is modern British with a bit of
globetrotting into Asian territory. Afternoon tea and
cocktails too.

Chef: Jeremy Bloor
Food Style: Modern British

Park Plaza County Hall London ◉
1 Addington Street, SE1 7RY
020 7021 1919
www.parkplazacountyhall.com/atrio-restaurant-bar
Open: All year

Chef: Stephen Rey
Food Style: Modern Italian

Inside the snazzy modern hotel next to County Hall on the South Bank, the hotel restaurant is
on a mezzanine level and has bags of style, including great views through the large glass wall.
The heart of the culinary action is a wood-fired oven.

Restaurant Story ◉◉◉◉◉ ♦NOTABLE WINE LIST
199 Tooley Street, SE1 2JX
020 7183 2117
www.restaurantstory.co.uk
Closed: August Bank Holiday, 25 December to 8 January

Chef: Tom Sellers
Food Style: Modern British

Located on a traffic island at the end of Tooley Street, this compact little restaurant is a simple
affair but it punches well above its diminutive size. The tables face bi-fold doors looking out
across a pretty sitting area. Inside, there's a polished concrete floor and bird mobiles suspended
from the ceiling. In the far corner, an open-plan kitchen where chefs create the small plates of
high quality food. There is constant evolution within this creative kitchen. Some dishes remain
throughout – with a tweak here and there – and others are new, but all are highly detailed,
with spot on flavours and textures. Creative and often with a sense of fun and theatre, the
highly technical skills and daring combinations are underpinned by classic technique. A grilled
Carlingford oyster is poached in chicken fat and XO sauce and dissolves in the mouth, the
textural contrast being a refreshing sea lettuce. A whole squab pigeon is served with roasted
artichoke purée, the bird's bones pressed and used to form a rich sauce with green peppercorns
and brandy. To finish, a signature dessert called 'Paddington Bear' is sandwich of marmalade,
cardamom biscuit and creamed foie gras.

MODERN PAN-ASIAN CUISINE AND LATIN BAR ON LONDON'S SOUTH BANK

FIND US
18 Albert Embankment
London SE1 7TJ

CONTACT
+44 207 769 2500
london@chinolatino.co.uk
chinolatino.eu

@chinolatinoeu

London SE1 *continued*

TĪNG ⬤⬤ 🍷NOTABLE WINE LIST
Shangri-La Hotel at The Shard, London,
31 St Thomas Street, SE1 9QU
020 7234 8008
www.ting-shangri-la.com
Open: All year

The Shangri-La occupies the 34th to 52nd floors of The
Shard, so the full-drop windows in TĪNG, the restaurant
on level 35, pack quite a punch. The dining room
is elegant, with a Chinoiserie feel, and the modern
European menu has Asian influences.

Chef: Paolo Belloni
Food Style: British, European, Asian

Trivet ⬤⬤⬤
36 Snowsfields, Bermondsey, SE1 3SU
020 3141 8670
www.trivetrestaurant.co.uk
Closed: Sunday, Monday

Chef: Jonny Lake
Food Style: Modern British

Tucked away opposite the historic Guinness Trust building, Trivet is refreshingly understated.
The glass-fronted space features a marble bar and two dining rooms with a focal-point open
kitchen, while Nordic-style woods and pastel shades add light and warmth. The menu bristles
with appeal, with confident, innovative cooking bringing top quality ingredients to life. Take
crispy veal sweetbreads with wild herb and confit kombu salad, which might precede a lovely
piece of citrus butter-poached John Dory paired with Tromboncino squash, spring onion and
Chardonnay butter sauce. Almond and plum tart with pistachio gelato is a delicious finale.

London SE10

The Market Brasserie ⬤
InterContinental London - The O2,
1 Waterview Drive, SE10 0TW
020 8463 6868
www.iclondon-theo2.com
Open: All year

Chef: Johan Rox
Food Style: Modern International

Views of the curving River Thames and bright lights of Canary Wharf skyscrapers through
full-drop windows provide a big-city backdrop for dining in this stylish cosmopolitan brasserie.
Expect prime British produce to form the backbone of hearty grills and modern European
dishes prepared with a touch of culinary theatre in the open kitchen.

Peninsula Restaurant ®®®

InterContinental London - The O2,
1 Waterview Drive, SE10 0TW
020 8463 6868
www.peninsula-restaurant.com
Closed: Bank Holidays

Chef: Aurelie Simon
Food Style: Modern European

It's all happening on the Greenwich Peninsula, which has gradually been transformed into a smart London quarter with its own cultural milieu, and a swish InterContinental Hotel to boot. The Peninsula Restaurant on the second floor has views of the whole district, with Canary Wharf hovering behind it, and amid the sleek contemporary design, a menu of cutting-edge cooking completes the picture. The influences are from modern and classic European cuisines which has created a menu reflective of the spice, exotic fruit and fresh fish trade that passed through East London's docks to be sold at London's Billingsgate.

London SE23

Babur ®®

119 Brockley Rise, Forest Hill, SE23 1JP
020 8291 2400
www.babur.info
Closed: 26 December

In business since the mid-1980s, Babur is a pioneer of modern Indian cuisine. Outside there's a life-sized model tiger on the roof, while inside is an upmarket, contemporary, brasserie-style space decorated with Indian artworks. Ingredients are never less than excellent, and they're put to good use in exciting, original cooking. Well-chosen, spice-friendly wine list.

Chef: Jiwan Lal
Food Style: Modern Indian

See advertisement on page 301

London SW1

NEW Al Mare ®®

1 Cadogan Place, SW1X 9PY
020 7235 1234
www.jumeirah.com/en/stay/london/the-carlton-tower
Open: All year

Chef: Marco Calenzo
Food Style: Italian, Seafood

The Carlton Tower Jumeirah is at the heart of Knightsbridge, and Al Mare is the place to dine on modern Italian cuisine. Set on the ground floor, it's the main restaurant for breakfast, lunch and dinner, with its own entrance, bar and private dining. The style fits the exclusive location and the high-end brand; classic with a contemporary feel.

London SW1 *continued*

Amaya ⊛⊛⊛ ⚡NOTABLE WINE LIST

Halkin Arcade, Motcomb Street, SW1X 8JT
020 7823 1166
www.realindianfood.com
Open: All year

Chef: Sanchit Kapoor
Food Style: Modern Indian

Discreetly tucked away in exclusive Belgravia, hot-ticket Amaya is part of the avant-garde Indian restaurant movement that has brought glitz, pizzazz and sophistication to the cooking of the subcontinent. From sleek cocktail bar to seductive dining room, there's a buzzy mood and glossy good looks in its leather seating, vivid artworks and terracotta statues, not to mention the theatre kitchen that delivers the real wow. The fashionable grazing menu features small-plate sharing dishes; green chutney chicken tikka, slathered with fresh herbs and green chilli, while foie gras gets the tandoori treatment. The more traditional ideas include curries (spicy Kerala prawn) and shahi chicken biryani with Persian barberries. Expect spot-on service and a classy wine list (plus inventive cocktails).

A. Wong ⊛⊛⊛

70 Wilton Road, Victoria, SW1V 1DE
020 7828 8931
www.awong.co.uk
Closed: 23 December to 8 January

Chef: Andrew Wong
Food Style: Chinese

Andrew Wong points out informatively that China has no fewer than 14 national borders, a phenomenon that has seen it absorb disparate culinary traditions throughout its own vast gastronomic history, and which informs the energetic and thrilling experimentation going on at his smart Victoria venue. So, take a culinary journey with the 'Touching the Heart' experience which includes clear shrimp dumpling, sweet chilli; rabbit and carrot glutinous puff; abalone flaky tart with aged balsamic vinegar; and Xian 'lamb burger' with sesame, coriander, chilli and Xinjiang pomegranate salad. Desserts are a little more restrained – coconut water ice, bird's nest, fermented coconut, dried mulberries, yogurt and mochi.

Caxton Grill ⊛⊛

St Ermin's Hotel, 2 Caxton Street,
St James's Park, SW1H 0QW
020 7227 7777
www.caxtongrill.co.uk
Open: All year

Set in the Victorian splendour of St Ermin's Hotel, Caxton Grill is all soothing colours, striking modern art and designer furniture. Although there's plenty to choose from, the Josper grill is the focus, offering prime British steaks, pork and more. A lot of the veg comes from their own kitchen garden, and honey comes from the bees on the roof.

Food Style: Modern European

London SW1 *continued*

Chutney Mary ⚫⚫⚫ 🍷NOTABLE WINE LIST

73 St James's Street, SW1A 1PH
020 7629 6688
www.chutneymary.com
Open: All year

Chef: Achal Aggarwal
Food Style: Modern Indian

New meets old at this stylish St James's restaurant with its hybrid of classical and modern decor. A visit to this classy venue begins at the glittering Pukka Bar for cocktails. But its main dining room is the real jewel in the crown complete with mirrored columns and soft lighting. The creative Indian cuisine runs to inspiring combinations with luxurious touches and well-dressed presentation. Goa crab cakes with chilli raita and punchy tamarind chutney fire up the tastebuds before an authentic Toddy shop cod Kerala fish curry richly flavoured with coconut, tamarind and fresh curry leaves. Almond halwa apple tart with cinnamon ice cream is a storming dessert.

Colbert ⚫

50–52 Sloane Square, Chelsea, SW1W 8AX
020 7730 2804
www.colbertchelsea.com
Closed: 25 December

Inspired by the grand boulevard cafés of Paris, the Colbert is a very popular Sloane Square destination and bustles with a wonderful feel-good vibe from breakfast to late evening. The lengthy all-day menu offers something for every occasion. The essence of the cooking is clean simplicity, defined by premium ingredients and flavour. The street-side alfresco tables are a hot ticket.

Chef: Sascha Rieb
Food Style: French

Curry Room ⚫

The Rubens at the Palace, 39 Buckingham Palace Road, SW1W 0PS
020 7834 6600
www.rubenshotel.com/dining-and-drinks
Open: All year

Not your average Indian restaurant, the opulent Curry Room is in the Rubens at the Palace hotel, and it's all rich jewel colours, Rajasthani hand embroidery, and dark red leather seating. Table settings sparkle, while staff are relaxed but attentive, and happy to help you through the menu. Traditional dishes are freshly made, vibrant, and very well spiced.

Chef: Arun Kumar
Food Style: Indian

Dinner by Heston Blumenthal ⊛⊛⊛⊛ ♦ NOTABLE WINE LIST

Mandarin Oriental Hyde Park,
66 Knightsbridge, SW1X 7LA
020 7201 3833
www.dinnerbyheston.co.uk
Closed: late August

Chef: Jon Bowring
Food Style: British

Dinner is located within the Mandarin Oriental Hotel in Knightsbridge, where a surprisingly simple dining room – unclothed tables, views over Hyde Park – features a centrally sited kitchen, viewed through floor-to-ceiling glass walls which allow you to see the unique pulley system, historically accurate, that rotates the spit over an open fire. If this sounds eccentric, it's because this is the culinary equivalent of a research institute, feeding Blumenthal's fascination with the history of British dining. The dishes on the menu are all taken from the recipes of the past, from the 14th to 19th centuries, allowing you to time-travel via the pleasures of the Meat Fruit of 1500 (mandarin jelly covers a chicken liver parfait, making a stunning 'faux orange') perhaps to roast turbot and green sauce (c.1440) or perhaps the more straightforward Hereford beef (c.1830) with mushroom ketchup and triple cooked chips. You might be surprised to learn that brown bread ice cream was being enjoyed in 1808 – this version comes with salted butter caramel, pear and malted yeast syrup. An early 18th-century spring tart, with Gariguette strawberries, rose, lovage and basil yogurt and goats' milk ice cream is delightfully light and fresh.

The English Grill ⊛⊛

The Rubens at the Palace, 39 Buckingham Palace Road,
SW1W 0PS
020 7834 6600
www.redcarnationhotels.com
Closed: Sunday, Monday

This elegant dining room is part of a hotel that has been run by the same family since 1912. Banquette seating along one wall provides views of large glass doors into the kitchen, where classic cooking techniques are employed for a menu that appeals to all.

Chef: Ben Kelliher
Food Style: Modern British

What are the most common misconceptions you face?

That we ask for a specific (traditional) style; that service plays a part in the award when assessing for AA Rosettes.

AA Inspector

London SW1 *continued*

Enoteca Turi 🏵️🏵️ 🍷NOTABLE WINE LIST
87 Pimlico Road, SW1W 8PH
020 7730 3663
www.enotecaturi.com
Closed: 25–26 December, 1 January

Run by the same family since 1990, Enoteca Turi has definitely put its roots down in the bustling Pimlico Road. It's a modern Italian restaurant which feels really welcoming with its long dining room and exposed red brick walls. The focus is on regional Italian flavours, with the menu highlighting the origins of each dish.

Chef: Stefano Tortelli
Food Style: Modern Italian

NEW Fallow 🏵️🏵️
2 St James's Market, SW1Y 4RP
www.fallowrestaurant.com
Closed: 24–25 December

This new kid on St James's Market is certainly firing on all cylinders, with its buzzy West End mood and cheffy action providing culinary theatre at the open kitchen. The aim is to 'elevate humble produce to new heights' so expect big flavours and some interesting combinations.

Chef: Jack Croft, Will Murray
Food Style: British Sharing Plates

The Game Bird at The Stafford London 🏵️🏵️ 🍷NOTABLE WINE LIST
16–18 St James's Place, SW1A 1NJ
020 7518 1234
www.thegamebird.com
Open: All year

Tucked away in a discreet street near Green Park, The Stafford is a luxurious St James's address that is worth tracking down. Under the direction of Lisa Goodwin-Allen, The Game Bird is inspired by great seasonal, British produce and the bustle of historic St James's. The kitchen delivers a menu overflowing with innovative combinations and ambitious dishes.

Chef: Jozef Rogulski
Food Style: Classic British

GBR (Great British Restaurant) 🏵️🏵️
Dukes London, 36 Little St James's Street, SW1A 1NY
020 7491 4840
www.dukeshotel.com
Closed: Monday

Buttoned banquettes, mirrored walls, herringbone
parquet and high leather stools at the marble-topped
bar add up to a glam setting in this classy all-day
Mayfair eatery. The initials stand for Great British
Restaurant, and that's a clear pointer to the kitchen's
inventive and up-to-date style of cooking.

Chef: Nigel Mendham
Food Style: British

The Goring 🏵️🏵️🏵️ 🍷NOTABLE WINE LIST
Beeston Place, SW1W 0JW
020 7396 9000
www.thegoring.com
Open: All year

Chef: Richard Galli
Food Style: Traditional British

Run by the Goring family since 1910, this sophisticated Edwardian treasure holds a Royal
Warrant and remains one of London's most luxurious hotels. In the restaurant you'll find
David Linley furnishings in soothing shades of gold and cream, while blossom-like Swarovski
chandeliers change colour with the light from outside. Service is polished and professional,
while the exquisitely conceived and beautiful dishes are a perfect combination of classic
traditions and state-of-the-art cooking. Roast Orkney scallop might start things off, with
cauliflower, pear William and roe butter sauce. A main of stuffed Norfolk baby chicken comes
with crusted globe artichoke, preserved lemon and thyme.

Hans' Bar & Grill 🏵️
164 Pavilion Road, Chelsea, SW1X 0AW
020 7730 7000
www.hansbarandgrill.com
Open: All year

Hans' Bar & Grill is part of 11 Cadogan Gardens
Hotel, not far from Sloane Square. Due to its position,
the restaurant has its own entrance. The style is
contemporary, with light, calming colours and lots of
artificial plants and mood lighting. Tables are marble-
topped, and the kitchen is partially open. Food is
modern but not too fussy.

Chef: Stefanos Kariofyllis
Food Style: Modern British

London SW1 *continued*

Ikoyi ⊛⊛⊛

1 St James's Market, SW1Y 4AH
020 3583 4660
www.ikoyilondon.com
Closed: Sunday

Chef: Jeremy Chan
Food Style: Modern West African

Set in the St James's Market development just south of Piccadilly, Ikoyi is named after an affluent Lagos neighbourhood in Nigeria. The modern, glass-fronted intimate space comes with dangling clay lamps, bright artwork and mustard-coloured banquette seating catching the eye, while its dinky upfront bar offers views into the semi-open kitchen. Chef-patron Jeremy Chan presents highly innovative, intriguing small plates delivering his translation of West African spice-based cuisine, punctuated by bold, balanced flavour and some unusual ingredients. 'Blind tasting menus' might include a signature plantain dish, with blackberry salt and smoked kelp emulsion, or perhaps 5-week Cornish lamb teamed with St George mushroom sauce, nespoli emulsion and celeriac crisps. Spice-friendly wines and inventive cocktails hit the spot too.

Kahani ⊛⊛

1 Wilbraham Place, SW1X 9AE
020 7730 7634
www.kahanidining.com
Closed: 1 January, 25–26 December

Just off Sloane Square, this upmarket and chic restaurant uses prime British ingredients for its contemporary Indian dishes. The innovative style is typified by a samosa platter of Punjabi aloo, kolhapuri chicken and chettinad venison to start. For mains, there's grilled stone bass coated with brown garlic and sundried tomato purée alongside a sweet and smoky sauce.

Chef: Peter Joseph
Food Style: Modern Indian

NEW Maison François Awaiting Inspection

34 Duke Street, St James's, SW1Y 6DF
020 3988 5777
www.maisonfrancois.london
Closed: Sunday

Food Style: French

Just round a few corners from Buckingham Palace, Maison François is a real Mayfair jewel. The exterior is very inviting, promising a real French restaurant experience, and inside the decor is most impressive. Wood and glass windowed panels in an art deco style with white leather banquettes and tables in booths. The menus offer very tempting French cuisine.

Marcus 🟢🟢🟢🟢🟢 ⓘ NOTABLE WINE LIST

Wilton Place, Knightsbridge, SW1X 7RL
020 7235 1200
www.marcusrestaurant.com
Closed: Sunday

Chef: Marcus Wareing
Food Style: Modern European, British

Located in Knightsbridge's Berkeley Hotel since 2008, the dining room's contemporary look is calmly stylish, with button-backed banquettes in dark brown leather, pale blue chairs, sparkling glassware and muted light glowing off burnished wood panelling. It's a welcoming place thanks to the excellent front of house team, and tables are laid with crisp white cloths, on which burn small tealights in smart opaque white glass bowls. Dining options are flexible, with a range offering light lunch up to eight-course tasting menus. Wareing works with head chef Craig Johnston to design modern, flexible dining options, from a light three-course lunch to the five- and seven-course tasting menus. An early summer lunch might feature chalk stream trout with rose, cucumber dill and gin, followed by Herdwick lamb, while tasting menus might offer risotto with wild nettle, Galloway beef with carrot, pine nut and garlic, or Gigha halibut with onion, chive and artichoke. This is internationally renowned cooking from a kitchen at the top of its game, every dish conceived with care and produced with precision.

The Mayfair Lounge & Grill 🟢🟢

The Cavendish London, 81 Jermyn Street, SW1Y 6JF
020 7930 2111
www.thecavendish-london.co.uk
Closed: 1 January, 25–26 December

Chef: Nitin Pawar
Food Style: Modern European

The Cavendish sits in a prime spot among the gentlemen's outfitters of St James's. The food in its Lounge and Grill cuts quite a dash too with its modern British styling and well executed dishes delivered by a skilled kitchen team that draws on thoroughbred suppliers for its materials.

Muse 🟢🟢🟢🟢

38 Groom Place, Belgravia, SW1X 7BA
020 3301 2903
www.musebytomaikens.co.uk
Open: All year

Chef: Tom Aikens
Food Style: Modern British

In a discreet Belgravia mews, Muse is a compact and intimate restaurant set across three levels, the first of which has highly prized seats by the chef's counter. Understated decor, brass-edged marble topped tables and sage green banquettes add a stylish edge and the atmosphere from well informed waiting staff is chatty and warm. Chef-patron Tom Aikens and his team bring dishes to the table and there's nothing in the least bit stuffy despite its swanky address. An intensity and purity of flavours permeates the elegant, beautifully presented food, which might begin with an inventive dish of lobster, asparagus and truffle. Move on to charcoal grilled loin and fillet of lamb with a glazed sweetbread, turnip, wild garlic, Tropea onions and sweet pea purée. The high quality, innovation and humour continues through to a dessert called 'when love and hate collide' – a multi-layered chocolate and orange delight.

London SW1 *continued*

Osteria Dell'Angolo
47 Marsham Street, SW1P 3DR
020 3268 1077
www.osteriadellangolo.co.uk
Closed: Bank Holidays, 1–2 January, 24–27 December

The neutral tones of this Westminster Italian bring
an air of Mediterranean sophistication to Marsham
Street. Leather seating and white linen add class, and
large windows fill the space with light, while a glass-
panelled wall offers a glimpse of the chef in action as
staff deliver regional classics and inventive modern
interpretations, with simplicity and flavour to the fore.

Chef: Demian Mazzocchi
Food Style: Italian

Pétrus by Gordon Ramsay
1 Kinnerton Street, Knightsbridge, SW1X 8EA
020 7592 1609
www.gordonramsay.com/petrus
Closed: 26–28 December

Chef: Gilad Peled, Ben Waugh
Food Style: Modern French

Pétrus by Gordon Ramsay is very much a fine dining environment with service of the highest
order. The dining room has a circular dynamic with a glass wine cellar in the middle. It's
comfortable, modern and light; think leather chairs and white linen, and pastel tones jazzed up
by splashes of claret. All crockery, cutlery and glassware is of the highest standard. The menu
may start with an organic egg with sweet corn, bacon and black truffle, continue to Cornish cod
with violet artichoke, pine nuts, courgette and olive, and wind up in a delicious hazelnut soufflé
with salted caramel ice cream. Outstanding wine list.

Quilon
41 Buckingham Gate, SW1E 6AF
020 7821 1899
www.quilon.co.uk
Closed: 25 December

Quilon is part of St James' Court Hotel, but has its own
entrance and feels like a stand-alone restaurant. Decor
is sleek and ultra-modern, and the separate areas in
the L-shaped space make it feel quite intimate. Cuisine
is south-west Indian from Kerala and Goa, a mix of
straightforward traditional dishes and more modern
ideas, all based on top-class produce.

Chef: Sriram Aylur
Food Style: Indian,
South-west Coastal

Sette ◉◉
4 Knightsbridge Green, SW1X 7QA
020 7151 1025
www.settelondon.co.uk
Open: All year

Food Style: Modern Italian

The first thing you notice in Sette is how gleamingly contemporary the whole place is. All mirrors, metal surfaces, high ceilings and remarkable lighting. The food is authentic modern Italian, based on Manhattan's Scarpetta restaurant family. The term 'scarpetta' comes from the Italian tradition 'fare la scarpetta,' which means to indulge in a meal down to the very last taste.

Seven Park Place by William Drabble ◉◉◉◉ 🍷NOTABLE WINE LIST
St James's Hotel and Club,
7–8 Park Place, SW1A 1LP
020 7316 1600
www.stjameshotelandclub.com
Open: All year

Chef: William Drabble
Food Style: Modern French

Tucked away in the heart of St James's, this luxurious hotel is home to one of London's most seductive dining experiences, where the talented William Drabble has been producing dynamic and creative modern French cuisine since 2009. The dining room is a gem, small but perfectly formed, shimmering with rich, warm colours and bold contemporary artworks. This is an elegant and refined dining experience with the modern cooking rooted in the classics. Expect big punchy flavours, precise execution and classic combinations with plenty of innovation. A high quality piece of seared foie gras is cooked precisely and teamed with smooth pear purée, tender confit pear and warm gingerbread. A well-executed grilled fillet of super fresh turbot is paired with Jerusalem artichokes and a sumptuous roasted chicken emulsion. To finish, pineapple is slow cooked in vanilla and rum and served with coconut sorbet and a punchy pina colada foam.

Wild Honey St James ◉◉◉
Sofitel London St James,
6 Waterloo Place, SW1Y 4AN
020 7968 2900
www.wildhoneystjames.co.uk
Open: All year

Chef: Anthony Demetre
Food Style: French

This high-ceilinged dining room with enormous windows, plus impressive lighting and pale blue velvet banquettes brings French style to the splendid Sofitel London St James. In fact, it sets the scene for Anthony Demetre's precise and honest seasonal cooking. The chef proprietor leads a technically accomplished team, and his great understanding of taste, flavour and produce are always to the fore. Kick off perhaps with the wild mushroom tart, ragout of Scottish girolles with sweet young peas and hazelnut sabayon. Move on to an exceptional roast and slow cooked Denbighshire Welsh lamb with grilled Vesuvio tomato and trombetta courgette. Finish with a well-made Paris Brest.

London SW3

Claude Bosi at Bibendum ❀❀❀❀❀ ♦NOTABLE WINE LIST

Michelin House, 81 Fulham Road, SW3 6RD
020 7581 5817
www.bibendum.co.uk
Closed: 1–7 January, 14–22 April, 23–26 December

Chef: Claude Bosi
Food Style: Modern French

This fabulous post-art nouveau building in Chelsea was once the UK headquarters of the French tyre company, Michelin, and Bibendum himself (featuring in the exuberant stained glass of the dining room) is their famously pneumatic mascot. The ornate pillared entrance leads into the ground-floor, all-day Oyster Bar (offering spectacular seafood platters as well as the eponymous mollusc), while upstairs you'll find the beautiful dining room, surely one of the airiest and most elegant in London. Home to Claude Bosi's modern French cooking since 2016, classical techniques and seasonal ingredients underpin reassuringly precise presentation, and perfectly timed dishes deliver every promised flavour with elegant simplicity. From the à la carte might be hand-dived scallop, cold consommé of roasted scallop beard and elderflower vinegar, or push the boat out to enjoy duck jelly, onion, smoked sturgeon and special selection caviar. Follow on with Brittany rabbit, Scottish langoustine and French tarragon, or for two to share – roast chicken de Bresse, Scottish girolles and English peas. A glorious finish would be the Bibendum double chocolate soufflé with Madagascan vanilla ice cream. If your whole party is willing, you might choose the 'tastes of season' or 'our classics' menu. The impressive wine list is mainly French and Italian.

Elystan Street ❀❀❀ ♦NOTABLE WINE LIST

43 Elystan Street, Chelsea, SW3 3NT
020 7628 5005
www.elystanstreet.com
Closed: 25 December

Chef: Philip Howard,
Toby Burrowes
Food Style: Modern British

An expansive, light-flooded space with chairs in two colours at bare-topped tables is the location for Phil Howard's Chelsea operation, a sophisticated take on informal contemporary eating. His cooking, as befits his many years at The Square, displays a level of fine-tuned attention to detail in every element of a dish, from the parsley linguine with brown shrimp, shallot and shellfish bisque to the creamy parmesan polenta and sharply soused red onion that accompany delicious home-made venison, lardo and green peppercorn sausage. To finish, the Brillat-Savarin cheesecake is already legendary, its blood orange sauce, Aleppo chilli and poppy seeds adding a balancing tang.

The Five Fields ❀❀❀❀ ♦NOTABLE WINE LIST

See page opposite

London SW3

NOTABLE WINE LIST

The Five Fields

8–9 Blacklands Terrace, SW3 2SP
020 7838 1082
www.fivefieldsrestaurant.com
Closed: 25 December, 2 weeks January, 2 weeks August

Chef: Taylor Bonnyman,
Marguerite Keogh
Food Style: Modern British

The Five Fields might be billed as a 'neighbourhood restaurant' but that's where any illusions of a cheap and cheerful local hangout end. Befitting its swish address, this is the very essence of Sloane Square finesse and style. The team delivers intuitive modern dishes centred around top-drawer ingredients. Expect exquisite looking plates of precise, inventive food, whether you go for the eight-course tasting at dinner or the slightly shorter lunchtime offering. The kitchen garden supplies the chefs with much of produce on a daily basis and it ends up in highly accomplished, modern dishes with interesting and challenging textures and pairings. A starter of roasted lobster tail and chopped claws is paired with pickled carrots, sea buckthorn purée and summer cabbage. It might be followed by a perfectly pink and tender roasted saddle of fallow deer with beetroot and pickled chard. A delicate black cherry tart is one way to finish, accompanied by kombu seaweed ice cream and wood sorrel to achieve the correct salty and sweet contrast.

London SW3 *continued*

Kutir

10 Lincoln Street, Chelsea, SW3 2TS
020 7581 1144
www.kutir.co.uk
Closed: Monday, 1–3 January, 25–27 December

An elegant townhouse in the heart of Chelsea is home to Kutir, a stylish Indian restaurant. Across a series of intimate rooms, with coloured panelling and beautiful details, including a fabulously patterned bar, Kutir is a discreet, pleasurable dining experience. Menus provide an innovative and refined exploration of the ingredients and dishes of India's many regions and cultures.

Chef: Rohit Ghai
Food Style: Pan-Indian

See advertisement opposite

NEW No. Fifty Cheyne

50 Cheyne Walk, Chelsea, SW3 5LR
020 7376 8787
fiftycheyne.com
Closed: Monday, Tuesday, 25–27 December

This one-time Cheyne Walk Brasserie was relaunched with panache as No. Fifty Cheyne back in 2019 by owner Sally Greene – the theatre impresario and proprietor of Ronnie Scott's – after a classy makeover. Service is both cheery and unpretentious, the atmosphere relaxed and fun whilst the kitchen delivers classically informed, generously portioned, high-end comfort dishes.

Chef: Iain Smith
Food Style: Modern British

London SW3 *continued*

The Restaurant at The Capital ◉◉
Basil Street, Knightsbridge, SW3 1AT
020 7591 1202
www.capitalhotel.co.uk
Open: All year

Food Style: British, Seafood

Located in the Capital Hotel in the heart of Knightsbridge you will find a smart, tall-ceilinged dining room with tall windows offering street views. British-inspired cuisine, using local and seasonal ingredients sourced from trusted suppliers, is produced from the kitchen with a touch of elegance. Service is attentive.

Restaurant Gordon Ramsay ◉◉◉◉ ♦ NOTABLE WINE LIST
68 Royal Hospital Road, SW3 4HP
020 7352 4441
www.gordonramsayrestaurants.com
Closed: 25 December to 1 January

Chef: Matt Abé
Food Style: French

The flagship of the Gordon Ramsay global empire remains a strong contender in London's high-end dining scene. From the discreet exterior to the surprisingly intimate dining room – just 45 or so seats – you'll feel confident that everything has been taken care of. Clean-lined, art deco-influenced looks and plush, pastel-hued tones give a sophisticated sheen to the space. In the kitchen, Matt Abé has been running things here for more than a decade. What keeps this venue in the premier league is its rejection of unnecessary experimentation and tawdry effects: what you get is superb ingredients, harmoniously combined in exemplary dishes executed with pin-sharp precision. If you're looking for the RGR experience on a budget (relatively speaking), the fixed-price lunch menu is the best entry point. Pitch-perfect service is supervised by Jean-Claude Breton, while sommelier James Lloyd and his team steer the way through a satisfying list of the world's best producers.

London SW4

Trinity Restaurant ◉◉◉ ♦ NOTABLE WINE LIST
4 The Polygon, Clapham, SW4 0JG
020 7622 1199
www.trinityrestaurant.co.uk
Closed: 1–2 January, 24–27 December

Chef: Adam Byatt
Food Style: British, European

In the Old Town, just a short stroll from Clapham Common tube, Adam Byatt's high-riding neighbourhood restaurant "is the kind of place you can take your heart and never be let down". The open, street-level dining room is smart in pastel tones, complete with open-to-view kitchen and outside terrace, while the wised-up service team maintain a sunny natured, relaxed mood. Byatt's inventive, light, modern European cooking has its feet firmly grounded in French classicism, driven by deceptive simplicity, balance and layers of flavour, with saucing that raises the bar; take sardine bolognese raviolo with a 'knockout' tomato butter sauce and basil, while to finish, perhaps salted caramel custard tart.

London SW7

190 Queen's Gate by Daniel Galmiche ◉◉

The Gore, 190 Queen's Gate, SW7 5EX
020 7584 6601
www.gorehotel.com
Open: All year

Chef: Daniel Galmiche,
Helder Andrade
Food Style: British, French

Close to the Royal Albert Hall, this venerable venue features a wood-panelled cocktail bar where the launch party for the Rolling Stones' Beggars Banquet album was held. French maître Galmiche oversees proceedings in the chandeliered, gilt-mirrored dining room, where modernised classic English dishes are served.

Bombay Brasserie ◉◉

Courtfield Close, Courtfield Road, SW7 4QH
020 7370 4040
www.bombayb.co.uk
Closed: 25 December

This glamorous South Ken institution (first opened back in 1982) still packs in the crowds for its authentic, melting-pot Mumbai (one-time Bombay) pan-Indian cuisine. Reworked modern interiors evoke that Raj-era spirit. The kitchen deals in freshly-ground, lightly toasted spices to impart maximum flavour.

Chef: Sriram Aylur
Food Style: Indian

The Town House ◉

The Kensington, 109–113 Queen's Gate, SW7 5LP
020 7589 6300
www.doylecollection.com
Open: All year

Food Style: Modern British

Located in chic West Kensington, The Town House at The Kensington is a stylish mix of vintage style and unfussy calm, with Farrow & Ball colours, pastel velour banquettes and elegant mood lighting. An attentive team delivers some wonderful dishes from a menu that features a variety of international cuisine depending on season.

How do you keep yourself under the radar?

By adopting plenty of aliases, have 'reasons' to be in the area – perhaps looking at a property or undertaking consultancy work down the road.

AA Inspector

London SW10

Medlar Restaurant ⚜⚜⚜ 🍷NOTABLE WINE LIST
438 King's Road, Chelsea, SW10 0LJ
020 7349 1900
www.medlarrestaurant.co.uk
Closed: 1 January, 25 December

Chef: Joe Mercer Nairne
Food Style: Modern European

A welcoming little restaurant in Chelsea's World's End quarter, Medlar radiates a smart appearance yet relaxed, unpretentious ambience. Colourful modern art, antique mirrors and mint-green banquettes or beige upholstered chairs add to the neat setting, while a few pavement tables are highly prized when the sun's shining. The precise modern European dishes are underpinned by classic French technique with well-defined and balanced flavours. Crab raviolo with samphire, brown shrimps, fondue of leeks and bisque sauce is a winning signature opener, while sparkling-fresh chargrilled Cornish monkfish, perhaps teamed with gnocchi, wild garlic pesto, braised radish and white French asparagus, could inspire at mains. Spot-on service is sunny natured and unobtrusive.

Myrtle Restaurant ⚜⚜⚜
1A Langton Street, SW10 0JL
020 7352 2411
www.myrtlerestaurant.com
Closed: Sunday, Monday

Chef: Anna Haugh
Food Style: Modern European, Irish

First solo venture from Irish-born chef Anna Haugh (known to a wider audience from her TV appearances on the BBC's *Morning Live* or *Saturday Kitchen*), Myrtle sees her deservedly step out into the limelight after working in some of London's top kitchens for celebrated chefs like Philip Howard, Shane Osborne and Gordon Ramsay. Small, two-floored, light-filled and relaxed, Myrtle speaks with a soft, endearing Irish accent, with Haugh's intelligently simple yet refined, elegant dishes driven by top-notch Irish produce: witness, Clonakilty black pudding wrapped in crispy string potato with Bramley apple and pearl barley, and to follow, oat-crusted hake with smoked mackerel chowder and spinach.

London SW17

AA RESTAURANT OF THE YEAR FOR LONDON 2022–23

Chez Bruce ⚜⚜⚜ 🍷NOTABLE WINE LIST
2 Bellevue Road, Wandsworth Common, SW17 7EG
020 8672 0114
www.chezbruce.co.uk
Closed: 1 January, 24–26 December

Chef: Bruce Poole, Matt Christmas
Food Style: French, Mediterranean

A fixture on the London dining scene since the mid-nineties, Chez Bruce is set in small row of shops and has the airy charm of a neighbourhood restaurant. The dining area spans two rooms with plenty of natural daylight, and the mood is elegant and subtly refined, much like the food. Seasonally changing menus provide the very best modern dishes, based loosely on classical and regional French/Mediterranean cuisine. Begin with a delicate, fresh starter of salmon and leek with smoked eel, horseradish, pickled rhubarb and dill, before moving on to a beautifully executed dish of Barbary duck breast with cabbage, celeriac purée, sarladaise potato and sauce poivrade.

Hotel du Vin Wimbledon ⚘

Cannizaro House, West Side,
Wimbledon Common, SW19 4UE
020 8879 1464
www.hotelduvin.com/locations/wimbledon
Open: All year

Chef: Kauff Diop
Food Style: Modern British,
European

Located in Cannizaro House, a rather posh late-Georgian mansion, this Bistro du Vin occupies an expansive orangery-style space with soaring floor-to-ceiling glass walls looking over the park. From the menu you can expect the HdV house style of classic French bistro cooking based on well-sourced seasonal materials.

116 at The Athenaeum ⚘⚘

116 Piccadilly, W1J 7BJ
020 7640 3333
www.athenaeumhotel.com
Open: All year

The Athenaeum Hotel's 116 restaurant features a wonderful array of choice from the all-day menu, including afternoon tea and private dining, and offers inspiring, seasonal menus that champion local producers. The hotel bar is renowned for its range of cocktails.

Chef: Ian Howard
Food Style: Modern, Classic British

Alain Ducasse at The Dorchester ⚘⚘⚘⚘ ⚑NOTABLE WINE LIST

The Dorchester, 53 Park Lane, W1K 1QA
020 7629 8866
www.alainducasse-dorchester.com
Closed: First week January, Easter, 3 weeks August

Chef: Jean-Philippe Blondet,
Thibault Hauchard, Alberto Gobbo
Food Style: Contemporary,
Modern French

Alain Ducasse at The Dorchester is the main restaurant at the iconic hotel on Park Lane and there is a renewed energy and excitement from the young team in the kitchen. The glamorous grill room has retained many of its original features such as parquet floors, striking Murano chandelier and intricate gilded ceiling but a contemporary tone has been added bringing it right up to date including a pudding bar where guests can take a seat in front of the open kitchen. Expect highly professional and friendly service from a well-drilled team complete with a highly knowledgeable sommelier. Strong technical execution is evident from the start, with a well-timed veal sweetbread, truffle-topped potato pancake, cabbage and bacon foam. Follow it with a first-rate piece of Cornish turbot, borlotti beans and grelot onion. Yogurt soft serve, apricots, London honey and almonds is one of the delightful desserts.

London W1 *continued*

**Amaranto at Four Seasons Hotel London
at Park Lane** 🌸🌸
Hamilton Place, Park Lane, W1J 7DR
020 7319 5206
www.fourseasons.com/london/dining/restaurants/
amaranto_restaurant
Open: All year

Chef: Romuald Feger
Food Style: Italian

Four Seasons stands in modern grandeur at Hyde Park Corner, a distinctly plutocratic node of London. In the restaurant, carefully-crafted Italian dishes embrace the simplicity that everyone seeks in Italian food. The garden terrace is just the ticket in the summer.

Bellamy's 🌸
18–18a Bruton Place, W1J 6LY
020 7491 2727
www.bellamysrestaurant.co.uk
Closed: Bank Holidays

Bellamy's effortlessly classy good looks and slickly professional service epitomise the chic, timeless French brasserie genre. Leather banquettes, tasteful French artworks, white linen and staff in bow ties and waistcoats add to the authentic look. The kitchen excels in simple, clear-flavoured dishes. Fabulous all-French wines, an afternoon oyster bar and a chic evening cocktail bar complete the experience.

Chef: Stéphane Pacoud
Food Style: French

Benares Restaurant 🌸🌸 🍷NOTABLE WINE LIST
12a Berkeley Square, W1J 6BS
020 7629 8886
www.benaresrestaurant.com
Closed: 1 January, 25 December

Chef: Brinder Narula
Food Style: Modern Indian

In the heart of Mayfair, this restaurant has the buzz of a glamorous nightclub but takes a serious approach when it comes to dining. Combining high-end British ingredients with spices and aromatics the Anglo-Indian cooking always excites with its innovative ideas, precise technique and enticing presentation.

Bentley's Oyster Bar & Grill ⊛ 🍷NOTABLE WINE LIST
11–15 Swallow Street, W1B 4DG
020 7734 4756
www.bentleys.org
Closed: 1–26 January, 25 December

Now over a hundred years old, the illustrious oyster bar is a highly popular, feel-good rendezvous, its canopied terrace a hot ticket for slithering-fresh fish and seafood on a balmy day. Prices lean toward West End scary, but then the ingredients are second to none, the service slick and the wines a superb bunch.

Chef: Nick Simmons
Food Style: British, Irish

Berners Tavern ⊛ ⊛ 🍷NOTABLE WINE LIST
The London EDITION, 10 Berners Street, W1T 3NP
020 7908 7979
www.bernerstavern.com
Open: All year

Chef: Phil Carmichael,
Jason Atherton
Food Style: Modern British

This palatial space with a magnificent plaster ceiling, chandelier, and walls crowded with pictures, is nothing like a tavern. Jason Atherton oversees the cooking, which is in his contemporary brasserie style. Restyled classics such as lobster and prawn cocktail get things going nicely.

Blanchette ⊛ ⊛
9 D'Arblay Street, Soho, W1F 8DR
020 7439 8100
www.blanchettesoho.co.uk
Closed: 23–26 December

Opened by three brothers from across the Channel, Blanchette delivers creative modern bistro-style French cuisine, including a range of charcuterie, and cheese and honey pairings, rife for sharing. The setting feels every bit Parisian boulevard bistro, yet is oh-so relaxed Soho too, with its counter seats and alfresco tables upfront and vintage Francophile bits and bobs. Great-value set menu too, and wines with a Gallic accent.

Chef: Maxime Alary
Food Style: Modern, Traditional French Tapas

See advertisement on page 321

London W1 *continued*

Bocca di Lupo

12 Archer Street, W1D 7BB
020 7734 2223
www.boccadilupo.com
Closed: 23–30 December

High-energy, high-octane and fantastic fun, Bocco di
Lupo rocks. Grab a stall at the long bar's 'chef's counter'
to enjoy the culinary theatre, or head to the restaurant
area proper. Leather seating, flower displays and feature
lighting catch the eye, while simple regional Italian
grazing plates shout flavour; think spaghetti with squid
ragù to grilled calves' liver, red onion and balsamic.

Chef: Jacob Kenedy
Food Style: Italian

Café Biltmore Restaurant & Terrace

44 Grosvenor Square, W1K 2HP
020 7629 9400
lxrhotels3.hilton.com/lxr/biltmore-mayfair
Open: All year

Food Style: Modern Mediterranean

Café Biltmore Restaurant & Terrace is a contemporary dining experience located within The
Biltmore, Mayfair, just across from Grosvenor Square. Luxurious, yet relaxed, with modern
interiors of a very high standard and a menu to match. The seasonally-driven output features
beautifully presented dishes of wood-fired fish and meats, fresh seafood, signature salads and
plant-based plates.

Charlie's Restaurant at Brown's Hotel

Brown's Hotel, Albemarle Street, Mayfair, W1S 4BP
020 7493 6020
www.roccofortehotels.com
Open: All year

Food Style: Modern British,
European

Charlie's Restaurant is a well-established Mayfair eating place, its antique wooden panelling
interspersed with large mirrors, complemented by interior designer Olga Polizzi's bright
botanical wallpaper. British dishes include modern classics, for example, daily roasts carved
on the trolley, and there are French, Italian and Spanish influences too. All is backed up by a
comprehensive wine list and an enthusiastic sommelier.

See advertisement on page 323

Blanchette

GASTRONOMY IS NOT ONLY ABOUT EATING
IT IS ALSO ABOUT PLEASURE, FRESHNESS AND CONVIVIALITY

Blanchette Soho is a French bistro serving simple, classic and inventive French food. Our concept is based on the idea of sharing, from smaller snacks to larger traditional dishes with a Blanchette twist. A fine selection of drinks, including a variety of French wines and classic cocktails, are also available.

Founded in 2013 by brothers Maxime, Malik and Yannis, the quintessentially Parisian restaurant is named after their mother.

London W1 *continued*

The Chesterfield Mayfair ⊚⊚
35 Charles Street, Mayfair, W1J 5EB
020 7491 2622
www.chesterfieldmayfair.com
Open: All year

Chef: Ben Kelliher
Food Style: Traditional British

A fine Georgian property jam-packed with antiques and run with a touch of old-school charm. A suckling pig's cheek croquette looks tempting, with a sliver of black pudding and sweetcorn purée. There's a pre-theatre menu, and afternoon tea is served in the conservatory.

China Tang at The Dorchester ⊚⊚
53 Park Lane, W1K 1QA
020 7319 7088
www.chinatanglondon.co.uk
Closed: 24–25 December

Chef: Chong Choi Fong
Food Style: Classic Cantonese

This opulent homage to 1930s Shanghai, with smart carpets, upholstery and wallpaper, elevates classic Cantonese cuisine to a higher level; remember, though this is The Dorchester, so don't expect normal high-street prices. Familiar-sounding, nevertheless, are dim sum, vegetarian soups, roast duck mixed platter, and Szechuan peppercorn-braised Dover sole. Vegetarian, halal and gluten free options are all available.

The Colony Grill Room ⊚
The Beaumont, 8 Balderton Street, Mayfair, W1K 6TF
020 7499 9499
www.colonygrillroom.com
Open: All year

On the south side of Oxford Street, not far from Selfridges, The Beaumont is a burnished slice of Mayfair elegance. The dining room's grill concept sees crustacea, grills and steaks arrive as simply honest, hearty fare, all delivered in a richly decorated room with an art deco theme. A number of dishes are prepared at the table to add further theatre.

Chef: Ben Boeynaems
Food Style: British, American

COMO Metropolitan London ⊚⊚
Old Park Lane, W1K 1LB
020 7447 1000
www.gridironlondon.com
Open: All year

Food Style: Modern British

One of several dining possibilities at this urbane Park Lane hotel, Gridiron is a quietly luxurious grill restaurant. Sit up close and personal with the fiery action at the marble counter overlooking the open kitchen, or park at a leather seat or banquette to tuck into precision-seared meats and fish of the highest quality.

CHARLIE'S

Tucked away in London's most fashionable neighbourhood, Charlie's by Adam Byatt is a cheerful blend of much loved tradition and modern excellence. The menu evolves frequently with the seasons, using exceptional, local produce, to offer British dishes including the great classics with a present-day twist. There are Italian, French and Spanish influences too.

Charlie's is a romantic, stylish, warmly-lit, memory-making place with a welcome touch of theatre. Scottish smoked salmon and irresistible, daily roasts are carved on the trolley. Come early evening, cocktails are shaken and stirred at Charlie's Bar.

ALBEMARLE STREET, LONDON, W1S 4BP
020 7518 4004

London W1 *continued*

Corrigan's Mayfair 🏵🏵🏵 🍷NOTABLE WINE LIST

28 Upper Grosvenor Street, W1K 7EH
020 7499 9943
www.corrigansmayfair.co.uk
Closed: Bank Holidays, 25 December

Chef: Richard Corrigan,
Aidan McGee
Food Style: British, Irish

Just off Park Lane, Richard Corrigan's eponymous restaurant has become a firm favourite ever since the doors opened in 2008. A clubby, convivial feel is created with dark wood floors, studded chairs and white linen and the room oozes understated luxury. Corrigan's Mayfair redefines modern British and Irish cuisine, fusing seasonal produce with Richard's unmistakable flair. Salt-baked heritage beetroot, goats' curd, hazelnuts and aged balsamic is a robust starter and could lead on to tender pork belly, charred hispi cabbage, apple purée and a well-balanced mustard jus. End with burnt honey custard tart, Yorkshire rhubarb, vanilla and ginger.

CUT at 45 Park Lane 🏵🏵🏵

45 Park Lane, W1K 1BJ
020 7493 4554
www.dorchestercollection.com/en/london/45-park-lane/restaurants-bars/cut-45-park-lane
Open: All year

Chef: Elliott Grover
Food Style: Modern American

The Park Lane glitz of a swanky hotel in the Dorchester stable makes a suitably top-end joint for one of US chef and restaurateur Wolfgang Puck's über-glam international steakhouses. With an extravagant decor, no-one could fault the jet-set vibe of this temple to top-grade beef sourced from all over the world. Take your pick: Australian and Japanese Wagyu, South Devon Angus, USDA rib-eye steak with fries, all expertly aged, sold by weight, and precision timed on the grill, with eight sauces to go with it. There's also seared scallops, or steamed sea bass 'Hong Kong' style, plus a delectable baked Alaska to finish.

Dehesa 🏵

25 Ganton Street, W1F 9BP
020 7494 4170
www.saltyardgroup.co.uk/dehesa
Closed: 25 December

Dehesa comes from the same stable as Salt Yard and Opera Tavern and, like them, is a charcuterie and tapas bar serving up a lively hybrid of Spanish and Italian dishes. It's a small, buzzy place where you sit elbow-to-elbow at high-level tables.

Chef: William Breese
Food Style: Spanish, Italian

Galvin at Windows Restaurant & Bar ⚜⚜⚜ 🍷NOTABLE WINE LIST

London Hilton on Park Lane, 22 Park Lane, W1K 1BE
020 7208 4021
www.galvinatwindows.com
Open: All year

Chef: Joo Won, Chris Galvin
Food Style: Modern French

High up on the 28th floor, the views of London's iconic skyline are spectacular whether you visit at lunch or dinner. The stylish interior matches the vista with a bold contemporary design and smartly appointed tables. The kitchen here produces a mesmerising take on modern European cuisine with Asian influences. Begin with marinated Iberico pork, house pickles and Korean ssamjang paste, followed by spring lamb rump, breast ragout, offal pastry, anchoïade and olives, or, perhaps, lobster tail, scallop, sea bream and rouille. Things come to a satisfying finale with a perfect banana and chocolate soufflé and peanut butter ice cream.

Gauthier Soho ⚜⚜⚜ 🍷NOTABLE WINE LIST

21 Romilly Street, W1D 5AF
020 7494 3111
www.gauthiersoho.co.uk
Closed: Bank Holidays, 25 December

Chef: Gerard Virolle,
Alexis Gauthier
Food Style: Modern French, Vegan

In the heart of the West End, Gauthier Soho is set across three floors of a handsome Regency townhouse. Previously a formal French restaurant, it has reinvented itself as a relaxed vegan venue. Plant-based French fine dining is now the mantra but the sophisticated cooking is still underpinned by classic technique and presentation. Kick off with black truffle risotto, rich umami sauce, freshly grated truffle and vegan cheese, perhaps continuing with a main course fondant boulangère comprising layers of potato, fennel and celeriac with a confit tomato crisp and basil velouté. Finish with praline, almond, hazelnut and dark chocolate.

Goodman ⚜ 🍷NOTABLE WINE LIST

26 Maddox Street, W1S 1QH
020 7499 3776
www.goodmanrestaurants.com
Closed: Bank Holidays, 1 January, 25 December

Chef: Lukasz Doktor
Food Style: British,
Classic American

There's plenty of red meat action going on for die-hard carnivores in this upscale New York-inspired steakhouse serving prime slabs of US and UK beef. Choose your cut, from rib-eye, through bone-in sirloin to porterhouse, and it arrives precision timed and served with béarnaise, pepper or Stilton sauces.

The Grill at The Dorchester ⚜⚜⚜ 🍷NOTABLE WINE LIST

See page 326

London W1

 NOTABLE WINE LIST

The Grill at The Dorchester

53 Park Lane, W1K 1QA
020 7317 6531
www.dorchestercollection.com/en/london/the-dorchester/restaurants-bars/the-grill-at-the-dorchester
Open: All year

Chef: Tom Booton
Food Style: Modern British

First established in 1931, The Dorchester is one of London's iconic restaurants set in the heart of well-heeled Park Lane. The glamorous Grill restaurant is now run by an energetic and enthusiastic young team although it has retained many of its original features. There are still the parquet floors, striking chandelier and intricate gilded ceiling but a contemporary tone has been added, bringing it right up to date including a pudding bar in front of the open pastry kitchen. This is where guests can take part in the pre-dessert challenge and can try to identify the flavours. Highly professional and friendly service from a well-drilled team complete with a highly knowledgeable sommelier. Start with a technically perfect veal sweetbread with potato pancake, bacon and cabbage topped with generous shavings of truffle and frothy bacon foam. Continue with a first-rate piece of Cornish turbot served with a rustic accompaniment of borlotti beans and grelot onion. Yogurt soft serve, apricots, London honey and almonds is a harmonious finale.

London W1 *continued*

Hakkasan Mayfair ⊕⊕⊕ 🍾 NOTABLE WINE LIST

17 Bruton Street, W1J 6QB
020 7907 1888
www.hakkasan.com
Closed: 25 December

Chef: Tong Chee Hwee,
Tan Tee Wei
Food Style: Modern Cantonese,
Chinese

The Mayfair branch of the now global, super-cool Hakkasan group features a pulsating, contemporary mix of seductive design and dazzling east-meets-west Cantonese cuisine. Up first, the ground-floor dining room with its sexy low-slung leather seating, while downstairs the more nightclubby, low-lit space comes decked out with intricately carved-wood screens and scintillating, high-energy atmosphere. But, wherever you sit, an in-place, high-gloss, high-octane approach abounds; from the slick, informed service to the kitchen's vibrant reimaginings of traditional Cantonese dishes designed for sharing. From divine dim sum like crispy lobster with cheese and Prunier caviar, to house speciality mains like grilled Chilean seabass in honey or smoked beef ribs with jasmine tea that have helped clinch Hakkasan's high-end reputation. Desserts prolong the thrill factor, likewise a stunning wine list.

Hélène Darroze at The Connaught ⊕⊕⊕⊕⊕ 🍾 NOTABLE WINE LIST

16 Carlos Place, W1K 2AL
020 3147 7200
www.the-connaught.co.uk/restaurants-bars/
helene-darroze-at-the-connaught
Open: All year

Chef: Hélène Darroze
Food Style: French

Parisian designer Pierre Yovanovitch has brought a more colourful, contemporary look to this intimate dining room. Almost everything is custom-made, emphasising the levels of care you can expect to find in every element of a visit here. Light oak panelling and colourful, comfortable seating in enticing shades of blush pink, along with exposed wooden tables and blue blown-glass chandeliers bring a warmer, more welcoming ambience. Service is polished and engaging, and menus change seasonally. The precise, classic French cooking makes the very best of fantastic British produce, and the wine list is superb, with amazing depth and a great range by the glass. This is stunning cooking and a meal here is sure to count as one of the significant events of your culinary life. Menu descriptions are terse, just listing ingredients. 'Jerusalem artichoke Guanciale' is a true celebration of this humble vegetable, delicate pasta forming truly excellent ravioli with melt in the mouth guanciale (Italian cured pig's cheek), the freshness of radish and warming notes from Kenyan estate coffee. A delightful main course of super fresh turbot with swede – what an unsung ingredient – here making a wonderful purée and filled 'parcels', is completed by tender razor clams.

London W1 *continued*

Hide Above ◉◉◉ ♪ NOTABLE WINE LIST

85 Piccadilly, W1J 7NB
020 3146 8666
www.hide.co.uk
Closed: 1 January, 25 December

Chef: Martin Carabott
Food Style: Contemporary

Hide Above is the top-end, first-floor restaurant of chef Ollie Dabbous's glossy drinking and dining venue. A magnificent oak staircase curves upwards to the sleek designer space where wall-to-wall glass gives great views over the snarl of Piccadilly traffic to the leafy canopy of Green Park. Five- and eight-course tasting menus bring on cooking of exceptional precision, taking in pea tartlet with fragrant herbs and elderflower vinegar, and a main dish of John Dory with courgettes and crushed nasturtium broth. Dessert heaven could be soaked cherry blossom teacake with Tahitian vanilla ice cream. Vegetarians have their own variety of menus too.

Hide Ground ◉◉

85 Piccadilly, W1J 7NB
020 3146 8666
www.hide.co.uk/restaurant/ground
Closed: 1 January, 25 December

Floor-to-ceiling windows look onto bustling Piccadilly and Green Park beyond at this multi-floored, hipster, all-day dining operation. Slick, polished service serves up inspired, light, modern British/European dishes of flavour, intrigue and panache, alongside stunning wines and a high-energy vibe. A designer oak staircase coils up to 'Above', the fine-dining restaurant, or down to the basement bar called 'Below'.

Chef: Ollie Dabbous
Food Style: Modern British

JW Steakhouse ◉

Grosvenor House Hotel, Park Lane, W1K 7TN
020 7399 8460
www.jwsteakhouse.co.uk
Open: All year

The expansive JW brings American-style steakhouse dining to the Grosvenor House in an ambience of black and white ceramic floor tiles and parquet, dressers and a menu offering variations of cuts and sauces. The beef is either thoroughbred USDA-approved or grass-fed Aberdeen Angus.

Chef: Robert Stephens
Food Style: American

Kitchen Table ⚫⚫⚫ 🍷NOTABLE WINE LIST
70 Charlotte Street, W1T 4QG
020 7637 7770
www.kitchentablelondon.co.uk
Closed: Sunday, Monday, Tuesday, Summer (check website for details), 25 December

Chef: James Knappett
Food Style: Modern British

Advance through the hot dogs and champagne going on out front, and behind a curtain at the back is what feels like a secret gourmands' club, where devotees gather round a counter for an up-close interface with the sizzles and scents of a kitchen in full gear. A daily-changing tasting menu chalked up in abbreviations on the board is the drill, delivering small morsels of outstanding, always surprising food. Each course focusses on a single ingredient such as mackerel, pigeon, oyster and truffle. Vegetarian tasting menus plus wine pairings and soft pairings are all part of the mix.

Kitty Fisher's ⚫⚫
10 Shepherd Market, W1J 7QF
020 3302 1661
www.kittyfishers.com
Closed: 1 January, Easter, 25–26 December

Closely packed tables and stools at the bar offer diners two options in this low-lit, atmospheric, Bohemian-style restaurant with red velvet banquettes, retro light fittings and candles. The modern British food is driven by what's available at the market on the day.

Chef: Alice Massalongo
Food Style: Modern British

KOL Restaurant ⚫⚫⚫ 🍷NOTABLE WINE LIST
9 Seymour Street, W1H 7BA
020 3829 6888
www.kolrestaurant.com
Closed: Monday

Food Style: Mexican

The tagline at KOL is 'Mexican soul, British ingredients', which perfectly encapsulates the ethos at this innovative restaurant where fusion food is washed down with mezcal and agave spirits. Terracotta walls, brown leather banquettes and clay pots add to the rustic Latin American feel and the food is equally as robust and colourful. Meltingly tender confit pork cheek served in a clay pot to share turns up with cabbage, black beans and gooseberry and pear salsa, while whole grilled octopus is teamed with bone marrow, pink fir potatoes and seaweed macha. Leave room for fig leaf cake, strawberries and marigold.

London W1 *continued*

NEW La Brasseria Milanese ⚜
42 Marylebone High Street, W1U 5HD
020 7486 3753
www.labrasseria.com
Closed: 25 December to 3 January

Smack on upmarket Marylebone High Street, this
bustling neighbourhood Italian, with its go-to alfresco
tables, proves a hotspot in any weather. Open all day
from breakfast, the kitchen delivers straightforward
Italian staples like pizzas and pastas to more
restaurant-y dishes like grilled wild sea bass with a
tomato, olive and caper sauce served with caponata.

Chef: Francesco Sistu
Food Style: Modern Italian
& Mediterranean

Les 110 de Taillevent ⚜⚜⚜ ⓘ NOTABLE WINE LIST
16 Cavendish Square, W1G 9DD
020 3141 6016
www.les-110-taillevent-london.com
Closed: Sunday

Chef: Ross Bryans
Food Style: Modern French

Ornate high ceilings, tall windows, dark-green banquettes and a showpiece bar give this classy,
low-lit, wine-based outfit a romantic, high-end gloss. Sibling of much-worshipped Parisian
restaurant with the same moniker, it offers diners 110 by-glass wines as part of its corking list
that tops 1,500 bottles. Each dish is offered with four different wine pairings, in four different
price brackets and measures. Chef Ross Bryans' modern French roster delivers in well-dressed,
perfectly executed plates clean on flavour. High skill, flair and balance shine in dishes like
native lobster, seaweed, oxheart cabbage, calamansi vinegar, and British lamb saddle, vine leaf,
aubergine, Greek yogurt and lamb jus.

L'Escargot ⚜⚜
48 Greek Street, W1D 4EF
020 7439 7474
www.lescargot.co.uk
Closed: 25 December to 3 January

Chef: James Tyrrell
Food Style: French, Mediterranean

This near-century-old Soho institution serves the rich comforts of classic French cuisine.
Occupying a fine Georgian townhouse once home to the Duke of Portland, L'Escargot's
sumptuous colours and serious art collection set an elegant old-school scene for cooking that
reassures, comforts and thrills from the off.

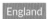

Le Gavroche Restaurant

43 Upper Brook Street, W1K 7QR
020 7408 0881
www.le-gavroche.co.uk
Closed: Bank Holidays, 1 January, 25 December

Chef: Michel Roux Jnr
Food Style: French

For over half a century Le Gavroche has been synonymous with classic French cuisine. Situated in a smart Mayfair basement, the room sticks to a refined and graceful look that is entirely in keeping with the kind of flawlessly courteous service that has all but disappeared from London's 21st-century dining rooms. Two generations of the Roux family have built a culinary empire on classical French cuisine of the Escoffier era, with discreetly applied modernist notes to tastes and textures. The dishes are virtuoso displays of culinary artistry, while main-course saddle of Herdwick lamb with turnip, beetroot and fennel is the ultimate in meaty comfort food.

Little Social

5 Pollen Street, Mayfair, W1S 1NE
020 8600 3600
www.5social.co.uk
Closed: Sunday, Monday

Chef: Frankie van Loo
Food Style: Contemporary, Bistro

In the heart of Mayfair, Little Social is a gem of a place, just across the street from Jason Atherton's flagship Pollen Street Social. This is a contemporary, neighbourhood dining bistro and wine bar showcasing the very best British seasonal produce – the elegant, airy dining room has an unstuffy vibe. A starter of cured Loch Duart salmon, avocado crème fraîche, pickled cucumber, salmon caviar makes for an impressive opening, followed by a succulent, well-seasoned Josper-grilled pork chop garnished with the smoothest pomme purée and braised hispi cabbage. A well-chosen wine list offers a French selection with a focus on all the famous regions and names in old-world winemaking.

Locanda Locatelli

8 Seymour Street, W1H 7JZ
020 7935 9088
www.locandalocatelli.com
Closed: 1 January, 24–26 December

Chef: Giorgio Locatelli
Food Style: Italian

TV star Giorgio Locatelli's culinary career began by the shore of Lake Comabbio. Italian classical cooking, gently modernised but staying true to its principles of honesty and simplicity, will never lack for devotees. Curving booth seating in stone-coloured leather, etched glass screens and mirrors make for an ambience of refined civility, naturally, but the generously proportioned tables are designed with convivial family dining in mind. Traditionally structured menus open with compendious antipasti salads, before pasta makes its appearance, perhaps via spaghetti with octopus. Principal dishes command the attention with majestic fish – monkfish with walnut and caper sauce, or pan-fried calves' kidneys with potato purée and stewed lentils.

London W1 *continued*

The Mandeville Hotel
Mandeville Place, W1U 2BE
020 7935 5599
www.mandeville.co.uk
Open: All year

Chef: Gauri Shankar
Food Style: Modern British

Set in Marylebone, the Mandeville is an impressive Victorian corner building that promises boutique luxury alongside old school hospitality. The restaurant is modern yet understated, showing some exposed brick with modern prints and large clocks. A Josper grill puts the heat on the meat, while uncomplicated, comfort-oriented dishes are the mainstay of the menu.

The Mayfair Chippy
North Audley Street, W1K 6WE
020 7741 2233
www.mayfairchippy.com
Closed: 25 December

As a pairing, Mayfair and Chippy breaks new ground, and so it should. This wealthy quarter of W1 has as much right to a quintessentially British fish and chip restaurant as anywhere else. And it certainly looks the part too.

Chef: Pete Taylor
Food Style: British

Mere   NOTABLE WINE LIST
74 Charlotte Street, W1T 4QH
020 7268 6565
www.mere-restaurant.com
Closed: Bank Holidays

Chef: Monica Galetti
Food Style: Modern European

You may know Monica Galetti best from her appearances as a judge on *MasterChef: The Professionals*, but she's also a former Michel Roux Jr/legendary Le Gavroche protégé and Mere (pronounced 'Mary') is her and sommelier husband David's first restaurant. It's classily understated, sophisticated and fashionable with a smart bar at ground level, while downstairs the dining room features contemporary Samoan pieces and is unexpectedly light, thanks to its double-height glass frontage. The cooking is classic French given contemporary spin and some South Pacific touches, backed by consummate skill, panache and standout flavours. Take pan-fried turbot T-bone with shellfish ragout, leek, fennel and potato, and a chowder sauce, and to follow, pistachio and raspberry tart.

The Montagu Kitchen ◉◉
Hyatt Regency London, The Churchill,
30 Portman Square, W1H 7BH
020 7299 2037
www.themontagurestaurant.co.uk
Open: All year

Food Style: Modern British

Located within a five-star hotel, this all-day dining destination features a relaxed and welcoming environment and serves up seasonally changing menus of smart, modern British ideas using British produce. There are great views over Portman Square and it's all just a short walk from Oxford Street and Marylebone.

Murano ◉◉◉◉ ⚑NOTABLE WINE LIST
20 Queen Street, W1J 5PP
020 7495 1127
www.muranolondon.com
Closed: 25 December

Chef: Angela Hartnett,
Emily Brightman
Food Style: Modern European,
Italian influence

With its exclusive Mayfair location, you'd rightly expect Murano to boast opulent trappings such as mirrored and marble surfaces, deep carpets and striking modern art. The elegant decor and sumptuous seats are matched by the well-pitched, faultless service but it's not fussy and could even be described as refreshingly informal at times. The kitchen is rooted in Italian classics with a real identity and clarity of flavours. Ravioli made with the thinnest, silkiest pasta are stuffed with spinach and goats' cheese and served with a rich walnut sauce with shaved walnuts on top for textural contrast. A main course of Cornish chicken is paired with a deeply flavoured mushroom purée, barbecued hen of the woods funghi and a sauce punctuated with trout roe. Desserts maintain the high standard with a buttery frangipane tart, rhubarb and crème fraîche, and the Italian-leaning wine list also boasts plenty of French classics.

The Ninth ◉◉◉
22 Charlotte Street, W1T 2NB
020 3019 0880
www.theninthlondon.com
Closed: Bank Holidays, 24 December to 4 January

Chef: Jun Tanaka
Food Style: Modern French,
Mediterranean

The Ninth is chef-patron Jun Tanaka's debut solo venture where he swaps the fine-dining folderol of his past for relaxed good looks and an on-trend menu of French- and Italian-inspired dishes that are all about big, gutsy flavours. Spread across two floors with a small bar on each, the decor goes for a stripped-back cool look, with exposed brick walls and bistro-style marble tables. Underpinned by Tanaka's classic French grounding, dishes are bursting with refined simplicity, confidence, flavour and seasonality. Take spot-on cuttlefish malloreddus with crispy squid and bottarga, then the peasant gutsiness of a roasted turbot head with brown shrimps, fennel and langoustine sauce. The knockout pain perdu celebrates classics puddings with gusto.

London W1 *continued*

Nobu London Old Park Lane ◉◉
COMO Metropolitan London, Old Park Lane, W1K 1LB
020 7447 4747
www.noburestaurants.com/london-old-park-lane
Open: All year

Since opening 35 years ago, Nobu's brand of Japanese-Peruvian cooking remains highly popular. Classics include hot yellowtail sashimi with jalapeño, and cold baby tiger shrimp with three different sauces. On the seemingly endless menu too are sushi, grilled or stir-fried yakimono dishes, and omakase – tasting dishes that the chef chooses. Anticucho rib-eye steak is a Peruvian representative.

Chef: Kyle Marston
Food Style: Japanese, Peruvian

Ormer Mayfair ◉◉◉◉ ⬧NOTABLE WINE LIST
See page opposite

Orrery ◉◉◉
55–57 Marylebone High Street, W1U 5RB
020 7616 8000
www.orrery-restaurant.co.uk
Closed: 1 January, Easter Monday, Summer Bank Holiday, 26–28 December

Chef: Igor Tymchyshyn
Food Style: Modern French

Above the Conran shop, on the first floor of a former stable block, Orrery is something of a veteran of the Marylebone scene. A well groomed venue, the full-length skylight and arched windows provide verdant views across Marylebone church gardens and a roof terrace provides ample alfresco opportunities. The French-inspired dishes are refined and modern but respectful of classic technique. Roasted cauliflower florets, celeriac and truffle makes for a flavour-packed opener and might lead on to duck magret à l'orange and chou farci. Craquelin choux pastry, preserved apple and manjari chocolate is one of the skilful desserts.

Pied à Terre ◉◉◉ ⬧NOTABLE WINE LIST
34 Charlotte Street, W1T 2NH
020 7636 1178
www.pied-a-terre.co.uk
Closed: 25 December to 8 January

Chef: Asimakis Chaniotis
Food Style: Modern French

A venerable venue for four decades, Pied à Terre has aged as well as any elder statesman. The design provides a sophisticated edge with traditional white linen on the tables and rich autumnal colours on the walls. The cooking is luxurious and creative, with well presented dishes displaying finesse and sound technique. Go for smoked quail, celeriac, winter truffles, Piedmont hazelnuts and confit egg yolk before Gigha halibut, crushed potatoes, mussels, saffron, sea urchin, sea sand wort and Centennial grapes. Milk chocolate namelaka, salted caramel, pretzel, almonds, whisky ice cream is a stand out dessert. The wine list is encyclopaedic.

Ormer Mayfair

7-12 Half Moon Street, Mayfair, W1J 7BH
020 7499 0000
www.flemings-mayfair.co.uk
Open: All year

Chef: Sofian Msetfi
Food Style: Modern, Classic

Close to Green Park and Buckingham Palace, this stylish hotel restaurant boasts a premium postcode in the heart of London. Intimate and traditional with a classy art deco look, the oak panelling is offset by striking geometric-striped marble floors. Low lit with crisp white linen, it makes for an elegant setting to enjoy the accomplished cooking of top-drawer ingredients. Flavours are big and technique is precise, but it's all executed with a lightness of touch. Rich veal sweetbreads are imaginatively matched with pear purée, ripe slices of fresh pear and a well judged mustard cream. Moist and sweet lightly poached native lobster is paired with Italian tomatoes, pine nuts and tiny basil leaves, with an assertive langoustine hollandaise. Intensely flavoured Garriguette strawberries – pieces of fresh fruit, gel and coulis – turns up with a yogurt-like kefir foam and a dusting nitro-frozen extra virgin olive oil on top.

London W1 *continued*

Podium 🏵🏵

London Hilton on Park Lane, 22 Park Lane, W1K 1BE
020 7208 4022
www.podiumrestaurant.com
Open: All year

Chef: Anthony Marshall
Food Style: Modern European

This swish all-day eatery in the Park Lane Hilton fits the bill when you're tootling around Mayfair and fancy a relaxed pit-stop with an eclectic, comfort-oriented menu. The kitchen delivers the goods via unpretentious and well-executed modern European dishes constructed from well-sourced materials, while the service team do their bit with friendly professionalism.

Pollen Street Social 🏵🏵🏵🏵🏵 🍷NOTABLE WINE LIST

8–10 Pollen Street, W1S 1NQ
020 7290 7600
www.pollenstreetsocial.com
Closed: Bank Holidays

Chef: Jason Atherton,
Dale Bainbridge
Food Style: Modern British

Discreetly hidden away down a narrow Mayfair side street, Pollen Street Social is Jason Atherton's London flagship. Inside, it's all smooth dark wood, white linen and modern British art; soothing, calm, and the perfect setting for 'relaxed fine dining' which is as beautiful and uplifting to look at as it is joyful to eat. With a range of menus including vegetarian and vegan tasting menus, the cooking is deeply rooted in the classics, combined with modern presentation utilising the very best British produce. There is also plenty of Asian influences in the dishes, which have a wonderful lightness delivered through balance, texture and precision. A wonderful example of the very highest levels of modern British cooking, everything is executed brilliantly from the bread to the petits fours. A meal might begin with a vibrant dish of marinated Orkney scallop with a supporting cast of tomato water, lemon and apple, frozen dashi with wasabi, ponzu and dill oil. It could be followed by a superb piece of roasted Newlyn turbot, Loire Valley asparagus and warm roe butter, or roasted Creedy Carver duck, orange pickled chicory, cauliflower and koji purée. Finish off with Gariguettes strawberries, goats' cheese ice cream and geranium oil.

Portland 🏵🏵🏵 🍷NOTABLE WINE LIST

113 Great Portland Street, W1W 6QQ
020 7436 3261
www.portlandrestaurant.co.uk
Closed: 23 December to 3 January

Chef: Zach Elliot-Crenn,
Martin Labron-Johnson
Food Style: Modern British

Over the road from the BBC's Broadcasting House, Portland scores high in the understated cool stakes. The clean-lined, contemporary dining room has an intimate ambience, its Scandi-style darkwood tables and chairs illuminated by low-slung filament lights, and bright artworks leading the eye to the open kitchen at the back. This faultless modern take on new-Brit cuisine delivers in spades; brimming with innovation and seasonality, a classy lightness of touch, balanced and eye-catching presentation, but, above all, flavour. Take Isle of Mull scallop with a zippy mix of tomato, strawberry and wild fennel to start, then Cornish cod with Devon crab, burnt lemon purée, yuzu compressed apple and chorizo.

The Ritz Restaurant

150 Piccadilly, W1J 9BR
020 7300 2370
www.theritzlondon.com
Open: All year

Chef: John T Williams MBE,
Spencer Metzger
Food Style: British, French

You can read about The Ritz – Grade II listed, five star hotel, iconic setting – but you still can't really imagine it without a visit. It's everything they say it is and more, a haven of calm in the grand style, with old-school elegance and luxury at every turn. Begin with a glass of bubbly in the art deco Rivoli Bar to prepare your senses for the extravagant opulence of the dining room – a space to rival the Palace of Versailles, with its rich Louis XVI-inspired decor of murals, marble columns, painted ceilings, statues and glittering chandeliers reflecting from mirrored walls. An army of tailcoated waiting staff pulls off a correctly polite performance with classic, theatrical tableside service that avoids any hint of stuffiness. Extravagant ingredients are carefully prepared and make their appearance in suitably precise dishes, from native lobster with tomato and basil to Cornish turbot with asparagus or Bresse duck with apricot, almond and lavender.

Roka Charlotte Street

37 Charlotte Street, W1T 1RR
020 7580 6464
www.rokarestaurant.com
Closed: 25 December

Chef: Hamish Brown
Food Style: Modern Japanese

This super-cool go-to flagship of the Roka brand, an enduring magnet of the capital's beau monde since 2004, shows that London diners still have a big appetite for stylish contemporary Japanese robatayaki cooking. The light-flooded room's wrap-around plate-glass frontage looks onto a high-energy scene, with on-trend hardwood furniture and ringside views of the open kitchen's action. The menu's high-gloss fusion temptations (including a tasting option) run to a beguiling roster of sushi, sashimi and tempura to trump-card robata offerings, perhaps sea bass fillet served with yuzu-shisho and ginger seaweed salad, or lamb cutlets with Korean spices. Desserts, like baked cheesecake with guava and black sesame crumble, round off a classy act.

Roka Mayfair

30 North Audley Street, W1K 6ZF
020 7305 5644
www.rokarestaurant.com
Closed: 25 December

Chef: André Camilo
Food Style: Modern Japanese

Just a short stroll from Oxford Street, the Mayfair branch of London's Roka group proves a top draw for high-gloss contemporary Japanese food lovers; shoppers by day and the fashionable cocktail set after dusk. The ultra-cool interior's focus is squarely on the central robata grill, where hot-ticket counter seats offer ringside action of the chefs in the open kitchen, adding to the high-energy vibe. The grazing menu (including a tasting option) offers Roka robata favourites and umami flavours; take black cod marinated in yuzu or lamb cutlets with Korean spices, while a thoroughbred roll call of sushi, sashimi and tempura doesn't miss a beat either. For dessert try dark chocolate and green tea pudding with crunchy jivara and pear ice cream,

London W1 *continued*

Roux at The Landau ⊛⊛ ♣NOTABLE WINE LIST

The Langham, London, Portland Place, W1B 1JA
020 7636 1000
www.rouxatthelandau.com
Open: All year

Chef: Nicolas Pasquier
Food Style: Modern European, French

As we went to press Roux at The Landau was temporarily closed, please check their website for further information.
There's more of a brasserie feel to proceedings here with leather banquettes and snugs plus a marble-topped oyster and charcuterie island in the middle. The panelled oval restaurant is still a highlight of the hotel with excellent food and wine service.

Salt Yard ⊛⊛

54 Goodge Street, W1T 4NA
020 7637 0657
www.saltyard.co.uk
Closed: 25 December

Set in fashionable Fitzrovia, Salt Yard has a great ambience with upbeat music, elbow-to-elbow wooden tables, banquettes, and bare brick walls. There are stools at the bar, and windows that open onto a few pavement tables on bustling Goodge Street. The food is tapas-style small plates with a Spain-meets-Italy theme. Both familiar and creative.

Chef: Myumyun Ramadan Ali
Food Style: Italian, Spanish

Scott's ⊛⊛ ♣NOTABLE WINE LIST

20 Mount Street, W1K 2HE
020 7495 7309
www.scotts-restaurant.com
Closed: 25–26 December

Chef: Dave McCarthy
Food Style: Seafood

Glamour fills Scott's, from its charming service to the eye-catching mountain of seafood on ice in the swanky champagne bar. Apart from celebrities, there are mosaics, mirrors, oak-panelled walls, leather seats, and modern artworks to catch the eye, plus a menu brimming with top-notch seafood.

Sketch (The Gallery) ⊛⊛⊛ ♣NOTABLE WINE LIST

See pages 340-341

Sketch (Lecture Room & Library) ⊛⊛⊛⊛ ♣NOTABLE WINE LIST

See pages 342-343

Sketch (The Parlour) ⚛⚛

9 Conduit Street, W1S 2XG
020 7659 4500
www.sketch.london/the-parlour
Open: All year

Chef: Frédéric Don
Food Style: Modern European

Sketch (The Parlour) has a whimsical, Regency-inspired boudoir ambience, with dark gold walls, low lighting, and voile curtains that break up the split-level space. Lots of unusual art and colourful fabrics. The ambience might be a touch frivolous but there's nothing half-hearted about the food. Accurate cooking of good quality materials to produce some impressive flavours and textural combinations.

See advertisement below

London W1

@ @ @ NOTABLE WINE LIST

Sketch (The Gallery)

9 Conduit Street, W1S 2XG
020 7659 4500
www.sketch.london/the-gallery
Closed: 25 December

Chef: Pierre Gagnaire, Frederic Don
Food Style: Modern European

Upmarket brasserie dining in swanky location

Stylish venues combining food, drinks, music and art are reasonably commonplace these days, but Sketch certainly blazed a trail when it launched 20 years ago. A Grade II listed Georgian townhouse in the heart of Mayfair, all the venues at Sketch are unusual in terms of their interior design, and The Gallery is no exception. Under its astonishing glazed cupola roof, there are copper-coloured walls and beautiful yellow fabrics throughout, while the walls are adorned with specially commissioned pieces by British-Nigerian artist Yinka Shonibare.

Pierre Gagnaire's food is as vibrant and entertaining as the setting, exuberantly creative, playful and often accompanied by a live DJ, the modern French/European menus, which change every two months, demonstrate an endless stream of inventive, technically accomplished brasserie dishes.

The à la carte offers a choice of hot or cold starter – witness, perhaps, a featherlight haddock and scallop soufflé with a punchy Colman's mustard beurre blanc and intensely flavoured leek fondue, or red beetroot tartare, raspberry, redcurrants, Montgomery Cheddar and seaweed caviar. You might move on to perfectly timed fillets of crisp-skinned sea bream with silky and subtle anchovy butter, vibrant broccoli purée with and seaweed with a minerally ozone flavour. Lamb chop Milanese with onion, mint sauce, mustard, borlotti beans and red pepper salad is one of the meat options and vegetarians can enjoy dishes like braised endive with orange juice and grilled mushrooms or purple potato bavaroise, vegetables, golden raisins and balsamic vinegar.

These are precisely conceived, intelligently constructed dishes, and the dessert menu is a riot of equally precise and beautiful options, from iced lavender-honey galette, citrus marmalade with Kirsch, lemon opaline to Bramley apple terrine, lemon sponge, Limoncello and yuzu ganache.

The wine list is bursting with thoroughbred bottles perfectly selected to enhance the food.

"...food is as vibrant and entertaining as the setting."

London W1

NOTABLE WINE LIST

Sketch (Lecture Room & Library)

9 Conduit Street, W1S 2XG
020 7659 4500
sketch.london/the-lecture-room
Closed: 1–11 January, 21 August to 11 September, 25 December

Chef: Daniel Stucki
Food Style: Modern European

Polished service and fabulous setting for complex, innovative cooking

This Grade II listed Georgian townhouse in Mayfair might look sensible and sober from the outside, but once through the door you're in for a treat for all the senses. A jaw-dropping interplay between food and design, the interior's outrageously lavish colour scheme, a joyfully theatrical explosion of pink, orange and gold. It's a suitably unforgettable spot for some ground-breaking cuisine. The effortlessly polished service is exemplary, and the cooking is innovative, provocative and skilful, under the order of head chef Daniel Stucki.

There's a six-course tasting menu, with a vegetarian version also available, or you can go à la carte. The menu descriptions may be lengthy but the complexity they hint at is just that, a clue to the thrilling rollercoaster of extravagance and delight you're about to experience. A plethora of small plates will bring you more

ingredients, concepts and techniques than you could dream of. It's breathtaking, a clear demonstration of a chef and brigade at the very top of their game.

You might begin with Middle White pork shoulder gyoza, chargrilled Hispi cabbage chiffonade, gratin of Shetland mussel, braised Eric Roy's carrot, green panko fennel salad, herb sorbet, yellow and white peach marmalade, Tiger aubergine 'stiletto' with home-made focaccia. For your main, maybe slices of Irish beef bavette, Gubbeen cheese, jus infused with marjoram, celeriac cream with foie gras, sherry glazed radishes, millefeuille of Maris Piper potato with seaweed and nutmeg. Vegetarians could look to choosing asparagus ice cream, chopped rocket salad, Sicilian olive oil, tomato jam infused with rosemary, lemon gel, tempura of artichokes, green gnocchi, 36-month aged parmesan cream and spring onion. Chocolate soufflé may sound simple but involves a similar list of techniques and

ingredients; the 25 minutes waiting time will give you a chance to recover from the intensity of your meal so far.

> "It's breathtaking, a clear demonstration of a chef and brigade at the very top of their game."

London W1 *continued*

Social Eating House ⊛⊛⊛⊛ 🍷NOTABLE WINE LIST
58-59 Poland Street, W1F 7NS
020 7993 3251
www.socialeatinghouse.com
Closed: Bank Holidays, 25–26 December

Chef: Paul Hood
Food Style: Modern British

Part of Jason Atherton's dining empire, the stripped-back bistro-style vibe at the Social Eating House is vibrant and bang on trend, with switched-on, friendly and knowledgeable service. The team here will make you feel like a valued regular, while chef-patron Paul Hood's thoroughbred contemporary menu catches the mood to a T and delivers with precision, flair and panache, whether via carte or fixed-price lunch/early evening offerings; Cornish hake with spring peas, mint and garlic butter, jacket potato and bacon velouté is a delightfully appealing dish, or you might choose roast Cumbrian cob chicken, with ricotta gnudi and broad beans. Desserts – perhaps strawberries with whipped goats' curd mousse, vanilla custard and basil ash meringue – are refreshingly creative. Downstairs, the intimate kitchen chef's counter offers the ultimate 'tasting' experience, while a sparkling wine list and the upstairs Blind Pig bar complete a class act.

SOLA ⊛⊛⊛
64 Dean Street, W1D 4QQ
020 373 07883
www.solasoho.com
Closed: Sunday, Monday

Chef: Victor Garvey
Food Style: Californian

Victor Garvey brings an authentic slice of California and touch of class to Dean Street at the intimate SOLA, where pale slatted-wood walls, greenery lined windows and warm pendant lighting evoke memories of The Golden State. The contemporary cooking of America's Pacific West Coast is served from an open kitchen via tasting-menu format complete with a dash of theatre. Top-notch ingredients, precision and bold flavours characterise dressed-to-thrill dishes – a trio of wild Pacific salmon (roulade, terrine and ballotine), or the silkiest foie gras, innovatively teamed by stoned fruit, yuzu and smoked duck, while a finale Millot 74% (dark chocolate) is paired with passionfruit, peanut and caramel. Superb Californian-focused wines.

Tokii ⊛⊛
The Prince Akatoki London,
50 Great Cumberland Place, W1H 7FD
020 7724 0486
www.tokii.co.uk/contact
Open: All year

Chef: Gary Durrant
Food Style: Japanese

A short stroll from Marble Arch, this luxurious hotel restaurant has a pronounced Japanese influence. Rich in flavours and textures, the dishes are designed to be shared, whether it's delicate sushi, shrimp tempura with ginger dashi or a main course teriyaki-glazed duck breast, orange, toasted coconut and peanut salad.

Trishna ⚜⚜ 🍷NOTABLE WINE LIST

15-17 Blandford Street, W1U 3DG
020 7935 5624
www.trishnalondon.com
Closed: 1–3 January, 24–27 December

Chef: Karam Sethi
Food Style: Indian

Trishna takes a minimalist decorative line in two dining rooms done out with oak floors and tables, painted brickwork, mirrored walls, and hues of cream and duck-egg blue. The kitchen celebrates the coastal cuisine of south-west India in fresh, flavour-packed contemporary dishes.

Umu ⚜⚜⚜ 🍷NOTABLE WINE LIST

14–16 Bruton Place, W1J 6LX
020 7499 8881
www.umurestaurant.com
Closed: Bank Holidays, 1 January, 25 December

Chef: Yoshinori Ishii
Food Style: Japanese

While its smart Mayfair postcode may hint at its exclusivity, there's no questioning the seductive stylishness here, from the quality of its high-definition cuisine to the sparkling freshness of ingredients or the super-helpful service. Enter the discreet push-button sliding door and a greeting is called in the best tradition of Japanese hospitality, where a calm interior of delicate wood screens and subdued lighting comes into focus, heightened by the precision knifework of the brigade at the open kitchen. The food is firmly anchored in traditional ways, with an adherence to time-honoured techniques like Ikejime and Edo, delivered via Bento-box lunches, carte, classy sashimi and sushi rosters, and a high-end seasonal kaiseki (tasting) menu.

The Wolseley ⚜

160 Piccadilly, W1J 9EB
020 7499 6996
www.thewolseley.com
Open: All year

Decked out like a European brasserie, with plenty of brass, marble and tiled floors, The Wolseley used to be a car showroom, and is a really grand place to eat. Staff are waistcoated, and there's even a doorman. It's next to the Ritz, after all. Expect an all-day menu of classic European and British food, and a cracking wine list.

Chef: Edward Ross
Food Style: Traditional European

London W1 *continued*

Zoilo ⊛⊛
9 Duke Street, W1U 3EG
020 7486 9699
www.zoilo.co.uk
Closed: 2 weeks December

Much more Buenos Aires than Marylebone, this
hot-spot outpost of South American cuisine delivers
in spades. Bare brick or slate-blue walls, crimson-red
banquettes and a chequerboard tiled floor surrounding
a central bar and counter seats delivers an animated
backdrop for flavour-driven food and wines inspired by
Argentina's regions, including its renowned beef steaks.

Chef: Diego Jacquet
Food Style: Argentinian

London W2

Nipa Thai ⊛⊛
Royal Lancaster London, Lancaster Terrace, W2 2TY
020 7551 6039
www.niparestaurant.co.uk
Closed: Monday

Chef: Sanguan Parr
Food Style: Traditional Thai

Opposite Hyde Park, in the Thai-owned Royal Lancaster, an all-female, all-Thai kitchen
balances the five main flavours in a comprehensive offering of appetisers, soups, salads, curries,
pan-fried dishes, rices and noodles. Examples are crisp-fried prawn dumplings; a mixed seafood
curry, beef with onions, mushrooms and oyster sauce; and stir-fried chicken with chillies.
Set menus avoid making difficult decisions.

London W4

Le Vacherin ⊛⊛
76–77 South Parade, W4 5LF
020 8742 2121
www.levacherin.com
Closed: Bank Holidays

Le Vacherin brings a hit of Gallic bonhomie to Chiswick,
saving you a trip across the Channel when you're in the
mood for some classic French cooking. The place has
the look of a smart neighbourhood bistro, simple things
are done well by a skilful kitchen, and the prix-fixe
menu is particularly good value in any language.

Chef: Marc Wainwright
Food Style: French

See advertisement opposite

London W6

The River Café ◎◎◎

Thames Wharf Studios, Rainville Road, W6 9HA
020 7386 4200
www.rivercafe.co.uk
Closed: 24 December to 1 January

Chef: Ruth Rogers,
Sian Wyn Owen, Joseph Trivelli
Food Style: Italian

The timeless appeal of the River Café's Mediterranean food, constructed from unimpeachable ingredients, to which only the least complicating treatments are given, tells a story all of its own. A quartet of whole young squid emerge from the chargrill with their sea savour intact, the dressing a little rocket and chilli and as much lemon as you feel like squeezing. Similarly, the flawless crisp-skinned sea bass cooked over coals with wood-roasted yellow peppers, olives and spinach is a banner-waving exemplar of the style. Finish with moistly alluring pear and almond tart alongside a slick of crème fraîche.

Le Vacherin is a Classic French bistro with a Parisian style, serving modern yet authentic regional dishes. The restaurant caters for 72 covers, with a private room if required providing for parties of any number. It currently holds two AA rosettes, it has been voted by Zagat 2014 as 5th best French bistro in London, holds two forks and knives on Michelin guide.

Le Vacherin		Opening Times	
76-77 South Parade	**Telephone** 0208-742-2121		
Chiswick	**Website** www.levacherin.com	**Lunch Hours**	**Dinner Hours**
London	**Email** foh@levacherin.com	**Mon – Sat** 12pm – 2:30pm	**Mon – Sat** 6pm- 10:30pm
W4 5LF	**Instagram** @le_vacherin	**Sun** 12pm – 9pm	**Sun** 12pm- 9pm
	Facebook @levacherin		

London W6 *continued*

Sam's Riverside ◎◎
1 Crisp Walk, W6 9DN
020 8237 1020
samsriverside.co.uk
Closed: 24–30 December

Chef patron Sam Harrison is certainly making his mark at his uptempo, high-profile brasserie that commands river and sauce. Hammersmith Bridge views. Smartly designed, there's huge windows letting in lots of light and a cool marble topped bar. The open kitchen delivers crowd-pleasing, clean-cut, elegant dishes; witness Fosse Meadow chicken schnitzel, parmesan, lemon and caper.

Chef: Sam Harrison, Ashley Tinoco
Food Style: Modern European, Anglo-French

London W8

Cheneston's Restaurant ◎◎ ⬥ NOTABLE WINE LIST
1 Kensington Court, W8 5DL
020 7917 1000
www.milestonehotel.com
Open: All year

Formed from three red-brick Victorian townhouses, this venerable hotel in affluent Kensington offers old-school service in the elegant, wood-panelled dining room, right down to the roast-of-the-day trolley. Start with lobster and Devon crab topped with caviar and move on to Suffolk lamb cooked three ways; or whole piri-piri baby chicken.

Chef: Dan Putz
Food Style: Modern British

Kitchen W8 ◎◎◎ ⬥ NOTABLE WINE LIST
11–13 Abingdon Road, Kensington, W8 6AH
020 7937 0120
www.kitchenw8.com
Closed: Bank Holidays, 25–26 December

Chef: Mark Kempson
Food Style: Modern British

Just off bustling, fashionable Kensington High Street, Kitchen W8 shrewdly delivers a winning neighbourhood-cum-destination format. A smart, relaxed, light, contemporary decor combines with friendly service to seal the relaxed, unpretentious vibe, while a confident kitchen delivers clean, creative, well-presented modern dishes with a strong emphasis on quality ingredients, flavour and seasonality. Maybe open with scorched Cornish mackerel teamed with smoked eel, golden beets, sweet mustard and oyster leaf, while, staying with the fish theme, perhaps grilled baby monkfish tail served with Portwood asparagus, wild garlic aïoli and spring onion arancini to follow. For a summery final flourish, perhaps English strawberry and elderflower fool with white chocolate and almond.

Launceston Place ⊛⊛⊛ ♦NOTABLE WINE LIST

1a Launceston Place, W8 5RL
020 7937 6912
www.launcestonplace-restaurant.co.uk
Closed: 25 December

Chef: Ben Murphy
Food Style: Modern European

Fashionably located in the heart of Kensington, Launceston Place occupies a Victorian townhouse that retains plenty of elegance from the period. Once settled on the sumptuous leather banquettes, you are in the safe hands of attentive waiting staff who display deep knowledge of the food and notable wine list. Start with a light and vibrant céviche of stone bass, calamansi, lovage and kohlrabi before shoulder of Iberico pork with a mini pea cream tart, wild garlic purée and potato terrine. A profiterole-style choux filled with lemon curd and jasmine cream is a light and zesty way to finish off.

London W11

Core by Clare Smyth ⊛⊛⊛⊛⊛ ♦NOTABLE WINE LIST

92 Kensington Park Road, W11 2PN
020 3937 5086
www.corebyclaresmyth.com
Closed: 25 December, 1 January

Chef: Clare Smyth, Jonny Bone
Food Style: British

Clare Smyth has become one of the UK's most acclaimed chefs, following a career that took in senior roles with Sir Terence Conran and Alain Ducasse, and then Gordon Ramsay who made her chef-patron of his eponymous Chelsea restaurant. The stripped-back setting at Core is as polished as the superlative service and food that are the restaurant's highlights; fine glassware, cutlery and crockery, yes, although tablecloths and carpets have been dispensed with. The service is precise and polished to match the food on offer, and the staff are very approachable. Smyth, and her kitchen team, work behind a glass partition, from where emerges beautifully crafted, delicious artisanal and sustainable food, as in the Core Seasons menu, on which you'll likely find trademark specialities like a starter of steamed Portland crab, sabayon, consommé and caviar; and girolle and toasted buckwheat tart with fresh almonds. 'Beef and Oyster' brings Highland Wagyu beef teamed with Porthilly oysters, and an à la carte treat is Cornish turbot, grilled mussels, leeks, fennel and pepper dulse. To finish, what Smyth calls a 'Core-teser', which on the plate translates as chocolate with malt and hazelnut. A Chef's Table tasting menu dinner for eight to 10 people makes a great gift.

What excites you most in your work?

Being surprised by something or someone.
The simple pleasure of tasting something truly delicious.

AA Inspector

London W11 *continued*

The Ledbury ⊛⊛⊛⊛ ⚑ NOTABLE WINE LIST
127 Ledbury Road W11 2AQ
020 7792 9090
www.theledbury.com
Closed: Summer Bank Holiday, 25–26 December

Chef: Brett Graham
Food Style: Modern British

A table at The Ledbury has been one of Notting Hill's hottest tickets in recent years and Brett Graham's highly accomplished food continues to deliver waves of striking and memorable flavours. With its smooth parquet floor, contemporary light fittings and battalions of attentive staff, the restaurant is far less formal than its forbidding dark exterior signifies. The standard menu is a four-course format, perhaps encompassing a lightly blowtorched, hand-dived scallop with wafer-thin shards of crunchy radish, samphire and dashi broth with ponzu and wasabi leaves. It might precede various cuts of hay-aged pigeon with Earl Grey tea sauce, smoky beetroot purée, radicchio leaves, carrot and forced rhubarb. Round things off with a light and crumbly sweet woodruff tart, with various forms of strawberry and toasted vanilla ice cream. For the full Ledbury experience, go nuts with the comprehensive eight-course taster. The quality wine list adds additional class.

London WC1

The Montague on the Gardens Hotel ⊛
15 Montague Street, Bloomsbury, WC1B 5BJ
020 7612 8416
www.montaguehotel.com
Closed: 25 December

You'll like the Blue Door Bistro at the Montague on the Gardens Hotel, a Georgian townhouse full of English charm. The top-hatted doorman at the entrance is a clue that this is a classy boutique hotel, on a quiet street next to the British Museum. The bistro is a welcoming and informal dining room, decorated with a frieze depicting London in around 1850 and an uncomplicated repertoire of comfort-oriented dishes.

Chef: Martin Halls
Food Style: British

Rosewood London ⊛⊛
252 High Holborn, WC1V 7EN
020 3747 8620
www.rosewoodhotels.com/london
Open: All year

Chef: Calum Franklin
Food Style: Modern European

This magnificent building on High Holborn is a fine setting, and the old East Banking Hall with its soaring marble pillars is an elegant restaurant. The Mirror Room offers a relaxed and social dining experience and the Art Afternoon Tea is well worth discovering.

London WC2

Clos Maggiore ⊛⊛⊛ ⚑NOTABLE WINE LIST

33 King Street, Covent Garden, WC2E 8JD
020 7379 9696
www.closmaggiore.com
Closed: 24–25 December

Chef: Marcellin Marc
Food Style: French, Mediterranean

A delightfully intimate place, immediately welcoming and a relief from the bustle of Covent Garden, Clos Maggiore is influenced by the country inns of both Provence and Tuscany. The dining rooms, set across two floors, are charming, the skylight and ceiling decorated with twining, flower-starred branches to resemble an Italianate courtyard. Seasonally changing menus provide a contemporary take on modern European cuisine and the wine list is stunning. An elegant, refined beef tartare makes for a delightful starter, while a classic rustic main course of chicken breast, chicken mousseline, celeriac purée and chicken jus makes the very best of high quality ingredients and demonstrates the skills on show in the kitchen.

Cora Pearl ⊛⊛

30 Henrietta Street, Covent Garden, WC2E 8NA
020 7324 7722
www.corapearl.co.uk
Closed: 1 January, Easter Sunday, Easter Monday,
25–26 December

Named after a 19th-century courtesan, this second restaurant from the team behind Mayfair's Kitty Fisher's occupies an elegant Covent Garden townhouse. Modern comfort food is the form here – a meal could begin with cow's curd agnolotti, pea and truffle, and follow on with plaice, fennel and brown shrimps. Finish with 'milk and cookies'.

Chef: Alex Kalaizidis
Food Style: Modern British

Frenchie Covent Garden ⊛⊛⊛

16 Henrietta Street, WC2E 8QH
020 7836 4422
www.frenchiecoventgarden.com
Closed: 1 January, 25 December

Chef: Gregory Marchand
Food Style: French, European

Smack in the heart of Covent Garden, Frenchie is the London outpost of chef-patron Gregory Marchand, who splits his time between his Paris restaurant and WC2. Cool, smart and buzzy, this relaxed modern French brasserie rocks, with spot-on service, innovative cuisine and on-trend good looks. Creative, ambitious modern French dishes have equal appeal, as in a well-balanced starter of pickled mackerel, dill, grape and crispy shallots. Follow that with Middle White Pork, barley, carrots and ras el hanout, or goats' curd agnolotti, stinging nettles and broad beans. To finish there's apricot and lavender cheesecake with herb sorbet or their cheese selection served with French honey.

London WC2 *continued*

Frog by Adam Handling ⚜⚜⚜ 🍷NOTABLE WINE LIST

34–35 Southampton Street, WC2E 7HG
020 7199 8370
www.frogbyadamhandling.com
Closed: 1 January, 24-26 December

Chef: Adam Handling,
Cleverson Cordeiro
Food Style: Modern British

Firmly established as a go-to Covent Garden fine-dining destination, Adam Handling's stylish flagship venue combines a sexy downstairs bar and contemporary street-level dining room. The open kitchen is the standout focus, while counter seats get the full-on action of the pass. Handling's 10-course tasting menu comes with brief titles, as chefs, and a talented service team, describe and add final flourishes at the table. It's highly innovative cuisine, combining deep skill and top-draw materials with dressed-to-thrill presentation, matched by bold flavours and some unusual combinations. Opening 'Snacks' wow from the off; including an oyster, buttermilk and cucumber tart perhaps, while Orkney scallop could be teamed with carrot and chilli and Herdwick lamb with sweetbread and morels. An abiding ethos for sustainability and zero waste is commendable.

Kerridge's Bar & Grill ⚜⚜⚜ 🍷NOTABLE WINE LIST

Corinthia Hotel London,
10 Northumberland Avenue, WC2N 5AE
020 7321 3244
www.kerridgesbarandgrill.co.uk
Open: All year

Chef: Tom Kerridge
Food Style: Modern British

Within the grand setting of Victorian-built Corinthia Hotel that's a short hop from Whitehall, Kerridge's Bar & Grill has all the hallmarks of Tom Kerridge's take on the modern British brasserie. Beneath the high vaulted ceiling, burgundy leather banquettes and striking bronze statues compete for attention with the rotisserie grill in the corner. Start, perhaps, with prawn Scotch egg, pickled mooli and lobster satay sauce before English lamb cutlet with baked red peppers, toasted cucumber, courgette and black olive caramel. The high standard continues through to desserts such as chocolate and whiskey parfait, frosted barley, honeycomb and pearl barley ice cream.

Margot ⚜⚜ 🍷NOTABLE WINE LIST

45 Great Queen Street, Covent Garden, WC2B 5AA
020 3409 4777
www.margotrestaurant.com
Closed: Sunday, Monday, 25 December

The dining room of this suave Italian looks as sharp as an Armani suit with its black leather banquettes and abstract artworks, and the slick service purrs along like clockwork. The seasonal menu is full of promise, with classic combinations and masterful home-made pasta.

Chef: Leonardo Pieri Buti
Food Style: Italian

The Northall ⊕⊕⊕

Corinthia Hotel London,
10a Northumberland Avenue, WC2N 5AE
020 7321 3100
www.corinthia.com/london/restaurants-bars/the-northall
Open: All year

Chef: Andrè Garrett
Food Style: British

This elegant restaurant is housed in the majestic surroundings of one of London's most highly regarded hotels. High ceilings, vast windows and mirrors create a bright and airy space with immaculate service from start to finish. Executive chef André Garrett's precise cooking makes good use of top drawer raw materials. A classic duck liver parfait is accompanied by mushroom brioche and Madeira jelly. Precisely timed chalk stream trout with confit Charlotte potato, Avruga caviar and chowder sauce is an elegant main and Pavlova with toasted coconut cream, pink grapefruit and lemon verbena delivers a perfect balance of flavour and texture.

The Opera Tavern ⊕⊕

23 Catherine Street, Covent Garden, WC2B 5JS
020 7836 3680
www.operatavern.co.uk
Closed: 25 December

This classic old London pub, has become a relaxed, two-storeyed tapas joint with the restaurant on the upper level and an intimate bar, with high stools, on the ground floor. You could go three-course if you're an old stickler, but little dishes are the principal bill of fare and they pack quite a punch.

Chef: Lukasz Kielbasiński
Food Style: Spanish, Italian

NEW Pivot by Mark Greenaway ⊕⊕

First Floor - 3 Henrietta Street,
Covent Garden, WC2E 8LU
020 3325 5275
www.markgreenaway.com/pivot-covent-garden
Closed: Sunday, Monday, Tuesday, 25–26 December

Notable Scottish chef Mark Greenaway's debut London venture, Pivot comes secreted away on the first-floor of a handsome Georgian townhouse overlooking Covent Garden's piazza. The intimate space, with its open kitchen, terracotta walls and red leather seating has a relaxed vibe. The evening tasting menu changes monthly with ingredient-led dishes of classic combinations and bold flavours.

Chef: Mark Greenaway
Food Style: Innovative British

London WC2 *continued*

Savoy Grill – Gordon Ramsay ⍟⍟

1 Savoy Hill, Strand, WC2R 0EU
020 7592 1600
www.gordonramsayrestaurants.com/savoy-grill/
Open: All year

Food Style: British

A handsome art deco room with lustrous panelling, antiqued mirrors, chandeliers and velvet banquettes, the Savoy's iconic Grill has always been the place to see and be seen. Built on classic Anglo-French foundations, the cooking aims for comfort. The Sunday lunch roasts are legendary.

Spring ⍟⍟

New Wing, Somerset House, Lancaster Place, WC2R 1LA
020 3011 0115
www.springrestaurant.co.uk
Closed: Sunday, Monday, Tuesday, 23 December to 4 January

After winning much acclaim at the rustic glasshouse restaurant of Petersham Nurseries, Skye Gyngell has brought her trademark style to the grander stage of Somerset House. The regularly-changing Mediterranean menu delivers good-looking plates of

Chef: Skye Gyngell
Food Style: European

seasonal fare with flavours that shine. Though prices are high, a fixed-price lunch option eases the bottom line.

Greater London

Bromley

Chapter One Restaurant ⊚⊚⊚ NOTABLE WINE LIST
See pages 356-357

Hounslow

La Belle Époque ⊚⊚ NOTABLE WINE LIST
Sofitel London Heathrow, Terminal 5,
Wentworth Drive, London Heathrow Airport,
TW6 2GD
020 8757 5029
www.la-belle-epoque.co
Closed: Bank Holidays, 25 December

Chef: Andrew Cole
Food Style: Modern French

There's something a touch counter-intuitive about looking for seriously good cooking in the environs of Heathrow Airport, but put aside your preconceptions and head over the covered walkway from Terminal 5 into the swanky Sofitel hotel. With its lush hues of purple and royal blue, La Belle Époque offers a suave change of mood from the airport mayhem.

Vivre Restaurant ⊚
Sofitel London Heathrow, Terminal 5,
Wentworth Drive, London Heathrow Airport,
TW6 2GD
020 8757 5027
www.sofitelheathrow.com
Open: All year

Chef: Carl Stockenstrom
Food Style: International

The Sofitel at Heathrow Terminal 5 boasts more decent eating than many airport hotels. As an alternative to the fine French goings-on in La Belle Époque, Vivre offers informal dining in an open-plan room of colourful contemporary design. The kitchen team are on view at their wokking and pizza-throwing, and service puts everyone at their ease.

What changes have you seen over the past few years?

A wonderful response to the hardships of Covid and Brexit –
the industry becoming more collegiate and collaborative.
The result is a focus on what really is essential to a restaurant.

AA Inspector

 **NOTABLE WINE LIST**

Chapter One Restaurant

Farnborough Common, Locksbottom, BR6 8NF
01689 854848
www.chapteronerestaurant.co.uk
Closed: 2–4 January

Chef: Andrew McLeish
Food Style: Modern European

Intelligent modern European food

Located on the busy road connecting the Kentish towns of Bromley and Orpington, chef-patron Andrew McLeish's upmarket Chapter One Restaurant has wide appeal. Whether you go for the relaxed brasserie and its covered terrace, or the more formal restaurant with its crisp linen tablecloths and vibrant gastronomic artwork, a meal here will live long in the memory. Now well established and ever popular with the locals, the ambience is friendly, with a well-drilled team in black waistcoats and aprons. You could go for the carte, or the wallet-friendly menu du jour, but either way McLeish strikes an inviting balance between assured modern European cooking and the desire to offer value.

Classic techniques deliver finely tuned dishes, while seasonal ingredients from a network of high-end suppliers mean that the menus change all the time, depending on what's best at the time and

what arrives in the kitchen. A beautifully presented confit duck and foie gras terrine with prune purée, pickled shimeji, toasted macadamia nuts and warm brioche gets the tastebuds standing to attention. The richness of the terrine is countered by blobs of prune purée and pickled shimeji, as do crunchy toasted nuts and excellent brioche with caramelised onion layers.

Main courses bring further evidence of intelligent flavour combinations via pan-fried halibut partnered with grilled celeriac, spring onions, sea-fresh cockles and chicken jus. The splendidly fresh tranche of halibut is perfectly timed, the slice of celeriac nicely seared and celeriac purée boasting a clear flavour. The dish is completed with sea fresh cockles, finely shredded lightly pickled spring onion, earthy wilted spinach and a rich chicken. Desserts continue the form with a perfectly risen mango and passionfruit

soufflé with a surprise base of spiced pineapple compôte and a sharp pineapple sorbet completing the hot/cold contrast.

"...McLeish strikes an inviting balance between assured modern European cooking and the desire to offer value."

Kew

The Glasshouse 🏵️🏵️🏵️ 🍷NOTABLE WINE LIST

14 Station Parade, TW9 3PZ
020 8940 6777
www.glasshouserestaurant.co.uk
Closed: 1 January, 24–26 December

Chef: Gregory Wellman
Food Style: Modern International

Light and airy as its name implies, and, from the same stable as Chez Bruce in Wandsworth and La Trompette in Chiswick, its pedigree is assured, pulling off neighbourhood fine dining with panache and an unbuttoned gloss. Neutral tones, textured walls, roman blinds, white linen, polished-wood floors and colourful artworks give the space a smart modern sheen, matching the highly polished light, contemporary cooking. Detailed, dressed-to-thrill dishes deliver high on precision, flavour and balance; witness a mains of sea-fresh roasted hake served with standout potted shrimp butter and crisp sarladaise potatoes, romanesco cauliflower and dill. Dessert is equally impressive; malt tart with stout ice cream, cocoa nibs and honeycomb. Corking wine list too.

Pinner

Friends Restaurant 🏵️

11 High Street, HA5 5PJ
020 8866 0286
www.friendsrestaurant.co.uk
Closed: 1–19 January, 15–31 August

Chef: Bradley Walford
Food Style: British

Occupying a 500-year-old timbered building in Betjeman's suburban Metro-Land, Friends' devoted local fan base turns up for top-grade meat and fish handled with skill and sound modern thinking. Perhaps seared scallops with parsnip purée, black pudding crumble, crispy bacon and truffle foam for your opener.

Richmond upon Thames

144 On The Hill 🏵️

144–150 Richmond Hill, TW10 6RW
020 8940 2247
www.richmondhill-hotel.co.uk
Open: All year

144 On The Hill sits on fashionable Richmond Hill next to Royal Richmond Park. There's a central bar between the lounge and the restaurant so you'll always find a bustling atmosphere. Everything is upscale yet friendly, including the cooking. The à la carte offers impressive choices, or you could try a charming takeaway picnic.

Chef: Jessen Valaydon
Food Style: Modern British

Bingham Riverhouse ⚜⚜⚜ ⚑NOTABLE WINE LIST

See pages 360-361 and advertisement below

The Dysart Petersham ⚜⚜⚜

135 Petersham Road, Petersham, TW10 7AA
020 8940 8005
www.thedysartpetersham.co.uk
Closed: 1 week January, 1 week August, 25 December

Chef: Kenneth Culhane
Food Style: Traditional European

The Dysart occupies a 1904 Arts and Crafts building with original leaded windows and wooden window frames facing south over Richmond Park. Sunshine streams in on bright days, and a low-key jazz soundtrack floats around the elegant room. Kenneth Culhane's confident and sure-footed cooking delivers some fascinating, intricately detailed dishes full of subtle interplays of taste and texture. Start with charred bream, radish ginger and champagne, before moving onto Middle White pork, lemon and caper purée, Petersham Swiss chard with wild apple jus. Finish with Earl Grey crème brûlée and walnut shortbread. Wine pairings are available with the tasting menus.

Richmond upon Thames

 NOTABLE WINE LIST

Bingham Riverhouse

61–63 Petersham Road, TW10 6UT
020 8940 0902
www.binghamriverhouse.com
Open: All year

Chef: Steven Edwards
Food Style: Modern British

Confident cooking by the river

Stylish restaurant-with-rooms Bingham Riverhouse is a short walk from Richmond town centre and occupies a lovely spot overlooking the River Thames. Set within a handsome pair of elegant townhouses, tables on the waterside-facing balcony are highly prized when it comes to summery alfresco dining.

Easy-on-the-eye neutral hues and a calm ambience set the tone in the elegantly relaxed dining room which has the sort of chic, faultless look often found on the pages of an interiors magazine.

Young and engaged waiting staff are attentive and friendly but not at all overbearing. An ambitious team in the kitchen displays strong technical skill and interesting flavour combinations. High quality ingredients are given the respect they deserve, and they are allowed to take centre stage with minimal interference from other elements on the plate. Before

the first course, excellent home-made bread is served with light and airy whipped seaweed butter. To start, a precisely cooked and well rested quail is served with burnt apple purée, bacon, swede and sherry vinegar to round things off. Another way to begin a meal could be smoked duck breast with duck liver parfait and blood orange.

For mains, an attractively presented piece of precisely timed butter-roasted sea bass is paired with cauliflower, caviar and a well-balanced, wine-enriched sauce. For meat eaters, the main course might present pork fillet with asparagus and puffed pork or lamb teamed with salsify, celery and mint.

For dessert, 'rhubarb and custard' is much more than its tersely written menu description, the light and creamy rhubarb and vanilla parfait enhanced by fiery stem ginger and crumble for added textural balance and flavour. A vegan option to close the meal is William pear with an intriguing accompaniment of coriander ice cream and honey.

See advertisement on page 359

"An ambitious team in the kitchen displays strong technical skill and interesting flavour combinations."

Surbiton

The French Table 🏵️🏵️ ♦ NOTABLE WINE LIST
85 Maple Road, KT6 4AW
020 8399 2365
www.thefrenchtable.co.uk
Closed: 24 December to 9 January

Chef: Richard Giles
Food Style: Modern French

Tucked away in leafy Maple Road, The French Table is a smart neighbourhood outfit. Dressed-to-impress modern French cooking punches above its weight on a fixed-price repertoire buoyed by a five-course taster. Breads are a triumph, while pastry impresses too – no surprise with its sibling boulangerie/patisserie bang next door.

Twickenham

A Cena 🏵️
418 Richmond Road, TW1 2EB
020 8288 0108
www.acena.co.uk
Closed: Sunday, Monday, 24 December to 1 January

A Cena is just the sort of informal neighbourhood bistro-style Italian we'd all like to live round the corner from. Comforting, authentic cooking, served with minimum fuss in a dining room done out with a woody mix of dark floorboards, church pew furniture and white walls hung with mirrors. The kitchen makes a good job of classic dishes.

Chef: James Allen Thompson
Food Style: Modern Italian

Merseyside

Riviera at Hillbark ◉◉
Hillbark Hotel & Spa, Royden Park, CH48 1NP
0151 625 2400
www.hillbarkhotel.co.uk/riviera
Open: All year

Chef: Craig Baker
Food Style: French, Mediterranean

This all-mod-cons spa hotel features a light-filled Riviera dining room, which embraces a sweeping Mediterranean arc all the way from Nice to Liguria, presented in the grazing format of little and large dishes, courtesy of a super-cool modern brasserie service.

Heswall

Burnt Truffle ◉◉
106 Telegraph Road, CH60 0AQ
0151 342 1111
www.burnttruffle.net
Closed: 25–26 December

Gary Usher, owner of the six-restaurant Elite Bistros group, opened his Wirral bridgehead in 2015, following a crowdfunding campaign; its name was decided by the Twitterati. Walls are decorated with food and wine pictures, old London restaurant menus and names of crowdfunding donors. Monthly changing menus offer bistro-style takes on modern British and international dishes. Outside is a heated terrace.

Chef: William Cole
Food Style: Modern British

Liverpool

The Art School Restaurant, Liverpool ◉◉ 🍷 NOTABLE WINE LIST
1 Sugnall Street, L7 7EB
0151 230 8600
www.theartschoolrestaurant.co.uk
Closed: 1–7 January, 3–11 August, 25–26 December

Chef: Paul Askew
Food Style: Modern International

Close to Liverpool's main attractions, The Art School Restaurant is accessed through a discreet side entrance and the stylish dining area sits in a glass-roofed courtyard with a window into the kitchen allowing diners to see the chefs at close quarters. The assured cooking is rooted in French classics.

Liverpool *continued*

Chez Mal Brasserie ◎
Malmaison Liverpool, 7 William Jessop Way,
Princes Dock, L3 1QZ
0151 229 5000
www.malmaison.com
Open: All year

Chef: Duncan Anderson
Food Style: Modern British

On the landward side of Princes Dock, Malmaison's first purpose-built hotel is a landmark for the maritime city. Echoing the city's industrial heritage, the exposed bricks, lighting gantries and air ducts of the double-height brasserie, are balanced by warm, plush, purple and black furnishings.

The London Carriage Works ◎◎ ⌁NOTABLE WINE LIST
Hope Street Hotel, 40 Hope Street, L1 9DA
0151 705 2222
www.thelondoncarriageworks.co.uk
Open: All year

Opposite the Liverpool Philharmonic sits The London Carriage Works, built in the mid-Victorian era, then converted into a hotel in 1998. The restaurant occupies the corner of the ground floor and has floor-to-ceiling windows allowing guests to look out (and in). Styling is minimal with bare boards and exposed brick. Menus show international influences with an Asian angle.

Chef: Mike Kenyon
Food Style: Modern British

NEW Manifest Awaiting Inspection
4a Watkinson Street, L1 0AG
07729129873`
www.manifestrestaurant.com
Open: Sunday, Monday, Tuesday, 1–11 January,
1 week August, 25–26 December

In a narrow street in the Baltic Triangle, Manifest draws inspiration from the city's historical shipping trade. Decor could be described as 'elegant industrial' while the food is more about passion, precision and local produce. Dine at the bar or in the restaurant, but wherever you sit you'll enjoy good food and that famous Liverpool hospitality.

Chef: Paul Durand
Food Style: Modern British

NEW Mustard & Co 🌸🌸
84 College Road, Crosby, L23 0RP
0151 931 3228`
www.mustardandco.co.uk

Food Style: British,
Modern European

Mustard & Co is a contemporary bistro with an open kitchen as the focal point. Naturally illuminated by day and candlelit in the evening, there's a well-appointed and sunny conservatory at the back, as well as alfresco tables on the terrace. The modern British food has a strong European accent.

Panoramic 34 🌸
34th Floor, West Tower, Brook Street, L3 9PJ
0151 236 5534
www.panoramic34.com
Closed: 1 January, 25–26 December

From the 34th floor the views from this modern revolving restaurant are spectacular. There's Liverpool and the Mersey estuary of course, but also the Welsh mountains, the Irish Sea and distant Blackpool. Stone, natural wood, glass and underlit tables set the interior scene, while the daily-evolving modern food includes international flavours such as miso and dukkah.

Chef: Nathan Booth
Food Style: Modern European

Wreckfish 🌸
60 Seel Street, L1 4BE
0151 707 1960
www.wreckfish.co
Closed: 25–26 December

Gary Usher used crowdfunding to get Wreckfish off the ground in this former derelict Georgian building in the cool Ropewalks district. Inside, wooden floors and tables, and exposed brickwork give it a stripped-back industrial feel. Staff know their stuff and make sound recommendations about dishes such as torched sea bream, braised featherblade of beef, pork osso buco and chocolate 'oblivion'.

Chef: Tanner Whiteside
Food Style: Modern British

Port Sunlight

Riviera at Leverhulme 🏵️🏵️
Leverhulme Hotel, Central Road, CH62 5EZ
0151 644 6655
www.leverhulmehotel.co.uk
Open: All year

Chef: Craig Baker
Food Style: French, Mediterranean

Lord Leverhulme opened the place in 1907 as a cottage hospital for soap works employees at his Port Sunlight garden village, and who wouldn't find their health restored amid such exquisite art deco surroundings? The comprehensive French-Mediterranean menu is a mix of small and large plates that come to the table 'as and when ready'.

Prescot

Pinion 🏵️
39 Eccleston St, L34 5QA
0151 4930660
www.pinionbistro.com
Closed: Monday, Tuesday

Chef: Jake Parry
Food Style: British

The sixth offering in the Elite Bistros group of neighbourhood restaurants, Pinion is a charming little bistro sitting on the pedestrianised high street in Liverpool's Prescott suburb. Decor is traditionally French in style, with chandeliers, mirrors and bare brick walls. Staff are friendly and very enthusiastic about the food, so they'll happily recommend their favourite dishes.

Southport

Bistrot Vérité ●●
7 Liverpool Road, Birkdale, PR8 4AR
01704 564199
www.bistrotverite.co.uk
Closed: 1 week February, 1 week August

French roots are very evident in this bustling, frill-free
restaurant with a strong local following, thanks in
part to its consistency, simplicity and informality. But
obviously the food also counts hugely and fish soup
and crab thermidor are staples, and crisp-fried frogs'
legs and snails (from Dorset) too, while mustard- and
herb-crusted lamb, and grilled swordfish also feature.

Chef: Jacques Vérité
Food Style: French, International

Thornton Hough

NEW Lawns Grill ●
Thornton Hall Hotel and Spa, Neston Road, CH63 1JF
0151 336 3938
www.thorntonhallhotel.com
Open: All year

The Victorian Thornton Hall Hotel is a popular place for
weddings, meetings and functions. The restaurant has
a notable leather ceiling, and Grecian frieze moulding,
which are part of the property's original features.
Staffing is structured and quite formal in delivery, but
smart casual dress rather than uniforms help keep
things intimate and informal.

Chef: Stephen Moore
Food Style: Modern British

Norfolk

Bawburgh

The Kings Head Bawburgh ●●
Harts Lane, NR9 3LS
01603 744977
www.kingsheadbawburgh.co.uk
Open: All year

Chef: Jake Armes, Geoff Smith,
Max Emmerson
Food Style: Modern British

The pub itself dates from the early 17th century, but the king in question is Edward VII (born
1841), chosen for his reputation as a bon viveur. There are real ales and the likes of fish and
chips up for grabs, plus low oak beams, real fires and plenty of character. Its reputation as a
dining pub is confirmed by its well-judged output.

Blakeney

The Blakeney Hotel ❀
The Quay, NR25 7NE
01263 740797
www.blakeney-hotel.co.uk
Closed: 24–27 December, 31 December

Those who like to be by the sea need look no further: this is in a perfect spot on the quay, with magnificent views over the estuary to Blakeney Point Area of Outstanding Natural Beauty. Well-sourced raw materials underpin the operation in the sea-facing restaurant.

Chef: Adam Thompson
Food Style: Modern British

Morston Hall ❀❀❀❀ 🍷 NOTABLE WINE LIST
Morston, Holt, NR25 7AA
01263 741041
www.morstonhall.com
Closed: January, 3 days at Christmas

Chef: Galton Blackiston,
Greg Anderson
Food Style: Modern British

Galton and Tracy Blackiston's handsome 17th-century manor house is truly an idyllic escape from the daily grind, with charming, individually designed bedrooms and lovely public areas. The atmosphere is calm and welcoming, and the conservatory dining room makes a soothing setting, especially when the sun is shining and the French doors are open. The Blackistons are passionate about the area and its magnificent produce, and the seven-course tasting menu presents the very best available ingredients, combining refined classical technique with contemporary verve and intricate yet seemingly effortless presentation. Dish descriptions are brief but enticing – Scottish langoustine, peanut, lime, for example, might be followed by spelt risotto with ewes' curd and peas on a spring menu, before moving on to wild Stiffkey bass with whey butter sauce and Middle White suckling pig. The wide-ranging global wine list has lots of gems among its pages.

Brancaster Staithe

The White Horse ❀❀
PE31 8BY
01485 210262
www.whitehorsebrancaster.co.uk
Open: All year

Platefuls of fantastic regional produce, including goodies smoked locally by Staithe Smokehouse, are what keep The White Horse firmly on the north Norfolk foodie map. And it's all the more enticing when you add in the big skies and unfettered views over the marshes from a table in the conservatory dining room or, on a balmy day, alfresco on the terrace.

Chef: Fran Hartshorne
Food Style: Modern British, Seafood

Burnham Market

AA RESTAURANT OF THE YEAR FOR ENGLAND 2022–23

Socius ⊛⊛
11 Foundry Place, PE31 8LG
01328 738307
www.sociusnorfolk.co.uk
Closed: Monday, Tuesday, 2 weeks early January,
24–25 December

Socius is Latin for joining in/partaking, and that's
the essence of this restaurant where the dishes are
designed to share and the theme is very much modern
British tapas. Well-chosen, locally sourced produce is
the order of the day. The open-plan kitchen/restaurant
has a contemporary feel and the team are very friendly
and demonstrate a high degree of professionalism.

Chef: Dan Lawrence
Food Style: Modern British

Coltishall

Norfolk Mead Hotel ⊛⊛
Church Lane, NR12 7DN
01603 737531
www.norfolkmead.co.uk
Open: All year

This handsome old house in the heart of the Norfolk
Broads is looking dapper with its contemporary,
country-chic finish. The smart restaurant follows the
theme, seamlessly blending period features with an
uncluttered style – white walls, abstract artworks,
and simple flower arrangements. On the food front,
the kitchen hauls in fine local ingredients and offers a
vibrant modern British menu.

Chef: Damien Woollard,
Kieran Barratt
Food Style: Modern British

Cromer

Bolton's Bistro ⊛
The Cliftonville Hotel, Seafront, NR27 9AS
01263 512543
www.cliftonvillehotel.co.uk
Open: All year

Chef: Paul Harvey
Food Style: Modern British

Seafood – including the famous Cromer crab and locally-caught lobster – is the draw at
Bolton's Bistro, the informal, family-run restaurant that forms part of the Cliftonville Hotel, an
Edwardian Grade II listed property overlooking the sea on Cromer's west cliff. Although there
are steaks on offer for carnivores, it's the attractively-presented, well-seasoned fish and shellfish
dishes that steal the show.

Cromer *continued*

The Grove Cromer

95 Overstrand Road, NR27 0DJ
01263 512412
www.thegrovecromer.co.uk
Closed: 1st 3 weeks January

A private path leads through woodland to the beach
from this north Norfolk hotel, a substantial white
Georgian house partly covered in creepers. In the
restaurant, it's all about clear, fresh flavours. You might
try Norfolk cheeses with quince jelly as an alternative
to dessert.

Chef: Reis Khalil
Food Style: British, Seafood

NEW The Red Lion Food and Rooms

Brook Street, NR27 9HD
01263 514964
www.redlion-cromer.co.uk
Closed: 25–26 December

Chef: Shahid Iqbal
Food Style: Modern British

In an elevated position at the heart of the town centre, overlooking the beach and the sea, the
Red Lion is a charming Victorian inn. The open-plan public areas include a lounge bar, a sunny
conservatory and the popular restaurant. A large backboard proclaims the 'catch of the day' and
the 'meat of the moment' depending on what's available.

Diss

NEW Weavers Wine Bar + Restaurant

24 Market Hill, IP22 4JZ
01379 642411
www.weaversdiss.com
Closed: 27 July to 3 August, 24–28 October,
25–26 December

Originally built as a guild chapel in the 15th century,
Weavers has been a wine bar for some time, but is
now more of an eatery. There are plain wooden tables
as well as banquette seating in some areas, making
for a nice mix of old and new. Service is relaxed but
attentive, while menus are seasonal modern British.

Chef: Joshua Atkin
Food Style: Modern British

Erpingham

NEW Saracen's Head ⊛
Wall Road, Wolterton, NR11 7LZ
01263 768909
www.saracenshead-norfolk.co.uk
Closed: Monday, Tuesday

Chef: Sam Rush
Food Style: Traditional,
Modern British

Built in 1806, and surrounded by lovely open countryside, the Saracen's Head isn't quite the typical Norfolk inn. It's more of a creeper-clad Tuscan villa with brick fireplaces, a small bar and its main attraction, a dining room offering between 25 and 40 covers. It's all nicely intimate with hands-on service from the owners and their team.

Fleggburgh

The Kings Arms ⊛⊛
Main Road, NR29 3AG
01493 368333
www.kingsarmsfleggburgh.com
Closed: 25 December

This 19th-century red-brick pub in the village of
Fleggburgh is split across a few areas with a bar feel to
the front and a slightly more formal style dining area
to the side with clothed tables. Service is attentive and
professional with a gastro pub feel to proceedings.

Chef: Jack Burrell
Food Style: Modern, Traditional

Great Yarmouth

Imperial Hotel ⊛⊛
North Drive, NR30 1EQ
01493 842000
www.imperialhotel.co.uk
Closed: 23 December to 2 January

Set at the quieter end of the seafront, the Imperial
Hotel is a friendly, family-run place with superb sea
views. The Café Cru is the restaurant, offering a relaxed
style with professional and attentive service. Frosted
glass panels divide the booths to give an extra feel of
intimacy. Classic dishes from the brasserie repertoire
are the stock-in-trade.

Chef: Peter Clarke
Food Style: Modern British

Great Yarmouth *continued*

The Prom Hotel
77 Marine Parade, NR30 2DH
01493 842308
www.promhotel.co.uk
Open: All year

Chef: Leigh Schofield
Food Style: Contemporary British

The Prom Hotel is on the seafront close to the bright lights and attractions of Marine Parade. The restaurant, Strollers, has recently received major refurbishment and is now a contemporary and stylish dining area with plush seating, colourful fabrics, and interesting decor. Although Yarmouth isn't the fishing town it was, fish and seafood still have their place on the menu.

Grimston

Congham Hall Country House Hotel
Lynn Road, PE32 1AH
01485 600250
www.conghamhallhotel.co.uk
Open: All year

Recently given a full makeover, the restaurant at Congham Hall has light wood flooring and tables, while seating is a mix of coloured tub chairs and benches. The room is really relaxed and the views of the grounds are lovely. The hall is an 18th-century manor in 30 acres of landscaped grounds and parkland.

Chef: James O'Connor
Food Style: Modern British, European

Heacham

Heacham Manor Hotel
Hunstanton Road, PE31 7JX
01485 536030
www.heacham-manor.co.uk
Open: All year

Chef: Richard Millar
Food Style: Mediterranean, European

The wide-open skies of Norfolk's fabulous coast make Heacham Manor an attractive prospect, and the place even comes with a coastal golf course. Built as an Elizabethan manor, the hotel has been brought smartly up-to-date and the conservatory-style Mulberry Restaurant has been extended and modernised.

Hevingham

Marsham Arms Coaching Inn 🏵
40 Holt Road, NR10 5NP
01603 754268
www.marshamarms.co.uk
Open: All year

A former coaching inn with a stylish white and grey exterior and good outdoor space, tables surrounded by flowers. The bar and dining area are homely and welcoming with a central wood-burning stove, and the dishes are modern British pub classics. The gin list is great, with a good selection of local varieties.

Chef: Jack Talbot
Food Style: Modern British

Holt

The Pheasant Hotel & Restaurant 🏵
Coast Road, Kelling, NR25 7EG
01263 588382
www.pheasanthotelnorfolk.co.uk
Open: All year

Chef: David Carter
Food Style: Modern British

With the never ending beaches and marshland of the north Norfolk coast on hand, The Pheasant is plumb in one of the country's most fashionable resort areas. Cooking is modern British, with seafood a strong suit. Afternoon teas are an abiding part of The Pheasant's appeal.

"

What is your advice for cooking great food?
Keep it simple, keep it fresh
AA Inspector

Hunstanton

Caley Hall Hotel 🏵
Old Hunstanton Road, PE36 6HH
01485 533486
www.caleyhallhotel.co.uk
Closed: 4–20 January, 20–27 December

Built around a manor dating from 1648, Caley Hall
is a short walk to the wide beaches on The Wash, a
twitcher's paradise. Its restaurant, in a former stable
block, is a relaxing-looking room. It's a popular place
offering precisely cooked, quality East Anglian produce.

Chef: Sean McGinlay
Food Style: Modern British

The Neptune Restaurant with Rooms 🏵🏵🏵
85 Old Hunstanton Road, Old Hunstanton, PE36 6HZ
01485 532122
www.theneptune.co.uk
Closed: 3 weeks January, 1 week May, 1 week November and 26 December

Chef: Kevin Mangeolles
Food Style: Modern European

Not far from the coast, The Neptune has the look of an old inn, with its creeper-covered
Georgian façade, but in fact it's a top-notch restaurant with rooms. The dining room is smart
and intimate, with just 18 covers. A lot of glorious regional bounty finds its way onto Kevin
Mangeolles' menus, and his cooking is full of good ideas; a well-constructed and flavoursome
terrine of chicken and foie gras terrine with pickled sultanas to start, then a seemingly effortless
main of Goosnargh duck with butternut purée, parsnip, pickled onion, dauphine potato, and red
cabbage, for example.

King's Lynn

NEW The Angel at Watlington Awaiting Inspection
41 School Road, PE33 0HA
01553 811588
www.theangelatwatlington.co.uk
Open: All year

Just outside of Kings Lynn, The Angel at Watlington has
undergone a major refurbishment not only in decor and
its food and drink offering, but in its very approach to
hospitality. Dining areas include one with a log burner
and six tables, and a second that is a conservatory with
large windows and plenty of natural light

Chef: Richard Crouch
Food Style: British

Loddon

The Loddon Swan ◉◉
23 Church Plain, NR14 6LX
01508 528039
www.theloddonswan.co.uk
Closed: Monday, 25 December

Close to the stunning River Chet, this 18th-century coaching inn retains traditional charm along with 21st-century styling. While much is made of local sourcing of ingredients, the menu mixes modern British dishes with Mediterranean classics.

Chef: Jason Wright, Shel Gibbs
Food Style: Modern British

North Walsham

Beechwood Hotel ◉◉
20 Cromer Road, NR28 0HD
01692 403231
www.beechwood-hotel.co.uk
Open: All year

Hospitality is top of the agenda at this charming country house hotel, with hands-on owners and plenty of staff ensuring that guests are well looked after. The kitchen sources most ingredients from within 10 miles of the hotel and sends out contemporary British ideas.

Chef: Scott Elden, Lawrence Gurney
Food Style: Modern British

Norwich

Benedicts ◉◉◉
9 St Benedicts Street, NR2 4PE
01603 926080
www.restaurantbenedicts.com
Closed: 29 July to 14 August, 23 December to 8 January

Chef: Richard Bainbridge
Food Style: Modern British

Benedicts is a switched-on operation where pared-back, Scandi-chic looks tick all the boxes of a big-city venue and make a suitably modernist setting for chef-patron Richard Bainbridge's innovative contemporary cooking. Diners can be assured of exciting 21st-century food with stimulating combinations of excellent materials such as Cromer crab with grapefruit and Morston samphire or Cornish wild sea bass with braised baby gem, lemon and lobster bisque. To finish, perhaps a lemon tart with raspberry sorbet or British summer trifle with English rose, Sharrington strawberries and raspberries. There's regularly changing five- or eight-course tasting options or a set lunch menu which offers remarkable value.

Norwich *continued*

Brasted's Restaurant ◉◉
Manor Farm Barns, Fox Road, Framingham Pigot,
NR14 7PZ
01508 491112
www.brasteds.co.uk
Open: All year

Brasted's is set in 20 acres of mature, landscaped
parkland on the outskirts of Norwich. The restaurant is
a bright and elegantly decorated converted barn, with
a raftered ceiling, oak floor and exposed brick. The
experienced kitchen team offers a menu of traditional
British dishes with a modern European twist.

Chef: Chris Busby
Food Style: Modern European

See advertisement opposite

Farmyard ◉◉◉
23 St Benedicts Street, NR2 4PF
01603 733188
www.farmyardrestaurant.com

Chef: John Walker
Food Style: Modern British

Despite its rural name, Farmyard is slap bang in the heart of Norwich and it's a modern bistro
with an uncompromising attitude to sourcing quality local produce. Everything is prepared in
the open kitchen, including the daily sourdough bread and hand-made butter. Meat, fish and
vegetables are cooked over charcoal on the 'Bertha' oven and there is an intelligently curated
wine list full of interesting bottles. Tender belly pork turns up at the starter stage with charred
baby leeks and Chinese XO sauce foam. To follow, there's slow-cooked belly and roasted rump
of lamb with celeriac, mushroom and fenugreek.

Maids Head Hotel ◉◉
Tombland, NR3 1LB
01603 209955
www.maidsheadhotel.co.uk
Open: All year

Maids Head Hotel is in the city centre, and lays
claim to being the UK's oldest hotel, having been
feeding and watering East Anglian travellers for
some 800 years. Dining is in the intimate Winepress
Restaurant or in the glassed-in Spring Courtyard with
its quarry-tiled floor and simple wooden tables.

Chef: Simon Dean
Food Style: Modern British

BRASTED'S

MULTI-AWARD WINNING
Fine Dining

Our award winning a la carte menus offer locally sourced ingredients and produce, resulting in traditional British dishes with a modern European twist. As a fine dining restaurant, service and food are paramount, resulting in the ultimate dining experience.

Restaurant Opening Times

Thursday, Friday & Saturday
6.30pm till 10.00pm
Thursday & Friday lunchtime
12.00pm till 2.30pm

AA ★★★★
Restaurant with rooms

AA ★★★★
Self Catering Accommodation

Eastern Daily Press Norfolk FOOD AWARDS
BEST RESTAURANT
3 TIMES WINNER

OpenTable
DINERS' CHOICE
3 TIMES WINNER

ACCREDITED MEMBER

EDP NORFOLK CHEF OF THE YEAR
WINNER 2005
CHRIS 'BUZZ' BUSBY

tripadvisor®
CERTIFICATE OF EXCELLENCE
2 TIMES WINNER

Norfolk food&drink WINNER
OUTSTANDING CUSTOMER SERVICE

Norfolk FOOD& DRINK
OUTSTANDING FRONT OF HOUSE
2 TIMES WINNER

Contact Us

01508 491112   brasteds.co.uk   Manor Farm Barns, Framingham Pigot, Norwich NR14 7PZ

Norwich *continued*

Roger Hickman's Restaurant ◉◉◉ ⚐NOTABLE WINE LIST

79 Upper St Giles Street, NR2 1AB
01603 633522
www.rogerhickmansrestaurant.com
Closed: 2 weeks in January

Chef: Roger Hickman
Food Style: Modern British

Squirrelled away near the cathedral in the Upper St Giles area, Roger Hickman's intimate restaurant is discreetly positioned but draws a crowd nonetheless. Elegant, calm and tastefully appointed with modern artwork and smartly laid tables, it's a comfortable setting for the modern British seasonal cooking. Whether ordering from the fixed-price or tasting menu, you might begin with crispy chicken, glazed wing, spring onion, sesame seed purée and mouli before braised beef short rib, Jerusalem artichoke, shallot and cashew nut. Chocolate fruit and nut, chestnut and pistachio is one way to round things off. The wine list has won awards.

Stower Grange ◉

40 School Road, Drayton, NR8 6EF
01603 860210
www.stowergrange.co.uk
Closed: 26-30 December

Chef: James Cox
Food Style: Modern British

The ivy-covered country house in its own wooded grounds a few miles out of Norwich is a charming family-run hotel where contemporary cooking based on quality ingredients aims to satisfy rather than startle. Try crisp-skinned sea bass with wild mushrooms, beetroot and puréed onions as a main course.

Reepham

The Dial House ◉◉◉

Market Place, NR10 4JJ
01603 879900
www.thedialhouse.org.uk

Chef: Andrew Jones
Food Style: Modern British

Occupying a splendid Georgian house, The Dial House offers a series of character spaces in which to dine, running from a chandelier-hung main dining room to a garden room with a terrace, and a cellar with bare brick walls. Wherever you choose, expect sparky modern cooking from a kitchen that likes to bang the drum for regional ingredients. There's a very relaxed and informal atmosphere, but with professional and attentive service. Go for the beautiful tender pork belly which almost melts in the mouth – lovely crisp skin, flavoursome carrots and the tartness of the rhubarb that complemented the dish. The two side dishes are extremely good; Norfolk greens with a salsa verde and triple-cooked chips.

Stalham

The Ingham Swan 🏵️🏵️🏵️

Sea Palling Road, Ingham, NR12 9AB
01692 581099
www.theinghamswan.co.uk
Closed: 25 December

Chef: Daniel Smith
Food Style: Modern British, French

In the heart of a village close to the north-east Norfolk coastline, the thatched Ingham Swan is a 14th-century former coaching inn which retains plenty of original features. You'll love the dining area with light wood flooring, dark wood tables, blue chairs and exposed brick walls that set the scene for modern British dishes such as Cromer crab cakes and wild garlic baked lobster, followed by barbecue fillet of beef and potato terrine. Service is relaxed yet very attentive and there's a good selection of well chosen wines available as well as a large selection by the glass.

Stoke Holy Cross

The Wildebeest 🏵️🏵️

82–86 Norwich Road, NR14 8QJ
01508 492497
www.thewildebeest.co.uk
Closed: 25 December

Set in a tranquil village, The Wildebeest is a haven of refined eating, serving-up innovated modern European dishes with pride. The interior is rich with beams, aged floorboards, wood-topped tables and leather-clad dining chairs. Much produce comes from a nearby farm.

Chef: Daniel Smith, Fabio Miani
Food Style: Modern European

Thetford

The Mulberry 🏵️

11 Raymond Street, IP24 2EA
01842 824122
www.mulberrythetford.co.uk
Closed: Sunday, Monday

This intimate restaurant in the heart of Thetford makes good use of local ingredients but looks to the Mediterranean for its inspiration on the plate. Go for the king prawn bruschetta, garlic prawns, tomato, chickpea, tarragon and lobster butter, perhaps followed by aged Norfolk beef sirloin tagliata with rocket, parmesan and red wine jus.

Food Style: Mediterranean, English

Thornham

The Chequers Inn ◉◉
High Street, PE36 6LY
01485 512229
www.chequersinnthornham.com
Open: All year

Chef: Liam Lingwood
Food Style: Modern British

This pretty village inn dates back to the 16th century and its location on the north Norfolk coast makes it a popular spot for people heading to the beautiful beaches of Brancaster and Holkham. Contemporary but rustic, the restaurant attracts locals as well as visitors.

The Lifeboat Inn ◉
Ship Lane, PE36 6LT
01485 512236
www.lifeboatinnthornham.com
Open: All year

Chef: David Mead
Food Style: Traditional British

Down a quiet lane behind the church, The Lifeboat Inn has been providing hospitality for more than 500 years. The terrace is a tranquil spot for a drink in summer, while the coastal location means plenty of local seafood. The dining room has smart flooring, stripped wood tables and chairs, and a relaxed modern atmosphere.

Titchwell

Titchwell Manor Hotel ◉◉◉
PE31 8BB
01485 210221
www.titchwellmanor.com
Open: All year

Titchwell Manor, once a Victorian farmhouse, is now a delightful boutique hotel. The red-brick building enjoys views across the RSPB reserve of Titchwell Marsh, and since 1988 it's been run by the Snaith family with genuinely warm-hearted efficiency. The chic Eating Rooms and light-filled conservatory restaurant make for a delightfully laid-back setting, the latter overlooking

Chef: Eric Snaith, Chris Mann
Food Style: Modern European

an abundant walled garden that supplies vegetables and herbs for the vibrant contemporary dishes. An Alsace bacon and langoustine pannacotta is a lovely starter, offering a perfect combination of textures and flavours, while main course pork collar is beautifully tender, with confit parsley root, quince purée, sauce charcutière and crackling.

Wiveton

Wiveton Bell 🌸🌸
The Green, Blakeney Road, NR25 7TL
01263 740101
www.wivetonbell.co.uk
Closed: 25 December

Chef: Simon Haynes
Food Style: Modern British

An authentic Georgian country pub on the village green, the Bell is near Blakeney and the salt marshes of north Norfolk and is done up in light and airy modern fashion. The cooking has a pleasingly traditional air about it.

Northamptonshire

Daventry

Fawsley Hall Hotel & Spa 🌸🌸
Fawsley, NN11 3BA
01327 892000
www.handpickedhotels.co.uk/fawsleyhall
Open: All year

Chef: Richard Walker
Food Style: Modern British

Plantagenets, Tudors and Georgians all played a part in the beguiling architectural mishmash seen today, and it screams 'grand' with its oak panels, stone arches and the Cedar Restaurant. However, a feeling of intimacy pervades the place, and the kitchen deals in imaginative 21st-century ideas.

Fotheringhay

NEW The Falcon Inn 🌸
PE8 5HZ
01832 226254
www.thefalcon-inn.co.uk
Closed: 25 December

Chef: Zak Perrin
Food Style: Modern British

Built from traditional Northampton stone in the historic village of Fotheringhay, The Falcon offers diners a selection of areas, from a traditional bar to a conservatory dining room, and the outdoor terrace offers plenty of alfresco options. Regional ingredients shine in dishes and local farms are namechecked on the menu.

Kettering

Kettering Park Hotel & Spa
Kettering Parkway, NN15 6XT
01536 416666
www.ketteringparkhotel.co.uk/food-drink
Closed: 1 January (excluding residents and pre-bookings), 25–26 December

Chef: Steven White
Food Style: Modern British

Kettering Park belies its business park location by having plenty of style and charm with its large open fire and sunny terrace, offering a relaxed and convivial atmosphere throughout the year. A mix of classic and contemporary dishes are served by a smart and attentive team. Raised pork pie with home-made pickle could precede chicken Kiev.

Tresham Restaurant
See pages 384-385

Nassington

The Queens Head Inn
54 Station Road, PE8 6QB
01780 784006
www.queensheadnassington.co.uk
Open: All year

Chef: Mark Baker
Food Style: Modern British

On the banks of the River Nene, The Queens Head Inn is built from delightful mellow stone and has been a hostelry for some two centuries. It still functions as a pub, but food is the main draw with a charcoal-fired Josper grill taking pride of place in the kitchen. Impeccably sourced steaks are a real treat.

Northampton

Hibiscus Fine Dining
Delapre Abbey, London Road, NN4 8AW
01604 911073
www.hibiscusfinedining.co.uk
Closed: Monday, Tuesday, Wednesday, 1 January, 25 December

Tucked away inside the Royal & Derngate theatre, Hibiscus is an intimate space, beautifully decorated in muted greys and silvers. Staff are smartly dressed and welcoming, and the menu changes seasonally with regular tweaks according to market availability. Begin with the marinated Cornish crab followed by roast lamb with lamb fat potato and wild garlic.

Chef: Bart Polinski
Food Style: Modern British

The Hopping Hare ⊛⊛
18 Hopping Hill Gardens, Duston, NN5 6PF
01604 580090
www.hoppinghare.com
Closed: 25 December

Chef: Karl Penny
Food Style: Modern, Traditional

Spacious, thoughtfully decorated and furnished, with an informal and atmospheric dining room and a popular bar. The modern, and inventive, British culinary output changes with the seasons – Balmoral venison loin bolognese with Szechuan pepper; shepherd's pie; hake fillet roasted in Marmite butter; crispy almond milk polenta and daily chef's specials.

Nuovo Restaurant ⊛
104a Abington Street, NN1 2BP
01604 601100
www.nuovo-restaurant.co.uk
Closed: Sunday, Bank Holiday Monday,
25–26 December, 1 January

A gem in a unique setting, hidden away down a passageway off the main drag. A long, narrow space, where the feature lighting and bold stripes create a great atmosphere. This is casual, relaxed dining, with a Venetian-inspired menu of cicchetti or Italian small plates; really tasty, well-executed, seasonally driven food.

Chef: Radu Biadu, Perry Langley, David Boszo
Food Style: Contemporary Italian

Oundle

The Talbot ⊛
New Street, PE8 4EA
01832 273621
www.thetalbot-oundle.com
Open: All year

Chef: Christian Koroma
Food Style: British

If The Talbot looks ancient, that's maybe because its stone façades, mullioned windows and grand timber staircase were recycled from Fotheringhay Castle in the 17th century. Nowadays, it does a brisk trade as a hotel, coffee house and eatery, aka the restaurant.

Kettering

Tresham Restaurant

Rushton Hall Hotel and Spa, Rushton, NN14 1RR
01536 713001
www.rushtonhall.com
Open: All year

Chef: Martin Allen
Food Style: Modern British

Dating back to the 15th-century, Grade I-listed Rushton Hall is an elegant country house hotel set amidst 30 acres of landscaped grounds and parkland and surrounded by open countryside.

With their roaring log fires and wooden floors, the stylish public rooms include a library and superb open-plan lounge bar with a magnificent vaulted ceiling and plush sofas. Now a sought-after wedding venue, the magnificent Orangery, with its intricate ceilings and crystal chandeliers, overlooks the immaculate gardens.

The stunning Tresham Restaurant, named after original Rushton Hall owner Sir William Tresham who fought with Henry V at Agincourt in 1415, is housed at the back of the brasserie in what was once the original kitchen of the house. It's an elegant room dominated by the large fireplace and walls dotted with photographs chronicling the house over the years. Tables are classically dressed with crisp cloths and high quality tableware, each with a tall crystal candleholder and fresh roses.

Although the kitchen is well schooled in classic technique, the food is contemporary and dishes are multilayered. The tasting menu is the best way to explore the full repertoire of the chefs and dinner might begin with lobster, cauliflower and lobster sauce before Dover sole, smoked leeks, oyster and nettle oil.

Next, the meat courses might bring saddle of rabbit with a pressing of confit leg and glazed carrot before Hereford beef fillet, sticky glazed short ribs, sprouting broccoli, burnt onion purée and Jerusalem artichoke gratin.

When it comes to the sweet courses, a palate-cleansing lemon and pine kernel ice cream with pink peppercorn mascarpone and maple syrup ice cream with honey sponge might lead on to a decadent hazelnut cremeux, tonka bean, caramel and milk chocolate cylinder. An affordable wine list offers a good selection by the glass.

"...the food is contemporary and dishes are multilayered."

Murrays ◉◉◉
Whittlebury Park, NN12 8QH
01327 850489
www.whittlebury.com
Closed: selected dates at Christmas, 31 December

Chef: Craig Rose
Food Style: Modern British,
European

Murrays is the pole-position dining option at Whittlebury Hall, a plush neo-Georgian hotel with a top-end spa and serious golfing just a short drive from Silverstone. While the slick front-of-house team help diners relax in the slow lane, the kitchen hits top gear with modern British cooking. A starter of Cornish sardine fillet, with heritage tomato and brioche grabs the attention with its fresh, clear flavours and textures, while chicken with sweetcorn, spinach and young turnips appear at the main course stage. For pudding, a cosy confection of apple crumble soufflé, Granny Smith purée and vanilla is a winner.

Northumberland

Magna ◉
39 Bridge Street, TD15 1ES
01289 302736
www.magnatandooriberwick.co.uk
Open: All year

Chef: Oliul Khan, Suman Ahmed
Food Style: Indian

Close to the bridge over the Tweed at the lower end of the walled town, Magna has earned a reputation for top-notch Indian cooking since it opened in 1982. Occupying a grand Victorian building, bright red chairs and colourful murals add a cheery glow to the place. The menu offers familiar curry-house staples making admirable use of local produce.

Lord Crewe Arms Blanchland ◉
Lord Crewe Arms, The Square, DH8 9SP
01434 675469
www.lordcrewearmsblanchland.co.uk
Open: All year

Chef: Emma Broom
Food Style: Traditional British

Built for the residents of Blanchland Abbey in the 1100s, this wonderfully historic inn has served everyone from monks to lead miners. It seems unlikely that the latter would have been interested in the architecture, not least the vaulted stone crypt, now an atmospheric bar.

Chathill

Doxford Hall Hotel & Spa ◉◉
NE67 5DN
01665 589700
www.doxfordhall.com
Open: All year

Doxford Hall's restaurant has chandeliers in ornate ceilings, a stone fireplace, deep-red walls and menus reflecting 21st-century dining expectations. Seared scallops with two croquettes of slowly cooked pig's cheek and celeriac remoulade is just one possible starter of intense, distinct flavours.

Food Style: Modern British

Cornhill-on-Tweed

NEW The Collingwood Arms ◉
Main Street, TD12 4UH
01890 882424
www.collingwoodarms.com

Food Style: Modern British

Set by the border, close to the River Tweed, the Grade II listed Collingwood Arms has been welcoming travellers for more than two centuries. Its main restaurant looks out onto the central gardens, and is a good mix of old and new with handsome wood tables, comfortable seating and classic northern hospitality. Much produce comes from the nearby Collingwood Gardens.

Hexham

The Barrasford Arms ◉
Barrasford, NE48 4AA
01434 681237
www.barrasfordarms.co.uk
Closed: Monday, Tuesday, 25–26 December

Set in a charming village close to the River North Tyne, The Barrasford Arms has three dining rooms. Each has bare wooden tables and is traditionally decorated pub-style. Sit on chairs and banquettes and enjoy punchy flavours from a modern British template, with the emphasis firmly placed on produce from local estates.

Chef: Michael Eames
Food Style: British

Hexham *continued*

Langley Castle Hotel ◉◉
Langley, NE47 5LU
01434 688888
www.langleycastle.com
Open: All year

In two parts, the restaurant at Langley Castle is in the 14th-century castle keep, with some walls being 7ft thick. The older part has plenty of period artwork and tapestries in line with the castle's history while the modern addition introduces natural daylight and views of the grounds. The kitchen produces straightforward flavoursome food without unnecessary distractions.

Chef: Frankie Shields
Food Style: Contemporary British, French

Longframlington

The Granby Inn ◉
Front Street, NE65 8DP
01665 570228
www.thegranbyinn.co.uk
Closed: 25-26 December

Situated in the heart of the peaceful Northumberland village of Longframlington, The Granby is a traditional village inn dating back over 250 years. Locally sourced produce appears throughout the appealing modern British menu, whether it's seared scallops, home-made black pudding and crushed peas or pork tenderloin wrapped in dry-cured streaky bacon, pork croquette, roasted broccoli and jus.

Chef: Michael Hall
Food Style: Modern British

Morpeth

Eshott Hall ◉◉
Eshott, NE65 9EN
01670 787454
www.eshotthall.co.uk
Open: All year

Eshott Hall is a compact boutique hotel in a handsome Georgian property – a perfect base from which to explore the National Park and end the day with dinner in the elegant restaurant, with its soothing gold colour scheme and a fire in cooler weather. Afternoon tea is worth checking out too.

Chef: Dan Curtis
Food Style: British, European

'Simply... Wow!'

The Duke of Wellington Inn

Newton, Stocksfield, Northumberland NE43 7UL

01661 844 446

info@thedukeofwellingtoninn.co.uk

www.thedukeofwellingtoninn.co.uk

Award winning food

The Cook and Barker Inn ⊚
NE65 9JY
01665 575234
www.cookandbarkerinn.co.uk
Open: All year

Chef: William Farmer
Food Style: British

Just off the A1 The Cook and Barker Inn has gained a great reputation for food, so the bar and restaurant are often full even on a Sunday or Monday night. The restaurant is large with a high pitched ceiling, while the bar and other small dining areas are more cosy and intimate, but it's all very welcoming.

The Duke of Wellington Inn ⊚
Newton, NE43 7UL
01661 844446
www.thedukeofwellingtoninn.co.uk
Open: All year

The Duke of Wellington Inn is only minutes from the A69, but it's so peaceful here that you'd never know it. It's reputedly one of Northumberland's oldest pubs, but the food is much more up to date than that. Also, you can be sure of a warm welcome if you're a cyclist, a walker, or want to bring the dog.

Food Style: Modern British

See advertisement on page 389

Nottinghamshire

Restaurant Bar 1650 ⊚
Ye Olde Bell Hotel & Spa, DN22 8QS
01777 705121
www.yeoldebell-hotel.co.uk
Open: All year

This hotel offers beauty therapies aplenty, and lots of room for functions. There's a bistro in the St Leger bar, but the main event is the oak-panelled Restaurant Bar 1650, with its art deco style in the bar area and modern chandeliers to add a touch of glamour.

Chef: John Blenkiron
Food Style: Modern British

Blidworth

The Black Bull ⑳⑳
Main Street, NG21 0QH
01623 490222
www.blackbullblidworth.co.uk
Open: All year

Chef: Lewis Kuciers, Craig Hadden
Food Style: Modern British

Not far from Sherwood Forest and Byron's Newstead Abbey is this classic Georgian timbered inn. Sand-blasted beams, a brick fireplace and checkered carpeting make for a modernised but still homely atmosphere for showcasing some creatively witty cooking. The inventive pace is sustained to the end.

Gunthorpe

Tom Browns Brasserie ⑳⑳
The Old School House, Trentside, NG14 7FB
0115 966 3642
www.tombrowns.co.uk
Open: All year

The homage to Thomas Hughes' plucky Victorian schoolboy denotes the fact that this large riverside building was a place of education in the 19th century. No risk of having to face school dinners here now, though, this is a robustly complex, well-considered brasserie cooking in the modern style.

Chef: Steve Hinch
Food Style: Modern British

See advertisement on page 393

Lowdham

NEW The Old Volunteer ⑳⑳
61 Caythorpe Road, Caythorpe, NG14 7EB
0115 966 5822
www.oldvolpub.co.uk
Open: All year

A few miles outside Nottingham, The Old Volunteer is a lovely country pub with a contemporary style; modern lighting, wallpapers, upbeat music, and a sparkling white piano lending a real air of sophistication. The restaurant consists of two rooms, both with well-spaced tables and unusual 'plant windows'. The Garden Bar has an open kitchen where sushi is served.

Chef: Jack Pearce
Food Style: Gastro Fushion

Newark-on-Trent

NEW Taylor's Fine Dining 🏵
25 Castle Gate, NG24 1AZ
01636 659986
www.taylorsfd.co.uk
Closed: Sunday, Monday, Tuesday,
24 December to 9 January

In a prominent location opposite Newark Castle and
the River Trent, Taylor's Fine Dining has two rooms,
both adorned with murals from a local artist. The
style is classic elegance, with white clothed tables
and attentive service. The cooking is modern British
with hints from around the world. Food is technically
accomplished and presentation is definitely a strength.

Chef: Stephen Taylor
Food Style: Modern British,
International

Nottingham

Alchemilla 🏵🏵🏵🏵 ▲ NOTABLE WINE LIST
192 Derby Road, NG7 1NF
0115 941 3515
alchemillarestaurant.uk
Closed: 31 July to 13 August

Chef: Alex Bond
Food Style: Modern British

A wall of green foliage is the only real clue in daylight that you've found this almost hidden gem.
A former coach house, derelict for a century and a half, with bare brick walls, an arched brick
ceiling and light flooding down from huge skylights onto the simply presented wooden tables
and open kitchen. This is modern cookery of the best kind, supported by an understanding of
classic techniques, and with an inspired take on the plant-based elements of dishes. Memorable
dishes include smoked eel, cep, scallop dashi and liquorice; and aged beef, burnt aubergine
and smoked egg yolk. As with all the dishes on the menus, the dessert options are concise
in their description – apple, buttermilk, sorrel – which downplays the complexity of flavours.
Not forgetting what comes at the very end, the petits fours are top notch too. Mindful of the
diverse expectations of today's diners, separate vegetarian and pescatarian menus plus wine
pairings are available.

Byrons 🏵
Colwick Hall Hotel, Racecourse Road, NG2 4BH
0115 950 0566
colwickhallhotel.com
Open: All year

Byrons restaurant is part of the grand Georgian country
house that is Colwick Hall Hotel. It's an appealing space
for any dining occasion, with views over the front
gardens and nearby racecourse. The restaurant isn't
named for the poet Byron, but rather for his ancestral
family who used to live here. The Big Sunday Roast
is recommended.

Chef: Paul Fredric Roopesh
Food Style: Modern

Nottingham *continued*

NEW The Griffin Inn ◎
Griffin Plumtree, Main Road, Plumtree, NG12 5NB
0115 697 5700
www.griffinplumtree.co.uk
Open: All year

Occupying a prominent position on the road into the
village, The Griffin Inn has recently added a barn-style
restaurant with high beams and lovely views of the
garden. Choose from a collection of well-appointed
and relaxed rooms to enjoy a menu of pub classics and
inventive modern dishes.

Chef: Callum Hawkins
Food Style: Modern British

Hart's Kitchen ◎◎
Hart's Hotel, Standard Hill, Park Row, NG1 6GN
0115 988 1900
www.hartsnottingham.co.uk
Closed: 1 January

Partly thanks to its proximity to Nottingham's Theatre
Royal, Hart's Kitchen is very popular with visiting
showbiz figures. One wall of this stylish modern
restaurant is covered with signed photographs from
the likes of Michael Palin, Bill Bailey and Ruby Wax. The
kitchen offers modern British food, clean and simple
with fresh ingredients.

Chef: Martin Sludds
Food Style: Modern British

MemSaab Restaurant ◎◎
12–14 Maid Marian Way, NG1 6HS
0115 957 0009
www.mem-saab.co.uk
Closed: 25 December

Easily able to cater for 200 covers, MemSaab is a pretty
big operation, but its size doesn't dilute the quality
of the outstanding menu and its stunning choice of
modern and traditional Indian cooking styles. The decor
demonstrates MemSaab's ethos, a mix of traditional
Indian design and themes, with a modern approach and
execution.

Chef: Majid Ashraf
Food Style: Indian

See advertisement opposite

MemSaab

RESTAURANT

Winner

Best Front of House Team

Nottinghamshire Restaurant of the Year Runner up

Nottingham Restaurant & Bar Awards 2018

PRIVATE DINING • CANAPÉ & DRINKS RECEPTIONS
CELEBRATION DINNERS • OUTSIDE CATERING
£13.95 EARLY EVENING MENU AVAILABLE

5 957 0009 12-14 MAID MARIAN WAY, NOTTINGHAM NG1 6HS WWW.MEM-SAAB.CO.UK CONTACT@MEM-SAAB.CO.UK

Nottingham *continued*

Park Plaza Nottingham 🌐🌐
41 Maid Marian Way, NG1 6GD
0115 947 7444
www.chinolatino.eu/nottingham
Closed: 25–26 December

Chef: Manol Dmitrov
Food Style: Pan-Asian, Peruvian

Latin America meets the Far East in this Nottingham branch of the Park Plaza. Set across two levels, this buzzy restaurant and bar fuses pan-Asian cooking with international cuisine on the globe-trotting menu. Thai and Korean dishes appear in the mains and there's a menu of cocktails to complement the food.

NEW The Red Lion 🌐
Southwell Road, Thurgarton, NG14 7GP
01636 830772
www.redlionthurgarton.co.uk
Open: All year

The Red Lion is the only pub in this charming small village, and it was nicely renovated back in 2019. An ale house has been here since the 16th century. Inside it's all well decorated and retains original features like beams, bricks, and wooden floors. Newer touches include some contemporary wall paper, pastel decor, and a modern British menu.

Chef: Kyme Howells
Food Style: Modern British

Restaurant Sat Bains with Rooms 🌐🌐🌐🌐🌐 🍷 NOTABLE WINE LIST
Lenton Lane, Trentside, NG7 2SA
0115 986 6566
www.restaurantsatbains.com
Closed: 1 week in April, 2 weeks in August, 2 weeks in December to January

Chef: Sat Bains
Food Style: Modern British

Satwant Singh Bains chose rather an unexpected location for his restaurant. Not only is it outside the city centre, and a little tricky to find some say, it's in a handsomely converted Victorian farmhouse and outbuildings down a narrow lane, with the River Trent flowing behind. Sat's reputation has elevated him to the ranks of this country's super-chefs. For him, it's all about research, development and creativity that goes into his dishes. And, of course, the produce itself – for example, around 40 per cent of the veg and herbs that end up on the tables come from the urban garden outside. There's a small courtyard, ideal for a pre- or post-prandial drink, as well. Dining options are several: Chef's Table, with dishes served by the very chefs you may well have watched preparing them; Kitchen Bench, where you sit on high chairs within the main body of the pastry kitchen while, again, the chefs themselves look after you; the Conservatory, and the main restaurant itself. Wine flights ensure food and drink matches are as perfect as everything else.

World Service ⊕⊕ 🍷 NOTABLE WINE LIST
Newdigate House, Castle Gate, NG1 6AF
0115 847 5587
www.worldservicerestaurant.com
Closed: Monday, Tuesday, 1 January, 25–26 December

With a real buzzy atmosphere, World Service is in the 17th-century Newdigate House which has strong connections to the local United Services Club. The other part of the restaurant's name reflects inspiration drawn from around the world, which has created a combination of British cuisine with global influences, using a blend of techniques and flavours.

Chef: Kieran Haugh
Food Style: Modern British

Oxfordshire

Banbury

The White Horse ⊕⊕
2 The Square, Kings Sutton, OX17 3RF
01295 812440
www.whitehorseks.co.uk
Closed: Monday, 25 December

This old pub has a clean, modern look, yet still ensures that you are reminded of its past. Clearly popular, it has received regional food accolades for its cooking. Perhaps choose breast and leg of Loomswood duck with carrot, cumin and lentil dhal as a main, and lemon cheesecake with stem-ginger ice cream to finish.

Chef: Dominika Dorota Piotrowska
Food Style: Traditional British, French influences

Burford

The Angel at Burford ⊕
14 Witney Street, OX18 4SN
01993 822714
www.theangelatburford.co.uk
Closed: 25-26 December

Just off the main street in pretty Burford, this welcoming Cotswold stone inn oozes character. Perfectly kept pints of Hook Norton lure drinkers to the cosy and bustling bar, with the all-day bar menu offering sandwiches, burgers and a charcuterie board alongside the main carte.

Chef: Rhys Hoare
Food Style: Classic British

Burford *continued*

The Bay Tree Hotel ❀
Sheep Street, OX18 4LW
01993 822791
www.cotswold-inns-hotels.co.uk/baytree
Open: All year

Chef: Raf Tiglao
Food Style: Modern British

Built in Cotswold stone, this is a stylishly appointed place and a menu of modern English food. Try perhaps torched cured trout with textures of onion followed by Norfolk chicken schnitzel, Granny Smith apple and fennel or courgette, fennel and peas lasagne, Isle of Wight tomatoes and goats' curd.

The Lamb Inn ❀❀
Sheep Street, OX18 4LR
01993 823155
www.cotswold-inns-hotels.co.uk/lamb
Open: All year

Chef: Pawel Stepien
Food Style: Modern British

Beautifully cosy and comfortable, with flagstone floors and open fires, The Lamb is your quintessential Cotswold inn, set in a quaint market town. The dining room, with its grey walls and skylight, makes a very classy setting for their chic food – complex, precise seasonal dishes.

The Maytime Inn ❀
Asthall, OX18 4HW
01993 822068
www.themaytime.com
Closed: 25 December

The Maytime Inn is a 17th-century Cotswold countryside pub that once had its own smithy. Inside, you'll find a traditional inn with a modern twist to the tasteful decor and seating; expect scrubbed wooden tables, a warming fire and plenty of atmosphere. There's a well-stocked bar which is proud of its gin choices (over 150!). Local ingredients abound. Dogs miss none of the fun – there are treats for them too.

Chef: Roger Williams
Food Style: Classic British

The Sir Charles Napier ⬡⬡⬡ 🍷 NOTABLE WINE LIST

Sprigg's Alley, OX39 4BX
01494 483011
www.sircharlesnapier.co.uk
Closed: 25–26 December

The red-brick and wooden-beamed Sir Charles Napier enjoys a peaceful countryside setting in the Chiltern Hills. Inside, the dining room has a cosy feel with double doors leading to the most delightful terrace with mature vines and honeysuckle. In the summer months, an alfresco meal here can be enjoyed gazing across the magnificent garden and manicured lawn. The cooking is equally as impressive, a meal perhaps kicking off with

Chef: Andy Lewis
Food Style: Modern British, European

barbecued lobster tail, white asparagus and buttermilk and chive dressing. To follow, perfectly pink saddle of lamb turns up with Wye Valley asparagus, pommes sarladaises and black garlic purée. Leave room for their millionaire's chocolate pot.

NEW Whistlers Restaurant ⬡⬡

9 Middle Row, OX7 5NH
01608 643363
www.whistlersrestaurant.co.uk
Closed: Sunday, Monday, Tuesday,
23 December to 31 January

Set in Chipping Norton, among the beautiful Cotswolds, Whistlers is something of a hidden gem. Behind its unassuming front you'll find plenty of character; walls decorated with theatre posters, lots of plants and relaxed mood lighting. The team's watchwords are 'quality' and 'consistency', and everything is hand-made and locally sourced.

Chef: Nathan Phelps
Food Style: Contemporary British

Fyfield

The White Hart 🏵🏵
Main Road, OX13 5LW
01865 390585
www.whitehart-fyfield.com
Closed: Monday (excluding Bank Holidays)

There's certainly no lack of character here – Fyfield is a proper picture-book village, and the White Hart, originally a chantry house, has all the flagstones, beams and period features you could hope for. Inside you can dine beneath the impressive vaulted ceilings and choose from a thoughtfully constructed menu of locally sourced, seasonally inspired dishes.

Chef: Mark Chandler
Food Style: Modern British

Great Milton

Belmond Le Manoir aux Quat'Saisons 🏵🏵🏵🏵🏵 🍷NOTABLE WINE LIST
Church Road, OX44 7PD
01844 278881
www.belmond.com/hotels/europe/uk/oxfordshire/belmond-le-manoir-aux-quat-saisons

Chef: Raymond Blanc OBE, Gary Jones, Benoit Blin
Food Style: Modern French

Besançon-born Raymond Blanc bought this beautiful 15th-century manor in 1983, opening it a year later as a country house hotel and restaurant. He still runs it today, although it is owned by the Belmond hotel and leisure group. With luxurious bedroom suites, it stands at the heart of glorious grounds with sculptures, an orchard, a Japanese tea garden and a bounteous, organic kitchen garden. It should be no surprise that maître d' Blanc, OBE, remains the life force of the place, with his long-standing executive head chef Gary Jones, chef-pâtissier Benoit Blin, and their amazing teams, loyally alongside him. The dining experience is never less than utterly pleasurable, from the warm greeting and the charming attention to, of course, the delicious, classic French cuisine that has made Le Manoir's five-, six-and seven-course menus, with vegetarian and vegan options, such a gastronomic success. In addition is the three-course carte and a children's menu. The French led wine list has just a few candidates from the New World. Cookery and gardening schools add to Le Manoir's mix, enabling everyone a chance to take knowledge home, together with wonderful memories.

Henley-on-Thames

The Baskerville 🏵
Station Road, Lower Shiplake, RG9 3NY
0118 940 3332
www.thebaskerville.com
Closed: 1 January

Chef: Jamie Herridge
Food Style: Classic European

This Baskerville is a handsome beast, a contemporary kind of inn that offers beer and bar snacks, comfortable rooms, and a restaurant that produces seriously good grub. Pub classics like steak, ale and mushroom pie and Sunday roasts play to the gallery.

Hotel du Vin Henley-on-Thames

New Street, RG9 2BP
01491 848400
www.hotelduvin.com
Open: All year

Chef: Dominic Scott
Food Style: European

Hotel du Vin always chooses impressive buildings, and the Henley branch is no exception: a Thames-side Georgian property that was the HQ of Brakspears brewery. Bistro classics plus a few less standard dishes are what to expect, all cooked just as they should be.

Orwells

Shiplake Row, Binfield Heath, RG9 4DP
0118 940 3673
www.orwellsrestaurant.co.uk
Closed: 2 weeks beginning January,
2 weeks beginning September

Chef: Ryan and Liam
Simpson-Trotman
Food Style: Modern British

The whitewashed Georgian pub stands on an Oxfordshire country road in the unruffled environs of Binfield Heath. Liam and Ryan Simpson-Trotman have transformed the place into a beacon of modern British gastronomy since they opened the place over 11 years ago. Today, Ryan heads up front of house and Liam continues to hold the fort in the kitchen. They're around 75% self-sufficient in fresh produce in the summer months, and the emphasis is very much on dining. Perhaps try an opener of flavour-drenched, lightly cooked mackerel with pickled cucumber and ozone-fresh sea veg. Acknowledgement of the original pub ethos is evident in a dish that builds a slew of shredded ham hock with a runny egg yolk, bitter endive and dots of fiery mustard on an underlay of crumbled black pudding. For main, there could be salt baked celeriac or a Bajan-spiced lamb rump. The Mill Lane honey sponge is a good shout to finish on.

Kingham

The Kingham Plough

The Green, OX7 6YD
01608 658327
www.thekinghamplough.co.uk
Closed: 25 December

An idyllic honey-hued stone inn on the green of a pretty Cotswolds village, the Plough presents a quintessentially English picture. Inside, the place has the sort of stylish rustic-chic decor – all venerable beams and exposed stone walls – that you'd hope for in a foodie pub, but kids and Fido are welcome so there's no standing on ceremony.

Chef: Ashleigh Farrand
Food Style: Modern British

Kingham *continued*

The Wild Rabbit 🏵🏵🏵 🍷NOTABLE WINE LIST

Church Street, OX7 6YA
01608 658389
thewildrabbit.co.uk
Open: All year

Chef: Sam Bowser
Food Style: Modern British

A wisteria-draped Cotswold country inn makes an appealing prospect when its outdoor tables under the sunshades fill up. Allied with the Daylesford Estate, an expansive organic farming business, it makes a virtue of the natural approach, with a menu informed by nose-to-tail butchery and locally grown produce. Slow-cooked Daylesford organic egg, nasturtium velouté, Morteau sausage, new season peas and brioche makes a cracking start. The Wild Rabbit might be miles from the sea, but it's worth choosing John Dory, bouillabaisse, squid, cod's cheek, saffron onion, sea vegetables and fennel. There are temptations galore at the finishing line, including baked Brillat-Savarin cheesecake, market garden strawberry and pistachio.

Milton Common

The Oxfordshire 🏵

Rycote Lane, OX9 2PU
01844 278300
www.theoxfordshire.com
Closed: 25 December, 31 December

Whether you're at this new-build hotel in the Chilterns for golf or pampering, the Sakura restaurant has sweeping views of the course and countryside from its picture windows as a backdrop to a broad-ranging menu of modern dishes spiked with global influences.

Chef: Zandi Beetge
Food Style: Modern British

Minster Lovell

Minster Mill 🏵🏵🏵

OX29 0RN
01993 774441
www.minstermill.co.uk
Open: All year

Chef: Tom Moody
Food Style: Modern British

Minster Mill has plenty going for it: a rather glamorous Cotswold-stone boutique hotel by the River Windrush with a sybaritic spa and an atmospheric restaurant replete with vaulted ceilings and original oak beams. The kitchen, led by Tom Moody along with his team of highly skilled chefs, sends out an appealing fusion of contemporary and classic British ideas built on top-quality ingredients. Thoughtful, sharply executed dishes kick off with a plump scallop, perfectly caramelised, topped with subtle tandoori spicing and balanced by the sharpness of yogurt, cucumber and apple. Main course brings 50 day-aged Belted Galloway beef with duck fat-roasted carrot and oxtail in onion petals. Finish with chocolate délice with peanut and popcorn ice cream. Set in a high gallery overlooking the restaurant, the Mill Bar serves selected fine wines and champagnes, along with perfectly shaken classic cocktails.

Murcott

The Nut Tree Inn 🌸🌸🌸 🍷 NOTABLE WINE LIST

Main Street, OX5 2RE
01865 331253
www.nuttreeinn.co.uk
Closed: Sunday, Monday, 2 weeks July, 25 December to 7 January

The Nut Tree has been home to Michael and Imogen North and their family for the last 16 years. In this time, it has become a fine pub with a reputation for great food, beer and wine. Its roots are solidly in classic cooking techniques using the best produce possible and treating the ingredients with integrity to offer

Chef: Michael North
Food Style: Modern European

balanced dishes full of flavour with a keen eye for presentation. Expect lots of local produce, including veg from the garden. The warm pig's head and Nut Tree black pudding terrine with English mustard, black garlic ketchup and fried quail's egg is a superb opener. You'll also find a friendly and upbeat service.

Oxford

Bear & Ragged Staff 🌸

Appleton Road, Cumnor, OX2 9QH
01865 862329
www.bearandraggedstaff.com
Open: All year

Chef: Ben Flynn
Food Style: Modern, Classic British

The Bear offers an appealing mixture of traditional atmosphere and contemporary design. Masses of artwork on cool green walls in the dining room offset the roughcast stone, and forward-thinking menus offer trend-conscious British food. They create a themed board with ingredients from sea, garden and butchery.

The Cherwell Boathouse 🌸

Bardwell Road, OX2 6ST
01865 552746
cherwellboathouse.co.uk
Closed: 25–30 December

With swans and punts paddling by on the River Cherwell, it's no wonder that this Victorian boathouse restaurant is one of the city's cherished institutions. Waterside tables are at a premium on fine days; inside, the ambience is cosy and humming with the chatter of happy diners tucking into a menu of inventive, modern British ideas.

Chef: Paul Bell
Food Style: Modern English

Oxford *continued*

Chez Mal Brasserie 🏵
Oxford Castle, 3 New Road, OX1 1AY
01865 268400
www.malmaison.com
Open: All year

Chef: Jason Farbridge
Food Style: Modern British, French

Oxford's old slammer is now leading a reformed life as a classy hotel, with seductive bedrooms in the cells and a moodily-lit brasserie in the former basement canteen. The cooking is a little bit French, a little bit British, and a little bit global.

Cotswold Lodge Hotel 🏵
66a Banbury Road, OX2 6JP
01865 512121
www.cotswoldlodgehotel.co.uk
Open: All year

Chef: Emile Crothez
Food Style: British, European

This stately Victorian villa is replete with period style, all high ceilings, sweeping staircases and expansive bay windows, but given a modern facelift. The kitchen deals in contemporary food with clear European accents, but you might choose to end with a plate of tempting Oxfordshire cheeses.

NEW Pompette 🏵🏵
7 South Parade, Summertown, OX2 7JL
01865 311166
www.pompetterestaurant.co.uk
Closed: 25–26 December, 1 January

Pompette – apparently French for 'tipsy' – is an independent restaurant and wine bar in Summertown. It has real character and personality, and a high-quality brasserie feel throughout, complete with polished wood flooring, marble tables, and walls filled with all kinds of art. There's also a charming front terrace for outdoor dining. Cooking is French regional, with a rustic-style presentation.

Chef: Zoltan Gothard
Food Style: Classic European, French

Ramsden

NEW The Royal Oak
High Street, OX7 3AU
01993 868213
www.royaloakramsden.com
Open: All year

Food Style: Modern British

At the heart of a tranquil Cotswold village, The Royal Oak's stylish barn-style restaurant extension has high beams, stone and wood panels, pale flooring, skylights above and large windows looking into the rear garden Also, chunky rustic tables, intersting artworks and a lively ambience. The menu is a mix of re-imagined pub classics and inventive specials board.

Swinbrook

The Swan Inn
OX18 4DY
01993 823339
www.theswanswinbrook.co.uk
Closed: 25–26 December

Chef: Hubert Antoine
Food Style: Modern British

The wisteria-clad, 16th-century Swan is the quintessential village pub, with an orchard to the rear and the Windrush River running by. The kitchen sources seasonal ingredients with care (traceability is a big deal here), and knows how to turn it into some skilfully rendered dishes.

Toot Baldon

The Mole Inn
OX44 9NG
01865 340001
www.themoleinn.com
Closed: 25 December

Cosy and traditional, The Mole Inn is a classic country pub with a lovely garden and lots of space for outdoor eating. It's only a few miles from central Oxford, and is always very busy, so booking is a must. Most ingredients come from local suppliers, and the steaks are all dry-aged and hung for at least 28 days.

Chef: Anthony Hohmann
Food Style: Modern European

Witney

The Hollybush, Witney ✿
35 Corn Street, OX28 6BT
01993 708073
www.hollybushwitney.com
Open: All year

The Hollybush is a modern dining pub with a buzzy vibe
and a hint of sophistication. Tuck into your favourite
pub dishes with an inventive twist. The small frontage
to the old property belies the tardis that lies within.
It has a cosy feel; tables set with candles and there's
a friendly team. Expect great pub classics as well as
sharing and grazing plates alongside tasty daily specials;
real ales too.

Chef: Leon Smith
Food Style: British

See advertisement opposite

NEW The Horseshoes, Witney ✿
78 Corn Street, OX28 6BS
01993 703086
www.thehorseshoeswitney.co.uk
Open: All year

Built of mellow local stone, in a lovely part of town,
the Horseshoes is a fine example of rustic hospitality,
all bare stone, stripped-back wood and open fires.
Food is locally sourced, seasonal, and best enjoyed
with company. This is a very friendly pub, always full of
conversation. The terrace and the garden are popular
meeting places.

Chef: Leon Smith
Food Style: Modern, Classic British

Woodstock

The Feathers Hotel ✿✿
Market Street, OX20 1SX
01993 812291
www.feathers.co.uk
Open: All year

A brick-built inn in a handsome Cotswold market
town, The Feathers offers an inviting restaurant with a
relaxed, stylish and informal ambience. Attractive decor
blends period and contemporary features, as well as
nicely co-ordinated colour schemes, all adding to the
overall appeal of the room. Blenheim Palace is only a
short distance away.

Chef: Luke Rawicki
Food Style: Modern British

THE HOLLYBUSH

Our inventive menus are inspired by the best seasonal local ingredients.
You'll find clean, pared-back dishes with weekly changing specials. Produce
is sourced locally from local farms, butchers, Cotswold cheesemakers and
vegetable growers. We make everything from scratch from bread to
ice cream.

While you'll find fish and chips, pies and burgers all with the Hollybush
twist, we also push out the boat with more sophisticated plates.

Hollybush Sunday roasts are popular - and of course, there are always
plenty of options for vegetarians and vegans.

Visit Us

35 Corn Street, Witney, Oxfordshire | info@hollybushwitney.com | 01993 708073

Woodstock *continued*

The White House 🏵
1 Grove Road, Bladon, OX20 1RQ
01993 811288
www.bladonwhitehouse.co.uk
Closed: Monday

Chef: Ben Bullen
Food Style: Traditional British
Pub Food

A warm welcome awaits at this friendly community-owned pub. Situated close to Blenheim Palace, The White House dates to the 16th century and is full of character, with a garden for warm days and a log fire for cold nights. *Masterchef* quarter-finalist Ben Bullen heads up the kitchen team, serving a selection of seasonal pub classics.

Wootton

The Killingworth Castle 🏵🏵
Glympton Road, OX20 1EJ
01993 811401
www.thekillingworthcastle.com
Closed: Monday, Tuesday, 1 week January, 25 December

The inn has been an integral part of its community since the 1630s. When the Alexanders (who also run the Ebrington Arms near Chipping Campden) took over in 2012, the old place received the investment it needed, while retaining its earthy charm and period character. Organic beers are brewed on site.

Chef: Adam Brown, Mike Lobue
Food Style: Classic British

Rutland

Clipsham

The Olive Branch 🏵🏵
Main Street, LE15 7SH
01780 410355
www.theolivebranchpub.com
Closed: Monday, Tuesday, 25 December, 31 December

Home-grown and foraged herbs and berries play a big part here, alongside local farm meats, English Channel fish and Norfolk shellfish. Daily-changing menus offer pan-fried pigeon breast with braised lentils; hake with mussels and curry sauce; rump of lamb with sweetbreads; and orzo pasta with chargrilled shallots. Forced Yorkshire rhubarb is a popular tailpiece.

Chef: Luke Holland
Food Style: British, European

Hambleton Hall ⊕⊕⊕⊕ ▲ NOTABLE WINE LIST
See pages 410-411

NEW Hitchen's Barn ⊕⊕
12 Burley Road, LE15 6DH
01572 722255
www.hitchensbarn.co.uk
Closed: Sunday, Monday, 1st 2 weeks January, 2 weeks in summer

Located in the UK's smallest county, Hitchen's Barn is on two levels, with the top floor used for private dining. The styling is simple and unfussy; an interesting collection of kitchen tools is on display on shelves, along with white walls, a faux timber ceiling and a proper wood floor. Cuisine is modern British with a great emphasis on provenance.

Chef: Neil Hitchen
Food Style: Modern British

The Lake Isle ⊕⊕
16 High Street East, LE15 9PZ
01572 822951
www.lakeisle.co.uk
Closed: 1 January, Bank Holidays

The property may be 350 years old but the cooking at this restaurant-with-rooms is thoroughly modern. Global influences are apparent across the menu, with a starter of Timothy Taylor ale-cured English Parma ham, poached duck egg and asparagus soldiers followed by sea bream, clams, samphire and lemon sorrel pesto.

Chef: Stuart Mead
Food Style: British, French

" What are the most common misconceptions you face?

That we ask for a specific (traditional) style; that service plays a part in the award when assessing for AA Rosettes.

AA Inspector

Oakham

@ @ @ @ 🍷 NOTABLE WINE LIST

Hambleton Hall

Hambleton, LE15 8TH
01572 756991
www.hambletonhall.com
Open: All year

Chef: Aaron Patterson
Food Style: Modern British

Assured cooking in historic setting

Back in the 1880s, fox hunting was an aspirational pursuit, and one wealthy Victorian brewer-built Hambleton as his hunting season holiday home, as any chap of substance would.

A water feature, otherwise known as Rutland Water reservoir (now a nature reserve) arrived on the hall's doorstep in 1970 to enhance the splendour of the setting, and Tim and Stefa Hart added the icing on the cake when they bought the place in 1979 and created a country-house hotel of distinction. It is a handsome place that delivers grandeur on a human scale and was always meant for entertainment and pleasurable pursuits, a laudable aim which continues today with elegant bedrooms, chic public rooms and a fabulous restaurant to complete the sybaritic picture. Chandeliers, oil paintings and linen-swathed tables provide reassuring formality, and the service

throughout is charming, professional and engaging.

The food is refined, creative and firmly rooted in sound culinary thinking. The hotel has its own bakery, so the bread is a cut above, and everything from the canapés to the petits fours is beautifully made and delivered via tasting and à la carte menus. Marinated scallop with crème fraîche and apple is a well-balanced and delicate starter. Slices of soft, sweet scallop are layered with translucent slices of apple and apple gel, with pops of salty black caviar. It might be followed by Launde Farm lamb, pickled aubergine, goats' curd, mint caviar – the two perfectly-timed, sweet and flavoursome pieces of lamb sitting on top of tender, dark green cavolo nero. Puffed rice and pumpkin seeds on top add more texture and a sweet, slightly smoky pepper stew topped with a sliver of aubergine completes a dish packed with flavour. Finish with a well-risen almond and Amaretto soufflé, quince and honey ice cream.

"...everything from the canapés to the petits fours is beautifully made."

Wing

Kings Arms Inn & Restaurant @@
13 Top Street, LE15 8SE
01572 737634
www.thekingsarms-wing.co.uk
Closed: 2–16 January, 10–24 October, 25 December

The Kings Arms is a traditional, rustic inn; all exposed
stone walls, open fires and quarry tile flooring, with decor
to match. It's full of charming little nooks and crannies, but
mind your head on some of those beams. The menu
is classic British with a modern twist, and be sure to look
out for the products of Jimmy's Rutland Smokehouse.

Chef: James Goss
Food Style: Traditional British

See advertisement below

Shropshire

NEW The Clock Tower 🌹🌹
Netley Hall, SY5 7JZ
01743 718339
www.netleyhall.com

Food Style: Modern British, Grill

The Clock Tower is part of Netley Hall, a luxurious Victorian country mansion set in 160 acres of landscaped grounds, a truly impressive location. It's named after, but not located in, the mansion's clock tower, and takes inspiration from the 1920s; unique Waterford Crystal chandeliers, exquisite tapestries and a stunning stained glass ceiling.

Hodnet

NEW The Bear Inn 🌹🌹
Drayton Road, TF9 3NH
01630 685214
www.thebearinnhodnet.com
Closed: 1st week in January

Once a coaching inn dating from the 16th-century, the Bear retains many original features including exposed beams and wall timbering, all enhanced by imported, aged Indian floor tiling. Stylish decor and eclectic original art is matched by period furnishing and artefacts. The menu is essentially modern British with international influences, and great emphasis is placed on flavour balance and presentation.

Chef: Martin Board
Food Style: Modern British

Ironbridge

White Hart 🌹
The Wharfage, TF8 7AW
01952 432901
www.whitehartironbridge.com
Closed: 25 December

Set just beyond Abraham Darby's famous bridge, the White Hart is located deep in the Severn Gorge and surrounded by reminders of the industrial revolution. Their Number Ten restaurant is a fine dining option with large windows that look out to the river.

Chef: Sam Morgan Butler
Food Style: Modern British

Ludlow

The Charlton Arms
Ludford Bridge, SY8 1PJ
01584 872813
www.thecharltonarms.co.uk
Closed: 1 January, 24–26 December

You can eat and drink not only by, but above, the River Teme here, because the lower of two outdoor decks projects over it; the views are delightful. On the modern British menu, a good selection of dishes includes ham hock Scotch egg with piccalilli coulis; and pan-fried hake fillet with crab and chorizo croquettes.

See advertisement below

Chef: Krisztian Balogh, Thomas Tudor
Food Style: Modern British

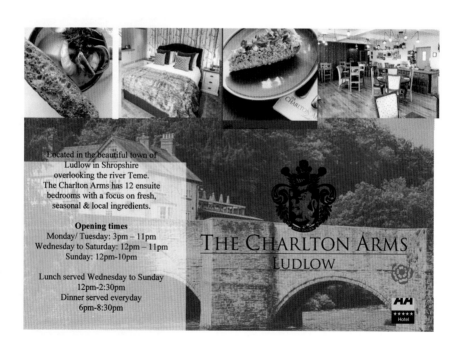

Located in the beautiful town of Ludlow in Shropshire overlooking the river Teme. The Charlton Arms has 12 ensuite bedrooms with a focus on fresh, seasonal & local ingredients.

Opening times
Monday/ Tuesday: 3pm – 11pm
Wednesday to Saturday: 12pm – 11pm
Sunday: 12pm-10pm

Lunch served Wednesday to Sunday
12pm-2:30pm
Dinner served everyday
6pm-8:30pm

THE CHARLTON ARMS
LUDLOW

The Cliffe at Dinham ◉◉
Halton Lane, Dinham, SY8 2JE
01584 872063
www.thecliffeatdinham.co.uk
Closed: 25–26 December

A handsome red-brick Victorian mansion beside
the River Teme with views across to Ludlow Castle,
The Cliffe has morphed into a stylish restaurant
with rooms with a breezily modern approach to
its interior decor. Sporting sage-green walls, bare
floorboards and unclothed tables, the restaurant is a
suitably contemporary spot for the kitchen's modern
bistro dishes.

Chef: Tom Jacks
Food Style: Modern British

The Clive Arms ◉
Bromfield, SY8 2JR
01584 856565
www.theclive.co.uk
Open: All year

The Clive Arms is based at the Ludlow Food Centre,
just two miles from the busy town of Ludlow. This
means that the Clive Restaurant has plenty of scope
for using local, seasonal produce at every meal. The
restaurant has white walls with a mixture of grey and
blue chairs, and local artwork on display.

Chef: Charles Westbrook
Food Style: Modern British

Fishmore Hall ◉◉◉
Fishmore Road, SY8 3DP
01584 875148
www.fishmorehall.co.uk
Closed: 2–13 January

Chef: Phil Kerry
Food Style: Modern British

Housed in the orangery extension of a restored Georgian pile, Forelles restaurant enjoys views
of the rolling Shropshire hills, which makes for a wonderful backdrop to the classic country-
house cuisine. As you might hope, it's built on pedigree materials sourced from within a 30-mile
radius (apart from seafood which comes from Devon and Scotland). Begin with an inventive
goats' cheese ice cream and mousse with intense parsley and cider gels before moving on to
rolled belly of lamb with aubergine, sweetbread, ricotta and courgette. A millefeuille layered
with raspberry, rose, lychee and almond is a beautifully constructed finale.

Ludlow *continued*

Old Downton Lodge ◉◉◉
Downton on the Rock, SY8 2HU
01568 771826
www.olddowntonlodge.com
Closed: 25 December

Chef: Nick Bennett
Food Style: Modern British

Not far from foodie Ludlow, idyllic Old Downton Lodge overlooks the Welsh Marches. Originally a farmhouse and cider mill, the lodge comprises a fascinating cluster of buildings – medieval, half-timbered, Georgian – around a courtyard filled with herbs and flowers. Dating from Norman times, the restaurant feels like the great hall of a castle with its stone walls, tapestry and chandelier. Nick Bennett's team follow the seasons. Start with well-balanced cod satay with pak choi, spring onion and coriander; continue with Creedy Carver duck with chicory braised in orange, and crunchy candied walnuts, then end it all with caramel chocolate mousse, hazelnut ice cream and praline.

Market Drayton

Goldstone Hall ◉◉ ⬧NOTABLE WINE LIST
Goldstone Road, TF9 2NA
01630 661202
www.goldstonehall.com
Open: All year

Chef: Kate Bradley
Food Style: Modern British

In the heart of the beautiful Shropshire countryside, family-run Goldstone Hall is surrounded by extensive grounds befitting its RHS garden partner status. Home-grown produce from the kitchen garden drives the menu, with unstuffy service whether you dine in the well-appointed restaurant or outside when the weather allows.

Much Wenlock

The Raven ◉◉
30 Barrow Street, TF13 6EN
01952 727251
www.ravenhotel.com
Closed: 24–27 December

With a 17th-century coaching inn as its heart, the dining room at the Raven is divided in two. One half a cosy, low-ceilinged affair, while the other has a high, vaulted ceiling and large patio doors overlooking an internal courtyard. On the dining front, things are positively 21st century, as the kitchen turns out smart, modern dishes.

Chef: Leigh Earing
Food Style: Modern British

Munslow

Crown Country Inn ◉◉
SY7 9ET
01584 841205
www.crowncountryinn.co.uk
Closed: some days during Christmas

Chef: Richard Arnold
Food Style: Modern British

In an Area of Outstanding Natural Beauty, the Crown dates from Tudor times and was first licensed in 1790. The kitchen has a 'Local to Ludlow' policy that might include a reworking of breakfast for black pudding croquettes with Boston beans, bacon and 'fried bread'.

Norton

The Hundred House ◉
Bridgnorth Road, TF11 9EE
01952 580240
www.hundredhouse.co.uk
Open: All year

Run by the Phillips family since the mid-1980s, The Hundred House is brimful of character and personality. The handsome Georgian coaching inn has stylish bedrooms, a bar serving pretty nifty pub grub, and a brasserie and restaurant producing classy dishes based on tip-top regional ingredients, many from the house's own bountiful gardens.

Chef: Stuart Phillips, Andy Nicholls
Food Style: British, French

Oswestry

Pen-y-Dyffryn Country Hotel ◉◉
Rhydycroesau, SY10 7JD
01691 653700
www.peny.co.uk
Closed: 12-29 December

A construction company built the rectory, church and village school here in 1840. Nowadays, the church is on the Welsh side of the border and the rectory is in England. With sweeping views over the valley, it is traditionally furnished in country-house style. A daily-changing menu is offered in the airy dining room.

Chef: Lewis Barton
Food Style: Modern British

Oswestry *continued*

Sebastians
45 Willow Street, SY11 1AQ
01691 655444
www.sebastians-hotel.com
Closed: 18–30 December

Sebastians is located in a 17th-century inn, full of
cossetting beamed character, but not stuck in the
past. Monthly-changing menus (with complimentary
appetiser and sorbet before mains) take you through
three courses of well-crafted, Gallic-influenced ideas.
This might translate as mushrooms, garlic, cream,
Roquefort cheese and watercress, and fish medley with
saffron potatoes.

Chef: Mark Fisher
Food Style: French

Shrewsbury

House of the Rising Sun
18 Butcher Row, SY1 1UW
01743 588040
www.hotrs.co.uk
Closed: 1 January, 25 December

Tucked away down a narrow lane, the two dining areas
here vary greatly – upstairs is very clubby with dark
walls and geisha-inspired artwork, while the ground
floor is more open plan with long tables. The staff are
well informed and clearly passionate about the food on
offer – imagine Asian street food meets Spanish tapas.

Chef: Robbie Simmonds
Food Style: Modern International

La Dolce Vita
35A Hill's Lane, SY1 1QU
01743 249126
www.ladolcevitashrewsbury.co.uk
Closed: 1 week January, Easter, 2 weeks September

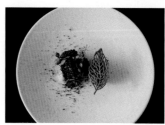

Tucked away but handy for the centre of town, this is
a traditional, family-run (dad out front, mum and son in
the kitchen) Italian restaurant, brought bang up to date
with modern cooking techniques and presentation. Low
key, simple decor puts the emphasis firmly on the food
and the quality of ingredients is second to none.

Chef: Gennaro Adaggio
Food Style: Modern Italian

Lion & Pheasant Hotel ◉◉
49–50 Wyle Cop, SY1 1XJ
01743 770345
www.lionandpheasant.co.uk
Closed: 25–26 December

This coaching inn has stood since the 16th century and
before the street called Wyle Cop became a bridge
over the River Severn. Its period façade gives way to a
contemporary New England-style interior, with neutral
tones and tongue-and-groove-panelling combining
harmoniously with the brickwork and beams.

Chef: Kaiofe O'Neill
Food Style: British

The Royalist Restaurant ◉
Prince Rupert Hotel, Butcher Row, SY1 1UQ
01743 499955
www.princeruperthotel.co.uk
Open: All year

Chef: Mike Peters
Food Style: Modern, Classic

As befits a former home of the grandson of King James I, the Grade II listed Prince Rupert Hotel
is a regal affair surrounded by cobbled streets and Tudor buildings. With tapestries and suits of
armour, the oak-panelled Royalist Restaurant provides a medieval ambience.

Telford

NEW The Ugly Duckling ◉
Long Lane, TF6 6HA
01952 257979
www.theugly-duckling.co.uk
Closed: Monday, 1 January, 25–27 December

The Ugly Duckling is anything but ugly. In reality
it's a charming light blue Georgian country pub just
outside Telford. Its interior is pleasingly eclectic, with
polished wood floors, original art, and bare brick
combining to create a welcoming, contemporary feel.
Cuisine is mostly modern British with Asian and
French influences.

Chef: Anthony Mason
Food Style: Modern British

Upton Magna

The Haughmond ◉◉◉
Pelham Road, SY4 4TZ
01743 709918
www.thehaughmond.co.uk
Open: All year

Chef: Martin Board
Food Style: Modern British

Light and modern, a stag theme running through the decor is a reminder that this is a traditional inn albeit one that now serves refined food. A pale green colour scheme and exposed brick walls add a rustic and relaxed edge to proceedings. In the kitchen, accomplished dishes display plenty of technical skill, as in a starter of trout mousse paired with beetroot, both pickled and in a pannacotta. Well judged pollock turns up with crumbed cauliflower slices, baby gem and tartare sauce, followed by a smooth salt caramel tart with banana purée and ice cream and white chocolate crumb.

Somerset

Bath

Bailbrook House Hotel ◉◉
Eveleigh Avenue, London Road West, BA1 7JD
01225 855100
www.bailbrookhouse.co.uk
Closed: 25 December, 31 December

Bailbrook is a handsome Georgian country mansion done out in classy contemporary boutique style. Its Cloisters Restaurant is the fine-dining option, an intimate split-level space. Flavours counterpoint well in fish dishes such as halibut fillet with pea and bacon fricassée, Jersey Royals and girolles.

Chef: Michael Ball
Food Style: Modern British

The Bath Priory Hotel, Restaurant & Spa ◉◉◉ ♦ NOTABLE WINE LIST
Weston Road, BA1 2XT
01225 331922
www.thebathpriory.co.uk
Open: All year

Chef: Jauca Catalin
Food Style: Modern European, French

Set within the magnificent Bath Priory Hotel, this is a true destination restaurant with classic country house dining. The formal dining room, in a long form, overlooks the beautiful grounds and gardens. Expect fine dining with a polished service to match, all done with minimal fuss which allows the food to be the star of the show. Start perhaps with a perfectly timed, tender and succulent squab pigeon breast with confit leg tart and a Madeira jus. Then move on to the Cornish wild turbot, again timed beautifully and pan roasted to a fine golden caramelised finish. End with a well-balanced Yorkshire rhubarb soufflé, pistachio ice cream and brightly coloured pistachio sauce.

The Circus Restaurant 🏵
34 Brock Street, BA1 2LN
01225 466020
www.thecircusrestaurant.co.uk
Closed: 25 December to 1 January

Located in a prime location between two of
Bath's most iconic locations, The Circus and the
Royal Crescent, this is an upmarket all-day eatery.
Its high-ceilinged dining rooms offer a bold, modern
setting for the monthly-changing, seasonally inspired
menu, based on fine West Country produce with
French influences.

Chef: Tom Smith
Food Style: Modern European

The Dower House Restaurant 🏵🏵🏵 ♦NOTABLE WINE LIST
The Royal Crescent Hotel & Spa, 16 Royal Crescent,
BA1 2LS
01225 823333
www.royalcrescent.co.uk
Closed: 30 September, 9 December

The Dower House is part of The Royal Crescent Hotel,
set in several houses in the famous Royal Crescent,
Bath's most elegant address. The restaurant overlooks
the immaculate landscaped gardens behind the hotel.
Head chef Martin Blake is settling in nicely, and has
certainly made his mark in the kitchen. Make a start

Chef: Martin Blake
Food Style: Modern British

with canapés of soft smoky cod roe wrapped in wafer thin tuile with confit lemon topping, then
try crisp-skinned halibut with curried mussel broth and a selection of heritage carrot textures.
Rhubarb, nutmeg custard and ginger makes a fine finish.

See advertisement on page 423

Gainsborough Brasserie Rosettes Suspended
The Gainsborough Bath Spa, Beau Street, BA1 1QY   Food Style: Modern British
01225 358888
www.thegainsboroughbathspa.co.uk
Open: All year

The Rosette award for this establishment has been suspended due to a change of chef and
reassessment will take place in due course.
If it's a blowout stay in Bath you're after, its hotels don't come with a more blue-blooded
pedigree than The Gainsborough Bath Spa. Named after the eponymous artist, an erstwhile
Bath resident, the place spreads across a handsome Grade II listed building dating from the
18th century. Looking elegantly understated with its unclothed tables, blue-and-white walls
and caramel leather seats, the dining room is a suitably contemporary setting for the
Gainsborough Brasserie.

Bath *continued*

The Hare & Hounds 🏵
Lansdown Road, BA1 5TJ
01225 482682
www.hareandhoundsbath.com
Open: All year

Chef: Chris Lynn
Food Style: Modern British

Standing nearly 750 feet above sea level on Bath's northern fringes, this pub is blessed with wide-ranging views from its terrace and gardens. Seasonal menus featuring dishes such as roasted chicken, wild mushroom and parmesan risotto, and plenty of classics, are bolstered by daily specials. Several lovely walks start and finish at the pub.

The Marlborough Tavern 🏵🏵
35 Marlborough Buildings, BA1 2LY
01225 423731
www.marlborough-tavern.com
Closed: 25 December

Chef: Jack Scarterfield
Food Style: Modern British

This Bath-stone corner local bills itself as offering 'great British food' — indeed it does. Perhaps, though, 'modern British' better describes the likes of sweet potato, coconut and chilli soup, or spiced venison burger with kimchi. Service is friendly and attentive, and outside is a walled courtyard that the Georgians must surely have built for today's drinkers and diners in mind.

Olio 🏵🏵
Abbey Lane, Freshford, BA2 7TB
01225 723731
www.homewoodbath.co.uk
Open: All year

A meal at Olio should not be missed. Expect a Mediterranean style mix of plancha and skillet dishes, lighter fresh salads, bites and sharing board tapas style along with more traditional classics. The fish is superb and very fresh, while for dessert the chocolate fondant, mint ganache and white chocolate ice cream is excellent.

Chef: James Forman
Food Style: Mediterranean, British

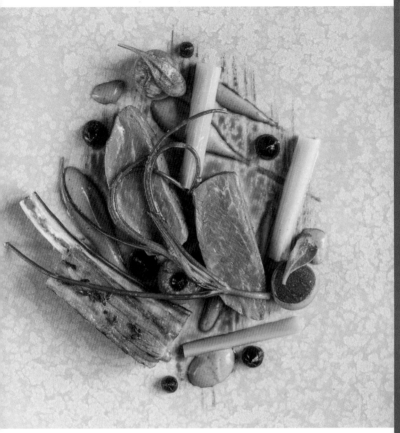

Bath *continued*

The Olive Tree at the Queensberry Hotel ⊕⊕⊕ ⛾NOTABLE WINE LIST
4–7 Russell Street, BA1 2QF
01225 447928
www.olivetreebath.co.uk
Closed: 20 to 27 April, 3 to 10 August,
2 to 9 November

This truly magnificent and uniquely stylish Georgian
townhouse is everything you could ask for in
a boutique hotel. It's the setting for chef Chris
Cleghorn's sharply contemporary cooking. The Olive
Tree restaurant is in the basement and revels in a
sophisticated, minimalist look. Two tasting menus (six

Chef: Chris Cleghorn
Food Style: Modern British

and nine courses) are offered, or you can choose à la carte from these, a thoughtful and flexible
approach that allows even those with a less robust appetite to experience his delightfully
conceived and constructed dishes. Smoked Devon eel, Isle of Wight tomato, and tarragon, and
Wiltshire lamb loin, anchovy, celery artichoke, Sarawak pepper are typical of his style.

NEW Raphael Restaurant ⊕
Gascoyne House, Upper Borough Walls, BA1 1RN
01225 480042
www.raphaelrestaurant.co.uk
Closed: 25–26 December

In the city centre, close to the Roman Baths and
Theatre Royal, Raphael has a romantic feel with its
candlelit tables and relaxed style. Friendly service and
an authentically European brasserie ambience makes
for the perfect setting to enjoy the modern food, taking
France and Italy as its main influence.

Chef: Miles Kesterton
Food Style: Modern British

The Scallop Shell ⊕
22 Monmouth Place, BA1 2AY
01225 420928
www.thescallopshell.co.uk
Closed: 1 January, 25–26 December

Behind a sky-blue frontage not far from Queen Square,
this popular venue offers a versatile range of fish and
seafood dishes in a relaxed café-style format where
food is ordered at the counter. Freshness is everything
at The Scallop Shell. There is no separate dessert menu,
just one sweet thing per day.

Chef: Dan Rosser
Food Style: British

Chard

NEW Candlelight Inn 🏵
Bishopswood, TA20 3RS
01460 234476
www.candlelight-inn.co.uk
Closed: 1st week January, 1st week November, 25–26 December

Chef: Aaron Ashworth
Food Style: Modern British

Winding lanes lead to this enchanting 17th-century village inn in deepest Somerset. The owners have fused traditional with contemporary to create an engaging ambience. After a pint or signature cocktail in the dog-friendly bar, head to the candlelit dining area to enjoy a menu featuring many fish specials.

NEW The Cotley Inn 🏵
Wambrook, TA20 3EN
01460 62348
www.cotleyinnwambrook.co.uk
Closed: Monday, Tuesday, 25 December

Once a farmhouse, The Cotley Inn dates back to the 17th century and thirsty local farmers still prop up the bar in this rustic venue. They happily mingle with diners who have navigated the country lanes in search of innovative dishes created with ingredients sourced within 25 miles, where possible.

Chef: Dan Brown
Food Style: Modern British

Cheddar

The Bath Arms 🏵🏵
Bath Street, BS27 3AA
01934 742425
www.batharms.com
Open: All year

Smack in the centre of Cheddar village and within footslogging distance of the eponymous gorge and caves, The Bath Arms has kept faith with those essential pubby virtues – real ales, a genuine welcome and great food. The kitchen turns out some impressive culinary action.

Chef: Martin Baker
Food Style: Modern British

Congresbury

Congresbury Arms 🏵️🏵️
High Street, BS49 5JA
01934 782283
www.congresburyarms.co.uk
Closed: Monday

Painted creamy-white, with a fine tiled roof, The
Congresbury Arms is welcoming roadside inn. Dine in
the bar, with its enormous flagstones, or the bright and
airy dining room, where pale green button banquettes
give a contemporary feel. The seasonal menus are
supplemented by regularly changing daily specials.

Chef: Martin Baker
Food Style: British

Dulverton

Woods Bar & Restaurant 🏵️🏵️
4 Banks Square, TA22 9BU
01398 324007
www.woodsdulverton.co.uk
Closed: 25 December

Chef: Ed Herd
Food Style: Modern British, French

On the edge of Exmoor, Woods is a pub cunningly disguised on the outside to look like a café.
The interior scene is cheered with a log fire in winter, and wooden partitions roughly divide the
place between the drinking of local ales and the eating of locally-sourced food. The kitchen
offers intricately worked modern British cooking.

Dunster

The Luttrell Arms Hotel 🏵️🏵️
Exmoor National Park, TA24 6SG
01643 821555
www.luttrellarms.co.uk
Open: All year

Just inside the Exmoor National Park, The Luttrell
Arms is a delightful 15th-century hotel, and Psalters
restaurant offers relaxed and comfortable dining
from a menu that presents a pleasing combination of
traditional style with a more modern country-house
feel. Try the venison with black pudding and star anise,
or the locally sourced Luttrell fish pie.

Chef: Allan Woodhall
Food Style: British

Holcombe

The Holcombe ⚘⚘
Stratton Road, BA3 5EB
01761 232478
www.theholcombe.com
Closed: Monday, Tuesday

The Holcombe is a textbook country inn with fires, local ales and amicable staff. Regional ingredients, including the produce of its own garden, supply the menus of mostly traditional fare. Desserts get creative with a raspberry and nougat parfait choc ice to accompany a Valrhona brownie.

Chef: Alan Lucas
Food Style: British, International, French

Hunstrete

THE PIG near Bath ⚘⚘ ▲NOTABLE WINE LIST
Hunstrete House, Pensford, BS39 4NS
01761 490490
www.thepighotel.com
Open: All year

Chef: Jack Stallard
Food Style: Modern British

Well positioned between Bristol and Bath, this chilled, shabby-chic country-house hotel is proud of its walled garden, which supplies much of the produce on the menu. Elephant garlic, chive crumpet and bacon jam might be followed by chargrilled pork tomahawk, garden greens, Somerset cider brandy and mustard sauce and triple-cooked chips.

Litton

The Litton ⚘
BA3 4PW
01761 241554
www.thelitton.co.uk
Closed: 25 December

The Litton's stylish interior is light and airy with bare stone walls, wood-burning stove, chesterfields, mix and match furniture and, definitely worth admiring, a long bar that's made from one solid piece of elm. There's also a whisky bar, terrace and gardens. The up-to-the-minute cooking is firmly rooted in the changing seasons.

Chef: Dan Jenkins
Food Style: British, European

Monksilver

The Notley Arms Inn ◉
Front Street, TA4 4JB
01984 656095
www.notleyarmsinn.co.uk
Open: All year

Chesterfields at an open fire, a mix of dining
chairs and pew-style seating, and attentive staff
add to the enjoyable experience of a visit to this
whitewashed village inn. The kitchen turns out
eloquently flavoured, well-executed dishes as well
as some pub classics.

Chef: Barrie Tucker
Food Style: Classic British

North Curry

NEW The Rising Sun Knapp ◉◉
Knapp Road, Knapp, TA3 6BG
01823 491027
www.therisingsunknapp.co.uk
Open: 1 week February, 25 December to 3 January

Set in a charming hamlet in some beautiful Somerset
countryside, the Rising Sun is a classic English inn that
may date back to before 1500. A great place to sit and
chat over a pint, while you contemplate some tempting
menus. The kitchen team work hard to produce fresh,
interesting and flavourful dishes using the best of
British suppliers.

Chef: Olly Jackson, Matthew Price
Food Style: Modern British

North Wootton

Crossways Inn ◉
Stocks Lane, BA4 4EU
01749 899000
www.thecrossways.co.uk
Open: All year

A thoroughly contemporary kind of inn these
days, the 18th-century Crossways looks much
the same as it always has from the outside, but a
21st-century makeover has opened-up the place.
It's the kind of inn where you can eat what you want
where you want.

Food Style: Modern British

Staffordshire

NEW The George Alstonefield Awaiting Inspection
DE6 2FX
01335 310205
thegeorgeatalstonefield.com
Closed: Monday, Tuesday, Wednesday,
25–26 December

The George Alstonefield is a classic English village pub, overlooking the village green, with a vegetable garden at the back. Inside there's a small bar, and a larger restaurant. Lots of original features, with a really intimate, friendly ambience. Service is nicely informal, presenting a weekly-changing menu as well as an evening tasting menu and Sunday roast.

Chef: Jordan Hemsil
Food Style: Modern British

NEW The Flintlock at Cheddleton ◉◉
11 Cheadle Road, Leek, ST13 7HN
01538 361380
www.theflintlockcheddleton.co.uk
Closed: Monday, Tuesday, Wednesday, 26 December to 5 January

The Flintlock at Cheddleton boasts a large terrace and window tables overlooking the adjacent Caldon Canal. A spacious lounge with comfortable sofas and armchairs makes for a relaxed space for pre-meal drinks before trying the imaginative modern cooking, which is underpinned by classic technique and steers away from pretension.

Chef: Thom Bateman
Food Style: Modern British

Ellastone

The Duncombe Arms ◎◎
Main Road, DE6 2GZ
01335 324275
www.duncombearms.co.uk
Closed: Monday, Tuesday

In the picturesque village of Ellastone, this attractive whitewashed country inn close to Alton Towers makes for an enjoyable pitstop for a pint but the modern food ensures visitors stay for much longer. Polished wooden tables, linen napkins and fresh flowers provide an informal setting and the cooking is creative, with intelligent flavour combinations.

Chef: Scott Law
Food Style: Modern British

Hoar Cross

The Ballroom Restaurant ◎
Hoar Cross Hall, Maker Lane, DE13 8QS
01283 575671
baronseden.com/hoar-cross-hall/food-drink
Open: All year

The Ballroom, as its name suggests, is a restaurant befitting of its grand home within Hoar Cross Hall, a stately home dating to 1871. Nestled in the countryside you will find chandeliers, William Morris wallpaper and views across the formal gardens, accompanied by a seasonal menu of local and Hall grown produce.

Chef: James St Claire-Jones
Food Style: Modern British

See advertisement opposite

Leek

Three Horseshoes Country Inn & Spa ◎
Buxton Road, Blackshaw Moor, ST13 8TW
01538 300296
www.3shoesinn.co.uk/food
Closed: 25 December

The stone-built inn overlooked by lowering gritstone outcrops in the southern stretches of the Peak District covers many bases. Original oak beams, exposed brick walls and dark slate tiles are matched to create contemporary styling, with an open-to-view kitchen augmenting the dynamic atmosphere.

Chef: Gareth Burnett
Food Style: Classic British

Decadent dining
at Hoar Cross Hall

Feel perfectly at home, yet utterly indulged at Hoar Cross Hall. Our award-winning Head Chef prides his matching of classic dishes with a contemporary twist. All spa overnight packages include a three-course dinner in our Ballroom, as well as a hearty breakfast.

Book your spa experience today.

Lichfield

The Boat Inn ◉◉◉ ♣NOTABLE WINE LIST
Walsall Road, Summerhill, WS14 0BU
01543 361692
www.theboatinnlichfield.com
Open: All year

Chef: Liam Dillon
Food Style: Modern British

The Boat occupies a rather unassuming location just off the busy A461 but once inside it's clear that this is a restaurant of substance with serious foodie credentials. An open kitchen with a chef's table takes pole position in a light, airy space that maintains a relaxed charm. And the menu? It has a sharp eye for the seasons and a love of big-hearted, well-matched flavours, as in Dorset crab with ribbons of kohlrabi, seaweed and wild cranberry, or pig's cheek with squash and sumac. Elsewhere, there's rose veal served with crisp sweetbreads and chanterelles and, for pudding, a lush chocolate gâteau with caramel ice cream.

The Larder ◉◉
Bore Street, WS13 6LZ
01543 471342
www.larderlichfield.com
Closed: 1 January, 25–26 December

Teal blue velvet chairs and gold banquettes glow against the otherwise muted colours in this smart urban dining room with its exposed brick and feature lighting. You can see the attention to detail in the cutlery and crockery as well as in the very precisely constructed dishes. There's a chef's table upstairs if you want to be part of the action, watching the preparation of the accomplished, seasonally focused cooking.

Chef: Alex Wickham
Food Style: Modern British

Swinfen Hall Hotel Rosettes Suspended
Swinfen, WS14 9RE
01543 481494
www.swinfenhallhotel.co.uk
Closed: Monday, 1 January, 26 December

Food Style: Modern British

The Rosette award for this establishment has been suspended due to a change of chef and reassessment will take place in due course.
Dating from 1757, this splendid mansion, complete with columns and pediment, is set in 100 acres of parkland, including a walled kitchen garden, deer park and formal gardens – hard to believe it's just half an hour from Birmingham's city centre. A careful restoration has created a stylish hotel, with elegant bedrooms and fine public areas with many period features. The oak-panelled dining room, with its ornate ceiling and heavily-swagged drapes, enjoys views across the terrace and gardens to the deer park.

NEW Upstairs by Tom Shepherd Awaiting Inspection
25 Bore Street, WS13 6NA
01543 268877
www.upstairs.restaurant
Closed: 1–17 January, Easter, 4–21 September,
25–26 December,

Its stylish interior decorated in shades of grey, with just
24 covers, Upstairs by Tom Shepherd is above Tom's
father's jewellery shop in the heart of Lichfield. Expect
flavour-led, produce-driven menus inspired by the
seasons and the local area. On offer are a seven-course
tasting menu and a four-course lunch menu.

Chef: Tom Shepherd
Food Style: Modern British

Stafford

The Moat House ＠＠
Lower Penkridge Road, Acton Trussell, ST17 0RJ
01785 712217
www.moathouse.co.uk
Closed: 25 December

The Moat House is a 17th-century timbered building, in
an idyllic canal-side setting. It's been skilfully extended
and does indeed have a moat. The Orangery is a bright,
spacious, chandelier-hung room with ample space.
Main courses on the seasonally-changing carte can be
complex but equally satisfying. Tuesday Grill night is
well worth checking out.

Chef: James Cracknell
Food Style: Modern British

The Shropshire Inn ＠
Newport Road, Haughton, ST18 9JH
01785 780904
www.theshropshireinnhaughton.co.uk
Closed: 25–26 December

The family-run Shropshire hasn't decamped to
Staffordshire, but has stood firm while county
boundaries have flowed around it. Its physiognomy is
a little different these days, with full-length windows
looking on to the garden, and gathered curtains in the
dining area creating an upscale ambience.

Chef: Michael Chapman
Food Style: Traditional British

Suffolk

Regatta Restaurant ◉
171 High Street, IP15 5AN
01728 452011
www.regattaaldeburgh.com
Closed: 25 December

In a fine building in the town centre, this long-running restaurant specialises in fresh fish and seafood, often locally landed. Daily specials support the carte, opening with Mediterranean fish soup and rouille, then continues with home-smoked whole prawns in garlic mayo; bradan rost (roasted salmon) with chilli chutney; and roast chicken breast in Parma ham.

Chef: Sam Tecklenberg
Food Style: Modern British

The Bildeston Crown ◉◉◉
104–106 High Street, IP7 7EB
01449 740510
www.thebildestoncrown.com
Open: All year

Chef: Chris Lee
Food Style: Modern and Classic British

A handsome Grade II-listed former coaching inn situated in a peaceful village location, The Bildeston Crown oozes chocolate-box charm. With its atmospheric beamed bar and smart restaurant, this is very much a pub that appeals to the 21st-century traveller and the food incorporates pub classics with more contemporary ideas from the kitchen. Belly of pork with scallops, black pudding beignet, apple and jus is a strong opener, followed by an Asian-influenced duck breast, udon noodles, pak choi and spicy duck broth. For dessert, lemon meringue and lemon curd ice cream is a refreshing way to end.

Best Western Brome Grange Hotel ◉
Norwich Road, near Diss, IP23 8AP
01379 870456
www.bromegrangehotel.co.uk
Open: All year

Chef: Matthew Cooke
Food Style: Modern British

It's easy to imagine horse-drawn carriages sweeping into the central courtyard of this 16th-century former coaching inn, with plenty of period details remaining inside and out. The Courtyard Restaurant, however, is a light and contemporary affair with vivid colours and well-spaced dark wood tables.

Bury St Edmunds

1921 Angel Hill ◉◉
IP33 1UZ
01284 704870
www.nineteen-twentyone.co.uk
Closed: 23 December to 8 January

Chef: Zack Deakins
Food Style: Modern British

It may occupy a timbered period building in the historic heart of Bury St Edmunds, but there's nothing old-fashioned about the modern British food here. Seasonal and local ingredients are at the fore in dishes like hay-smoked duck breast, rhubarb and celeriac, and fillet of coley, parsley root, snails and garlic velouté.

The Angel Hotel ◉◉
Angel Hill, IP33 1LT
01284 714000
www.theangel.co.uk
Open: All year

Overlooking the cathedral and abbey walls, The Angel is a quintessential Georgian coaching inn with a creeper-curtained façade. Inside, the generous spaces have been overlaid with a contemporary boutique look. The Eaterie's kitchen shows equally 21st-century sensibilities in its repertoire of upbeat brasserie food.

Chef: Arron Jackson
Food Style: Modern British

Best Western Priory Hotel ◉
Mildenhall Road, IP32 6EH
01284 766181
www.prioryhotel.co.uk
Open: All year

Chef: Matthew Cook
Food Style: Modern British, International

A peaceful atmosphere reigns throughout the Priory, including in the Garden Room restaurant, which offers soft lighting and a comforting feeling of being looked after by endlessly helpful staff. The kitchen produces dishes that pull in inspiration from all over the known world.

NEW The Brewers Rattlesden ◉◉
Lower Road, Rattlesden, IP30 0RJ
01449 736377
www.thebrewersrattlesden.co.uk
Closed: Monday, Tuesday

Chef: Sam Sturman
Food Style: Modern British

Saved from dereliction by local village families, The Brewers Rattlesden is a grand old pub that's now very much an eating place. Dining's split over several rooms, with striped wood tables, colourful padded chairs, a light wood floor, exposed brickwork and original beams. The kitchen team deliver strong, memorable flavours using local produce.

Bury St Edmunds *continued*

The Northgate ◉◉
13–14 Northgate Street, IP33 1HP
01284 339604
www.thenorthgate.com
Open: All year

The Northgate's modern British menu skilfully combines textures and flavours that make the most of local produce – accompanied by an impressive wine list, including a good selection by the glass. A relaxed and informal dining room belies the professional and attentive service – although diners who really want to get close to the action should book the 12-seat Chef's Table overlooking the kitchen.

The View Restaurant ◉◉
All Saints Hotel, Fornham St Genevieve, IP28 6JQ
01284 706777
www.allsaintshotel.com
Open: All year

Chef: Adam Spicer
Food Style: Modern British

Whether it's observing the chefs in action in the open kitchen or watching the sun set overlooking the adjacent golf course, The View certainly lives up to its name. Modern British with an Asian twist is the style: barbecue octopus, satay sauce, cucumber and mint followed by lamb rump, courgette stew, barbecue aubergine purée, potato terrine and broad beans.

The White Horse ◉
Rede Road, Whepstead, IP29 4SS
01284 735760
www.whitehorsewhepstead.co.uk
Open: All year

This stylishly made over, mustard-yellow village inn sits comfortably at the gastro pub end of the spectrum, but without losing any of the features one hopes for – smart and cosy rooms with a copper-sheathed bar serving Suffolk ales, a huge inglenook and country-style tables.

Chef: Lee Saunders
Food Style: Modern British

Dunwich

The Ship at Dunwich ◉
St James Street, IP17 3DT
01728 648219
www.shipatdunwich.co.uk
Open: All year

Chef: Liam Davidson
Food Style: Modern British

Climbing foliage adorns this red-brick pub in a coastal village. Surrounded by heathland and nature reserves, with a beach on hand and Southwold nearby, it's got the lot, including a garden with an ancient fig tree and a courtyard for outdoor dining.

Fox & Goose Inn 🏵🏵
Church Road, IP21 5PB
01379 586247
www.foxandgoose.net
Closed: Monday, 25 December to 1 January

The Fox & Goose is a Grade II* listed former Guildhall, dating back to 1509, full of period details and tons of atmosphere. It's the perfect setting for some really spot-on modern British cooking, where beef fillet might come with mustard gel, a pickled shallot, green bean and carrot salad, garlic mayonnaise and wild mushroom croquette potatoes.

Chef: Matt Wyatt
Food Style: Modern British

NEW The Kings Arms Awaiting Inspection
3 Old Street, IP14 3NT
01449 257120
www.thekingsarmshaughley.co.uk
Closed Monday, Tuesday

From the outside, The Kings Arms seems to be a proper rural village inn, but inside it's a little bit more sophisticated, although still as welcoming as you'd expect. The meals are mostly pub classics, but elevated to a higher level in ingredients and preparation. It's very family and dog friendly and a great place to spend a few relaxing hours.

Chef: Grant Newland
Food Style: British

Hintlesham Hall Hotel 🏵🏵
George Street, IP8 3NS
01473 652334
www.hintleshamhall.co.uk
Open: All year

Hintlesham Hall is a beautifully proportioned 16th-century, Grade I listed building with three wings, and a façade added in 1720. Its 175 acres of grounds make for a very relaxing location. The kitchen displays originality not commonly seen in such surroundings, producing thoughtfully-constructed and elegant dishes eminently suited to the stylish dining room

Chef: Jon Cole
Food Style: Modern British

Ipswich

milsoms Kesgrave Hall ⊛⊛
Hall Road, Kesgrave, IP5 2PU
01473 333741
www.milsomhotels.com
Open: All year

Chef: Stuart Oliver
Food Style: Modern International

Still deep in woodland after more than 200 years, milsoms at Kesgrave Hall is a large open-plan dining area, with rustic wooden floors and a range of stripped-wood tables and chairs. Service is slick but still relaxed and informal and the restaurant is always busy. Bookings aren't taken, and there's no dress code.

NEW The Peacock Inn – Chelsworth ⊛⊛
37 The Street, Chelsworth, IP7 7HU
01449 743952
www.thepeacockchelsworth.com
Open: All year

A lovely 14th-century timber-framed inn, The Peacock Inn is situated on the north shore of the River Brett in the heart of a pretty Suffolk village. Inside, an eclectic mix of wooden tables and chairs, mostly dark wood, alongside exposed brick and large open fires. Service is informal, relaxed and attentive. Outside is a nice garden with a terrace.

Chef: Sam Clover
Food Style: Modern British

See advertisement opposite

Salthouse Harbour Hotel ⊛⊛
No 1 Neptune Quay, IP4 1AX
01473 226789
www.salthouseharbour.co.uk
Open: All year

A harbourside warehouse makeover with eye-popping interior collisions of lime-green and violet, the Salthouse deals in brasserie food with look-at-me flavours. A gin and tonic arrives later than is conventional perhaps, in a dessert of apple and Hendrick's jelly, with cucumber sorbet and lime granita.

Chef: Luke Bailey
Food Style: Modern British

Peacock Inn Chelsworth

The Peacock Inn is a beautiful 14th Century timber-framed inn located in the stunning Suffolk village of Chelsworth. Recently awarded with two AA Rosettes, the pub offers a changing seasonal menu that showcases local Suffolk produce. As well as the restaurant, there is a cosy bar, private events room and a spacious country garden. With seven individual suites and a two bedroom cottage surrounding our lovely English cottage garden, why not pay us a visit and discover the delights of The Peacock Inn for yourself.

AA Rosette award for culinary excellence 2022

AA ★★★★ Inn 2022

The Peacock Inn
37 The Street, Chelsworth, Suffolk, IP7 7HU
+44 (0) 1449 743952
enquiries@thepeacockchelsworth.com
www.thepeacockchelsworth.com

Peacock Inn
CHELSWORTH

 @peacockinnchels   @peacockinnchelsworth   @peacockchelsworth

Ixworth

Theobald's Restaurant ◉◉
68 High Street, IP31 2HJ
01359 231707
www.theobaldsrestaurant.co.uk
Closed: 10 days in spring/summer

Theobald's Restaurant was converted from a Tudor inn in the early 1980s, but much of the historic atmosphere and many original features have been kept intact. It's an intimate venue, with only around 30 covers, and offers very nicely presented British dishes. Menus focus on locally reared meats and East Anglian fish.

Chef: Simon Theobald
Food Style: Modern British

Lavenham

The Great House ◉◉◉
Market Place, CO10 9QZ
01787 247431
www.greathouse.co.uk
Closed: January, 24–31 October

A 14th-century property in Market Place, this elegant restaurant with rooms brings a genuine flavour of France to historic Lavenham. The Great House oozes period charm, with efficient and attentive service in the dining room where local ingredients are transformed into creative Gallic-inspired dishes with a contemporary tweak. A beautifully presented starter of cured yellow fin tuna is served with dill gel, yellow beetroot, pomegranate 'caviar' and fresh herbs. To follow, grilled saddle of wild venison has a classic accompaniment of Jerusalem artichoke purée, sautéed fine beans and venison jus as well as parsley crisps and lemon gel.

Chef: Swann Auffray, Mathieu Gache
Food Style: Modern French

See advertisement opposite

Layham

The Marquis ◉◉
Upper Street, IP7 5JZ
01473 377977
www.themarquissuffolk.co.uk
Open: All year

Chef: Tom Bushell
Food Style: Modern British

The Marquis is an old coaching inn but on the inside it's very much 21st century. The floor to ceiling window that spans the length of the airy dining room offers spectacular panoramic views across the Brett Valley, making this a wonderful setting for the seasonal British dishes created in the open kitchen. Cornish crab tacos might start things off, followed by Josper grilled lamb with triple cooked chips.

NEW The Hog Hotel ⚘⚘
41 London Road, Pakefield, NR33 7AA
01502 569805
www.thehoghotel.co.uk
Closed: 1 week in January, 25 December

Close to the beach, the Hog Hotel has a very smart
brasserie style restaurant with dark tables, grey and
blue padded chairs, light oak flooring and an interesting
kind of retro-modern design. Service is relaxed,
attentive and professional. If you were wondering, the
Hog is a hedgehog, not anything of the porcine variety.

Chef: Terry Balme
Food Style: Modern British

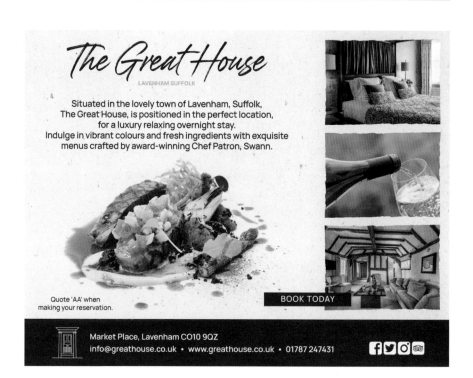

The Great House

LAVENHAM SUFFOLK

Situated in the lovely town of Lavenham, Suffolk,
The Great House, is positioned in the perfect location,
for a luxury relaxing overnight stay.
Indulge in vibrant colours and fresh ingredients with exquisite
menus crafted by award-winning Chef Patron, Swann.

Quote 'AA' when
making your reservation.

BOOK TODAY

Market Place, Lavenham CO10 9QZ
info@greathouse.co.uk • www.greathouse.co.uk • 01787 247431

Bedford Lodge Hotel & Spa ⊛⊛
Bury Road, CB8 7BX
01638 663175
www.bedfordlodgehotel.co.uk
Open: All year

This one-time Georgian hunting lodge offers plenty of top-end facilities to satisfy the modern epicure. The red-hued dining room sticks to a modern British mantra, starting perhaps with chicken liver parfait and moving on to seared fillet of Denham venison, smoked game sausage, celeriac dauphinoise and roasted baby turnips.

Chef: Lee Cooper
Food Style: British, Mediterranean

The Packhorse Inn ⊛⊛
Bridge Street, Moulton, CB8 8SP
01638 751818
www.thepackhorseinn.com
Open: All year

Chef: Win Hai (Sunny) Lau
Food Style: Modern British

Close to the racing at Newmarket, this modern country inn still pulls in local drinkers but it's the classy, inventive cooking that attracts foodies from far and wide. Suffolk produce is treated with respect in the kitchen and impressive pastry skills are evident in desserts.

NEW Tipi on the Stream ⊛⊛
High Street, Tuddenham St Mary, IP28 6SQ
01638 713552
www.tuddenhammill.co.uk
Open: All year

Food Style: Modern British

Located at Tuddenham Mill, a converted watermill, Tipi on the Stream is a very large tipi by the stream, offering around 30 covers. Furnished with natural wood tables and chairs as well as some bench seating; there are blankets and sheepskins if required, but the Tipi does have warm air heating. Service is informal but very attentive.

Upstairs at the Mill ⊛⊛⊛⊛ 🍷NOTABLE WINE LIST
See pages 444-445

Sibton

Sibton White Horse Inn
Halesworth Road, IP17 2JJ
01728 660337
www.sibtonwhitehorseinn.co.uk
Closed: 25–26 December

Chef: Ben Hegarty
Food Style: Modern British

This fascinating pub's Tudor origins – low ceilings, mighty ships' timbers, quarry tiles – are impossible to miss. The bar has a raised gallery, an elegant dining room and a secluded courtyard. The kitchen produces globally influenced modern cooking that's won a heap of awards.

Southwold

The Crown
90 High Street, IP18 6DP
01502 722275
www.thecrownsouthwold.co.uk
Open: All year

Chef: Stephen Duffield,
Robert Mace
Food Style: Modern British

The grand Georgian portico on Southwold's high street looks imposing, but once inside, bare floorboards and mismatched tables and chairs give The Crown a relaxed and pubby ambience. The kitchen draws on the local larder for a crowd-pleasing menu of uncomplicated modern British food, backed by a great roll-call of Adnams' beers and wines.

The Still Room Restaurant
The Swan, Market Place, IP18 6EG
01502 722186
theswansouthwold.co.uk/food-drink/
still-room-restaurant
Open: All year

Chef: Rory Whelan
Food Style: Modern British

The 17th-century Swan is the jewel in the Adnams empire's crown, and it's looking pretty buff after a top-to-toe refurb. Blending contemporary panache with its Georgian features, The Still Room's light and airy, modern and funky design references the house brewery and small-batch distillery as a backdrop to some inventive contemporary cooking.

Sutherland House
56 High Street, IP18 6DN
01502 724544
www.sutherlandhouse.co.uk
Closed: January, 25–26 December

Chef: Kinga Rudd
Food Style: Modern British,
Seafood

A period property of genuine charm, Sutherland House has wooden beams, ornate ceilings, coving and real fireplaces, with fixtures and fittings creating a chic finish. Likewise, the cooking impresses with its modern ambitions, passion for top-quality seafood and loyalty to locally-sourced ingredients.

Newmarket

🌹🌹🌹🌹 🍾 NOTABLE WINE LIST

Upstairs at the Mill

High Street, Tuddenham St Mary, IP28 6SQ
01638 713552
www.tuddenhammill.co.uk
Open: All year

Chef: Lee Bye
Food Style: Modern British

Assured modern cooking in renovated mill

The weatherboarded 18th-century mill, augmented in the Victorian era by a steam engine and towering brick chimney, may have ended its grinding days in the 1950s, but its heritage remains intact at the present-day boutique hotel.

For one thing, the fast-flowing stream that turned its waterwheel has been dredged of centuries of silt and is now a thriving wildlife habitat, while the majestic cast-iron wheel itself, framed by beams, glass walls and net curtains, forms a diverting centrepiece to the first-floor Upstairs at The Mill restaurant. This is what you might call a proper USP. It's a setting that seems to demand cooking with plenty of personality of its own and the talented team in the kitchen has an instinctive feel for combining ingredients from the surrounding region to good effect.

Thus, a typical opener strikes a balance between no-nonsense and contemporary

refinement via three succulent Loch Fyne king scallops, with a vibrant wild nettle butter, crunchy cobnuts and a fine julienne of apple. Juicy seven-hour-cooked shoulder of Norfolk Horn lamb served with two tender pieces of loin, Mr T's asparagus, green sauce, enoki mushroom and St Edmund's Ale is a straightforward but beautifully executed dish with lovely flavours.

Another clever construction might be ash-baked beetroot, Spenwood barley, red chicory and lovage. Desserts are executed with memorable dexterity, bringing entertaining plays of flavour and texture in ideas such as a millefeuille-style creation involving sea buckthorn, brown butter pastry, fig leaf ice cream and new season blackcurrants.

Again, it sounds straightforward in terms of the simplicity of the dish, but a bitter chocolate torte, coconut, meadowsweet caramel is a great combination. For a more casual dining experience, try the hotel's relaxed Tipi on the Stream set on the water's edge.

"...the talented team in the kitchen has an instinctive feel for combining ingredients..."

Sudbury

The Black Lion ⚜⚜
The Green, Long Melford, CO10 9DN
01787 312356
www.theblacklionhotel.com
Open: All year

Chef: Nicholas Traher
Food Style: Modern British

The Chestnut Group's imposing Black Lion has rapidly made a name for itself. There's no doubt that the discerning people of Suffolk have taken in a big way to the restaurant and its modern British cuisine.

Woodbridge

Seckford Hall Hotel ⚜⚜
IP13 6NU
01394 385678
www.seckford.co.uk
Open: All year

Chef: Luke Bailey
Food Style: Modern European, British

Approached by a sweeping drive through well-preened grounds, this blue-blooded Tudor pile impresses with its creeper-curtained brick façade, soaring chimneys and carved-oak front door. Culinary style is classical country house with a contemporary sensibility and the dessert menu offers old-school comforts.

The Unruly Pig ⚜⚜
Orford Road, Bromeswell, IP12 2PU
01394 460310
www.theunrulypig.co.uk
Closed: 25 December

Just five minutes from the market town of Woodbridge, this 16th-century pub is a lovely spot to enjoy a pint beneath original oak beams. Despite its age, The Unruly Pig has a contemporary look and feel with shabby-chic decor, a modern European menu, and relaxed, friendly service.

Chef: Dave Wall
Food Style: British, Italian

Yaxley

The Auberge ⚜⚜
Ipswich Road, IP23 8BZ
01379 783604
www.the-auberge.co.uk

Chef: John Stenhouse, Mark and Helena Bond
Food Style: Modern European

Ancient beams, panelling and exposed brickwork dating back to medieval times are clear evidence that The Auberge has been an inn for many centuries, but the current name – which is simply 'inn' in French – describes today's modern restaurant with rooms. The dining room is darkly intimate and French influences underpin modern, skilfully rendered food.

Surrey

Bagshot

Steve Smith at Latymer

Pennyhill Park, London Road, GU19 5EU
01276 471774
www.exclusive.co.uk/pennyhill-park/food/latymer
Closed: 1st 2 weeks January

Chef: Steve Smith
Food Style: Modern European

The Latymer is one of the top restaurants in the country, set in the creeper-covered Victorian manor at the heart of the 123-acre Pennyhill estate whose grounds encompass a high-powered hotel with elegant gardens, wild woodland, a less wild golf course and a swish spa. It's a genteel and luxurious space with panelled walls and rich floral fabrics all contributing to a formal and elegant setting for food of thrilling modernity, with Steve Smith's contemporary cooking techniques showcased on six-course tasting menus – allow 3 hours for the whole experience. The menu is highly seasonal and constantly evolving. You might have Delica pumpkin, cep, quail egg and Iberico ham; Brixham crab salad, buttermilk and dill; butter-poached Skrei cod, chanterelle and truffle; Herdwick lamb loin, artichoke and black garlic; pink grapefruit and burnt honey. This is British cooking at its best.

Chobham

Stovell's

125 Windsor Road, GU24 8QS
01276 858000
www.stovells.com
Closed: 19–25 August

Chef: Fernando Stovell
Food Style: Modern European

A 16th-century Tudor farmhouse in rural Surrey, this quaint building retains all of its original charm with an abundance of beams, low ceilings and open fireplaces. A welcome injection of contemporary style includes striking pictures of mushrooms on the walls of the restaurant, where the food is modern with bold flavours and creative presentation. Vibrant dishes change with the seasons with Mexican influences evident across the menu. Crisp blue corn tortilla topped with a refried bean purée, home-made cheese, pork dripping and minced chorizo might lead on to a well-timed wood roasted monkfish, chermoula and Israeli couscous.

How do you keep yourself under the radar?

By adopting plenty of aliases, have 'reasons' to be in the area – perhaps looking at a property or undertaking consultancy work down the road.

AA Inspector

Dorking

Sorrel ◉◉◉◉ 🍷NOTABLE WINE LIST

77 South Street, RH4 2JU
01306 889414
sorrelrestaurant.co.uk
Closed: 24-28 December

Chef: Steve Drake
Food Style: Modern British

Menus change seasonally at Sorrel, a 300-year-old Grade II listed brick building with a unique glass walled kitchen. There's a lovely cosy feel to the restaurant, rooms are divided by delightful exposed wooden beams which add both character and warmth. Immaculately set tables add to the luxury feel which is mirrored by the excellent and attentive service by the friendly, professional, well drilled front of house team complete with knowledgeable sommelier. Steve Drake's cooking is stylish and contemporary and his seasonal, ingredients-led compositions are full of creativity, with the kitchen delivering inspirational dishes via lunch and dinner menus. You might begin with pork belly, smoked cauliflower, ponzu, clams and monk's beard and follow on with turbot, gem lettuce, celeriac and lemon, dulse butter and Dublin Bay milk, or Cornish lamb, piquillo pepper, asparagus, haw-sin, lovage and wild garlic. Finish with blueberry ice cream, lavender cake, oregano and their own ginger tea.

Egham

The Estate Grill at Great Fosters ◉◉

Stroude Road, TW20 9UR
01784 433822
www.greatfosters.co.uk
Open: All year

The Estate Grill chefs use Old Spots pigs reared in the grounds and honey from the apiary, as well as Cumbrian fell-bred lamb. Sharing platters are a possibility – charcuterie to start and a selection of the estate-reared pork for main. In warmer months, eat out on the delightful terrace.

Chef: Ondřej Knedla
Food Style: Modern British

The Lock Bar and Kitchen at The Runnymede on Thames ◉

Windsor Road, TW20 0AG
01784 220999
www.runnymedehotel.com/food-drink
Open: All year

Chef: Adesh Bissonauth
Food Style: Modern

The scene could hardly be more 'Wind in the Willows', with the Thames burbling by, and outdoor tables and parasols set out by Bell Weir lock that lends its name to the kitchen and bar. The parquet-floored brasserie room has a light, breezy ambience.

Tony Parkin at the Tudor Room ⊛⊛⊛ ▲NOTABLE WINE LIST
Great Fosters, Stroude Road, TW20 9UR
01784 433822
www.alexanderhotels.co.uk/great-fosters
Closed: 2 weeks in January, 1 week at Easter, 2 weeks
in August

Chef: Tony Parkin
Food Style: Modern European

Great Fosters is a splendid, many-gabled red-brick
Tudor house with 50 acres of gardens and parkland.
The main dining room, with its ornately carved
fireplace and dramatic 17th-century Flemish tapestry,
is an intimate space of just seven tables. Here you'll
find restrained, sophisticated dishes, and fantastic
ingredients handled with skill and precision. The precise menu descriptions give little away. Start
the memorable journey with Jersey Royals, smoked eel, horseradish, Granny Smith; or Orkney
scallops, finger lime, ginger, spring onion, hot and sour broth, then Newlyn turbot, elderflower,
cucumber, jalapeño, or Cornish lamb, asparagus, pine, girolles and black truffle.

Epsom

Dastaan ⊛⊛
447 Kingston Road, Ewell, KT19 0DB
020 8786 8999
www.dastaan.co.uk
Closed: Monday, 25 December

Chef: Nand Kishore Semwal
Food Style: Indian

Forget the low-key location off a traffic-mobbed
dual carriageway in Epsom's hinterland, Dastaan is a
neighbourhood gem and anything but your regular
curry house. There's an open kitchen and the heady
whiff of spices, and the atmosphere's much more
Mumbai café than Surrey Indian. Even better, the
intelligently compact menu delivers a succession of
authentic flavours bursting with freshness, finesse and attitude.

Guildford

NEW The Grill ⊛
36–40 London Road, GU1 2AE
01483 303030
www.guildford.com
Closed: 25 December

Chef: Prithwiraj (Raj) Das
Food Style: Modern British

Part of the impressive Mandolay Hotel in Guildford's
city centre, The Grill can be bright and airy or
atmospherically intimate. Open tables and discrete
booths, woven mats, linen napery and quality
glassware, air conditioning and jazz music in the
background. As you'd expect, dishes from the grill make
up much of the menu, but there's still plenty of choice.

Guildford *continued*

The Long Bar & Grill ⊛

Guildford Harbour Hotel, 3 Alexandra Terrace,
High Street, GU1 3DA
01483 792300
www.guildford-harbour-hotel.co.uk
Open: All year

Chef: Steve Hubbert
Food Style: Classic British

Located within the Harbour Hotel, The Jetty has a separate entrance leading into a jolly ambience of sand- and sea-coloured seating. These signifiers announce a seafood bar and grill, the appealing menus built around main courses such as herby crab-crusted cod with creamy mash and peas.

Horley

Langshott Manor ⊛⊛⊛

Langshott Lane, RH6 9LN
01293 786680
www.langshottmanor.com
Open: All year

Chef: Giuseppina Terracciano
Food Style: Modern European

A 16th-century property just 15 minutes by car from Gatwick Airport, Langshott Manor oozes olde-worlde character with its wooden beams and oak panelling. Looking out across the lovely garden, the restaurant has a more modern feel with good quality furnishings, white linen tablecloths and tea lights adding plenty of relaxed ambience. The cooking is contemporary, too, a starter of melt-in-the-mouth cured trout flanked by pickled radish and cucumber pearls, cucumber ketchup and dill lemon emulsion. Follow it with mallard, foie gras and duck beignet, salt-baked root vegetables, Lyonnaise onion purée and port wine jus.

Leatherhead

NEW The Victoria Oxshott ⊛⊛⊛ 🍷NOTABLE WINE LIST

See page opposite

“

What changes have you seen over the past few years?

A wonderful response to the hardships of Covid and Brexit – the industry becoming more collegiate and collaborative. The result is a focus on what really is essential to a restaurant.

AA Inspector

NOTABLE WINE LIST

NEW The Victoria Oxshott

High Street, KT22 OJR
01372 238308
www.thevictoriaoxshott.com
Closed: Monday, Tuesday

Chef: Matt Larcombe
Food Style: Modern British

A charming village pub set located between Leatherhead and Esher, The Victoria Oxshott has a relaxed, welcoming vibe with open fires, friendly and attentive service. At the rear is a delightful garden area which comes into its own over the summer and there is a relaxed dining room.

The kitchen sticks to a tried-and-tested modern British take on pub food down to sharing boards and snacks. A typical meal could start with a light and flavour-packed mushroom parfait, sweet and sour onions and brioche, followed by a lovely piece of pan-fried halibut accompanied by plump St Austell Bay mussels, parsley and potatoes cooked in seaweed butter. A cheeky take on a Snickers bar turns up at the dessert stage – the precise square of aerated chocolate, roasted peanuts, nutty mousse and oozing caramel centre served with a scoop of ice cream.

Each course displays strong technical skill and serious intent from the kitchen together with a carefully curated wine list that combines affordable quaffers alongside rare bottles.

Ottershaw

Foxhills Club & Resort ◉◉
Stonehill Road, KT16 0EL
01932 704471
www.foxhills.co.uk
Open: All year

Chef: Paul Green
Food Style: Modern, Classic British

A short hop from Heathrow, this Victorian manor comes with a championship golf course, a spa and multifarious sporting pursuits spread around its 400-acre estate to help work up an appetite for contemporary, ingredient-led cooking in the Manor Restaurant. A starter of pressed pigeon might precede a main course of venison.

Redhill

Nutfield Priory Hotel & Spa ◉◉
Nutfield, RH1 4EL
01737 824400
www.handpickedhotels.co.uk/nutfieldpriory
Open: All year

Chef: Alec Mackins
Food Style: Modern British

The Priory is a classic Victorian Gothic extravaganza dating from the 1870s. Set in 12 acres on Nutfield Ridge, The Cloisters Restaurant has mullioned windows offering expansive views over the grounds towards the spine of the South Downs and makes an atmospheric backdrop for a creative, modern take on country-house cooking.

Ripley

The Anchor ◉◉
High Street, GU23 6AE
01483 211866
www.ripleyanchor.co.uk
Closed: 24–26 December

Dating back to the 16th century, the old brick-and-timber building's interior sympathetically blends old and new – think beams and exposed brick meets pastel tones and trendy leatherette seating, while a cosy snug, bar and alfresco courtyard add kudos. Light, adept, pretty, modern dishes fit the bill.

Chef: Michael Wall-Palmer
Food Style: Modern British

The Clock House 🏵🏵🏵 ⬩NOTABLE WINE LIST
High Street, GU23 6AQ
01483 224777
www.theclockhouserestaurant.co.uk

Chef: Paul Nicholson
Food Style: Modern British

Closed: 1 week in January, 1 week after Easter, 2 weeks in August, 1 week at Christmas

The namesake signature clock above the front door of this imposing Georgian building certainly draws the eye on well-healed Ripley's pretty High Street. Inside is equally elegant, with on-trend pastel shades and clean lines set against stripped-back old wall timbers and tall street-side windows. A relaxed vibe extends to the informed, sunny-natured service, while chef Paul Nicholson's thoroughbred modern cooking delivers via a roster of fixed-price menus, including tasting options. Simplicity, lightness of touch and flavour reign supreme in dressed-to-thrill dishes of panache; take 'sparkling-fresh' line-caught plaice with coco beans, pork and fennel to a Bakewell dessert with cherry and almond, while formal-code amuse-bouche and in-house bread are equally classy.

Shere

NEW Kinghams Restaurant 🏵🏵
Gomshall Lane, GU5 9HE
01483 202168
kinghams-restaurant.co.uk
Closed: Monday

Chef: Mohssine El Faddi
Food Style: Modern British

Kinghams Restaurant is at the heart of the Surrey Hills, in the picturesque village of Shere. It dates back to the 17th century, so as you'd expect it enjoys a wealth of characterful period features. The quality dishes have a slight Moroccan influence, and it's all fresh produce, sourced through local suppliers.

Stoke d'Abernon

Oak Room 🏵🏵
Woodlands Park Hotel, Woodlands Lane, KT11 3QB
01372 843933
www.handpickedhotels.co.uk/woodlandspark
Open: All year

Chef: John Stephens
Food Style: Modern British

Built in 1885 by William Bryant of the safety match dynasty, this magnificent pile is set in landscaped gardens and the grandeur extends to the oak-panelled restaurant. Provenance drives the menu, a typical meal starting with duck and goose liver terrine before sea bream, baby squid, samphire and red pepper marmalade.

Weybridge

Brooklands Hotel ❀❀
Brooklands Drive, KT13 0SL
01932 335700
www.brooklandshotelsurrey.com
Open: All year

This thrillingly modern structure overlooks the first purpose-built car-racing circuit in the world, opening back in 1907. There's a creative modern brasserie feel to the food, with the kitchen team keenly producing dishes that arrive on the plate dressed to thrill.

Chef: Jonathan Phillips
Food Style: British, European

Wonersh

Oak Room Restaurant ❀❀
Barnett Hill Hotel, Blackheath Lane, GU5 0RF
01483 893361
www.alexanderhotels.co.uk/barnett-hill
Open: All year

Barnett Hall is a handsome manor house that was once the home of Thomas Cook. The Oak Room Restaurant has a nicely formal atmosphere, with oak panelled walls, a large fireplace, ornate white ceilings and smartly upholstered grey chairs. The cooking shows style and innovation but doesn't fail to deliver comfort and generosity.

Food Style: Modern British

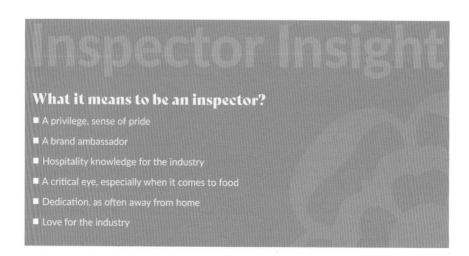

Inspector Insight

What it means to be an inspector?

- A privilege, sense of pride
- A brand ambassador
- Hospitality knowledge for the industry
- A critical eye, especially when it comes to food
- Dedication, as often away from home
- Love for the industry

East Sussex

The Powder Mills Hotel ⓐⓐ
Powdermill Lane, TN33 0SP
01424 775511
www.powdermillshotel.com
Closed: 9–22 January

Chef: Ahmed Shawkey
Food Style: Modern British

Powder Mills was once the site of a major gunpowder-making operation that helped defeat Napoleon. It stands in 150 acres of lush parkland with a seven-acre fishing lake. The owner's springer spaniels sometimes welcome arrivals, and dining takes place in the Orangery Restaurant. The kitchen offers high quality produce executed with accuracy and attention to detail.

64 Degrees ⓐⓐ
53 Meeting House Lane, BN1 1HB
01273 770115
www.64degrees.co.uk
Closed: 25–26 December, 1 January

In the heart of Brighton's famous Lanes, this bijou restaurant is big on small plates, the idea being convivial tapas-style sharing in a buzzy ambience focused on the counter at the open kitchen. The menu's economically worded fish, veg and meat options – four of each – reveal nothing of the creativity within each sharply crafted dish.

Chef: Tom Stephens
Food Style: Modern British

NEW Botanique ⓐ
31a Western Road, BN3 1AF
01273 567200
www.botaniquebrighton.com
Closed: Monday

This newcomer to the Brighton vegan restaurant scene has its own hydroponic kitchen garden, which helps tick all the boxes for zero food miles, seasonality and freshness of ingredients, all used imaginatively and served in a neutral, organic-looking setting with a friendly, laid-back ambience

Chef: Josephine Hawkins
Food Style: Vegan

Brighton *continued*

etch. by Steven Edwards 🏵🏵🏵 ⌁NOTABLE WINE LIST

214–216 Church Road, BN3 2DJ
01273 227485
www.etchfood.co.uk
Closed: 25 December, 1 January

Chef: Steven Edwards,
George Boarer
Food Style: Modern British

The eponymous restaurant from this former BBC *MasterChef: The Professionals* winner continues to impress with its buzzy air and thrilling food. The moody monochrome look and open kitchen adds a cool vibe to the place and the monthly-changing set menus have their heart in Sussex produce. Begin with a prime piece of line-caught brill, butter-roasted served with tarragon noodles and silky parsnip purée. Next, well-rested rump of soy and honey-marinated hogget and shredded braised shoulder turns up with buttered and roasted leeks and oyster leaf. Finish with blackberry parfait, sheep's yogurt and toffee tuile.

Hotel du Vin Brighton 🏵 ⌁NOTABLE WINE LIST

2–6 Ship Street, BN1 1AD
01273 718588
www.hotelduvin.com
Open: All year

Chef: Rob Carr
Food Style: Traditional British,
French

The Brighton branch of the chain has all the expected Francophile touches, its walls adorned with posters and risqué pictures, leather-look banquettes running back to back down the centre and small wooden tables. A glance at the menu reveals more than your average bistro fare.

Isaac At 🏵🏵

2 Gloucester Street, BN1 4EW
07765 934740
www.isaac-at.com
Closed: Sunday, Monday, Tuesday, 25 December to
1 Janaury

'Local' and 'seasonal' is the mantra in this ambitious, pocket-sized outfit in the trendy North Laine quarter – even the wines are from Sussex vineyards. Serving just 20 or so diners from an open kitchen in a stripped-back space, the venue fits the youthful Brighton mood, and the food keeps step with modern trends.

Chef: Caspian Armani
Food Style: Modern British

NEW Kusaki ◉
5-6 Circus Parade, New England Road, BN1 4GW
01273 620858
www.kusakibrighton.com
Open: All year

A buzzy newcomer to the Brighton foodie scene,
Kusaki looks the part with its minimal urban style,
bright abstract art, cherry blossom tree and Japanese
shoji panels. Expect some big palate-tingling Japanese
flavours on its creative menu of plant-based dishes.

Chef: Oli Grant
Food Style: Japanese Vegan

The Little Fish Market ◉◉◉
10 Upper Market Street, Hove, BN3 1AS
01273 722213
www.thelittlefishmarket.co.uk
Closed: 1 week March, 2 weeks September, 25 December

Chef: Duncan Ray
Food Style: Modern, Fish

In a little side street off Hove's Western Road, chef-patron Duncan Ray's modest little operation
certainly punches above its weight. After stints at The Fat Duck and Pennyhill Park, here he
works with meticulous attention to detail, producing stunning local and sustainable seafood
cooked with exemplary accuracy and an intelligent creative edge. The setting is a light-filled
space done out with a pared-back contemporary look and charming, well informed service –
delivered partly by the chef himself. The fixed-price menu offers dishes including 'Krabi' –
Thai-inspired crab meat with mango gel, puffed rice, peanut brittle and Thai green curry sauce.
The bright, clean flavours continue in stunning sea bass with mussels and scallop pointed up
with mussel veloute and chervil.

Terre à Terre ◉
71 East Street, BN1 1HQ
01273 729051
terreaterre.co.uk
Closed: 25–26 December

This trendsetting restaurant serves creative, classy
veggie-vegan food. It's just back from the seafront, and
the pared-back dining area stretches back to a small
terrace. The service team can help with the eccentric
menu's sometimes baffling descriptions. Inspiration
comes from around the globe.

Chef: David Marrow
Food Style: Modern Vegetarian

Camber

The Gallivant
New Lydd Road, TN31 7RB
01797 225057
www.thegallivant.co.uk
Open: All year

Overlooking the Camber shoreline near Rye and right on the beach, The Gallivant has its heart in New England, where that laid-back eastern seaboard style translates as oceans of space, light wood, and café furniture. Sourcing from within a 10-mile radius is an especially good idea when the radius takes in such impeccable meals.

Chef: Jamie Guy
Food Style: Modern British

Ditchling

The Bull Ditchling
2 High Street, BN6 8TA
01273 843147
www.thebullditchling.com
Open: All year

Chef: Steve Sanger
Food Style: Modern British

In the heart of Ditchling, The Bull has been a community hub for centuries, as the inglenook fire, half-timbered walls and old beams testify. The restaurant has a buzzing brasserie feel and the modern British cooking uses some produce so local that's its grown in their kitchen garden.

Eastbourne

The Mirabelle Restaurant
The Grand Hotel, King Edwards Parade, BN21 4EQ
01323 412345
www.grandeastbourne.com
Closed: Sunday, Monday

Part of the Grand Hotel at Eastbourne, The Mirabelle has very classy blue and grey decor, smartly upholstered chairs, linen clothed tables and crisp napery that brings a contemporary dash to the Victorian setting. The whole place is comfortable and spacious, creating a great place to relax and enjoy the sea views.

Chef: Michael Sutherland
Food Style: Modern, Classic European

East Chiltington

Jolly Sportsman ⚜
Chapel Lane, BN7 3BA
01273 890400
www.thejollysportsman.com
Closed: 25 December

Located deep in the South Downs hinterland, a GPS comes in handy for hunting down this weatherboarded country inn. There's a cosy bar area with casks on trestles and a rustic-chic restaurant. The kitchen delivers full-flavoured, contemporary cooking.

See advertisement below

Chef: Vincent Fayat
Food Style: Modern, Classic

Forest Row

The Anderida Restaurant 🏵🏵
Ashdown Park Hotel & Country Club, Wych Cross,
RH18 5JR
01342 824988
www.ashdownpark.com
Open: All year

Ashdown Park is a magnificent Victorian pile in acres of
grounds, and The Anderida Restaurant, with its elegant
drapes, sparkling glassware, double-clothed tables
and grand piano, is a fine setting for cooking that is a
sophisticated take on both classical and contemporary.

Chef: Tony Sanders
Food Style: Modern British

Hastings

NEW The Stag Inn Awaiting Inspection
14 All Saints Street, TN34 3BJ
01424 438791
www.staghastings.co.uk
Closed: 1 week January

At the top of All Saints Street in Hastings Old Town,
is the 16th-century Stag Inn. Inside, beamed ceilings
and bare floorboards create a great place to listen to
some live music and enjoy passionately prepared meals.
The large pub garden is also a kitchen garden, staff are
friendly, and the whole set-up is very welcoming.

Chef: Benjamin Cumberpatch
Food Style: European

Rye

Mermaid Inn 🏵🏵
Mermaid Street, TN31 7EY
01797 223065
www.mermaidinn.com
Open: All year

Near the top of a cobbled side street, the Mermaid
Inn dates back to 1420, with 12th-century cellars, and
was once well-known for its clientele of smugglers,
including the notorious 17th-century Hawkhurst
Gang. British and French-style food is on the table
under the black-and-white timbers of the atmospheric
dining room.

See advertisement opposite

Chef: Ollie Melfor,
Chayanin Selakan,
Food Style: British,
Traditional French

Webbe's at The Fish Café ⬡
17 Tower Street, TN31 7AT
01797 222226
www.webbesrestaurants.co.uk
Closed: 25–26 December, First 2 weeks January

A brick-built former warehouse dating from 1907 is home to this modern seafood restaurant. Exposed brickwork, high ceilings and fish-related artwork all feed in to the buzz of the smart dining room where the chefs work their magic in the open kitchen. Fish is king here, but meat eaters and veggies won't feel left out judging by the wide-ranging menu.

Chef: Paul Webbe
Food Style: Modern, Seafood

Welcome to the unique **Mermaid Inn**, rich in history, cellars dating from 1156 and the building rebuilt in 1420. The Mermaid Inn offers a totally different experience, sloping ceilings, creaking floorboards and numerous staircases. A history and a rich tradition that is maintained by careful stewardship. Experience a drink in the Giant's Fireplace Bar and imagine how the Hawkhurst Gang, local smugglers in the 1730s and 1740s, caroused in the bar. Can you see the secret passageway entrance?

Dine in the Linen Fold Panelled Restaurant, where you can enjoy the ambience of the large restaurant, the cosiness of The Dr Syn Dining Room or the privacy of the Boardroom for your evening meal, lunch and breakfast.

Head chef Ollie Melford is very focused on using quality, seasonal, local ingredients and cooking them perfectly. He is able to adapt to the requirements of the guest and the occasion.

The menu features local produce, such as Winchelsea Beef, Rye Bay Cod and Romney Marsh Lamb. There is an extensive wine list including wine from Chapel Down in nearby Small Hythe, Kent. All of these can be found on
www.mermaidinn.com

Mermaid Inn, Mermaid Street, Rye, East Sussex, TN31 7EY
Tel: 01797 223065, Fax: 01797 225069

Ticehurst

Dale Hill Hotel & Golf Club ⊛
TN5 7DQ
01580 200112
www.dalehill.co.uk
Open: All year

At Dale Hill Hotel & Golf Club, with its pair of 18-
hole courses, golf may be top of the agenda, but hill
views and a pair of restaurants are reason enough for
non-players to visit. The fine-dining Wealden View
restaurant is the star attraction; modern European
cooking is par for this particular course.

Chef: Adam Jaroszek
Food Style: Modern European

Uckfield

Buxted Park Hotel ⊛⊛
Buxted, TN22 4AY
01825 733333
www.handpickedhotels.co.uk/buxtedpark
Open: All year

Chef: Mark Carter
Food Style: Modern European

Offering the full country-house package, the hotel has hosted eminent guests, including William
Wordsworth and Marlon Brando, and indeed many others. Celebrity or not, diners will enjoy
good, honest modern European dishes, including textures of Cornish crab, pickled rhubarb
and avocado purée; pork fillet and belly with tomato and olive croquettes; and chocolate and
banana fondant.

Horsted Place ⊛⊛
Little Horsted, TN22 5TS
01825 750581
www.horstedplace.co.uk
Open: All year

Gothic Revivalist architect Augustus Pugin certainly
worked his wonders here at Horsted Place, hard on
the heels of his design for the interior of the new
Palace of Westminster. Done in elegant Victorian mode,
the rich green dining room is a calming space for well-
executed modern British dishes built from top-class
seasonal materials.

Chef: Lee Roberts
Food Style: Modern British

Wadhurst

NEW Sussex Pass ⊚
White Hart, High Street, TN5 6AP
01892 351230
www.sussexpassrestaurant.co.uk
Closed: Monday, Tuesday, 25 December

Chef: Adam Sear
Food Style: Modern classical

Set in the welcoming White Hart inn on the high street, the Sussex Pass is big on showcasing the finest produce from Sussex and Kent in its appealing menus. Expect well-executed, flavour-packed dishes from a kitchen team that puts its heart into its cooking.

Westfield

The Wild Mushroom Restaurant ⊚⊚
Woodgate House, Westfield Lane, TN35 4SB
01424 751137
www.wildmushroom.co.uk
Closed: Monday, Tuesday, 1 week November,
25–26 December, First 2 weeks January

Paul and Rebecca Webbe opened their restaurant in this former private house in 1998. They were inspired by their love of the natural ingredients on their doorstep, such as the sustainable fish and shellfish landed daily at Hastings, and the bounty from wild food foraging. Thus their 'Sussex by the Season' philosophy, which Paul teaches in his Fish Café in Rye.

Chef: Christopher Weddle
Food Style: Modern British

What excites you most in your work?

Being surprised by something or someone.
The simple pleasure of tasting something truly delicious.

AA Inspector

West Sussex

Amberley Castle 🏵️🏵️🏵️ ⏺NOTABLE WINE LIST
BN18 9LT
01798 831992
www.amberleycastle.co.uk
Open: All year

Chef: Paul Peters
Food Style: Classic European

Looking like the kind of place you'd happily pay the National Trust for the chance to look around, the Castle is a nearly millennium-old fortification at the foot of the South Downs that did time as a Royalist stronghold in the Civil War. Anywhere that is entered via a portcullis has more than a touch of class, an impression reinforced by the dining rooms with their armoury, tapestries, barrel-vault ceilings and lancet windows. Paul Peters produces assertive modern dishes with plenty to say for themselves, from an amuse-bouche of mushroom arancini and cheese gougère onwards. You might begin with a nicely-constructed scallop dish with caramelised cauliflower, hazelnut, golden raisin, caper, apple and Amberley ver jus. Main courses of wild sea bass, or veal (loin, cheek and sweetbread) are thoughtfully conceived and full of flavour. Bring things to a close with a beautiful pistachio bavarois with grapefruit and banana.

The Parsons Table 🏵️🏵️
2 & 8 Castle Mews, Tarrant Street, BN18 9DG
01903 883477
theparsonstable.co.uk
Closed: Sunday, Monday, 25 December to 5 January

Picture-perfect Arundel, laid out prettily beneath its majestic castle, is home to this bright, airy venue named not after a local cleric but the chef-patron. White walls and unclothed light wood tables furnish a neutral backdrop to thoroughgoing modern British culinary wizardry.

Chef: Lee Parsons
Food Style: British, European

NEW THE PIG-in the South Downs 🏵️🏵️
Madehurst, BN18 0NL
01243 974 500
www.thepighotel.com/in-the-south-downs/hotel-sussex

Food Style: Modern British

Located in a rural area, THE PIG-in the South Downs is a Palladian-style Georgian house that's been sympathetically renovated and extended. Its orangery-style restaurant has a quite minimal contemporary style of decor, and enjoys views of the gardens and grounds. The kitchen garden is the focus, with help from the forager, so menus are authentically seasonal.

Bosham

Sea School Restaurant ⚜️⚜️
Bosham Lane, PO18 8HL
01243 573234
www.millstreamhotel.com
Open: All year

The Sea School Restaurant is a quiet and charming place to enjoy a meal, and is part of The Millstream Hotel, created from a row of beautiful 17th-century red brick and flint cottages. The kitchen offers a happy blend of modern trends alongside traditional favourites. Seafood and Asian themed cooking are both particularly well served.

Chef: Neil Hiskey
Food Style: Modern British

See advertisement on page 467

Chichester

Earl of March ⚜️
Lavant Road, PO18 0BQ
01243 533993
www.theearlofmarch.com
Closed: 25 December

Just a short drive out of Chichester, this 18th-century coaching inn looks out over the South Downs. There's a small patio garden, but most of the action takes place inside, in the large dining area or the snug bar area with a fire and sofas.

Chef: Luke Cockram
Food Style: Modern British

Horse and Groom ⚜️⚜️
East Ashling, PO18 9AX
01243 575339
www.thehorseandgroom.pub
Closed: 25 December, 31 December, 1 January

Once a blacksmith's shop, the Horse and Groom has been the village pub for over 200 years, and retains many traditional features such as flagstone floors, wooden paneling, and exposed stone walls. The restaurant is full of art and interesting features, as well as fine seasonal modern British cooking. The chicken Wellington should make it well worth the visit.

Chef: Gary McDermott
Food Style: Modern British

Chichester *continued*

Potager Restaurant ⚜⚜
Crouchers Hotel, Birdham Road, PO20 7EH
01243 784995
www.crouchershotel.co.uk
Open: All year

Chef: David Smith
Food Style: Modern British

Over the past two decades as a stalwart of the Chichester dining scene, Crouchers has traded upwards from a simple B&B to a smart modern hotel near Dell Quay and the marina. Desserts maintain the high standards, as shown by the well-balanced flavours and textures.

The Ship Restaurant ⚜
57 North Street, PO19 1NH
01243 778000
www.chichester-harbour-hotel.co.uk
Open: All year

Chef: David Hunt
Food Style: British, Seafood

In the heart of Chichester, this hotel presents a sober, red-brick Georgian exterior, but inside the designers have unleashed a riot of boutique style. Murray's Restaurant is a split-level dining room that works a classy colonial look with palm trees, touchy-feely fabrics, exposed floorboards and unclothed dark wood tables. Brasserie-style menus tick the right boxes.

Goodwood

The Goodwood Hotel ⚜⚜
PO18 0QB
01243 775537
www.goodwood.com
Open: All year

Chef: Mark Forman
Food Style: Modern British

Part of the 12,000-acre Goodwood Estate, the Farmer, Butcher, Chef restaurant at this luxurious hotel uses pork, lamb and beef from the estate's organic home farm. Although there are plenty of fish and vegetarian options on the menu, home-reared meat dominates.

Hassocks

The Glass House Restaurant & Terrace ⚜
Wickwoods Country Club Hotel & Spa,
Shaveswood Lane, Albourne, BN6 9DY
01273 857567
www.wickwoods.co.uk
Closed: 25 December

As you might expect, The Glass House is a spacious, airy room with a skylight roof and floor-to-ceiling windows opening onto a heated and canopied terrace. It's all very chic, with low lighting, trendy chandeliers, and bare darkwood tables with tea lights. The menu has plenty from the chargrill, but there's no shortage of other options.

Chef: Neil Ruzicka
Food Style: Modern British

Kirdford

The Half Moon Inn ◉◉
Glasshouse Lane, RH14 0LT
01403 820223
www.halfmoonkirdford.co.uk
Closed: Monday, Tuesday, Wednesday

Owned by TV presenter and international model Jodie
Kidd, it ticks all the 'quintessential village pub' boxes –
oak beams, red-brick floors, an inglenook fireplace and
friendly staff. A tasty, indeed attractively presented,
opener is salmon and langoustine ravioli with rich
shellfish cream, peas and broad beans and decorated
with pub garden flowers.

Chef: Darren Velvick
Food Style: Modern British

Lodsworth

The Halfway Bridge Inn ◉
Halfway Bridge, GU28 9BP
01798 861281
www.halfwaybridge.co.uk
Open: All year

This classy 18th-century roadside inn makes an inviting
pitstop after a hike on the South Downs Way or a
leisurely perusal of Petworth's antique emporia. The
ambience is friendly and unbuttoned, while the kitchen
deals in pub classics given a contemporary tweak.

Chef: Clyde Hollett
Food Style: Modern British

What is your advice for cooking great food?
Keep it simple, keep it fresh

AA Inspector

The Camellia Restaurant at South Lodge ⊕⊕⊕ ⭐NOTABLE WINE LIST

Brighton Road, RH13 6PS
01403 891711
www.exclusive.co.uk/south-lodge
Open: All year

Chef: Josh Mann
Food Style: British

The Camellia is part of a handsome Victorian mansion hotel, its walls covered with wallpaper depicting red and pink camellias. There are lovely views of the garden as well. The cooking is modern British but with a sound foundation in the classics. Try a starter like hand-dived seared scallop with brawn, 'deconstructed piccalilli', scallop roe powder and smooth burnt leek purée. Follow up with roasted cod loin, confit chicken thigh, rose hip, wild cranberry and a vermicelli topping infused with hen of the woods mushroom powder. If there's room, try yogurt pannacotta with 'candy drop grapes' and a lavender goats' curd topping.

Restaurant Interlude ⊕⊕⊕

Leonardslee Gardens, Brighton Road, RH13 6PP
0871 873 3363
www.restaurant-interlude.co.uk
Closed: Monday, Tuesday, Wednesday

Chef: Jean Delport
Food Style: Modern British

Interlude occupies a glorious setting in the woodland gardens of the Leonardslee Estate. The grand old house doesn't lack for character with its high ceilings, ornate fireplaces, oil paintings and chandeliers, while the kitchen takes its cue from the seasons and makes full use of ingredients from its own gardens, as well as foraging and tapping into the local food network for top-notch Sussex produce. Expect bright, lively flavours in epic-length tasting format, from beef tartare smoked with gorse flowers, to poached plaice with parsley purée and knotweed vinegar, or 28 day-aged Middlewhite pork with wild garlic and capers.

The Chequers Inn ⊕

RH12 3PY
01403 790480
www.thechequersrowhook.com
Closed: 25 December

In business since the 15th century, The Chequers is a proper village local with flagstones, oak beams, chunky wooden tables, open fires and well-kept real ales on hand pump. A skilful kitchen keeps the food department in tune with modern tastes, with no pretensions, just bang-on-the-money pub classics and more modern ideas with a clear French influence.

Chef: Tim Neal
Food Style: British

Sidlesham

The Crab & Lobster ◉◉
Mill Lane, PO20 7NB
01243 641233
www.crab-lobster.co.uk
Closed: 25 December

The whitewashed 17th-century pub is an upscale restaurant with rooms, and looks spruce from top to bottom. On the edge of the Pagham Harbour nature reserve, it offers a stylish restaurant that aims to impress with ambitious, top-notch modern British food.

Chef: Clyde Hollett, Dan Storey
Food Style: Modern British

Turners Hill

AG's Restaurant at Alexander House Hotel ◉◉◉
East Street, RH10 4QD
01342 714914
www.alexanderhouse.co.uk
Closed: Monday, Tuesday, Wednesday

Chef: Johnny Stanford
Food Style: British, French

Set in 120 acres of countryside, Alexander House is convenient for Gatwick, but tranquil enough to serve as a real getaway. AG's Restaurant has painted panelled walls, turquoise and grey decor, a high plasterwork ceiling and a marble fireplace. The kitchen covers all dietary bases with vegetarian, vegan and dairy-free versions of set-price and tasting menus. Cooking is contemporary, with striking combinations of ingredients and heaps of visual artistry. First off, langoustine teams up with lardo and pine twigs. Next, there's sea trout with celeriac and preserved gooseberry or smoked cod roe with Jersey Royals and marsh greens.

Reflections at Alexander House ◉◉
Alexander House Hotel & Utopia Spa, East Street,
RH10 4QD
01342 714914
www.alexanderhouse.co.uk
Open: All year

Chef: Darrel Wild
Food Style: Modern British

The handsome 17th-century mansion has moved into boutique territory after a thoroughly modern makeover, with pampering facilities to delight spa enthusiasts and a buzzy brasserie – Reflections – to lift the spirits still further the fine-dining option is AG's Restaurant.

West Hoathly

Gravetye Manor Hotel ⚜⚜⚜⚜ 🍷 NOTABLE WINE LIST
See pages 472-473

Worthing

Indigo Seafood & Grill ⚜
Ardington Hotel, Steyne Gardens, BN11 3DZ
01903 230451
www.indigorestaurant.info
Closed: 25 December to 4 January

Chef: Luca Mason, John Wheatland
Food Style: Modern British, European

Just outside the town centre, and a few minutes' walk from the seafront, Indigo is a contemporary seafood and grill restaurant. Red leather banquettes and lavish chandeliers add a luxurious touch to the proceedings, although the vibrant, globally-influenced food is simple and well-defined.

PITCH Restaurant ⚜⚜
16 Warwick Street, BN11 3DJ
01903 952460
www.pitchrestaurant.co.uk
Closed: Monday

Local lad and *MasterChef* 2018 winner Kenny Tutt's aim is 'to cook food that makes people smile', and he's certainly ticking that box here judging by the burble of happy diners in his bright and breezy contemporary brasserie-style venue. Expect plenty of top-class local produce in skilfully cooked modern dishes.

Chef: Kenny Tutt
Food Style: Modern British

West Hoathly

 NOTABLE WINE LIST

Gravetye Manor Hotel

Vowels Lane, RH19 4LJ
01342 810567
www.gravetyemanor.co.uk
Open: All year

Chef: George Blogg
Food Style: Modern British

Wonderful historic setting for equally wonderful modern food

Built in the 1590s, Gravetye Manor set in acres of grounds, with some of England's most important historic gardens surrounding the sumptuous Tudor country house hotel with all the period details you could wish for, from the mullioned windows to the plasterwork ceilings and panelled walls. The stunning dining room is rather more modern, with floor-to-ceiling windows that overlook the beautiful gardens and create a wonderful setting for the dynamic, contemporary British cooking that makes the most of the produce from the huge kitchen gardens.

The daily-changing set menus (three course lunch, four course dinner) are seasonal, and dishes are pretty as a picture, as well as offering exceptional levels of skill and depths of flavour. Dishes are complex without being fussy or convoluted, be assured this is some of the best food in the country.

Begin with a luscious mousse of Dorset crab with apple and coriander, or an immaculately seared hand-dived scallop with delicate, crisp-skinned chicken wing and an intense cauliflower purée. Ryeland hogget with spring greens, onion and wild leek is a fabulous main, the loin pink and tender, the shoulder rich and gamey, the whole dish offering clear, deep flavours and great balance.

Pre-dessert might be sesame crisp with intensely lemony sorbet, light and cleansing, with a great nutty crunch in cracker and little bits of brittle. A top class forced rhubarb soufflé, risen to perfection, is light as air and beautifully pink, and comes with deeply flavoured stem ginger ice cream.

As you might expect, everything from bread – maybe black malted barley or seeded onion – to deliciously flavoured butters – chive and lemon, or tomato and paprika – and canapés like a melt-in-the-mouth truffle and Sussex Charmer cheese gougère or a beetroot and citrus gel tart – is exceptional, demonstrating the same high levels of skill and creativity.

"...dishes are pretty as a picture, as well as offering exceptional levels of skill and depths of flavour."

Tyne & Wear

Gateshead

Eslington Villa Hotel 🏵
8 Station Road, Low Fell, NE9 6DR
0191 487 6017
www.eslingtonvilla.co.uk
Closed: 25–26 December, 1 January

Originally built for a Victorian industrialist, today's hotel retains bags of period features, allied with contemporary verve and character. Dining goes on mainly in a light and airy conservatory extension with tiled floor and commanding views over the lawns, as well as in the interior room behind it.

Chef: Jamie Walsh
Food Style: Modern

Newcastle upon Tyne

21 Newcastle 🏵
Trinity Gardens, Quayside, NE1 2HH
0191 222 0755
www.21newcastle.co.uk
Closed: 25 December, 1 January

Located just off the Quayside, the spacious, glass-fronted brasserie is popular with the area's office folk but also with the people who 'do lunch'. Bright and welcoming, it remains as buzzy as ever, with slick and smooth service. The appealing modern brasserie-style dishes playing a big part in the attraction.

Chef: Chris Dobson
Food Style: Modern British

NEW Blackfriars Restaurant 🏵
Friars Street, NE1 4XN
0191 261 5945
www.blackfriarsrestaurant.co.uk
Closed: Bank Holidays

Amongst the ruins of the city wall and old monastery, aptly named Blackfriars Restaurant dates from the 13th century and has plenty of original features. Thick stone walls and stained glass windows remain with wooden floors and low ceilings. There's an impressive wine list to accompany skilful British cooking.

Chef: Christopher Wardale
Food Style: Modern, Traditional British

The Broad Chare ❀

25 Broad Chare, NE1 3DQ
0191 211 2144
www.thebroadchare.co.uk
Closed: 25–26 December, 1 January

Located just off the Quayside, this new kind of 'old' pub features stripped back rustic wood and exposed stone. Nothing fancy, nothing fussy, but great beer with quality produce simply put together to maximise flavour. The specials board changes on a regular basis. Local produce is used to good effect.

Chef: Dan Warren
Food Style: Modern British

NEW Dobson & Parnell ❀

19-21 Queen Street, NE1 3UG
0191 221 0904
www.dobsonandparnell.co.uk
Closed: Monday, Tuesday, Bank Holidays

Sitting on the city's quayside, Dobson & Parnell is named after the two architects responsible for its design, and is a bustling and reliable informal restaurant with more than a touch of Victorian glamour and comfort. Refined European cuisine is the order of the day, using local, ethically-sourced and sustainable produce.

Chef: Troy Terrington
Food Style: Modern British, European

Fern Dining Room & Bar ❀❀

Jesmond Dene Road, NE2 2EY
0191 212 3000
www.jesmonddenehouse.co.uk
Open: All year

Fern Dining Room is the fine dining operation at Jesmond Dene House, which is set in some lovely grounds next to a delightful wooded valley, yet is still very much part of the city. The Fern offers a top-class brasserie-style menu with a mix of relaxed dishes as well as those that demonstrate higher technical skills.

Chef: Danny Parker
Food Style: Modern British, European

Newcastle upon Tyne *continued*

NEW Hibou Blanc ®
13 High Bridge Street, NE1 1EN
0191 261 8000
www.hiboublanc.co.uk
Closed: Monday, 25 December

Set in the impressively elegant Sunlight Chambers, built in 1902 for the Lever Brothers, Hibou Blanc is a remarkably attractive place. The colour scheme is brown and ochre with camel coloured leather banquettes and wooden library shelves. Tables are set in classic style and laid with thick white brasserie plates. Service is professional and friendly.

Chef: Neil Jefferson
Food Style: French, Bistro

Hotel du Vin Newcastle ® 🍷NOTABLE WINE LIST
Allan House, City Road, NE1 2BE
0191 229 2200
www.hotelduvin.com
Open: All year

The converted red-brick Edwardian warehouse of the Tyne Tees Steam Shipping Company enjoys commanding views of the city's many bridges, while, as might be expected from this well-established chain, the restaurant has the look of a French bistro, with dark wood floors and wooden-topped tables.

Chef: Kevin Bland
Food Style: British, French

House of Tides ®®®® 🍷NOTABLE WINE LIST
See pages 478-479

Leila Lily's ®
Grey Street Hotel, 2–12 Grey Street, NE1 6EE
0191 230 6777
www.greystreethotel.co.uk
Closed: 25 December, 1 January

Leila Lily's is located in Grey Street Hotel in the heart of Newcastle. The bar and restaurant flow into each other and are equally as popular for non-residents as it is for house guests. The marble centre table is a real feature, off set with neon lights and flower displays. Food-wise, expect a modern grill with Asian influences.

Chef: Chris Finnigan
Food Style: Modern, Asian

Ury Supasatra Restaurant ◉

27 Queen Street, NE1 3UG
0191 232 7799
www.uryrestaurants.co.uk
Closed: 25 December, 1 January

An ury is a clay pot used for storing preserved food, a traditional feature of Keralan homes in south India, which is where the regional specialities hail from in this large, exuberantly decorated restaurant just off the quayside. Mains run from turmeric-spiked lamb cooked with coconut and curry leaves to chemmeen masala.

Chef: Yusuf Mukkat
Food Style: Indian, Sri Lankan & Oriental

AA Restaurant of the Year for England 2022–23

◉◉ **Socius**
Burnham Market, Norfolk
Page 369

AA Restaurant of the Year for Scotland 2022–23

◉◉◉ **The Cellar**
Anstruther, Fife
Page 580

AA Restaurant of the Year for Wales 2022–23

◉◉◉ **Gem 42**
Newport
Page 644

AA Restaurant of the Year for London 2022–23

◉◉◉ **Chez Bruce**
Wandsworth SW17
Page 316

Chefs' Chef of the Year 2022–23

Mark Birchall,
Chef Patron, Moor Hall Restaurant with Rooms, Aughton, Ormskirk, Lancashire
Page 266

Lifetime Achievement Award 2022–23

John Williams, MBE
Executive Chef, The Ritz Restaurant, London W1
Page 337

AA Food Service Award 2022–23

◉◉◉◉◉ **Hélène Darroze at The Connaught,**
London W1
Page 327

AA Restaurant with Rooms for England 2022–23

◉◉◉◉ **The Angel at Hetton**
Hetton, North Yorkshire
Page 521

AA Restaurant with Rooms for Scotland 2022–23

◉◉ **The Bonnie Badger**
Gullane, East Lothian
Page 604

AA Restaurant with Rooms for Wales 2022–23

◉◉ **Crug Glâs Country House**
Solva, Pembrokeshire
Page 653

AA Wine Award for England & Overall Winner 2022–23

◉◉◉ **The Vineyard**
Stockcross, Newbury, Berkshire
Page 46

AA Wine Award for Scotland 2022–23

◉◉◉ **UNALOME by Graeme Cheevers**
Glasgow
Page 594

AA Wine Award for Wales 2022–23

◉◉◉◉ **The Fernery**
Narberth, Pembrokeshire
Page 646

AA College Restaurant of the Year 2022–23

Senara Restaurant
Truro & Penwith College, Penzance, Cornwall

Award Winners
also see pages 22–33

Newcastle upon Tyne

🌸🌸🌸🌸 ▮ NOTABLE WINE LIST

House of Tides

· 28–30 The Close, Quayside, NE1 3RF
0191 230 3720
www.houseoftides.co.uk
Closed: See website

Chef: Kenny Atkinson
Food Style: Modern British

Assured cooking in characterful dockside building

This elegant Grade I listed, 16th-century merchant's townhouse in the shadow of the iconic Tyne Bridge, is the flagship enterprise of local culinary hero Kenny Atkinson. As witness to Kenny's ingenuity and skill, his dishes were chosen for two of the BBC's *Great British Menu* banquets. House of Tides is a contemporary restaurant set across two floors that has brought top-flight modern cooking to Newcastle's bustling quayside.

Expertly crafted cocktails in the downstairs bar are a curtain-raiser to the main event, which is delivered via a tasting menu in the refined beamed dining room with its sloping floors and lopsided ceilings. Although produce from the north-east is the cornerstone of the modern British menus, the kitchen isn't afraid to look globally for inspiration. Everything that appears from the kitchen is top-drawer, starting with

the warm crispy crusted sourdough and creamy cultured butter. Seafood is exceptional, whether it's mackerel, apple, buttermilk and dill, or halibut, hazelnuts, turnips and razor clams. Meat is a strong point, too, so don't overlook dishes like Kenny's salt-aged lamb served with kohlrabi, broccoli and marjoram, or precisely cooked veal sweetbread with apple, lovage and truffle.

A separate tasting menu for vegetarians is certainly no afterthought and includes such intelligent dishes as the silky kohlrabi ravioli with pine nuts, pak choi and chive; and braised heritage carrot, baby gem, sea buckthorn and black garlic.

Texture and temperature tend to be the template for the inventive desserts which might include peach tart, lemon verbena and almonds, or dark chocolate crémeux, Thai basil and lime. The attention to detail continues with the intricate petits fours. Although the carefully chosen wine pairings by the glass with the tasting menu are spot on, there is also an excellent list which showcases Atkinson's favourite bottles from around the world.

"...contemporary restaurant set across two floors that has brought top-flight modern cooking to Newcastle's bustling quayside."

Warwickshire

Alderminster

Ettington Park Hotel ◉◉
CV37 8BU
01789 450123
www.handpickedhotels.co.uk/ettingtonpark
Open: All year

A magnificent example of mid-Victorian Gothic
architecture, Ettington Park stands in 40 acres of
grounds in the Stour Valley. The interior bursts with
antiques and walls hung with paintings, plus several
friezes. Staff are friendly as they serve up some modern
contemporary cooking.

Chef: David Guest
Food Style: Modern,
Traditional British

Armscote

The Fuzzy Duck ◉◉
Ilmington Road, CV37 8DD
01608 682635
www.fuzzyduckarmscote.com
Closed: 25–26 December, 31 December, 1 January

This upmarket gastro pub is looking pretty swanky
these days with decor that makes the most of the
original character of the place. It's been doing the
business as a coaching inn since the 18th century and
now has a bit of contemporary style. Good honest
food, done very well.

Chef: Andrew Edwards
Food Style: Seasonal,
Modern British

Henley-in-Arden

Cheal's of Henley ◉◉
64 High Street, B95 5BX
01564 793856
www.chealsofhenley.co.uk
Closed: Monday, Tuesday, 25–26 December, 1 January

Chef: Matt Cheal
Food Style: Modern European

The black-and-white timbered façade of Cheal's slots in unobtrusively among the wonky
beamed buildings of the affluent 'Henley Mile' high street. Inside, the dining room is as you'd
hope, all gnarly beams and tables dressed up smartly with white linen. The kitchen sends
out confidently executed, well conceived dishes bursting with sharply defined flavours and
contemporary verve.

Ilmington

The Howard Arms Ilmington 🏵️
Lower Green, CV36 4LT
01608 682226
www.howardarms.com
Open: All year

History seeps from every stone of the Howard, a 400-year-old inn on a Warwickshire village green to the south of Stratford. A big old stone fireplace, weathered armchairs and unclothed tables make for a relaxing ambience, and the cooking is in the modern country-pub mould.

Chef: Christopher Ellis
Food Style: British

Kenilworth

The Cross at Kenilworth 🏵️🏵️🏵️ 🍾 NOTABLE WINE LIST
16 New Steet, CV8 2EZ
01926 853840
www.thecrosskenilworth.co.uk
Closed: 25–26 December, 1 January

Chef: Adam Bennett
Food Style: Modern British

This whitewashed 19th-century inn in Old Kenilworth makes the most of its beams and exposed brickwork, set against contemporary oak tables and a tasteful modern makeover in the dining room. Rooted in classic European ideas, the kitchen delivers modern refinement in spades, opening with velvety celeriac soup poured over diced poached pear and roast chestnut. Next up, perhaps a piggy plateful of pork belly, tender cheek and a croquette of head meat, helped along by crackling, smoked onion, salted apple purée, sage jus and braised barley. To finish, a sublime Tahitian vanilla custard tart alongside tart Yorkshire rhubarb sorbet and crystallised ginger provides a final flourish.

Long Compton

The Red Lion 🏵️
Main Street, CV36 5JS
01608 684221
www.redlion-longcompton.co.uk
Closed: 25 December

Built as a coaching stop in 1748, The Red Lion is a textbook country inn, right down to its inglenook fireplace, settles and eclectic furniture and local artwork. The cooking takes traditional pub food to a higher level, both in terms of preparation and presentation.

Chef: Sarah Keightley
Food Style: Traditional British

Royal Leamington Spa

The Brasserie at Mallory Court Hotel ❀❀
Harbury Lane, Bishop's Tachbrook, CV33 9QB
01926 453939
www.mallory.co.uk
Open: All year

Chef: Paul Evans
Food Style: European,
Traditional British

As well as the main dining room, Mallory Court boasts a more contemporary-looking brasserie just a short stroll from the main house, serving modern European and traditional British classic food. No mere adjunct to the main action, this is a fine venue in its own right, with art deco-style lines and glass-topped wicker tables.

The Dining Room at Mallory Court Hotel ❀❀❀ ♨NOTABLE WINE LIST
Harbury Lane, Bishop's Tachbrook, CV33 9QB
01926 330214
www.mallory.co.uk
Open: All year

Chef: Simon Haigh
Food Style: Modern British

Set in 10 acres, Mallory Court dates from the early 20th century and has a comfortably authentic country-house feel. Restaurant tables are smartly dressed, staff are attentive without being intrusive, and everything feels relaxed and grown-up – rather like the cooking. The seven-course tasting menu changes daily and seasonally to make best use of what's available from the garden and locally. Home-made bread and Lincolnshire Poacher lightly salted butter makes a good intro for a starter of Mallory garden salad, goats' curd and black olive, and then bavette of Highland Wagyu beef, crown pumpkin, morel Madeira sauce. Manjari chocolate mousse, raspberries and candied hazelnut to finish.

Stratford-upon-Avon

Hotel du Vin Stratford upon Avon ❀ ♨NOTABLE WINE LIST
7–8 Rother Street, CV37 6LU
01789 613685
www.hotelduvin.com/locations/stratford-upon-avon
Open: All year

Food Style: Bistro

Set in a building dating from Georgian times, this branch of the HdV chain combines blond wood tables and midnight-blue banquettes to stylish effect in its sleek contemporary bistro. Expect classic French favourites such as snails in garlic butter, then sea bass en papillote, and tarte au citron for pudding.

No 44 Brasserie on The Waterside ◉◉
The Arden Hotel, Waterside, CV37 6BA
01789 298682
www.theardenhotelstratford.com
Open: All year

Just across the river from the theatres of the Royal
Shakespeare Company, this contemporary brasserie
offers a champagne bar and enterprising modern
cooking. Expect fashionable twists on the classics –
for example a dessert of dark chocolate pavé with a
deconstructed garnish of griottine cherries, cherry
sorbet and Chantilly cream.

Chef: Lee Cresswell
Food Style: Modern British

Salt ◉◉◉
8 Church Street, CV37 6HB
01789 263566
www.salt-restaurant.co.uk
Closed: 25 December

Chef: Paul Foster
Food Style: Modern British

In the heart of Stratford-upon-Avon, this charming little restaurant occupies two rooms, one of
which has an open view of the kitchen. Neutral colours, chunky tables and flagstone floors add
to the rustic look but the food is modern, big on flavour and deceptively complex. When they
are in season, you might begin with Jersey Royals – skin on pieces cooked in seaweed butter –
with a home-made salad cream and sea lettuce. Then it could be a carefully cooked, juicy piece
of Isle of Gigha halibut with Wye Valley asparagus, crème fraîche and a drizzle of verdant
lovage oil.

Warwick

Tailors Restaurant ◉◉
22 Market Place, CV34 4SL
01926 410590
www.tailorsrestaurant.co.uk
Closed: 25 December

Chef: Dan Cavell, Mark Fry
Food Style: Modern British

In a pint-sized room centred on an old brick fireplace, the cooking is complex, with much
technical skill. The seafood cocktail consists of prawns and brown shrimps, Marie Rose
dressing deep-fried in breadcrumbs, red pepper purée and a gel of preserved lemon; all in all a
conceptual triumph.

The Belfry ☺
B76 9PR
01675 238600
www.thebelfry.com
Open: All year

Surrounded by 550 acres of lovely countryside, the Ryder Grill restaurant in this luxurious golf and spa resort serves a range of classic dishes. A contemporary space with a relaxed ambience, high quality tableware and atmospheric lighting sets the scene for steaks and fish cooked with skill on the chargrill.

Chef: Robert Bates
Food Style: British, European

West Midlands

Nailcote Hall ☺
Nailcote Lane, Berkswell, CV7 7DE
024 7646 6174
www.nailcotehall.co.uk
Closed: 31 December

Chef: Daniel Topa
Food Style: Traditional European

Built on the eve of the Civil War, Nailcote is a stately home on a modest scale, with 15 acres of grounds containing what are reputedly some of England's oldest yew trees. Old-school service extends to tableside steak-flambéing, but otherwise the mood is modern.

Adam's ☺ ☺ ☺ 🍷 NOTABLE WINE LIST
New Oxford House, 16 Waterloo Street, B2 5UG
0121 643 3745
www.adamsrestaurant.co.uk
Closed: Easter, 2 weeks Summer, 2 weeks January

Slap bang in the financial district, Adam's is a cosmopolitan and contemporary fine dining restaurant at the heart of Birmingham city centre. Midnight blue banquettes, marble-patterned carpet and abstract artworks create a chic look and there is an upbeat and buzzy vibe throughout. The modern British food is cooked through a Europe-wide prism so things might begin with chalk stream trout, cucumber, mint and

Chef: Adam Stokes,
James Goodyear
Food Style: Modern British

grapefruit beurre blanc before a perfect piece of monkfish served with romesco sauce, sweet and sour onions, buttery roasted cauliflower and parsley oil. There is a notable wine list with 20 by the glass.

Carters of Moseley ⊛⊛⊛
2c Wake Green Road, Moseley, B13 9EZ
0121 449 8885
www.cartersofmoseley.co.uk
Closed: 1–17 January, 24 April to 3 May, 11–21 August

Chef: Brad Carter
Food Style: Modern British

Away from the crowds in one of Birmingham's more peaceful suburbs, Brad Carter's understated venue doesn't quite prepare diners for the culinary magic that awaits them. This is a restaurant that works as closely as possible with the best producers around the UK, but also local allotment growers. This farm-to-table approach is evident at every stage of the tasting menus. A meal might kick off with Evesham tomatoes, chilled shrimp broth and Exmoor caviar before Gigha halibut with drawn butter and seaweeds. A palate-cleanser of Cornish saffron yogurt could be followed by chocolate, Cotswold sherry and cobnuts.

Chez Mal Brasserie ⊛
Malmaison Birmingham, 1 Wharfside Street,
The Mailbox, B1 1RD
0121 246 5000
www.malmaison.com
Open: All year

Chef: Pete Brown
Food Style: Modern, Traditional

The Malmaison team bring their brand of boutique swagger to this place in The Mailbox, a swanky shopping and eating venue. The Brasserie, with its floor-to-ceiling windows and contemporary finish, is a relaxed yet lively spot offering a menu of globally inspired, contemporary dishes.

Harborne Kitchen ⊛⊛
175 High Street, Harborne, B17 9QE
0121 439 9150
www.harbornekitchen.com
Closed: 17–26 July, 23–30 October, 25–26 December,
1–9 January

A neighbourhood restaurant with an already very excellent local reputation, this former butcher's shop has been transformed into a modern and bright dining venue with a bar area at the front. The kitchen is open plan and a tiled wall is also used as a white board to run the service. The restaurant team of three are welcoming and knowledgeable. A small garden to the rear provides seasonal fruit and vegetables.

Chef: Tom Wells
Food Style: Modern British

Hotel du Vin & Bistro Birmingham ⊛ ⌁NOTABLE WINE LIST
25 Church Street, B3 2NR
0121 200 0600
www.hotelduvin.com
Open: All year

Chef: Greg Pryce
Food Style: British, French

Light floods through the tall windows of this hotel dining room in Birmingham's financial area. The Gallic-inspired decor is backed up by a menu of bistro classics. A typical meal could begin with steak tartare, followed by roast cod with braised Puy lentils, button onions and pancetta, and finish with crème brûlée.

Birmingham *continued*

NEW Le Petit Bois ⊛⊛
143 Alcester Road, Moseley Village, B13 8JP
07599 161334
www.lepetitboismoseley.com
Closed: Sunday, Monday, Tuesday

A friendly, modern brasserie combining classics and
seasonal dishes, Le Petit Bois flies the flag for all things
France. A blue and mustard colour scheme, exposed
brick walls and unclothed tables add a rustic air. Enjoy a
pre-meal drink in the rear small bar with its
Gallic-inspired artwork.

Chef: Ben Taylor
Food Style: French

Opheem ⊛⊛⊛
Summer Row, B3 1JJ
0121 201 3377
www.opheem.com
Closed: 25–29 December

Opheem is on Summer Row close to University College
Birmingham, and offers modern Indian cuisine with a
real view to test boundaries. The cooking inspiration
comes from all over the world, not least from a number
of different Indian regions and ethnicities which are
well represented on the impressive 10-course tasting
menu. Among the starting dishes, perhaps choose

Chef: Aktar Islam
Food Style: Modern Indian

Rassam featuring heritage tomatoes, coriander and basil. Mains might be the well-timed Rogon
Josh with bold and wonderfully punchy sauce. End with the Anaabnaas, a pineapple roasted in
a tandoori style – a slight char to one side creates contrast with the deep roasting that really
brings out the sweetness and sugars.

NEW The Oyster Club by Adam Stokes ⊛⊛
43 Temple Street, B2 5DP
0121 643 6070
www.the-oyster-club.co.uk
Closed: Monday, 8–23 August, 24–27 December,
2–17 January

With its marble-topped tables, plentiful mirrors and
counter seating, The Oyster Club has a smart look
that's matched by high quality cooking. Just off Temple
Row and close to the cathedral, modern British seafood
and fish dishes lead the field here and the intelligent
wine list has broad appeal.

Chef: Rosanna Moseley
Food Style: Seafood, Grill

Purnell's ⊛⊛⊛ ♨ NOTABLE WINE LIST

55 Cornwall Street, B3 2DH
0121 212 9799
www.purnellsrestaurant.com
Closed: Easter, 25 December, 1 January

Chef: Glynn Purnell
Food Style: Modern British

Glynn Purnell's personality shines through on his menus and the old red-brick warehouse in the financial district has surely never looked so sleek and smart with its dark and moody palette and splashes of abstract artworks. Glynn's menus include a keenly priced 3 or 5-course lunch and an 8-course tasting menu. Silky smooth and seriously punchy, chicken liver parfait, with red wine poached pear, toasted grains and sorrel gets things off the blocks. Main course unites superb cod with pickled kohlrabi, St Austell mussels, and a sublime parsley sauce, while dessert is a knockout combo of 35% milk chocolate and hazelnut delice, mango sorbet and jelly, coffee cream and candied pistachio. Go for broke with flights from the impressive wine list.

NEW Restaurant 8 ⊛⊛⊛

8 Centenary Square, B1 2EA
0333 772 9329
www.about8.co.uk
Closed: Sunday, Monday, Tuesday, 24 December to mid-January

Inside Birmingham's International Convention Centre, Restaurant 8 is an interactive experience that starts with diners watching an explanatory video in a red velour booth before being shown through to counter-style seating. Neon lights, TVs and DJs add to the theatre and dishes boast numerical titles like 'Square

Chef: Andrew Sheridan
Food Style: Modern British

root of 8' – a deep-flavoured lamb broth with caramelised lamb belly, carrot, capers, garlic and anchovies. It might be followed by a decadent dish of seared Wagyu beef with beef jus, caviar and truffle. Finish with nitrogen-frozen dill with vanilla ice cream, freeze-dried raspberries and lemon drizzle cake crumb.

NEW Restaurant Folium ⊛⊛⊛

8 Caroline Street, B3 1TW
0121 638 0100
www.restaurantfolium.com
Closed: 3–10 October, 24 December to 9 January

A glass-fronted venue in Birmingham's bustling city centre, Restaurant Folium has a stylish, minimalist interior with parquet floor, exposed red brick wall and Edison bulbs. The chefs in the open kitchen specialise in modern, clean cooking with precise flavours and plenty of innovation. Exmoor caviar with first of the season asparagus and a sauce made from fermented

Chef: Ben Tesh
Food Style: Modern British

wild garlic and mussel stock is one way to start a meal. Move on, perhaps, to Woolley Park guinea fowl with rich cep aïoli and vibrant spinach. Frozen meringue with rhubarb root and salted meringue ice cream is one of sweet options.

Birmingham *continued*

Simpsons ⊛⊛⊛ 🍷NOTABLE WINE LIST

20 Highfield Road, Edgbaston, B15 3DU
0121 454 3434
www.simpsonsrestaurant.co.uk
Closed: Bank holidays

Chef: Luke Tipping
Food Style: Modern British

Tucked away in leafy Edgbaston, Simpsons may occupy a converted mansion but the airy interior has a strikingly contemporary Scandi-style. The focal point of this modern dining space is a central chef's table where the brigade of chefs are in full sight of diners. The intuitive cooking is as vibrant and highly crafted as the room. Carrot broth, smoked cheese dumpling, black garlic, hen of the woods, chickweed and fennel pollen might lead on to venison loin, parsnip purée, wilted kales, barley and elderberry vinegar sauce. Banoffee pie soufflé, banana ice cream and caramel sauce is a must-order.

The Wilderness ⊛⊛⊛

27 Warstone Lane, Jewellery Quarter, B18 6JQ
0121 233 9425
www.wearethewilderness.co.uk
Closed: 25 December, 1 January

Chef: Stuart Deeley, Alex Claridge
Food Style: British

Finding The Wilderness is something of an adventure. In the city's jewellery quarter a doorway leads down a small alley, identified by simple but effective signage. Inside, the kitchen is centre stage in the dining room, and cutlery and glass polishing are unashamedly in full view; a mixture of gimmick and necessity. Nearly everything is black or grey, with dashes of gold, but the space feels airy thanks to glass panels in the roof. Start with cod in XO and Iberico ham, move on to Scottish venison with faggot and barbecued brassica. End with a clever riff on banoffee pie.

Royal Sutton Coldfield

The Bridge at New Hall ⊛⊛

Walmley Road, B76 1QX
0121 378 2442
www.handpickedhotels.co.uk/newhall
Open: All year

Chef: Matthew Brookes
Food Style: Modern British

Before Birmingham's suburban sprawl engulfed the village of Sutton Coldfield, this 800-year-old moat house stood in empty countryside. Nowadays, it's cushioned from the hurly-burly by 26 acres of grounds. The Bridge Restaurant is the top-end dining option at New Hall, where mullioned stained-glass windows blend with modern decor.

The Oak Room Restaurant @

Moor Hall Hotel & Spa, Moor Hall Drive, Four Oaks,
B75 6LN
0121 308 3751
www.moorhallhotel.co.uk
Closed: Monday, Tuesday, Wednesday, Thursday

A family-run country-house hotel set in parkland, Moor
Hall's panelled Oak Room restaurant has a real sense of
grandeur and lovely views over the grounds, including
the golf course. The contemporary British cooking from
a young kitchen team emphasises quality ingredients.

Chef: Edward Dutton
Food Style: Modern British

Solihull

NEW Grace & Savour @ @ @ @

Hampton Manor, Swadowbrook Lane,
Hampton-in-Arden, B92 0EN
01675 446080
www.hamptonmanor.com/grace-savour
Open: All year

Chef: David Taylor
Food Style: Modern, Innovative

Within the walls of Hampton Manor's Victorian walled garden, Grace & Savour is an immersive
dining experience where diners can see where the kitchen sources much of the produce on the
plates in front of them. The chefs embrace a pre-industrial approach to food, so the focus of
the growing is on soil health, bio-diversity and sustainability. Minimalist with an open kitchen
and counter where chefs assemble dishes, a meal here is certainly interactive. The 15-course
tasting menu at dinner is a tantalising journey of flavours and textures, starting with a vibrant
opener of Isle of Wight tomatoes in smoked lamb heart broth with sweet cicely. Impressively
tender lamb leg and braised shoulder appears with an intense jus, topped with turnip and
liver crumble. Warm rice pudding with unrefined Colombian cane sugar, double cream and a
nostalgic ripple of raspberry coulis is one of the sweet courses.

What changes have you seen over the past few years?

A wonderful response to the hardships of Covid and Brexit –
the industry becoming more collegiate and collaborative.
The result is a focus on what really is essential to a restaurant.

AA Inspector

Solihull *continued*

Peel's Restaurant 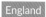 NOTABLE WINE LIST
Hampton Manor, Swadowbrook Lane,
Hampton-in-Arden, B92 0EN
01675 446080
www.hamptonmanor.com
Closed: 21 December to 6 January

Chef: Monty Stonehewer
Food Style: Modern British

This Tudor Gothic-style manor house, dating to 1855 and set in lovely gardens, was built for the MP son of Prime Minister Sir Robert Peel. Now it's home to the Hill family, who, inspired by the beautiful setting, have worked hard to make this a proper food-focused destination. They arrange special two-night stays, which might include wine tasting or bread making courses, as well as dinner in Peel's Restaurant, where the delightful dining room perfectly blends traditional period features and modern design elements, like the half-panelled walls with hand-painted Fromental wallpaper above. The highly seasonal tasting menu reflects what's going on in the kitchen gardens, and a late spring meal features a vibrant green, silky smooth wild garlic velouté served with potato dressed in crème fraîche. A delicate Cornish crab main is served with micro coriander, lime gel and lemongrass jelly. A crispy tapioca cracker with crab mayonnaise tops the white crab, while intensely flavoured crab consommé is poured round. To make a wonderful experience complete, the wine list is exceptional.

The Regency Hotel
Stratford Road, Shirley, B90 4EB
0121 745 6119
www.theregencysolihull.com/
Open: All year

Chef: Nigel Cooke
Food Style: Modern, Classic

Less than 20 minutes from Birmingham Airport and the NEC, The Regency is well-positioned for visitors, but its stylish restaurant appeals equally to locals. Decorated in grey tones and bare darkwood tables that are well spaced around the periphery of the room, the kitchen offers inventive British dishes inspired by international flavour combinations.

NEW Smoke
Shadowbrook Lane, Hampton-in-Arden, B92 0EN
01675 446080
www.hamptonmanor.com
Closed: Monday, Tuesday

Smoke was the old furnace house at Hampton Manor, but now it's a delightful dining room that's been updated but has still kept many original features. With bare brick walls and floor, there's a five-metre table down the middle, ideal for a large party or two tables of four. In fine weather diners can also eat in surrounding greenhouses.

Chef: Stuart Deeley
Food Style: Modern British,
Wood-fired specialities

Wolverhampton

Bilash 🏵
2 Cheapside, Civic Centre, WV1 1TU
01902 427762
www.thebilash.co.uk
Closed: Bank Holidays, 25 December to 9 January

These days the family-run Bilash is something of a
Wolverhampton institution, popular with the pre-
theatre crowd as well as football fans heading to or
from Molineux Stadium. The stylish interior is all neutral
colours with cream chairs, booths, banquette seating
and walls hung with sparkling mirrors. The creative
menu is a mix of modern Indian and Bangladeshi dishes.

Chef: Sitab Khan
Food Style: Indian, Bangladeshi

Wiltshire

Beanacre

Beechfield House Restaurant 🏵🏵
SN12 7PU
01225 703700
www.beechfieldhouse.co.uk
Open: All year

Beechfield House is set in eight beautiful acres with its
own arboretum. The restaurant is a collection of four
different dining rooms, and during warmer weather
there's also dining on the outdoor terrace in the walled
garden. The kitchen garden supplies much of the
produce used, and you're free to visit the polytunnels.

Food Style: Modern British

Bradford-on-Avon

The Bunch of Grapes 🏵🏵
14 Silver Street, BA15 1JY
01225 938088
www.thebunchofgrapes.com
Closed: Monday, 2 weeks August, 25 December

Very much a food-oriented hostelry in the
contemporary vein, The Bunch of Grapes has a dapper
pared-back decor with a rich blue finish, bare wood
tables and floors – a look that's more bistro than
boozer. The kitchen draws on high quality ingredients
to deliver a modern British menu full of up-to-date
ideas and big flavours.

Chef: Tony Casey
Food Style: Modern British

Bradford-on-Avon *continued*

The George at Woolley 🌸🌸

67 Woolley Street, BA15 1AQ
01225 865650
www.thegeorgebradfordonavon.co.uk
Open: All year

On the outskirts of historic Bradford-on-Avon stands
the comfortably spacious George at Woolley, where
seasonally changing modern British food awaits diners.
The management's long-standing, high-end experience
is evident throughout. In the dining room, typical dishes
include rack of lamb with mini shepherd's pie, grilled
fillet of black bream, cheese and potato gnocchi, and
traditional pub favourites.

Chef: Alexander Venables
Food Style: Modern British

See advertisement opposite

NEW The Weaving Shed 🌸

3 Bridge Yard, Kingston Mills, BA15 1EJ
01225 866519
www.weaving-shed.co.uk
Closed: 25–26 December

Next to the river in the centre of the former wool town
of Bradford-on-Avon, The Weaving Shed is a modern
bistro with a large outdoor dining area. Open all day
from breakfast or coffee and cakes through to lunch
and dinner, the contemporary cooking has a global
perspective.

Chef: Richard Synan
Food Style: Modern British

Calne

NEW The Dumb Post Inn Awaiting Inspection

Dumb Post Hill, Bremhill, SN11 9JZ
01249 813192
www.thedumb-post.com
Open: All year

A picturesque 18th-century village pub in charming
Wiltshire countryside, The Dumb Post Inn enjoys
beautiful views over the nearby Bowood Estate. On
offer are quality cask ales and home-cooked food
made with locally sourced ingredients. Try one of their
'Pub Classics', or maybe something from the grill. The
Sunday roast is very special.

Chef: Daniel Mack
Food Style: Modern British,
Pub Classics

The George

There are three unique dining spaces to choose from at this Wiltshire inn, so whether you want to cosy up by the inglenook fire on a chesterfield, or watch the team of chefs in the theatre kitchen or catch up with friends in the pantry dining room, there's a spot for every occasion. Supper is best started with a G&T, the bar boasts a healthy selection, before browsing the à la carte menu of modern British and European influenced dishes. Experienced head chef and owner Alex Venables oversees the classically trained brigade. Expect favorites such as beef Wellington, executed with skill and style. The whole experience can be topped off with a night in one of the charming bedrooms.

67 Woolley Street, Bradford on Avon, Wiltshire BA15 1AQ

T: 01225 865650   W: thegeorgebradfordonavon.co.uk   E: info@thegeorgebradfordonavon.co.uk

Calne *continued*

The Shelburne Restaurant ⊛⊛
Bowood Hotel, Spa and Golf Resort, Derry Hill,
SN11 9PQ
01249 822228
www.bowood.org
Open: All year

Part of Bowood Hotel, an elegant boutique country
house set on the Bowood Estate, The Shelburne
Restaurant is an impressive space. An elegant, curved
room with window-shaped mirrors, French windows
with wonderful views and a mural. There's also a
terrace for summer dining. Seasonal menus make the
modern British most of produce from the estate.

Chef: Rupert Taylor
Food Style: Modern British

Strand Room ⊛⊛
The Lansdowne, The Strand, SN11 0EH
01249 812488
www.lansdownestrand.co.uk
Closed: Monday, 25 December

Dating from the 16th century, The Lansdowne pub
is owned by Arkell's Brewery and the Strand Room
restaurant is at the very heart of the place. The modern
cooking keeps things simple on the plate, allowing local
produce to shine.

Chef: Joel Lear
Food Style: Modern British

The White Horse Inn ⊛⊛
Compon Bassett, SN11 8RG
01249 813118
www.whitehorse-comptonbassett.co.uk
Closed: 25 December

The White Horse Inn takes its name from the giant
chalk carving at nearby Cherhill. It's a charming
18th-century village inn set in Wiltshire countryside.
Meals can be taken in the bar, the dining room, or
weather permitting, out in the garden. The approach is
modern British and the home-made pie of the day is a
best seller.

Chef: Kieron Mondahl
Food Style: Modern British

See advertisement opposite

THE WHITE HORSE INN

COMPTON BASSETT

Nestled in the beautiful Wiltshire countryside, we are a traditional Free House with good homemade food and welcoming accommodation.

Nr Calne SN11 8RG 01249 813118
www.whitehorse-comptonbassett.co.uk

Castle Combe

Bybrook at The Manor House Hotel ⊛⊛⊛ ⅃ NOTABLE WINE LIST
SN14 7HR
01249 782206
www.exclusive.co.uk
Open: All year

Chef: Robert Potter
Food Style: Modern British

Quality underpins everything at the Bybrook, named after the river that runs through the hotel grounds. There's a formal air, as you'd expect at a luxury hotel, yet the team remain approachable and friendly. The room gives off a real sense of history with stained glass and many other features, while Robert Potter's kitchen offers something more modern, with hyper-seasonal, seven course tasting menus. Cooking is elegant and light, with carefully constructed dishes such as a starter of Chalk Stream trout, wasabi and lime squid croustade, with a perfect crunch. Huntsham Farm Ryeland lamb with morel and asparagus makes for a memorable main.

The Castle Inn ⊛⊛
SN14 7HN
01249 783030
www.thecastleinn.co.uk
Open: All year

Food Style: British

Exposed stone walls, wooden floorboards and antique furnishings are all signs that you're in a proper old English inn. The Castle Inn is just such a place, in a picturesque village with views of the church. On offer is excellent and comforting pub food that has reached an impressively high standard.

Colerne

The Brasserie ⊛⊛
Lucknam Park Hotel & Spa, SN14 8AZ
01225 742777
www.lucknampark.co.uk
Open: All year

Chef: Hywel Jones
Food Style: Modern British

The Brasserie is the less formal dining option at Lucknam Park. Located within the walled garden, with a wall of glass of its own, it has a classy finish and serves up high-end food from its open kitchen and a wood-burning oven.

Restaurant Hywel Jones by Lucknam Park ⊚⊚⊚ ⌁NOTABLE WINE LIST
Lucknam Park Hotel & Spa, SN14 8AZ
01225 742777
www.lucknampark.co.uk
Open: All year

Chef: Hywel Jones
Food Style: Modern British

Luxurious Lucknam Park is a beautiful Palladian mansion set in 500 acres of unspoilt parkland. For the last 30 years it has been a top-end hotel and spa. The dining room, with its curved walls, cloud-painted ceiling and pristine double-clothed tables, is the perfect setting for Hywel Jones' sophisticated, focused cooking. This is not fanciful stuff at the whim of fashion, but mature and well directed, where great produce is treated with respect. To begin, roast Scottish diver scallop, brown shrimp, razor clam and cucumber, then follow on with Wiltshire lamb, new seasons asparagus, cep mushroom and wild garlic.

Corsham

Guyers House Hotel ⊚
Pickwick, SN13 0PS
01249 713399
www.guyershouse.com
Open: All year

An elegant country house in handsome grounds with a relaxing dining room patrolled by friendly staff, and menus with a real sense of creative elan. Save room for an up-to-the-minute Earl Grey and lavender crème brûlée with pistachio brittle and mullet wine sorbet.

Chef: Dave Waine
Food Style: Modern European, British

Devizes

The Peppermill ⊚⊚
40 St John's Street, SN10 1BL
01380 710407
www.peppermilldevizes.co.uk
Closed: 26–29 December

This family-run restaurant with rooms impresses with its contemporary, feel-good menu. In the evening you might start with BBQ-infused, slow-roasted pork belly with carrot 'slaw', or potted shrimps with home-made brioche. It is a popular place so it's worth booking ahead.

Chef: Benjamin Gale, Declan McArdle
Food Style: British

Edington

Three Daggers ◎◎
47 Westbury Road, BA13 4PG
01380 830940
www.threedaggers.co.uk
Closed: 25 December

Once a humble 18th-century wool barn, this is now
the Three Daggers, a pub that offers rooms as well as
excellent dining. Meals can be enjoyed in the bar or a
number of different dining areas. There's also a farm
shop and a brewery on the premises, and Bratton Camp
and its White Horse are nearby.

Chef: Guy Browning
Food Style: British

Great Bedwyn

Three Tuns Freehouse ◎
1 High Street, SN8 3NU
01672 870280
www.tunsfreehouse.com
Closed: Monday, Bank Holidays, 25 December

Chef: James Wilsey
Food Style: British

A welcoming and dog-friendly pub on the edge of the Savernake Forest, the Three Tuns
combines the traditional charms of a local village inn with an excellent selection of carefully
prepared, tempting dishes. Everything from bread to ice cream is made on the premises.

Lacock

Sign of the Angel ◎◎
6 Church Street, SN15 2LB
01249 730230
www.signoftheangel.co.uk
Open: All year

Ageing beautifully, the Sign of the Angel is a 500-year-
old, timbered inn that is the very personification of
classy Cotswold charm. Low-beamed ceilings, walk-in
fireplaces and cosy nooks and crannies are all present
and correct, and candlelit tables add to the cosseting
mood. On the food side, the kitchen takes local
sourcing very seriously.

Chef: Ashley Jackson
Food Style: British

Malmesbury

Grey's Restaurant ◉◉
Whatley Manor Hotel and Spa, Easton Grey, SN16 0RB
01666 822888
www.whatleymanor.com/eat-drink
Closed: Monday, Tuesday, 31 December, 24 January to 7 February

Chef: Ricki Weston
Food Style: British

Grey's location within Whatley Manor is undeniably a major draw. Another is the food, served in a stylish dining room furnished in muted tones of grey, appropriately enough, and pink. Start maybe with pan-fried mackerel, pickled beetroot, horseradish and chervil, followed by chorizo and scallop risotto, or slow-cooked pork belly, perhaps while listening to live jazz (on selected dates). Expect a relaxed ambience and a changing à la carte menu featuring seasonal produce.

The Dining Room ◉◉◉◉ ▲NOTABLE WINE LIST
See page 500

Marlborough

NEW Crown and Anchor ◉
Ham, SN8 3RB
01488 503040
www.crownandanchorham.co.uk
Open: All year

Chef: Gert Pienaar
Food Style: Modern British

The Crown and Anchor is a delightful, traditional country pub, in a peaceful village within easy reach of Hungerford and Marlborough. It's got plenty of character, as evidenced in its oak panelling and flagstone floors. Meals offer a very good selection of quality dishes showing international influences. The garden and rear terrace are very popular in summer.

NEW The Marlborough ◉
90 High Street, SN8 1HF
01672 515011
www.themarlboroughgroup.co.uk
Open: All year

The Marlborough is a Grade I listed, traditional 15th-century inn, located on the high street. It's retained many original features including wood panelling along the bar, and some uneven floors, small steps, low ceilings and exposed beams. Staff are friendly and relaxed while the food ranges from pub classics to more adventurous dishes.

Chef: Thomas Price
Food Style: Modern British

Pewsey

Red Lion Freehouse ◉◉◉
See pages 502-503 and advertisement on page 501

Malmesbury

NOTABLE WINE LIST

The Dining Room

Whatley Manor Hotel and Spa, Easton Grey, SN16 0RB
01666 822888
www.whatleymanor.com/eat-drink
Closed: Monday, Tuesday, Wednesday,
23–30 December, 2–3 January, 24 January to 7 February

Chef: Ricki Weston
Food Style: Modern British, Asian influences

A beautiful country house hotel set in the Wiltshire countryside surrounded by charming gardens, The Dining Room is the principal restaurant at luxurious Whatley Manor and split across three modern, light rooms. The restaurant itself is an understated space with cream walls, bare floors and generously spaced tables. Embossed tablecloths and refined table appointments add a luxurious touch, and dinner often starts in the state-of-the-art kitchen where you meet the chefs and enjoy the first couple of snacks at the pass.

Local sourcing is key to the modern British food – the neighbouring organic farm supplies the beef and a local beekeeper looks after four hives located in the garden – and there is also a kitchen garden. Start with a céviche of hand-dived Orkney scallop, ponzu, cucumber, trout roe, seaweed and verjus, perhaps moving on to an immaculate turbot, fermented hispi cabbage and frothy hollandaise or a well presented plate of lamb with asparagus and black olive. Finish with an elegant and fragrant plum custard and apple blossom.

Red Lion Freehouse
TROUTBECK GUEST HOUSE

COUNTRY PUB & RESTAURANT WITH ROOMS
FAMILY OWNED & RUN SINCE 2008

EAST CHISENBURY, PEWSEY SN96AQ

Red Lion Freehouse

East Chisenbury, SN9 6AQ
01980 671124
www.redlionfreehouse.com
Closed: First 2 weeks January

Chef: Guy Manning, Daniel Barker,
Brittany Manning
Food Style: Modern British

Confident country pub cooking

Hidden from view down narrow lanes in an idyllic corner of Wiltshire, The Red Lion has retained its pubby element for the locals but also draws foodies from far and wide. If it's just a drink and a snack you're after, there's a range of local beers on tap and carefully selected ciders plus Scotch eggs, kid's burgers and even doggie treats on the bar.

Family-owned and -run since 2008, you can eat in the smartly attired and relaxed dining areas or the tranquil, tree-shaded beer garden behind the thatched pub. The owners rear their own pigs and rescue hens nearby so there's always a plentiful supply of eggs and good quality pork to supplement the rest of the local ingredients.

Start, perhaps, with fish pie packed with chunks of top-notch cod, tiger prawns and topped with sliced quail eggs, or maybe tagliatelle of Fowey mussels and

wild prawns with heritage tomatoes and gremolata is more your style. Move on to chargrilled Wiltshire lamb rump with imam bayildi, crisp falafel, courgette and cucumber raita, or there's tender and pink Creedy Carver duck breast with crisp duck leg pastilla, butternut squash, whole cooked apricots and a rich duck sauce.

The high quality cooking and impeccable presentation continues right through to the dessert stage with an intense passionfruit and coriander sorbet, coconut marshmallow, macadamia praline and gooey meringue cubes.

Poached apricot millefeuille with vanilla custard and crème fraîche ice cream is another way to finish but if you are looking for a more savoury finale, a board of Baron Bigod, Rachel, Bath Blue and Godminster cheeses with Red Lion chutney and biscuits is just the ticket. And if you find

it too tricky plucking dishes from the à la carte, there's a five-course set menu covering all bases.

See advertisement on page 501

> "The high quality cooking and impeccable presentation continues right through to the dessert stage..."

Rowde

The George & Dragon ◉◉
High Street, SN10 2PN
01380 723053
www.thegeorge-and-dragon.co.uk
Closed: 25 December

Chef: Christopher Day, Tom Bryant
Food Style: Seafood

This Tudor coaching inn in the unassuming village of Rowde has a reputation as a destination dining venue. The rustic country finish is part of its charm, while the menu makes a speciality of seafood hauled in from the boats at St Mawes in Cornwall.

South Wraxall

The Longs Arms ◉◉
BA15 2SB
01225 864450
www.thelongsarms.com
Closed: Monday, Tuesday, 2 weeks January,
2 weeks May, 2 weeks September

Across the road from the church in the picturesque village of South Wraxall, The Longs Arms is a welcoming stone-built pub with traditional flagstone floors and a wood-burning stove in the fireplace. Everything here is made on the premises including the delicious bread.

Chef: Robert Allcock
Food Style: Seasonal Modern British

Swindon

The Angel ◉
47 High Street, Royal Wootton Bassett, SN4 7AQ
01793 851161
www.theangelhotelwoottonbassett.co.uk
Closed: 25 December

Ancient oak panelling and flagstone floors confirm the pedigree of this veteran coaching inn, which continues life as a high-street hub of local goings-on into the 21st century. The kitchen keeps up with the times, sending out starters such as seared pigeon breast accompanied by a Merlot-poached pear.

Chef: Oliver Williams
Food Style: Modern British

Chiseldon House Hotel 🏵

New Road, Chiseldon, SN4 0NE
01793 741010
www.chiseldonhouse.com
Open: All year

Conveniently located for access to the M4, Chiseldon House is a very pretty Regency manor house in a quiet location by the Marlborough Downs. The restaurant offers a selection of carefully prepared dishes, making the best of high quality produce. Guests are welcome to enjoy the pleasant garden and its outdoor seating.

Chef: Paul Suter
Food Style: Modern European, British

Trowbridge

NEW The Hidden Chef Brasserie 🏵🏵

13 St Georges Mews, Silver Street, BA14 8AA
01225 754967
www.thehiddenchef.net
Closed: Monday, Tuesday, Wednesday

Tucked away down a quiet alley in the town centre, the appropriately named Hidden Chef Brasserie is a small and intimate venue with limited covers that makes booking in advance advisable. The kitchen sticks to the seasons and a range of pre-booked tasting menus are available for larger groups.

Chef: Dean Toon
Food Style: French, Modern English

Whiteparish

Betony by Matt Tomkinson 🏵🏵

The Kings Head, The Street, SP5 2SG
01794 884004
www.thekingshead.co.uk
Open: All year

Food Style: Modern British

You'll find Matt Tompkinson's latest venture, Betony, in The Kings Head, a lovely old village pub. The stylish, intimate dining room, with its mix of old and new, is the perfect setting for an evolving menu that centres local produce. It's small, so book ahead for the chance to try things like confit duck croquette with smoked Morteau sausage and pickled pear; and fish-of-the-day with braised artichokes and fresh borlotti beans.

Worcestershire

Badgers ◉◉
Stockton Road, WR6 6AT
01299 896666
www.theelmshotel.co.uk
Open: All year

Dating from 1710, The Elms' grand Queen Anne manor house has been a country house hotel since 1946, with 10 acres of grounds including tennis courts and croquet lawns. Seasonal produce from the hotel's kitchen garden forms the basis of the offering at Badgers – good food in elegant surroundings.

Chef: Adam Maddock
Food Style: Modern British

The Manor Arms ◉
The Village, WR6 6BN
01299 890300
www.themanorarms.co.uk
Open: All year

Chef: Stuart Foreman
Food Style: Modern British

Originally dating from the 17th century, today's pub is a valuable part of the community, appreciated by locals and visitors alike (note the six classy bedrooms). The traditional decor inside is entirely in keeping and the finish is smart but informal.

The Back Garden ◉◉◉ ⬥NOTABLE WINE LIST
Dormy House Hotel, Willersey Hill, WR12 7LF
01386 852711
www.dormyhouse.co.uk
Open: All year

Chef: Martin Burge
Food Style: Modern

The Back Garden is one of the eating options at Dormy House, a 17th-century former farmhouse built of honey-coloured stone, perched on a hill above Broadway. Its elegant, contemporary design scheme is worthy of an interiors magazine, with its use of calming greys, blues and honey yellows. Big windows allow views out of the walled garden that supplies a lot of the veg used in the kitchen. Start dinner with smoked salmon lasagne, nasturtium oil and vermouth sauce, continue with braised veal cheek, Swiss chard, polenta and Madeira sauce, and finish off with passionfruit baked Alaska with coconut and lime.

Foxhill Manor
Farncombe Estate, WR12 7LJ
01386 852711
www.foxhillmanor.com
Open: All year

Chef: Richard Thorpe
Food Style: Modern Classic

Foxhill Manor is a relaxed and home-away-from-home where the residents-only dining can be taken anywhere in the property, be it an intimate table for two or while catching a movie in the cinema room – even discussions with the chef are encouraged. The brasserie-style, modern, yet classic cooking has a focus on high quality ingredients and there's a compact well-chosen wine list too.

Hook by Martin Burge
The Fish Hotel, Farncombe Estate, WR12 7LJ
01386 858000
www.thefishhotel.co.uk
Closed: 23–26 December

Set in a forest in the Cotswolds, The Fish Hotel is not your average. As well as rooms and suites it also has huts and treehouses. Hook the restaurant is similarly quirky, set right among the trees and decorated with Scandi-chic charm. Part of a 400-acre estate, this Fish is miles from the sea.

Chef: David Hall
Food Style: British

The Lygon Grill
High Street, WR12 7DU
01386 852255
www.lygonarmshotel.co.uk
Open: All year

Food Style: British, Grill

The Lygon Grill is at the heart of the village of Broadway, and has been for some 600 years. When you step into this amazing space you can see how unspoilt the place is, with its beautiful barrelled ceiling, large windows, minstrels' gallery and well-kept wood panelling. The popular grill-based menu is well executed and there's a decent vegan offering too.

What is your advice for cooking great food?
Keep it simple, keep it fresh

AA Inspector

Broadway *continued*

MO ✪✪✪

Dormy House Hotel, Willersey Hill, WR12 7LF
01386 852711
www.dormyhouse.co.uk

Chef: Sam Bowser
Food Style: Modern British

Up on the hill above Broadway, that quintessential Cotswolds honeypot, 17th-century Dormy House is a slinky designer retreat with a glossy spa. The place is also a beacon of culinary pleasures and in MO, an intimate and interactive dining experience, that takes place around a marble-topped counter. With just a dozen guests to serve, the chefs can deliver a remarkable level of precision in the seven-course exploration of tastes and textures. Starting with scrambled duck egg served in the shell with Jerusalem artichoke foam and grated truffle, and ending with a confection of orange, rhubarb and cheesecake.

Tattersall's Brasserie ✪✪

The Green, High Street, WR12 7AA
01386 852401
www.broadway-hotel.co.uk/brasserie
Closed: Few days in early January

Chef: Steve Smith
Food Style: Traditional British

The Broadway Hotel, overlooking the green, has its roots in the 16th century, so Tattersall's Brasserie, in a contemporary light-filled atrium, is in sharp contrast to its traditional surroundings. The kitchen focuses on quality seasonal produce and has an assured sense of what will work.

Callow End

The Refectory ✪

Stanbrook Abbey, Jennet Tree Lane, WR2 4TY
01905 409300
www.stanbrookabbey.com
Open: All year

Food Style: Modern British

Unsurprisingly, the impressive Stanbrook Abbey hotel was converted from an old abbey, and The Refectory was originally the nuns' dining room. It's clear from the architecture; wood panelling, vaulted ceilings, large high windows, and pictures that reflect the place's history, but this has also given way to an elegant contemporary design, reflected in a modern British menu.

Chaddesley Corbett

Brockencote Hall Country House Hotel 🏵🏵🏵
DY10 4PY
01562 777876
www.brockencotehall.com
Open: All year

Chef: Tim Jenkins
Food Style: Modern British

Brockencote, standing in 70 acres of landscaped gardens and parkland, now blends original features with a sprinkle of contemporary pizzazz. Sweeping pastoral views are best appreciated from either a seat in the Le Colonial lounge-bar or a table in the linen-swathed elegance of the Chaddesley Restaurant. Tim Jenkins is in charge of the gastronomic show, setting high standards with precisely executed modern dishes. Open with pan-fried scallops, pickled quince and chestnut velouté, then roasted venison loin, Jerusalem artichoke, Oxford Blue cheese and elderberry jus. The technical dexterity is once again in abundance at dessert – iced muscovado parfait with pear textures is a beautifully presented dish.

Malvern

The Cottage in the Wood 🏵🏵
Holywell Road, Malvern Wells, WR14 4LG
01684 588860
www.cottageinthewood.co.uk
Open: All year

The Cottage in the Wood is delightfully Georgian, with a panoramic view across the Severn Valley from its position high up on a wooded hillside. The aptly named Outlook Restaurant makes the best of its situation while the kitchen's rather refined, classically inspired yet modern output is a distraction in itself. Pan-roasted cod loin is a standout.

Chef: Rob Mason
Food Style: Modern British

The Inn at Welland 🏵🏵
Hook Bank, WR13 6LN
01684 592317
www.theinnatwelland.co.uk
Closed: Monday, Tuesday, First week January

The proprietors at this pub have a long history with the AA, having previously held Rosettes elsewhere. In its modern farmhouse-style interior, a friendly, mostly young team serves seasonally driven, modern British dishes and specials such as stone bass fillet with pickled seaweed, and char-griddled woodland pork cutlet. Wines are listed by style rather than region.

Chef: Dominic Weeks
Food Style: Modern, Classic

Malvern *continued*

L'amuse-Bouche Restaurant ◉◉

The Cotford Hotel, 51 Graham Road, WR14 2HU
01684 572427
www.cotfordhotel.co.uk
Open: All year

L'amuse-Bouche is a converted faux-Tudor Victorian
chapel in the grounds of a house originally built as
a summer home for the Bishop of Worcester. Inside,
the decor is champagne pink and burgundy, while the
high ceilings give a real sense of space and light. Large
windows mean guests can enjoy great views across the
beautiful gardens.

Chef: Christopher Morgan
Food Style: Modern French

See advertisement below

Awards
Winner - Best Restaurant, Visit Worcestershire Awards for Excellence 2016, 2017 and 2019
Runner-up - Best Hotel of the Year, Visit Worcestershire Awards for Excellence 2016, 2017 and 2019
Two AA Rosettes awarded for Culinary excellence since 2010
Michelin recommended since 2010

AA
◉◉
Rosette award for
culinary excellence
2022

Ombersley

The Venture In Restaurant
Main Road, WR9 0EW
01905 620552
www.theventurein.co.uk
Closed: 25 December to 1 January, 2 weeks summer,
2 weeks winter

Behind the half-timbered façade of this 15th-century
property is a bar with an open fire, comfortable sofas
and low tables and a restaurant with bags of ancient
character from its ceiling beams and standing timbers.
Chef-patron Toby Fletcher stamps his style on the
Anglo-French repertoire.

Chef: Toby Fletcher
Food Style: British, French

Tenbury Wells

Pensons Rosettes Suspended
Pensons Yard, WR15 8RT
01885 410333
www.pensons.co.uk
Open: All year

Food Style: Modern British

The Rosette award for this establishment has been suspended due to a change of chef and
reassessment will take place in due course.
A labour-of-love project has transformed derelict farm buildings into this high-flying newcomer.
Located on the Netherwood Estate on the Herefordshire/Worcestershire border, Pensons
occupies a stripped-back, barn-like space with sturdy rafters soaring to the vaulted roof, bare
brickwork and a stylishly minimalist decor.

What are the most common misconceptions you face?

That we ask for a specific (traditional) style; that service
plays a part in the award when assessing for AA Rosettes.

AA Inspector

East Riding of Yorkshire

Beverley

NEW The Beverley Arms ⬡
25 North Bar Within, HU17 8DD
01482 296999
www.beverleyarms.co.uk
Open: All year

The Beverley Arms is at the heart of the historic town that shares its name. It's a 17th-century coaching inn that's been thoroughly modernised. The restaurant is a stylish orangery-style room with an open kitchen, and there's also a sizable alfresco terrace area under cover with an outside pop-up bar. Food ranges from classic pub to adventurous table d'hôte.

The Westwood Restaurant ⬡⬡
New Walk, HU17 7AE
01482 881999
www.thewestwood.co.uk
Closed: 1 August to 5 September, 23 December to 3 January

Owned by twins Matt and Michelle Barker, the Westwood began life as a courthouse and the building is full of character. Decorated in dark colours with copper and gold highlights, it has a contemporary feel, with an open kitchen and a terrace for outdoor dining. The kitchen produces confident modern British cooking, with simple, effective flavour combinations.

Chef: Matthew Barker
Food Style: Modern British

North Yorkshire

Arkengarthdale

Charles Bathurst Inn ⬡
DL11 6EN
01748 884567
www.cbinn.co.uk
Closed: 25 December

Chef: Gareth Bottomley
Food Style: British

The CB – to its friends – is named after a Georgian parliamentarian, and the beamed dining room is done out with pale wood and generously spaced tables. Local farmers and fishermen supply its seasonally-changing menus of modern Yorkshire cooking.

Asenby

Crab & Lobster Restaurant ◉◉
Crab Manor, Dishforth Road, YO7 3QL
01845 577286
www.crabandlobster.co.uk
Open: All year

Chef: Steve Dean, Stephen Thomas
Food Style: Modern British

The Crab & Lobster Restaurant offers various settings in which to dine, from a garden terrace to a room hung with a profusion of fishing nets and pots. Traditional seafood specialities cooked with flair include fresh plump blue-shelled mussels in a hearty marinière.

Austwick

The Traddock ◉◉
LA2 8BY
01524 251224
www.thetraddock.co.uk
Open: All year

A lovely building set in a lovely garden in a rural location, The Traddock is built on a historical traddock, or 'Trading Paddock'. The dining room is quite traditional and is split across two rooms. Walls are a grey-blue colour and there's lots of flowery artwork. Cooking is very much modern British using some quite advanced technical elements.

Chef: Ryan Shilton
Food Style: Modern British

Bainbridge

Yorebridge House ◉◉◉ 🍷 NOTABLE WINE LIST
See page 514

Birstwith

The Station Hotel ◉
Station Road, Birstwith, HG3 3AG
01423 770254
www.station-hotel.net
Open: All year

Chef: Peter Allen
Food Style: Modern British

The Station is a venerable building in a village on the edge of Nidderdale. The pick of the eating areas is the smart room that looks over the garden, but the main menu of classical cooking is served throughout. The terrace area is a highlight and is very well tended.

Bainbridge

NOTABLE WINE LIST

Yorebridge House

DL8 3EE
01969 652060
www.yorebridgehouse.co.uk
Open: All year

Chef: Daniel Shotton
Food Style: Modern British

Set in the heart of the Yorkshire Dales National Park, Yorebridge House was once the old grammar school and headmaster's house. Now a stylish restaurant with rooms, the magnificent Orangery houses the dining room, with large windows offering panoramic views of the beautiful Yorkshire Dales and French doors leading down onto the terrace and lawns, overlooking fields and hills as far as the eye can see. It's a smartly presented dining room with well-appointed tables, and a focal point open kitchen that allows diners to watch the chefs in action. The modern British menu evolves with the seasons and proudly lists all local suppliers on the menu. Start, perhaps, with pink and succulent French squab pigeon served with purple sprouting broccoli purée and pine nuts before an accurately cooked piece of top-quality wild halibut teamed with caramelised cauliflower and hazelnut butter. Finish with an unctuous 'Caramac' parfait, the richness countered by the sharpness of poached Yorkshire rhubarb. A comprehensive and AA award-winning wine list offers around 20 by the glass.

Bolton Abbey

The Burlington Restaurant ⚜️⚜️⚜️ NOTABLE WINE LIST
The Devonshire Arms Hotel & Spa, BD23 6AJ
01756 718100
www.devonshirehotels.co.uk/
devonshire-arms-hotel-spa
Open: All year

Chef: Chris O'Callahan
Food Style: Modern British

The hotel name may suggest a cosy village pub, but the Devonshire Arms (named for the owners, the eponymous duke and duchess) is actually a rather splendid country house, with beautiful grounds, set in 30,000 acres of wonderful Yorkshire Dales countryside. The Burlington Restaurant is the star of the show, an elegant space with a classic look and a stylish glasshouse extension. There's modern British cooking on the seasonally changing menu, with emphasis on local ingredients, including some produced in the kitchen garden or on the estate. A cured sea trout starter is pretty as a picture and full of contrasting textures.

The Devonshire Brasserie & Bar ⚜️
The Devonshire Arms Hotel & Spa, BD23 6AJ
01756 710710
www.thedevonshirearms.co.uk
Open: All year

Chef: Ross Forder
Food Style: Traditional British

The Devonshire Arms has a lot going for it, from its fabulous position on the vast estate, the luxe bedrooms and the high-end restaurant, but don't forget about the Brasserie & Bar. The menu deals in upscale brasserie food, with a Yorkshire flavour.

Burnsall

The Devonshire Fell ⚜️⚜️
BD23 6BT
01756 729000
www.devonshirefell.co.uk
Open: All year

The informal, friendly service here feeds into the easy-going vibe of The Devonshire Fell. The please-all menus are driven by quality ingredients, with simple pubby classics such as fish and chips or steaks thrown into the mix. There's a very good use of quality, local produce and the dishes are honest and well balanced.

Food Style: Modern British

Gilling East

The Fairfax Arms ◉◉
Main Street, YO62 4JH
01439 788212
www.thefairfaxarms.co.uk
Closed: 25 December

Popular with the local farming community, The Fairfax
guards the village crossroads, one of which leads
to Gilling Castle, prep school for the well-known
Ampleforth College. The pub's black-beamed,
open-plan bar and dining area leads out to a beer
garden bordered by a stream. Expect crowd pleasing
dishes, done well.

Chef: Michael Kenworthy
Food Style: Classic British

Goathland

Mallyan Spout Hotel ◉
YO22 5AN
01947 896486
www.mallyanspout.co.uk
Closed: 25–26 December

Chef: Ross Oram
Food Style: Modern British

Named after the tumbling 70-ft waterfall behind the hotel, the Mallyan Spout clings
comfortingly to a traditional style of furnishing and decor – textured wallpaper, mirrors,
high-backed upholstered chairs, that sort of thing. The menus rely on local suppliers and Old
and New World wines are well balanced on the 50-bin list.

Goldsborough

Goldsborough Hall ◉◉◉
Church Street, HG5 8NR
01423 867321
www.goldsboroughhall.com
Closed: 24–26 December

Chef: Josh Barnes
Food Style: British

Goldsborough Hall is a Jacobean stately home that was once home to HRH Princess Mary.
Canapés are served in the lounge before guests are shown through to an intimate dining
space with linen-swathed tables, a baby grand, and a splendid marble fireplace. Modern British
cooking raids the kitchen garden. Jerusalem artichoke tart with Alsace bacon and maple syrup,
or mosaic of foie gras and corn-fed chicken with trompette mushroom, smoked prune purée
and pickled shimeju are excellent starters, while poached cod loin with scallop mousse, red
dulse, chicken jus, and koji is an equally outstanding main. Finish off with poached Yorkshire
rhubarb, soy ginger and white chocolate.

Grassington

Grassington House ◉◉
5 The Square, BD23 5AQ
01756 752406
www.grassingtonhouse.co.uk
Closed: 25 December, First 2 weeks January

Grassington House is a smart restaurant-with-rooms at the heart of the Yorkshire Dales. There's a small bar area to the front where you can enjoy a drink before going into the smart dining area. A colour scheme of cream and grey, with plenty of wood makes for an informal atmosphere combined with attentive service.

Chef: John Rudden, Andrew Collop
Food Style: Modern British

Guisborough

Gisborough Hall ◉
Whitby Lane, TS14 6PT
01287 611500
www.gisborough-hall.com
Open: All year

The hall is an imposing creeper-covered country-house hotel situated in well-kept grounds, and Chaloner's restaurant occupies a large space with pillars and a fireplace in what was once the billiard room. The kitchen team turns out some rather interesting dishes.

Chef: David Sotheran
Food Style: Modern British

Harome

The Star Inn ◉◉ NOTABLE WINE LIST
Helmsley, YO62 5JE
01439 770397
www.thestaratharome.co.uk
Open: All year

Chef: Andrew Pern, Steve Smith
Food Style: Modern British

Following a devastating fire in November 2021, this much loved 14th-century thatched pub in a moorland village has been sympathetically rebuilt, retaining much of its character and history. With a phased reopening due in Autumn 2022 expect the return of modern 'Yorkshire' food with big, rugged flavours and friendly hospitality.

Harrogate

Clocktower ◉◉
Rudding Park, Follifoot, HG3 1JH
01423 871350
www.ruddingpark.co.uk/dine/clocktower
Closed: Monday, Tuesday

Chef: Callum Bowmer
Food Style: Modern British

Rudding Park's Clocktower boasts food that's worth a detour. It's all vibrant, colourful spaces, from the long limestone bar to the grand conservatory with its Catalonian olive tree, and a dining room complete with an eye-catching pink glass chandelier.

NEW The Drum and Monkey Seafood Restaurant ◉
5 Montpellier Gardens, HG1 2TF
01423 502650
www.drumandmonkey.co.uk
Closed: Sunday, 25–26 December, 1 January

Located in the heart of the popular Montpellier quarter, The Drum and Monkey is Harrogate's go-to seafood restaurant. Run by the same family for the past decade, the bistro-style decor makes for an elegant setting for memorable fish and shellfish dishes, as well as meat and vegetarian options.

Chef: Paul Warner
Food Style: Seafood

The Fat Badger Grill ◉
2 Cold Bath Road, HG2 0NF
01423 505681
www.whiteharthotelharrogate.com
Open: All year

The White Hart is a Harrogate landmark, having provided bed and sustenance to travellers since the Georgian era. The Fat Badger Grill is its main eating space, serving up classic British food with a bit of a contemporary twist.

Chef: Richard Ferebee
Food Style: Classic British

Horto Restaurant ◉◉◉
See page opposite

Horto Restaurant

Rudding Park, Follifoot, HG3 1JH
01423 871350
www.ruddingpark.co.uk/dine/horto-restaurant
Closed: Monday to Tuesday

Chef: Callum Bowmer
Food Style: Modern British

Located in the modern spa area of Harrogate's Rudding Park hotel, Horto enjoys something of a double life. By day, it's an informal spa café but in the evening, it blossoms into a relaxed fine dining restaurant. Meaning 'garden' in Latin, Horto certainly lives up to its name by utilising the seasonal produce grown in the hotel's kitchen garden. Unclothed tables, modern art on the walls and smart but casually attired staff add to the informality of the restaurant where dinner could begin with cauliflower tart, the crisp pastry case containing intensely flavoured roasted cauliflower purée, aged parmesan and golden sultanas. Alternatively, you might kick off with delicate chalk stream trout, kohlrabi and grapefruit. Follow with mallard pithivier served with a rich Madeira-based jus, elderberries and silky parsnip purée, or if seafood is your preference, there's native lobster with tomato and garden herbs. Kitchen garden beetroot with saké-soaked raspberries and rich almond custard is one way to round things off, or maybe you could choose buckwheat with caramelised chocolate and cep.

Harrogate *continued*

Hotel du Vin & Bistro Harrogate 🏵 🍷NOTABLE WINE LIST

Prospect Place, HG1 1LB
01423 856800
www.hotelduvin.com/locations/harrogate
Open: All year

Chef: Walter Marskamp
Food Style: British, French,
European

The Harrogate outpost of the HdV chain occupies a luxuriously converted terrace of eight Georgian townhouses opposite the 200-acre Stray Common. With hops around the windows and mustard-coloured walls, the place bears the group's corporate stamp, and the kitchen makes a virtue of simplicity.

Orchid Restaurant at The Studley Hotel 🏵

28 Swan Road, HG1 2SE
01423 560425
www.orchidrestaurant.co.uk
Closed: Monday, 25–26 December

In the Studley Hotel's Orchid Restaurant, a multinational brigade of chefs delivers authentic regional flavours in an eclectic pan-Asian melting pot of cuisines. Mango and darkwood interiors divided by Japanese lattice-style screens make for a classy and contemporary setting for enjoying interesting dishes.

Chef: Jim Hao
Food Style: Pacific Rim, Thai

West Park Hotel 🏵

West Park, HG1 1BJ
01423 524471
www.thewestparkhotel.com
Open: All year

Chef: Pawel Cekala
Food Style: Traditional British

West Park is a contemporary boutique hotel that occupies a lovely spot overlooking the Harrogate Stray, an open area of 200 acres of grassland at the centre of the historic spa town. You can dine in the comfortable modern dining room or in the alfresco courtyard. The dining room is all stylish turquoise with polished chrome and silver.

Hebden

The Clarendon Country Pub With Rooms 🏵

BD23 5DE
01756 752446
clarendoninn.co.uk
Open: All year

Chef: Lionel Strub
Food Style: French, British Modern

With most ingredients on the menu sourced from farmers and growers within the village, The Clarendon is rightly proud of the fresh, local produce it showcases. In the main, dishes based on Yorkshire Dales venison, and nearby Grimwith Estate wood pigeon are skilled, balanced and modern, and delivered by knowledgeable waiting staff in an unpretentious pub-style environment.

Feversham Arms Hotel & Verbena Spa ◉◉
1–8 High Street, YO62 5AG
01439 770766
www.fevershamarmshotel.com
Open: All year

Sophisticated cooking built on fine regional ingredients is the order of the day here in The Weathervane Restaurant. The seared scallop with warm apple jelly, black pudding and smoked roe emulsion seems appropriate for a hotel in an affluent market town.

Chef: Jon Appleby
Food Style: Modern British

The Pheasant Hotel ◉◉ ⬧NOTABLE WINE LIST
Mill Street, Harome, YO62 5JG
01439 771241
www.thepheasanthotel.com
Open: All year

Although The Pheasant might sound like a simple pub – it was once the blacksmith's and village shop overlooking the duckpond in the charming village of Harome – its current incarnation is a rather refined hotel with bags of smart country style. There are different menus to choose from, including tasting and à la carte menus and even one for children too.

Chef: Vincenzo Raffone
Food Style: Modern British

AA RESTAURANT WITH ROOMS OF THE YEAR FOR ENGLAND 2022–23

The Angel at Hetton ◉◉◉◉
BD23 6LT
01756 730263
www.angelhetton.co.uk
Closed: 25 December, 2 weeks January

Chef: Michael Wignall
Food Style: Modern European

Now a Yorkshire dining destination, The Angel at Hetton has been an inn for more than 500 years. Under experienced new custodians, a recent makeover has brightened and modernised the pub with sleek grey interiors to contrast with the more traditional wooden features. There are still stoves and fires to warm customers and the warren-like restaurant spaces make for an intimate dining experience. Tables adorned with rustic hessian runners, linen napkins and stoneware is offset by modern cutlery and gleaming glasses. The precision cooking is highly seasonal and intricate dishes display layers of crystal clear flavours and contrasting textures. Marinated hand-dived scallops are teamed with an intense dill gel and apple purée. It might be followed by super fresh Cornish turbot with winter artichokes, Périgord truffle, a well-balanced Fino sherry butter sauce and monk's beard. Finish with caramel tart, poached pear, frozen custard and condensed milk ganache.

Hovingham

The Worsley Arms Hotel ⊚⊚
High Street, YO62 4LA
01653 628234
www.worsleyarms.co.uk
Open: All year

Chef: Andrew Jones
Food Style: British

Well positioned in a pretty village against a spectacular backdrop of the Howardian Hills, The Worsley Arms is a Victorian hotel of mellow local stone. With its red walls, white linen and floral drapes, the restaurant is an elegant and traditional setting for fine-tuned dishes. The friendly and hard-working team make a visit here really special.

Kirkby Fleetham

Black Horse Inn ⊚
7 Lumley Lane, DL7 0SH
01609 749010
www.blackhorseinnkirkbyfleetham.com
Open: All year

Chef: David Davies
Food Style: Modern British

A short spin from the whirling traffic at Scotch Corner, this stone-built traditional inn pushes all the right buttons for a northern country hostelry. The main dining room overlooks the back garden and delivers classic and modern British dishes.

Malham

The Lister Arms ⊚
BD23 4DB
01729 830444
www.listerarms.co.uk
Open: All year

Food Style: Modern British

The Lister Arms, facing the green, is a country pub with pride of place in the village. Inside – open fires, low ceilings and snug areas. The specials are what drives this place, although all of the other food offerings look really sharp – regardless of whether it's a simple burger, fish and chips or their excellent pies.

Marton-cum-Grafton

The Punch Bowl Inn ⊚
YO51 9QY
01423 322519
www.thepunchbowlmartoncumgrafton.com
Closed: Monday, Tuesday

Chef: Alex Wood
Food Style: Modern British

The Punch Bowl Inn is a traditional village pub. It's a timber frame and York stone building with a beer garden to the rear. Inside, the central bar has five other rooms around it. There's lots of natural light, with open beams and local artwork. The menu is seasonal with an emphasis on honest, flavourful cooking.

Masham

Samuel's at Swinton Park ◉◉
Swinton, HG4 4JH
01765 680900
www.swintonestate.com
Closed: 2 days January

With its baronial tower and castellated walls hung
with creeper, Swinton Park makes quite an impression.
Samuel's restaurant is suitably grand, with its high
gilded ceilings, carved fireplace and views of the lake
and gardens. The kitchen celebrates the produce from
Swinton's four acres of walled kitchen garden as well as
from the local area.

Food Style: Modern British

The Terrace ◉
Swinton Park, HG4 4JH
01765 680900
www.swintonestate.com
Open: All year

Chef: Andrew Mangan
Food Style: Modern, International

The Swinton Park estate is well known for the impressive Samuel's in the main hotel, but if
you're looking for casual dining with a relaxed atmosphere then The Terrace restaurant serves a
globally inspired menu throughout the day and there's a cosy bar area with a range of cocktails.
The seasonally changing menus are focused around small grazing plates.

Middleham

The Tack Room Restaurant ◉◉
Market Place, DL8 4PE
01969 622093
www.thewensleydalehotel.com
Closed: 1 week January or February

In the charming hill town of Middleham, The Tack Room
has a horse racing theme that reflects the local industry
of breeding thoroughbreds, and comes with wooden
floors and plenty of natural light. The menu has an
old-school French brasserie feel, but also serves up a
decent collection of English classics for Sunday lunch.

Chef: Rui Barradas
Food Style: Pan-European, Classical

Middlesbrough

Chadwicks Inn Maltby ◉◉
High Lane, Maltby, TS8 0BG
01642 590300
www.chadwicksinnmaltby.co.uk
Closed: 26 December, 1 January

In a quiet village on the edge of the North Yorks Moors, you can dine either in the bar, with its wood-burner and sofas, or in the comfortable restaurant. Wherever, the dinner menu guarantees your full attention by listing Whitby crab and curry; pan-roasted Neasham beef with oxtail dumpling; and Hartlepool-landed halibut with lobster ravioli.

Chef: Steven Lawford
Food Style: Modern British

Middleton Tyas

The Coach House ◉◉
Middleton Lodge, DL10 6NJ
01325 377977
www.middletonlodge.co.uk
Closed: Saturday, Sunday

Part of the tranquil Middle Lodge estate that provides much of the produce for the kitchen, The Coach House is a truly memorable venue. There are walks and cycle tracks for guests to explore, as well as a superb spa facility. Dining involves a menu based on Yorkshire and estate produce. Skilled, friendly staff make any visit here worthwhile.

Chef: Ross Forder
Food Style: English, Mediterranean

Forge Rosettes Suspended
Middleton Lodge, DL10 6NJ
01325 377977
www.middletonlodge.co.uk
Closed: Sunday, Monday, Tuesday

The Rosette award for this establishment has been suspended due to a change of chef and reassessment will take place in due course.
Forge has been created from a long-neglected barn at Middleton Lodge, a classic example of a Palladian country house in 200 acres of beautiful English

Food Style: Contemporary British

countryside, with views across North Yorkshire. Forge makes extensive use of produce from the estate's two-acre kitchen garden and from the team's local foraging expeditions, and much of the food is cooked on open fires.

Moulton

NEW Black Bull 🌸
DL10 6QJ
01325 377556
www.theblackbullmoulton.com
Open: All year

Chef: Alexander Liam Wood
Food Style: Modern British

Set in the Yorkshire Dales, the Black Bull Inn is open-plan with large bay windows and plenty of natural light. Large wooden tables are surrounded by a choice of upholstered chairs and booths, and a terrace is available in warmer months. Modern British menus feature seasonal and local produce, some of which comes from their kitchen garden.

Oldstead

The Black Swan at Oldstead 🌸🌸🌸🌸 🍷 NOTABLE WINE LIST
Main Street, YO61 4BL
01347 868387
www.blackswanoldstead.co.uk
Open: All year

Chef: Tommy Banks
Food Style: Modern British

On a farm on the edge of the North York Moors, is where the Banks family calls home. With foraging forays to supplement the growing of fresh produce and then fermenting and pickling to create even more options, it's a very modern enterprise. James Banks runs a tight ship out front, while his brother Tommy works wonders in the kitchen. It's worth a wander around the kitchen gardens to get an idea on how your dinner will eventually come together. The tasting menu, showcasing the very best seasonal produce, opens with the customary nibbles, and posts notice of the intent straight away, although the menu dishes give little away as to the complexity of flavours to follow. For instance, lobster tail, turnip, fennel pollen; halibut, razor clam, garden herbs; lamb, Maris Bard, garden herbs. A glance at the cocktail menu shows that their creativity extends to infusing, distilling, drying and freezing techniques to offer unique drinks like a Sea Buckthorn Sour.

Osmotherley

The Cleveland Tontine 🌸🌸
Staddlebridge, DL6 3JB
01609 882671
www.theclevelandtontine.com
Closed: Tuesday

Once an overnight stop for travellers using the London to Sunderland mail coach, this has been an iconic restaurant for the past four decades. Now modernised for contemporary diners, the candlelit dining room oozes atmosphere with its stone fireplace and rustic carvings.

Chef: Alex Wood
Food Style: Modern British, French

Reeth

NEW 1783 Bar & Restaurant ⊛
On The Green, DL11 6SN
01748 884292
www.theburgoyne.co.uk
Closed: 2–13 January

Part of The Burgoyne hotel, at the top of the village
green with delightful views over the Swaledale Valley,
the 1783 Bar & Restaurant is at the heart of the
building. Decor is stylish: Farrow and Ball colours, low
lighting, local art. There are 10 tables, and the cooking
is modern country house style.

Food Style: Modern Country House

Ripon

NEW Bar Restaurant Eighty Eight ⊛
Grantley Hall, HG4 3ET
01765 620070
www.grantleyhall.co.uk/dining/eightyeight
Open: All year

Part of the extensive Grantley Hall complex by the
River Skell, Bar Restaurant Eighty Eight offers a
Pan-Asian menu combining the best of Yorkshire
produce with innovative Far Eastern flavours, all against
a backdrop of ornamental Japanese gardens. The decor
has an exciting glamour to it; intimate, colourful and
very chic.

Chef: Samira Effa
Food Style: Pan-Asian

Fletchers ⊛⊛
HG4 3ET
01765 620070
www.grantleyhall.co.uk/dining/fletchers-restaurant
Open: All year

Fletchers is the more relaxed of the two dining options
located in the original part of Grantley Hall. Offering
all-day dining, the wood-panelled restaurant has
banquette-style seating around the room's edges. It's
far more than your usual brasserie operation and the
main course offers great flavours and appearance. The
hotel features a state-of-the-art spa, gym and private
wine tasting areas.

Chef: Craig Atchinson
Food Style: Modern British

Shaun Rankin at Grantley Hall ⚜️⚜️⚜️ 🍷 NOTABLE WINE LIST
HG4 3ET
01765 620070
www.grantleyhall.co.uk
Open: All year

Shaun Rankin's set-up in the Palladian splendour of
Grantley Hall is unlikely to disappoint when you're
up for the full Monty. When you're done exploring
the vast swathes of grounds, spa and elegant public
rooms, Shaun and his team deliver cooking of serious
quality and distinction in opulent surroundings. There's
much to applaud, from chicken terrine with truffle-
topped brioche and artichoke textures to an exquisitely constructed dish of venison loin
with barbecued celeriac and blackcurrant gel. After that, terrine of quince and elderflower is
matched with yogurt ice cream.

Chef: Shaun Rankin
Food Style: Modern British

Saltburn-by-the-Sea

Brockley Hall Boutique Hotel & Fine Dining Restaurant ⚜️⚜️
Glenside, TS12 1JS
01287 622179
www.brockleyhallhotel.com
Closed: 25–26 December

Brockley Hall is a remarkable Gothic-style building
close to the seafront. Boutique is the watchword here.
The restaurant is a large space with a dark and opulent
theme. The hotel is generally quirky but the restaurant
draws its decor specifically from the likes of Moulin
Rouge, Raffles and the Orient Express.

Chef: Matthew Johnston
Food Style: Modern British

See advertisement on page 529

Scarborough

Clark's Restaurant ⚜️
40 Queen Street, YO11 1HQ
01723 447373
www.clarksrestaurant.co.uk
Closed: Sunday, Monday

A very tempting frontage is your gateway into this
neighbourhood restaurant where the tables are made
from Singer sewing machine bases. The room is
dominated by the bar/servery and a big display of gins,
including products from Scarborough and Yorkshire.
Locally-caught lobsters are a feature of the menus,
which are seasonal and dependent on the catch of
the day.

Chef: Rob Clark
Food Style: British, Seafood

Scarborough *continued*

NEW The Farrier
89 Main Street, Cayton, YO11 3RP
01723 861432
www.the-farrier.co.uk
Open: All year

The Farrier is a former blacksmith's workshop on North
Yorkshire's captivating coast, only a short drive from
Scarborough. It's an elegant restaurant with high-quality
country-style decor, wooden furnishings, and a tasteful
equestrian theme throughout. Service is professional
and attentive, and there's a cosy lounge area with a fire
and sofas. Meals are hearty and unpretentious.

Chef: Peter Gibson
Food Style: British

NEW The Plough Scalby
21–23 High Street, Scalby, YO13 0PT
01723 362622
www.theploughscalby.co.uk
Open: All year

The Plough is a friendly red-brick inn, sat in the quiet
village of Scalby, just a short drive from Scarborough.
The restaurant is beautifully cosy, with lots of wood,
bare brick, clocks, mirrors and general countryside
items on the walls. On the dinner menu, tapas and
'small plates' starters, followed by 'large plates' and
tasty desserts.

Chef: Jon Smith
Food Style: Modern British

Scawton

The Hare ⊛⊛⊛
YO7 2HG
01845 597769
www.thehare-inn.com
Closed: See website for details

Chef: Paul Jackson
Food Style: Modern British

There's a wire sculpture of two boxing hares outside The Hare, and it's possible that they're
arguing about who gets to sit down at one of the restaurant's 12 covers. It's a luxurious
venue with minimalist design, exposed stonework, and a rich colour palate of dark blues. The
approach is a little bit different too; tasting menus all the way. Choose from six or eight courses,
which the chef suggests may take around three or four hours respectively. Dishes come with
a suggested wine, and may include tomato and goats' cheese; rump steak with beetroot and
elderberry; or bass, razor clam and courgette.

BROCKLEY HALL
BOUTIQUE HOTEL · SALTBURN

Modern British Food providing an exciting gastronomic journey through each course

Brockley Hall Boutique Hotel and Restaurant is situated in the beautiful town of Saltburn By The Sea, which has just been recognised as one of the top 10 places to live in Britain.

Saltburn is famous for its Pier, water powered funicular Cliff Lift and Victorian pleasure gardens as well as its vibrant arts scene and huge variety of eating places celebrated in the annual food festival.

Brockley Hall is a beautiful Victorian building which has been restored in an individual and quirky style with a range of double, twin and family rooms and individually designed suites with freestanding feature baths, perfect for romantic breaks.

The Hotel has a spectacular restaurant in which to enjoy our award winning fine dining menu, we also serve well known favourites from our a la carte menu. Our delightful hand painted conservatory and sumptuous lounge are ideal for sampling our lunch menu and handcrafted afternoon teas.

Our restaurant was awarded 2 rosettes in the first year of opening for its fine dining menu.

Our head chef, Mathew Johnston, and his team of talented and inventive chefs will take you on a journey of taste with our unique menus which make the most of fabulous, locally sourced, ingredients. We are working with some of the UK's finest wine suppliers to provide exciting wines to compliment your dining experience.

www.brockleyhallhotel.com

Reservations: 01287 622179

Thirsk

NEW The Carpenters Arms
Felixkirk, YO7 2DP
01845 537369
www.thecarpentersarmsfelixkirk.com
Open: All year

Food Style: Modern British

Sitting in a tiny village on the North York Moors, The Carpenters Arms is a very welcoming place to eat and relax. The restaurant is split between the stone-flagged, bare brick pub area and a more modern extension with large bifold doors that lead out to a decked terrace with lovely views. Expect staunchly seasonal cuisine.

Timble

The Timble Inn
LS21 2NN
01943 880530
www.thetimbleinn.co.uk
Open: All year

Retaining all that makes a village pub such an asset, this Grade II listed, 18th-century coaching inn is squirrelled away in the beautiful Washburn Valley inside the Nidderdale Area of Outstanding Natural Beauty. Five miles from the Yorkshire Dales National Park, it's a popular pit stop for walkers in search of a pint of local ale. Warmed by a real fire, the comfortable restaurant showcases prime regional ingredients.

Chef: Jamie Cann
Food Style: Modern British

West Witton

The Wensleydale Heifer
Main Street, DL8 4LS
01969 622322
www.wensleydaleheifer.co.uk
Open: All year

Chef: Craig Keenan
Food Style: Modern British, Seafood

Locally famous for its fish and chips, The Wensleydale Heifer offers plenty of super-fresh fish and seafood options at the heart of the beautiful Yorkshire Dales National Park. This chic 17th-century inn with boutique rooms draws foodies from far and wide for its piscine pleasures. The place also has its own sense of fun, it's unique and quirky.

Whitby

Estbek House ⊛⊛
East Row, Sandsend, YO21 3SU
01947 893424
www.estbekhouse.co.uk
Closed: Monday, Tuesday, 25–26 December

Chef: Tim Lawrence
Food Style: Modern British

Overlooking the North Sea just north of Whitby, Estbek House is perfectly positioned to source its materials from the chilly waters out front and the rolling moors behind. It all takes place in a handsome Regency house that operates as a restaurant with charming rooms.

The Star Inn The Harbour ⊛
Langborne Road, YO21 1YN
01947 821900
www.starinntheharbour.co.uk
Closed: 25–26 December

An ideal harbourside location is the setting for this spacious restaurant with its delightfully styled fishing/ nautical-themed interior. Catch-of-the-day fish and meat specials, sometimes from local game, feature. A separate ice cream parlour provides the desserts, but is also open to non-restaurant clientele. All in all, it's very tempting indeed.

Chef: Joseph Lees
Food Style: British, Seafood

Yarm

The Conservatory ⊛⊛ ⚑NOTABLE WINE LIST
Judges Country House Hotel, Kirklevington Hall,
TS15 9LW
01642 789000
www.judgeshotel.co.uk
Open: All year

Chef: Dave McBride
Food Style: Modern British

Judges Country House Hotel sits in 22-acre grounds that include a walled kitchen garden. The dining room is appointed in keeping with the style of the property, with double-clothed tables set with silver cutlery and fresh flowers. Service is on the formal side, but staff are friendly and keen to engage. First-class ingredients underpin the kitchen's output.

Yarm *continued*

Crathorne Hall Hotel
Crathorne, TS15 0AR
01642 700398
www.handpickedhotels.co.uk/crathorne-hall
Open: All year

While the decor and furnishings of The Leven
Restaurant are all early 20th century – oak
half-panelled walls, heavy drapes at the tall sash
windows, oil paintings, and a gilt-edged coffered ceiling
– the cuisine tends towards modern British sensibilities,
with sound, classical technique on display throughout
the seasons.

Chef: Dave McBride
Food Style: Modern British

York

The Bow Room Restaurant at Grays Court
Chapter House Street, YO1 7JH
01904 612613
www.grayscourtyork.com
Closed: 24–27 December, 3–18 January

Chef: Adam Jackson
Food Style: Modern British

The Bow Room Restaurant is part of the historic Grays Court, which has been inhabited in
one form or another since the 11th century. The 90ft-long gallery is delightful, and features a
bow window with views out to the hotel grounds and city walls beyond. An impressive kitchen
garden supplies the all-day food options, which features exciting contemporary British dishes.
Menu descriptions may be terse, serving to disguise the huge amount of skill involved. Trout,
wasabi, beetroot and caviar is one of the successful flavour combinations, as is a dessert of
Gariguette strawberry, pistachio and yuzu curd.

NEW Chez Mal York
2 Rougier Street, YO90 1UU
01904 946 060
www.malmaison.com/locations/york

Food Style: Pan-Asian

Part of boutique hotel Malmaison York, newly converted from a former office block, Chez Mal
York is stylishly functional, all black and blue, with tiles and wooden flooring. There's an open
kitchen, and plenty of natural light. Dining is along the lines of classic brasserie dishes with lots
of Pan-Asian fusion.

Dean Court Hotel 🏵
Duncombe Place, YO1 7EF
01904 625082
www.deancourt-york.co.uk
Open: All year

The buildings that now make up Dean Court Hotel were built to house clergy, so it's no surprise that it's directly opposite stunning York Minster. The restaurant decor is calming and neutral, which means diners aren't distracted from the view, or the food. The modern British menu is well-balanced and seasonal.

Chef: Benji Thornton
Food Style: Modern British

NEW Fish & Forest 🏵
110 Micklegate, YO1 6JX
01904 220587
www.fishandforestrestaurant.com
Closed: Sunday, Monday, 25–30 December

At the top of Micklegate, Fish & Forest is an unpretentious sustainable fish and game bistro with a vibrant atmosphere and welcoming staff. Split across two rooms, this pop-up-turned-permanent is a long, narrow place, with rustic, minimalist, almost industrial-style decor. The self-taught chef-owner uses every part of his ingredients to create a constantly evolving menu which produces little waste.

Chef: Stephen Andrews
Food Style: French, Bistro, Modern British

Hotel du Vin & Bistro York 🏵 🍷 NOTABLE WINE LIST
89 The Mount, YO24 1AX
01904 557350
www.hotelduvin.com
Open: All year

Chef: James Skinner
Food Style: European, French

The York billet of the HdV group is a late Georgian townhouse in the vicinity of the Minster's Gothic splendour and the city racecourse. Bare tables and wooden floor fit in with the unbuttoned ethos, and the menu offers sturdy French domestic fare with minimal flounce.

York *continued*

The Judge's Lodging ◉
9 Lendal, YO1 8AQ
01904 638733
www.judgeslodgingyork.co.uk/food-drink
Open: All year

Chef: Katie Hoskins
Food Style: Modern British

The Georgian townhouse hard by the Minster has been reinvented as a modern inn of much character with a plethora of eating and drinking options. Dining can be elegantly panelled or domestic-cosy, and the all-day menus offer a wide range of international favourites.

NEW The Lime Tree Inn ◉
Branton Lane, Great Ouseburn, YO26 9RS
01423 324100
www.thelimetreeinn.com
Closed: Monday, Tuesday, 25–26 December,
2–17 January

Located in Great Ouseburn, between York and Thirsk, The Lime Tree Inn is a family-run country-pub with vintage wooden tables and candles in wine bottles. Service is relaxed but professional, and home-made food is a definite USP here; everything from vinegar to ketchup, jams, bread and mayonnaise. There's no doubt that the cuisine here comes from the heart.

Chef: Rob Mitchell
Food Style: Modern British

NEW Melton's Restaurant ◉◉
7 Scarcroft Road, YO23 1ND
01904 634341
www.meltonsrestaurant.co.uk
Closed: 23 December to 7 January

Away from the city centre, off a busy neighbourhood shopping area, Meltons has a bistro-style look and feel. The off-street entrance puts you straight into the eight-table restaurant, with its rich purples and lilacs. On the walls, hand-painted friezes show local landmarks and a restaurant scene. Service is low-key, and the menu is modern British.

Chef: Calvin Miller
Food Style: Modern British

Middlethorpe Hall & Spa ⊛⊛ ♦NOTABLE WINE LIST
Bishopthorpe Road, Middlethorpe, YO23 2GB
01904 641241
www.middlethorpe.com
Open: All year

This majestic old building stands in 20 acres of gardens and parkland. The kitchen offers a fashionable surf 'n' turf combination of diver-caught roasted scallop with sticky pork belly, kohlrabi and apple purée. The cracking wine list offers good advice on food and wine matching.

Chef: Ashley Binder
Food Style: Modern British

NEW The Rattle Owl Awaiting Inspection
104 Micklegate, YO1 6JX
01904 658658
www.rattleowl.co.uk
Closed: Monday, Tuesday

Set on one of York's many historic streets, The Rattle Owl occupies a restored Grade II* listed building and is now an independent, casual-dining restaurant with a focus on tasting menus that bring local produce and foraged elements to the fore. During the restoration a Roman house was discovered and is now preserved under the restaurant.

Chef: Tom Heywood
Food Style: Modern British

NEW The Rise ⊛
Station Rise, YO1 6HT
01904 380038
www.thegrandyork.co.uk
Open: All year

The Rise is the main restaurant here at The Grand in York. Built in 1906 as 'A Palace of Business', the building was meant to be impressive and majestic, and so it remains. Rise is in a new extension and presents as a restaurant very much in keeping with its early 20th-century location, offering serious metropolitan luxury alongside contemporary dining.

Chef: Nicolas De Visch
Food Style: Modern British

York *continued*

Roots York 🏵🏵🏵
68 Marygate, YO30 7BH
www.rootsyork.com

Chef: Tommy Banks, Sean Wrest
Food Style: Modern British

Closed: Sunday, Monday, Tuesday

Set in a characterful 19th-century building on Marygate in the heart of historic York, Roots is sister restaurant to The Black Swan at Oldstead. A high-end operation offering seasonal farm-to-table tasting menus, diners eat in a spacious room illuminated by leaded windows and an open kitchen. Tommy Bank's family farm supplies much of the produce destined for dishes such as a beef tartare with horseradish panacotta and charcoal oil, which could lead on to perfectly timed lamb saddle with mint, lovage emulsion, kohlrabi and pickled ramsons. Strawberry, elderflower and woodruff is a typical way to finish.

Skosh 🏵🏵
98 Micklegate, YO1 6JX
01904 634849
www.skoshyork.co.uk
Closed: Monday, Tuesday, 21 August to 7 September, 25–27 December, 1–4 January

Skosh has made a big splash on the local and national food radar. Occupying a former shop in central York, a slate grey and vivid yellow colour scheme adds a bright and cheery vibe, as does the jeans and T-shirt attire of the relaxed staff.

Chef: Neil Bentinck
Food Style: Modern, International

The Star Inn The City 🏵
Lendal Engine House, Museum Street, YO1 7DR
01904 619208
www.starinnthecity.co.uk
Closed: 25–26 December, 1 January

This former pump engine house in a stunning riverside setting in the centre of York has been redeveloped into a modern bustling restaurant. There are various dining spaces, including a terrace and a cellar, but overall the decor has a pub-like feel.

Chef: Jack Wheatley, Ian Polinar
Food Style: Modern British

South Yorkshire

Sheffield

JÖRO Restaurant 🏵🏵🏵 🏅NOTABLE WINE LIST

Krynkl, 294 Shalesmoor, S3 8UL
0114 299 1539
www.jororestaurant.co.uk
Closed: 5-11 July, 20-26 September, 20-27 December, 1-15 January

Chef: Luke French, Joe Bains
Food Style: British, Scandinavian, Japanese

A converted shipping container on the outskirts of Steel City doesn't sound too inviting a prospect, but Jöro's urban edginess is bang in tune with the contemporary trend for neo-Nordic-influenced eating. Inside, the space has a minimalist feel with bare wood floors and tables decorated with flowers and baby vegetables, the buzz of an open kitchen adding to the convivial vibe. Despite the urban surrounds, the kitchen team maintains a close bond to nature, working with local farms and foragers to provide a steady flow of seasonal ingredients, and the small plate concept encourages diners to try a salvo of different dishes.

Juke & Loe Awaiting Inspection

617 Eccleshall Road, S11 8PT
01142 680271
www.jukeandloe.com
Closed: Monday, Tuesday, 1 week January, 1 week August

Chef: Joseph & Luke Grayson, Thomas Vardy
Food Style: Modern British

At time of going to press this establishment is due to relocate in Sheffield and reassessment will take place in due course. Juke & Loe serves up modern British fare in a relaxed and informal atmosphere. Expect rustic-style wooden tables and contemporary, seasonal dishes which are good on flavour and natural presentation.

Nonnas 🏵

535–541 Eccleshall Road, S11 8PR
0114 268 6166
www.nonnas.co.uk
Closed: 25 December, 1 January

Nonnas is a bustling, good-natured Italian restaurant with friendly staff, café-style marble-topped tables and green walls. This is an imaginative kitchen turning out properly cooked, highly original dishes. Among accomplished dishes could be Merlot-braised oxtail with beetroot mash and horseradish canederli (bread dumplings), and grilled sea bass fillet, borlotti bean and tomato stew with rosemary aïoli.

Chef: Ross Sayles
Food Style: Modern Italian

Sheffield

Rafters Restaurant

220 Oakbrook Road, Nethergreen, S11 7ED
0114 230 4819
www.raftersrestaurant.co.uk
Closed: 22–30 August, 19 December to 3 January

Chef: Daniel Conlon
Food Style: Modern British

Located in a parade of shops in a residential corner of Sheffield, first-floor restaurant Rafters is concealed in a row of shops and accessed via a flight of stairs. The room has an unusual shape, with a couple of round windows and high beams that inspired the name of the restaurant. Decorated in grey with plenty of exposed brick, there are only around 24 covers, which makes it a pleasantly intimate dining experience. The modern British cooking showcases simple but innovative flavour combinations and clean, precise flavours.

Kick off with a fresh and zingy starter comprising cubes of fresh, raw Loch Duart salmon, fermented beetroot, blood orange segments and melt in the mouth buttermilk 'snow'. Move on to an accurately timed piece of Scottish venison with an offal and barley faggot, honey-roasted parsnips, kale and blackcurrant gel with a hint of pine oil. Finish with a bright, modern take on rhubarb and custard with forced Yorkshire rhubarb teamed with white chocolate, gingerbread crumb and apple and sorrel granita.

Rafters Restaurant ⍟⍟⍟
See page opposite

NEW The Stag Restaurant ⍟
Lightwood Lane, Middle Handley, S21 5RN
01246 434800
www.devonshirearmsmiddlehandley.co.uk
Open: All year

Part of the Devonshire Arms, a honey-stoned hostelry
in a tastefully renovated period village, the Stag has a
bright spacious restaurant that strives to deliver great
hospitality and efficient service. Food is locally sourced
and a monthly fish night is a feature. Hard to believe it's
only about nine miles from the centre of Sheffield.

Chef: Gareth Nightingale
Food Style: Pub Classics

Wortley

The Wortley Arms ⍟
Halifax Road, S35 7DB
0114 288 8749
www.wortley-arms.co.uk
Open: All year

Chef: Andy Gabbitas
Food Style: Modern British

The Wortley Arms is an appealing spot for a pint of local ale and some modern gastro-pub
cooking. Timeless staples (beer-battered fish and chips with home-made tartare sauce, or
gammon steak with griddled pineapple) rub shoulders with more up-to-date ideas.

West Yorkshire

Bradford

Prashad ⍟⍟
137 Whitehall Road, Drighlington, BD11 1AT
0113 285 2037
www.prashad.co.uk
Closed: Monday, 25 December

There is strong competition in Bradford when it comes
to authentic Indian cooking, but Prashad's meat-free
repertoire ensures a loyal local following. A mural
depicting an Indian street scene provides a vibrant
look, and food has its roots in the vegetarian cuisine
of the Gujarat.

Chef: Minal Patel
Food Style: Indian Vegetarian

Halifax

Shibden Mill Inn ⚜️⚜️
Shibden Mill Fold, Shibden, HX3 7UL
01422 365840
www.shibdenmillinn.com
Closed: 25 December

With milling abandoned long ago, it's left to the beams
and exposed stone to remind us of its history. An
inviting menu covers a lot of ground, ranging from a
starter such as cured chalk stream trout, to mains like
65-day salt-aged pavé of beef with ox-cheek crumble;
and vegetarian cauliflower arancini.

Chef: William Webster
Food Style: Modern British

See advertisement opposite

Ilkley

Box Tree ⚜️⚜️⚜️ NOTABLE WINE LIST
35–37 Church Street, LS29 9DR
01943 608484
www.theboxtree.co.uk
Closed: 27–31 December, 1–8 January

Chef: Simon Gueller
Food Style: Modern,
Classic International

An iconic restaurant for six decades, The Box Tree continues to thrive under current custodians
Simon and Rena Gueller. A stone-built property on the road through Ilkley, the abundant
hanging baskets and pretty garden enhance the cottage-like feel. Linen tablecloths and
impeccable service add a touch of luxury and the modern food is underpinned by classical
techniques. Dinner might begin with glazed veal sweetbreads, crispy chicken, local corn, pickled
shallot, burnt cauliflower purée, followed by Anjou squab pigeon, foie gras parfait, cherries,
salsify and port. Finish with strawberry soufflé, clotted cream, oat crumble, pickled pine berries
and basil.

Leeds

Chez Mal Brasserie ⚜️ NOTABLE WINE LIST
Malmaison Leeds, 1 Swinegate, LS1 4AG
0113 398 1000
www.malmaison.com
Open: All year

Chef: Simon Silver
Food Style: Modern British

The Malmaison group's Leeds branch is decorated and furnished to a high standard and the
brasserie is no exception, with plush leather booths and fireplaces under its elegant ceiling. The
cooking is built on quality ingredients, and talented chefs are clearly at work.

AN AWARD WINNING COUNTRY INN
NESTLED IN THE FOLD OF THE GLORIOUS SHIBDEN VALLEY.

OFTEN DESCRIBED AS A HIDDEN GEM,
TUCKED AWAY DOWN COUNTRY LANES,
THIS AWARD WINNING SEVENTEENTH
CENTURY INN IS THE PERFECT
COUNTRY ESCAPE.

Halifax, West Yorkshire, HX3 7UL. 01422365840

www.shibdenmillinn.com

Leeds *continued*

HOME

3 Brewery Place, LS10 1NE
0113 430 0161
www.homeleeds.co.uk
Closed: 25 December to 5 January

HOME's loft-style location is accessed through a very
discrete entrance from a pedestrian shopping area of
Leeds city centre. Up two flights of darkened stairs,
you'll reach the bar first, which is laid out with sofas
and quite minimal decor in dark colours. The brighter
restaurant is well-spaced and clothed tables are set
only with candle, flowers and napkins. The team from

Chef: Elizabeth Cottam
Food Style: Modern British

the open kitchen are very knowledgeable, clearly professional and helpfully explain most
courses and their reimagined British flavours.

The Man Behind The Curtain ⊛⊛⊛⊛

68–78 Vicar Lane, Lower Ground Floor Flannels,
LS1 7JH
0113 243 2376
www.themanbehindthecurtain.co.uk
Closed: 21 December to 13 January

Chef: Michael O'Hare
Food Style: Modern European

With its skateboard and surfboard artwork, graffiti and blaring rock music, The Man Behind
The Curtain has the edgy feel of a nightclub rather than a fine dining restaurant. A cavernous
basement in the heart of the city centre, the mirrors and marble add a stylish edge as do staff
in contemporary uniforms. Tasting menus are the form here, with signature dishes regularly
joined by new ones as the seasons roll. Although classic techniques underpin the cooking, the
cutting edge style and presentation is unique and dazzling, not least because a black and white
theme that runs through the dishes. A smoky barbecued red prawn appears with warming,
fragrant tikka spices and might lead on to a silky iced tomato consommé with vanilla. Called
'Emancipation', a dish of cured cod, charred gem, dashi and vinegar is a playful deconstruction
on fish and chips. Finish with chocolate crowdie and black olive.

Salvo's Restaurant ⊛
115 Otley Road, Headingley, LS6 3PX
0113 275 5017
www.salvos.co.uk
Closed: 25–26 December, 1 January

Forty-five years ago, Salvatore Dammone opened this Headingley restaurant, not far from the famous cricket ground. Today, it's the second and third generations of the family who maintain Salvo's simple approach to providing contemporary Italian food, including interesting pastas and pizzas. Great items are brought in from the motherland, especially for tasting menu dishes from different Italian regions.

Chef: Gip Dammone, James Darbyshire
Food Style: Italian

Thorpe Park Hotel & Spa ⊛
Century Way, Thorpe Park, LS15 8ZB
01132 641000
www.thorpeparkhotel.co.uk/food-drink
Closed: 25 December, 31 December

With quick access into Leeds or the countryside, the modern Thorpe Park Hotel is a handy base for exploring the area. The split-level dining room has a contemporary finish with artwork on the walls, and black leather-type chairs. The populist menu offers feel-good stuff.

Chef: Paul Woodward
Food Style: British, French

Pontefract

Wentbridge House Hotel ⊛⊛ 🍷NOTABLE WINE LIST
The Great North Road, Wentbridge, WF8 3JJ
01977 620444
www.wentbridgehouse.co.uk
Open: All year

Set in 20 acres of landscaped grounds in a conservation village, Wentbridge is a stone-built grand manor house. There's a degree of glossy formality, where candy-coloured upholstery creates a light, bright effect, and the cooking reaches out in all directions for its references.

Chef: Dan Ward
Food Style: Modern British

Ripponden

NEW The Fleece Countryside Inn 🌸🌸
Barkisland, HX4 0DJ
01422 820 687
www.fleece-inn.com
Open: All year

There's a focus on promoting the best of Yorkshire food at The Fleece, a sympathetically restored 18th-century inn with stunning views over Ripponden and the Calder Valley. Lots of original features and cosy lighting make for a pleasant dining area, and the food fits in just right. Careful sourcing ensures fresh and very seasonal seafood including shellfish in season.

Chef: Darren Parkinson
Food Style: Modern British

Wetherby

Wood Hall Hotel & Spa 🌸🌸
Trip Lane, Linton, LS22 4JA
01937 587271
www.handpickedhotels.co.uk/woodhall
Open: All year

Chef: Rohan Nevins
Food Style: Modern British

High on a hill with fine views, the Georgian Wood Hall retains much of its original detailing. Its dining room is an elegant, relaxing space where a rigorous dedication to Yorkshire produce is observed, and the cooking is marked by clear, distinct flavours.

Inspector Insight

Why is the scheme so important?

- Objective benchmarks
- Reliable consumer advice
- Professional inspections
- Respected and trusted
- Heritage - 60+ years of publication
- Aspirational
- Assures potential guests of quality levels

CHANNEL ISLANDS

Guernsey

St Martin

La Barbarie Hotel 🏵
Saints Road, Saints Bay, GY4 6ES
01481 235217
www.labarbariehotel.com
Closed: 7–20 November

This former priory is now a comfortable hotel –
La Barbarie – with a soothing vibe and a restaurant
using the peerless fresh produce of Guernsey's
coasts and meadows. The kitchen looks to the French
mainland for inspiration in their repertoire of simply
cooked and presented dishes.

Chef: Colin Pearson
Food Style: Traditional British

St Peter Port

The Duke of Richmond Hotel 🏵
Cambridge Park, GY1 1UY
01481 726221
www.dukeofrichmond.com
Open: All year

At the Duke of Richmond, the Leopard Bar and
Restaurant has a very distinctive style with its black
banquettes and widespread use of faux leopard skin.
Diners can get a good view of the team toiling away in
the open kitchen or sit out on the large sunny terrace
and enjoy views of the sea and the marina.

Chef: Richard Frankham
Food Style: Modern, British, French

The Old Government House Hotel & Spa 🏵
St Ann's Place, GY1 2NU
01481 724921
www.theoghhotel.com
Open: All year

Chef: Robert Newall
Food Style: Modern European

The beautiful white Georgian building was once the island governor's harbourside residence,
converted into a hotel in 1858. Among several dining options at the hotel, The Brasserie is the
place to be, offering fresh Guernsey fish as part of the menu at lunch and dinner.

St Pierre Park Hotel, Spa and Golf Resort 🏵️
Rohais, GY1 1FD
01481 736676
www.handpickedhotels.co.uk/stpierrepark
Open: All year

Chef: Aaron Sarre
Food Style: British

One mile from St Peter Port, this peaceful hotel is surrounded by 35 acres of grounds and a golf course. Overlooking the garden and with its own terrace and water feature, the bright and contemporary Pavilion Restaurant offers a crowd-pleasing menu with something for everybody.

Jersey

Gorey

Sumas 🏵️🏵️
Gorey Hill, JE3 6ET
01534 853291
www.sumasrestaurant.com
Closed: late December to mid January

The seasonal menus in this family-run restaurant are mainly modern British, featuring abundant fish and seafood, maybe hand-dived scallops and John Dory, although hints of French and Asian cooking appear too. Dining on the terrace overlooking Gorey harbour and Mont Orgueil Castle is rather enjoyable, especially when it's sunny. An affordable wine list ranges worldwide.

Chef: Dany Lancaster
Food Style: Modern British

Rozel

Château la Chaire 🏵️🏵️
Rozel Bay, JE3 6AJ
01534 863354
www.chateau-la-chaire.co.uk
Closed: Tuesday

Chef: Daniel Teesdale
Food Style: Classic, Traditional

Snuggled into a wooded valley, and yet only moments from the seashore, La Chaire is an early Victorian edifice with grounds laid out by the Kew Gardens luminary Samuel Curtis, and interiors full of oak panelling and intricate plaster scrollwork. The conservatory dining room capitalises fully on the majestic green views.

St Aubin

The Boat House ⚜

1 North Quay, JE3 8BS
01534 744226
www.randalls-jersey.co.uk/the-boat-house
Open: All year

Chef: Filipe Vieira Ribeiro
Food Style: British

With its full-drop glass walls overlooking the harbour and town, The Boat House has staked its claim to the best spot in St Aubin. Light and airy with an open kitchen, the first-floor restaurant deals in fresh, modern and traditional food, mixing fine ingredients and confident technique.

St Brelade

L'Horizon Beach Hotel and Spa ⚜⚜

St Brelade's Bay, JE3 8EF
01534 743101
www.handpickedhotels.co.uk/lhorizon
Closed: 25 December

The view over the bay is a big draw here but the Grill restaurant really puts the place on the map. It's a smart room with neutral colours, and the menu makes excellent use of the island's bounty, in bright, modern dishes. This daily menu is driven by what the fishermen have caught that day.

Chef: Andrew Soddy
Food Style: Modern British

Ocean Restaurant at The Atlantic Hotel ⚜⚜⚜⚜ ⌁ NOTABLE WINE LIST

Le Mont de la Pulente, JE3 8HE
01534 744101
www.theatlantichotel.com
Closed: January

Chef: Will Holland
Food Style: Modern British

Overlooking the wild dunes of St Ouen's Bay, the Ocean Restaurant is the jewel in the crown of The Atlantic Hotel, a boutique retreat amid exotic palm trees in a conservation area. The timeless sea views are best savoured from the louvred windows of the dining room, a gloriously light and airy setting with a soft-focus palette of blue, white and beige, and modern artwork on the walls. The stellar cooking is the real draw here. You might open with accurately timed pan-roasted foie gras with pain perdu, well-seasoned raspberry and beetroot purée, potato galette and fresh raspberries, a visually appealing and well executed starter. That could be followed by lamb – roast fillet and braised neck – with a crispy sweetbread and deep-flavoured basil pomme purée. One showstopping finale is a smooth and creamy iced honey parfait with white chocolate and yogurt crumb and crème fraîche 'snow'.

Best Western Royal Hotel ⊛

David Place, JE2 4TD
01534 726521
www.morvanhotels.com
Open: All year

Chef: Robert Scott
Food Style: Modern European

Seasons, the restaurant at Best Western Royal Hotel, has a light and airy feel, mainly due to the white colour scheme and lightwood flooring. Flowers on the tables and comfortable leather chairs help the elegant atmosphere, appropriate surroundings for some polished cooking. Unfussy, modern British and European dishes.

Bohemia Restaurant ⊛⊛⊛⊛ ♦ NOTABLE WINE LIST

The Club Hotel & Spa, Green Street, JE2 4UH
01534 880588
www.bohemiajersey.com
Closed: 24–30 December

Chef: Callum Graham
Food Style: Modern French, British

Bohemia Restaurant is in the shadow of Fort Regent, the island capital's 19th-century fortifications, and from the hotel rooftop terrace there is a good view across St Helier. Part of the Hotel Club & Spa, it's reached from the street via a separate entrance. Bistro-style decor is the setting for precise and accurate cooking and presentation using premium ingredients from the island's lavish supplies along with British and French produce to create both a surprise five-course and tasting menus to delight the palate. Things might begin with a Jersey brown crab pannacotta with Granny Smith apple sorbet. Follow with a main course of roasted saddle of lamb, braised lamb-stuffed courgette flower, red pepper and harissa, courgette and basil 'ratatouille' and intense lamb jus. Close with a Mojito unlike any you've experienced - a white chocolate mousse boasting a central layer combining classic mojito mint, lime and rum flavours.

Inspector Insight

Why is the scheme so important?

- Objective benchmarks
- Reliable consumer advice
- Professional inspections
- Respected and trusted
- Heritage - 60+ years of publication
- Aspirational
- Assures potential guests of quality levels

St Helier *continued*

Sirocco@The Royal Yacht Rosettes Suspended

The Weighbridge, JE2 3NF
01534 720511
www.theroyalyacht.com
Open: All year

Food Style: Australasian inspired

The Rosette award for this establishment has been suspended due to a change of chef and reassessment will take place in due course.
Curvaceous, wave-shaped balconies echo the maritime location at this contemporary harbourfront bolt-hole. It's a slick, upmarket affair, with a glossy spa centre, plus ample dining and drinking opportunities to keep you refuelled and refreshed, the pick of the bunch being the snazzy Sirocco with its huge terrace opening up sweeping views over the marina through full-drop windows.

Tassili ⊛⊛⊛⊛

Grand Jersey Hotel & Spa, The Esplanade, JE2 3QA
01534 722301
www.handpickedhotels.co.uk/grandjersey
Closed: 25 December, 1–30 January

Chef: Nicolas Valmagna
Food Style: British, French

Just a stone's throw from the waters of St Aubin's Bay, The Grand Jersey is a rather glamorous late-Victorian hotel, and Tassili, is a darkly luxurious space that comes into its own in the evenings. Service is excellent, and you can expect high-level French technique from Nicolas Valmagna and his team, taking inspiration from the island's produce and ideas from farther afield, providing an often thrilling culinary exploration of some of the best ingredients France has to offer. An early summer menu might include pan-roasted Nantes goose liver with fermented rhubarb and dukkah, while beautifully fresh Jersey Royal potatoes join smoked eel, lovage purée, sea lettuce and a fabulous baked potato consommé. Turbot appears in a saffron risotto, along with mussels, cockles, sea vegetables, Exmoor caviar, and there's milk fed lamb with asparagus, wild garlic, morels and black garlic purée. Follow that with an artisan cheese plate or move straight on to citron de Menton with St Ouen's honey and Brittany sablé biscuit.

How do you keep yourself under the radar?

By adopting plenty of aliases, have 'reasons' to be in the area –
perhaps looking at a property or undertaking
consultancy work down the road.

AA Inspector

St Peter

Greenhills Country Hotel ☀

Mont de L'Ecole, JE3 7EL
01534 481042
www.greenhillshotel.com
Closed: 23 December to 12 February

Chef: Lukasz Pietrasz
Food Style: Modern,
Mediterranean, British, French

There is much to like about this relaxed country hotel with its riotously colourful gardens, heated outdoor pool and bags of traditional charm. The kitchen team turns out a wide-ranging menu taking in everything from a classic straight-up fillet steak to more ambitious ideas.

Mark Jordan at the Beach ☀☀

La Plage, La Route de la Haule, JE3 7YD
01534 780180
www.markjordanatthebeach.com
Closed: 23 December to 15 January

Get yourself a table with a sea view – or out on the terrace if the weather is kind – for enjoying skilful cooking with a relaxed approach. You'll see plenty of local produce, especially fish, on the menu, and there's a great choice of wines by the glass.

Chef: Mark Jordan
Food Style: Anglo-French

St Saviour

Longueville Manor Hotel ☀☀☀ ⬩NOTABLE WINE LIST

JE2 7WF
01534 725501
www.longuevillemanor.com
Open: All year

Chef: Andrew Baird
Food Style: Modern Anglo-French

The grande dame of the Jersey hotel scene, Longueville Manor occupies a fabulous location within 18-acres of woodland complete with lake and kitchen garden. It's the latter that supplies much of the produce on the Anglo-French menu served in the handsome Oak Room. It makes for a refined setting for a meal that might begin with quail Scotch egg, black pudding, garden shoots, mustard mayonnaise and honey-scented jus, perhaps, followed by an accurately cooked piece of cod with oxtail ravioli, kale, salsify and white bean velouté. End with a perfect plum soufflé, sake sauce and chocolate sorbet.

SCOTLAND

Aberdeen

Aberdeen

Chez Mal Brasserie ⦿
Malmaison Aberdeen, 49-53 Queens Road, AB15 4YP
01224 327370
www.malmaisonaberdeen.com
Open: All year

Chef: Adam Parzniewski
Food Style: Modern French

Built from the solid granite that gives the city its moniker, the Aberdeen Mal is suitably dashing, with boutique allure and a cool industrial-chic finish. The brasserie is at the heart of the operation, with an open-to-view kitchen revealing the Josper grill.

IX Restaurant ⦿⦿
The Chester Hotel, 59–63 Queens Road, AB15 4YP
01244 327777
www.chester-hotel.com
Open: All year

Chef: Kevin Dalgleish
Food Style: Modern Scottish

The kitchen team behind this glossy contemporary grill are on a mission to be one of Aberdeen's top restaurants, and their switched-on menu is heading straight for that target. Happily, the food here is about great flavours rather than ego.

Moonfish Café ⦿
9 Correction Wynd, AB10 1HP
01224 644166
www.moonfishcafe.co.uk
Closed: 25–26 December, 1 January,
First 2 weeks January

Chef: Brian McLeish
Food Style: Modern British

Tucked away in a medieval wynd, or narrow lane, Moonfish Café has that fit-for-purpose, ready-to-go look about it. And go it does, with innovative modern British cooking, perhaps opening with crispy potato, cheese custard and Madras curry, then hake with onion, rice and brown butter, ending with rhubarb millefeuille, mascarpone and vanilla.

NEW Scullery Restaurant ⦿
Oldmeldrum Road, Newmachar, AB21 0QD
01651 862636
www.newmacharhotel.co.uk
Closed: Monday, Tuesday, 25–26 December,
1–2 January

The Scullery is the fine dining option at the Newmarchar, something more than just a village inn. It has plenty of historic character but just as much contemporary decor and design. The restaurant has individual booths as well as stand-alone tables and enjoys lots of natural daylight. There's also a terrace for dining on nicer days.

Chef: Matthew Stewart
Food Style: Modern Scottish

Aberdeenshire

Balmedie

The Cock and Bull
Ellon Road, Blairton, AB23 8XY
01358 743249
www.thecockandbull.co.uk
Closed: 25–26 December, 1–2 January

Open fires and modern artworks bring cossetting
warmth to this creeper-clad, stone-built coaching
inn standing in open farmland north of Aberdeen.
You can be sure of a well-kept pint and no-nonsense
food ranging from pub classics to more accomplished
dishes based on Peterhead-landed fish and shellfish, or
regionally sourced meats.

Chef: Stuart Kelly
Food Style: Modern Scottish,
British

Banchory

The Falls of Feugh Restaurant
Bridge of Feugh, AB31 6NL
01330 822123
www.thefallsoffeugh.com
Closed: Monday, Tuesday, January

In a bucolic spot by the river, surrounded by trees,
the sound of running water is particularly evocative if
you're sitting on the small terrace. There's a charming
café, but the main draw is the modern French- and
Scottish-inflected food on offer in the restaurant.

Chef: John Chomba
Food Style: Modern French,
Scottish

Ellon

Eat on the Green
Udny Green, AB41 7RS
01651 842337
www.eatonthegreen.co.uk
Closed: 1 week January

In a picture-perfect Scottish stone house with a gloriously
inviting interior of rich colours, Eat on the Green
continues to go from strength to strength. Attention
to detail is everything from the 'kilted chef' here, with
vegetables and herbs picked from their own gardens
and meat and game arriving from local farms. They
have a 'Gin Garden' too.

Chef: Craig Wilson
Food Style: British, Scottish,
European

Inverurie

The Green Lady 🌹

AB51 5NT
01467 621643
www.crerarhotels.com/thainstone-house-hotel
Open: All year

Chef: Antonio Cappucio
Food Style: Scottish

This elegant hotel welcomes its guests with traditional Scottish hospitality and The Green Lady showcases the best of seasonal local produce – from 28 days matured Scotch beef, cooked on the Josper, to market fish-of-the-day from the nearby fishing ports. High ceilings, brass chandeliers, and flickering candles set an elegant scene for dinner.

Kildrummy

Kildrummy Inn 🌹🌹

AB33 8QS
01975 571227
www.kildrummyinn.co.uk
Closed: Monday, Tuesday, 26–27 December, January

Chef: Alexandria Hay,
David Littlewood
Food Style: Modern Scottish

Kildrummy Inn has an authenticity that appeals to tourists and locals, while the output from its dynamic kitchen has put it on the foodie map. Menus reveal classical sensibilities and a contemporary touch and flavours hit the mark when it comes to desserts, too.

Peterhead

Buchan Braes Hotel 🌹

Boddam, AB42 3AR
01779 871471
www.buchanbraes.co.uk
Open: All year

Chef: Paul McLean
Food Style: Modern Scottish,
European

Close to some rugged Scottish coastline, Buchan Braes is a splendid contemporary hotel with a rural aspect and up-to-date wedding and conference facilities to boot. There's also the Grill Room restaurant, with its open kitchen and warmly colourful decor. The kitchen's approach is modern Scottish, with a focus on local produce from the sea.

What excites you most in your work?

Being surprised by something or someone.
The simple pleasure of tasting something truly delicious.

AA Inspector

Tarland

Douneside House
Tarland, AB34 4UL   **Food Style:** Classic
013398 81230
www.dounesidehouse.co.uk
Open: All year

Surrounded by 17 acres of stunning grounds, Douneside House spent many years as an establishment for military guests. Family portraits still hang on the walls of this colonial-style property which has enjoyed a contemporary makeover, successfully blending period style features with its varied and colourful history. The kitchen utilises modern skills to create dishes of wonderful clarity and depth of flavour. Exciting and interesting dishes incorporate the best estate produce including ingredients from the splendid kitchen garden. Wonderful views of the garden and terrace are available from the light-filled, elegant restaurant.

Angus

Carnoustie

Carnoustie Golf Hotel & Spa ⚘
The Links, DD7 7JE
01241 411999
www.bespokehotels.com/carnoustiegolfhotel
Open: All year

Calder's Bistro enjoys a stunning location overlooking the 1st tee and 18th green of the world-famous Carnoustie Links golf course. With floor-to-ceiling windows providing impressive views of the golf course, this makes a pleasant place to sample an eclectic range of dishes.

Chef: Andrew Pavlantis
Food Style: Bistro, Scottish, European

Forfar

Drovers ⚘
Memus By Forfar, DD8 3TY   **Chef:** Sam Chalmers
01307 860322   **Food Style:** Modern Scottish
www.the-drovers.com
Closed: 25–26 December

Surrounded by beautiful glens, Drovers is the kind of wild place you want to be stranded when the weather closes in. Although a modern pub in many ways, the walls of antlers remind you this rustic bolt-hole has been around for many years.

Gordon's 🏵🏵🏵

Main Street, DD11 5RN
01241 830364
www.gordonsrestaurant.co.uk
Closed: January

Chef: Garry Watson
Food Style: Modern Scottish

Inverkeilor is a tiny coastal hamlet and Gordon's has put the village on the map of gastronomic destinations. Thanks to the Watson family's efforts over 30-odd years, the place ticks all the boxes for a food-and-sea-themed getaway. Gordon's son Garry heads up the kitchen, keeping visitors happy with his precise modern Scottish cooking. Dinner might open with a perfectly timed roast Orkney scallop with cauliflower velouté and leek oil. A fish main might involve Loch Fyne salmon with a spiced rice cracker, wonderful smoked mussel cream, avocado and citrus. Finish with Seahills Farm strawberries, tarragon ice cream and star anise meringue.

Argyll & Bute

Restaurant at Isle of Eriska 🏵🏵🏵

PA37 1SD
01631 720371
www.eriska-hotel.co.uk

Chef: Ernst Van Zyl
Food Style: Modern British

A 19th-century mansion on a private tidal island, Restaurant at Isle of Eriska boasts a unique setting. Surrounded by grounds, woods and shoreline, this luxurious hideaway has a traditional restaurant in keeping with the house itself. Although fine dining is the concept here, staff are unstuffy and chatty. The modern British food makes the most of the local area, including vegetables from the kitchen garden. Scottish seafood is a strength, as in a delightful starter of scallop, chervil root, quince and dashi. It might be followed by an accurately timed pancetta-wrapped pork fillet with squash, sprouts and prunes.

Sugar Boat 🏵🏵

30 Colquhoun Square, G84 8AQ
01436 647522
www.sugarboat.co.uk
Closed: 25–26 December, 1 January

On a square in the heart of town, with tables out front and back, Sugar Boat is an all-day bistro with real foodie credentials. The design is done out in natural colours of earth and sea, with a marble topped bar and viewable kitchen. The hearty modern bistro cooking features big flavours and an essentially simple approach to treating Scottish produce with care and attention and not a little European flare.

Chef: Oli Nodwell
Food Style: Modern Scottish

Inveraray

Loch Fyne Hotel & Spa ⊚
Shore Street, PA32 8XT
01499 302980
www.crerarhotels.com/loch-fyne-hotel-spa
Open: All year

The Cladach Mòr Bistro, from the Gaelic for 'great shore', takes its inspiration from both land and sea. Open fires, rich tones and stone walls set the scene. Expect seafood, meats and produce, locally sourced whenever possible, to reflect and celebrate each season. You can enjoy beautiful loch views as you indulge in the carefully crafted dishes.

Food Style: Classic Traditional

Kilchrenan

The Dining Room ⊚
Ardanaiseig Hotel, PA35 1HE
01866 833337
www.ardanaiseig.com
Open: All year

Chef: Martin McCluskey
Food Style: Classic

The elegant Dining Room at Ardanaiseig Hotel offers a daily rolling menu of dishes on a classical basis with some modern touches to bring it all up to date. There's a strong emphasis on local larder and very commendable wine choice. Expect a balanced blend of old and new world wines with a few options to tempt the connoisseur.

Faodail at Taychreggan Hotel ⊚⊚
PA35 1HQ
01866 833211
www.taychregganhotel.co.uk
Closed: 19 December 2022 to 3 February 2023

Faodail means 'lucky find' and your dining experience may be just that when you discover this 17th-century former coaching inn nestled in its own private bay on the shores of Loch Awe. The kitchen delivers set dinner menus and there's always a friendly team waiting to welcome you. Plus there are 14 individual bedrooms so you can retire in comfort after a good meal.

Chef: Gerard McCluskey
Food Style: Classic Scottish

Lochgoilhead

The Lodge on Loch Goil ◉◉
Loch Goil, PA24 8AE
01301 703193
www.thelodge-scotland.com
Open: All year

Chef: Daniel Holleren
Food Style: Modern Scottish

At the head of a sea loch, the beautifully restored lodge offers three dining spaces: the Orangery, the Treehouse and the lochside Arts and Crafts restaurant. Scottish produce leads the menu; indeed, many ingredients are grown in the lodge's gardens or at least locally foraged. With the sea so close, expect seafood too.

Oban

Etive Restaurant ◉◉
43 Stevenson Street, PA34 5NA
01631 564899
etiverestaurant.co.uk
Closed: Monday, Tuesday, 19–27 December

A small and intimate restaurant in Oban, Etive offers modern, fresh menus which clearly reflect the unbridled passion of its owners John McNulty and David Lapsley. So, expect quality Scottish ingredients, and high-calibre cooking of a classical nature with some added novel concepts, all culminating in a fun dining experience with attentive friendly service.

Chef: John McNulty, David Lapsley
Food Style: Modern Scottish

Grill Room ◉
Corran Esplanade, PA34 5AE
01631 564395
www.crerarhotels.com/oban-bay-hotel/grill-room
Open: All year

You'll like the Grill Room. The port of Oban provides the backdrop and much of the produce on seasonal menus offering an accessible grill room format. Focused cooking here might include scallops simply paired with Stornoway black pudding, rich linguine with lobster, cray fish and prawns or Crerar's own red deer.

Chef: Dawid Spychalski
Food Style: Modern Scottish

Oban *continued*

Tigh an Truish 🏵
Clachan Seil, PA34 4QZ
01852 300242
www.tighantruish.com
Closed: 24–25 December

Located on Seil Island just over the iconic 'Bridge Over the Atlantic', Tigh an Truish has been serving islanders for over 250 years and has undergone a total make-over. It enjoys some picture postcard views as well as warm, friendly service and fantastic food that makes the most of what the Argyle larder has to offer.

Chef: William Rocks
Food Style: Modern Scottish

Port Appin

Airds Hotel and Restaurant 🏵🏵🏵 ⟍NOTABLE WINE LIST
PA38 4DF
01631 730236
www.airds-hotel.com
Closed: Closed 28 November to 9 December

Chef: Calum Innes
Food Style: Modern Scottish

Airds has long enjoyed a loyal following, and is a great example of Scottish hospitality. The dining room has 12 tables, each with a fantastic view. Low ceilings makes the space cosy yet tables are spaced enough to provide privacy. Lilac wicker chairs, ironed white linen and bright modern decor. Food's engaging too. Start with a tian of crab with salt baked kohlrabi, sesame tuile and green chilli gazpacho. Move on to perfectly cooked seared stone bass with scallop tortellini, herb gnocchi, chervil and caviar butter sauce. Finish with rhubarb and vanilla pannacotta, rhubarb sorbet and gingerbread gel.

The Pierhouse Seafood Restaurant 🏵🏵
The Pierhouse Hotel, PA38 4DE
01631 730302
www.pierhousehotel.co.uk
Closed: 25–26 December

The Pierhouse enjoys a wonderful location at the edge of Loch Linnhe, opposite the pier from which a small ferry takes people to and from Lismore. Whitewashed walls inside and out with fantastic artwork, wood-burning stoves and a variety of seating. The main restaurant looks out onto the water and has some wonderful views.

Chef: Michael Leathley
Food Style: Scottish Seafood

Strachur

Inver Restaurant ⊛⊛⊛
Strathlachlan, PA27 8BU
01369 860537
www.inverrestaurant.co.uk
Closed: 25 December, January to February

Chef: Pamela Brunton
Food Style: Modern Scottish

An isolated and wild location on the shores of Loch Fyne is the perfect setting for the cooking of chef Pam Brunton, who previously worked at Noma in Copenhagen. A whitewashed cottage with unfussy Scandi designs, it's a minimalist backdrop for the sharp-edged cooking and bold flavours. Wild and foraged ingredients, plus shellfish from nearby lochs, dominate the menu, which might kick off with grilled squid, yellow tomatoes and a spicy red sausage. A signature main of Gigha halibut, mussels and coastal greens could lead on to raspberry and burnt honey meringue pie with raspberry sorbet and lemon curd.

South Ayrshire

Ayr

Fairfield House Hotel ⊛
12 Fairfield Road, KA7 2AS
01292 267461
www.fairfieldhotel.co.uk
Open: All year

With its views across to the Isle of Arran, this seafront hotel puts contemporary cooking at the forefront of menus in Martin's Bar & Grill with its walls displaying modern Scottish artwork. Pedigree local produce is the cornerstone of big-flavoured dishes like breast of duck, black cabbage, plum, potatoes and redcurrant jus.

Chef: Stuart Gemmel
Food Style: Modern, Traditional

Ballantrae

Glenapp Castle ⊛⊛⊛ ⬧NOTABLE WINE LIST
KA26 0NZ
01465 831212
www.glenappcastle.com
Open: All year

Chef: Joe Gould
Food Style: Modern British

There really is no beating a castle for dramatic impact, and the approach to Glenapp certainly won't leave you disappointed. The charming restaurant overlooks the splendid grounds and has a real sense of grandeur, with high ceilings and tables clothed in crisp linen. It's elegant and formal without being stuffy, and a grand setting for the daily-changing menu. The style is timeless, with simple, elegant compositions designed to showcase the top quality ingredients. Meltingly tender Ibérico pork shoulder might kick things off, while a main course of stone bass demonstrates impressively thoughtful textural contrasts from lemon quinoa, broccoli and braised baby gem.

Troon

Walkers Lounge ⊛
15 Craigend Road, KA10 6HD
01292 314747
www.piersland.co.uk
Open: All year

Chef: John Rae
Food Style: Traditional Scottish

Piersland House is a delightful, historic hotel, once home to the Johnnie Walker whisky family, and set in its own grounds in the heart of Troon. Walkers Lounge, the elegant bar/restaurant with its carved fireplaces and dramatic beamed ceiling, is a comfortable, elegant setting for classic, traditional dining. Begin with something simple – warming vegetable soup, perhaps – before moving on to a main course of enticingly presented poached fillet of sole, served with a cheese and leek glaze. A crisp pastry tart of white chocolate and raspberry, accompanied by raspberry sorbet, makes for an indulgent finale.

Dumfries & Galloway

Dumfries

The Auldgirth Inn ⊛⊛⊛
Auldgirth, DG2 0XG
01387 740250
www.auldgirthinn.co.uk
Open: All year

Chef: Robert McAleese
Food Style: Modern Scottish

Discover a relaxing dining experience at this 500-year-old inn where the locally sourced produce is transformed into contemporary cuisine with a classical basis, finished with more modern techniques and innovative touches. The menu features a collection of bold and ambitious dishes, all with good balance of flavour and clarity, which is evident in the taste. The feature open-plan kitchen is a conversational focal point, as is the dry ageing chamber on display with some superb local beef and game featuring on menus. Large aspect windows flood the area with natural light, for the benefit of diners at breakfast and dinner.

NEW The Globe Inn Awaiting Inspection
56 High Street, DG1 2JA
01387 323010
www.globeinndumfries.co.uk
Closed: Sunday, Monday, Tuesday, 25–26 December, 1–2 January

As Scottish pubs go, the 17th-century Globe Inn has the strongest connection of any eatery to Robert Burns, Scotland's National Bard. It was one of his favourite haunts (or 'howff') and has rooms dedicated to him, still almost as he left them. Meals makes the best of Scottish produce, and is served in rooms Burns himself dined in.

Chef: Jonathan Brett
Food Style: Classic

Gretna

Smiths at Gretna Green
Gretna Green, DG16 5EA
01461 337007
www.smithsgretnagreen.com
Closed: 25 December

Chef: Phillip Woodcock
Food Style: Modern British,
International

Smiths at Gretna Green is a contemporary, stylish restaurant, with booth seating down one wall, and large mirrors. Bespoke light shades and individual spot-lit tables alongside neutral, dark-toned decor ensures a memorable dining experience. The imaginative menus are especially good at game, and don't miss the excellent bread, which comes in a plant-pot.

Moffat

Brodies
Holm Street, DG10 9EB
01683 222870
www.brodiesofmoffat.co.uk
Closed: 25–27 December

The first thing you notice about Brodies is the decor, a display of colour, eclectic and eccentric wallpapers, and mixed fabrics. It's a lovely place for dining or for a very popular afternoon tea. The gin lounge is incredible, while the menu has a classic base with some novel touches such as the Annanwater hogget tasting plate.

Chef: Russell Pearce, Billy Armitage
Food Style: Modern British

See advertisement on page 564

Portpatrick

Knockinaam Lodge 🏅 NOTABLE WINE LIST
DG9 9AD
01776 810471
www.knockinaamlodge.com
Open: All year

Chef: Anthony Pierce
Food Style: Modern Scottish

Churchill and Eisenhower planned D-Day at this boutique country house hotel, built in the 19th century as a hunting lodge, but don't worry, you won't have to think about anything more taxing than what you might have for dinner. An elegant double-aspect dining room makes the most of stunning views over manicured lawns and beyond to the sea, a comfortable setting for the daily-changing set menu, where locally sourced produce is the backbone of the simple but effective cooking. A cappuccino of ceps and tarragon with poached quail's egg is a light and delicate starter, followed by roast loin of tender, deeply flavoured Carsluith red deer.

Sanquhar

Blackaddie House ⚜️⚜️
Blackaddie Road, DG4 6JJ
01659 50270
www.blackaddiehotel.co.uk
Closed: 24–26 December

Close to the River Nith, 16th-century Blackaddie House has a traditional restaurant in character with the building's heritage and style. Its high, ornate plastered ceiling gives a real sense of space, and in the evenings the atmosphere is enhanced by the opulent crystal chandelier. Modern artwork of highland cattle adds a little contemporary twist to the theme.

Chef: Paolo Recina
Food Style: Modern British

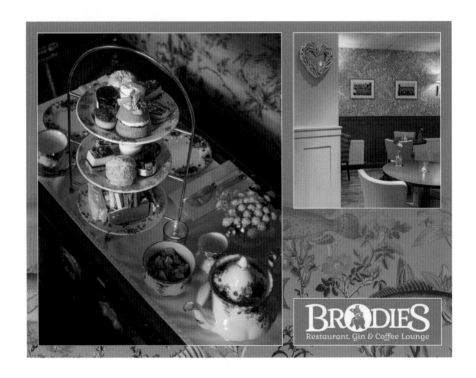

West Dunbartonshire

Balloch

The Cameron Grill ❀❀
Cameron House on Loch Lomond, G83 8QZ
01389 310 777
www.cameronhouse.co.uk
Open: All year

Chef: Gary Townsend
Food Style: Modern British

After a catastrophic fire in 2017, the Five Star Cameron House resort fully re-opened in September 2021 following a spectacular renovation which combines Scottish country-house finery and pin-sharp contemporary style. The Cameron Grill enjoys the signature stunning views across Loch Lomond and you can expect precise grill room cooking and wholesome natural dishes in an intimate setting.

NEW Tamburrini & Wishart ❀❀❀
Cameron House on Loch Lomond, G83 8QZ
01389 722504
www.cameronhouse.co.uk/dining-bars/
tamburrini-wishart
Closed: 25–26 December, 1 January

Chef: Paul Tamburrini,
Martin Wishart
Food Style: Modern Scottish,
European

Enter the elegant wood-panelled dining room at Cameron House and the expectation of what Paul Tamburrini and Martin Wishart may bring is almost palapable. The thought and imagination put into the food served here is first class as is the quality of the provenance. The dishes are modern Scottish with influences from Paul's motherland (Italy) but always balanced. Here, the accuracy of cooking is without doubt as are the flavours and technical skills showcased. Choose, perhaps, for your main course a perfectly timed Aberdeenshire lamb complemented with barbecued aubergine, black curry and yogurt. The accompanying wine list is very detailed.

Clydebank

Golden Jubilee Conference Hotel ❀
Beardmore Street, G81 4SA
0141 951 6015
www.goldenjubileehotel.com
Open: All year

Chef: Iain Ramsay
Food Style: Modern British

A hotel and conference centre next to the Jubilee Hospital, the Golden Jubilee Conference Hotel is a multi-purpose hub for business meetings, fitness workouts and aspirational dining with a new spin on some classics. Ecclefechan tart with toffee ice cream is a fine regional speciality.

Dundee

Dundee

Chez Mal Brasserie ⊛
Malmaison Dundee, 44 Whitehall Crescent, DD1 4AY
01382 339715
www.malmaison.com/locations/dundee
Open: All year

Chef: Paul Duncan
Food Style: British, French

The Dundee branch of the Malmaison chain is a majestic old hotel with a domed ceiling above a central wrought-iron staircase, with the trademark sexy looks, which run through to the candlelit brasserie's darkly atmospheric colour scheme. The menu plays the modern brasserie game from Thai noodle salad to steaks cooked on the Josper grill.

The Tayberry ⊛⊛
594 Brook Street, Broughty Ferry, DD5 2EA
01382 698280
www.tayberryrestaurant.com
Closed: 25–27 December

Chef: Adam Newth
Food Style: Scottish

This relaxed, contemporary operation has made quite a splash on the local culinary scene. Spread over two floors, its purple-toned decor is a nod to the namesake berry, and views across the River Tay from the first-floor tables are a real bonus. Focused, modern dishes allow local produce to shine.

Inspector Insight

Why is the scheme so important?

- Objective benchmarks
- Reliable consumer advice
- Professional inspections
- Respected and trusted
- Heritage - 60+ years of publication
- Aspirational
- Assures potential guests of quality levels

Edinburgh

Edinburgh

21212 ◎◎◎◎ 🍾 NOTABLE WINE LIST

3 Royal Terrace, EH7 5AB
0131 523 1030
www.21212restaurant.co.uk
Closed: 2 weeks January, 2 weeks September

Enjoying a lofty position on cobbled Royal Terrace, views from 21212 stretch across Edinburgh and the Forth towards Fife. This Georgian townhouse has been painstakingly transformed into the stylish restaurant with rooms it is today. The restaurant and kitchen occupy the ground and first floors with quality decor, striking artwork and booth seating. Ultra-modern cooking and flavour combinations that are eclectic

Chef: Paul Kitching
Food Style: Modern French

and often challenging make for a though-provoking dining experience. A starter of 'cheesy barley pudding' with panko and Taleggio is a wonderful combination of flavours and textures showcasing sound technical skills. An accurately timed piece of halibut is cooked with thyme and a soy dressing, the freshness of the fish shining through. Lemon meringue 'bombe' and coconut has the right hit of lemon acidity contrasted by the buttery snap of the shortbread base and creamy lemon curd sauce. The interesting global wine list offers plenty of choice.

The Brasserie - Norton House Hotel & Spa ◎

Ingliston, EH28 8LX
0131 333 1275
www.handpickedhotels.co.uk/nortonhouse
Open: All year

Chef: Graeme Shaw
Food Style: Scottish

Located on the outskirts of the city, in its own grounds, Norton House Hotel is a Victorian mansion that used to belong to a major brewing family. The Brasserie is the major dining option, with leather banquettes, warm wood colours, lovely views of the garden and good use of daylight. Menu is traditional Scottish with a modern twist.

Chez Mal Brasserie ◎

Malmaison Edinburgh, One Tower Place, Leith, EH6 7BZ
0131 468 5000
www.malmaison.com/locations/edinburgh
Open: All year

Chef: Andrew Mcconnell
Food Style: British, French

This was the first opening for the Malmaison chain, housed in a renovated seamen's mission on the waterfront in the old part of Leith, and is nowadays the grande dame of the boutique chain. The restaurant overlooks the docks with a terrace for alfresco dining.

Edinburgh *continued*

Dean Banks at The Pompadour ◉◉◉
Waldorf Astoria Edinburgh, The Caledonian,
Princes Street, EH1 2AB
07770451668
www.deanbanks.co.uk
Closed: 2 weeks January

Chef: Dean Banks
Food Style: Fine Dining,
Asian-influenced

One of the grande dames of Scottish hospitality, Waldorf Astoria - The Caledonian still offers
a genuine wow factor after more than a century. Dean Banks at The Pompadour is the fine
dining option on the mezzanine floor of the hotel, the in-demand tables overlooking Lothian
Road and up to the castle. High ceilings, intricate plasterwork and walls of striking artwork
makes for a grand setting for the modern Scottish cooking with an Asian influence. A fresh and
vibrant starter of North Sea hake, Thai basil and coconut might lead on to grass-fed beef cheek,
gochujan, ponzu and black sesame.

Divino Enoteca ◉ 🍷NOTABLE WINE LIST
5 Merchant Street, EH1 2QD
0131 225 1770
www.vittoriagroup.co.uk/divinoenoteca
Closed: Sunday

Chef: Francesco Ascrizzi
Food Style: Modern Italian,
International

A hip venue with contemporary artworks on the walls, exposed brickwork and displays of
wine bottles wherever you look: it's dark, moody, and a lot of fun. The kitchen's Italian output
includes an excellent range of antipasti plus some more modern interpretations of the classics.

The Dungeon Restaurant at Dalhousie Castle ◉◉
Bonnyrigg, EH19 3JB
01875 820153
www.dalhousiecastle.co.uk
Closed: 24–26 December, 31 December, 1 January

Dalhousie Castle is a 13th-century fortress in wooded
parkland on the banks of the River Esk, so you know
you're in for something special at The Dungeon
Restaurant. The cooking here has its roots in French
classicism and a bedrock of top-class Scottish
ingredients.

Chef: Pedro Barreira
Food Style: Traditional European

The Gardener's Cottage
1 Royal Terrace Gardens, London Road, EH7 5DX
0131 677 0244
www.thegardenerscottage.co
Closed: Monday, Tuesday, Wednesday,
25–26 December, 1 January

Chef: Edward Murray, Dale Mailley
Food Style: British

With its blackboard menu in the gravel outside, this restaurant with full-on royal connections is an oasis of pastoral calm in the bustling city. Cosy up in wicker chairs at big communal tables for Scottish cooking that takes pride in its carefully sourced prime materials. That's clear from a starter of mutton and roe-deer meatballs in maltagliati pasta.

Grazing by Mark Greenaway
Waldorf Astoria Edinburgh - The Caledonian,
Princes Street, EH1 2AB
0131 222 8888
markgreenaway.com/grazing-restaurant
Open: All year

Grazing by Mark Greenaway is the buzzy, informal dining room of the Waldorf Astoria Edinburgh – The Caledonian. High ceilings, leather and wood, reflect its Victorian railway station heritage. The kitchen presents a wide-ranging menu of solid bistro cooking – from small sharing plates to traditional starters and mains, and everything from comfort classics to displays of technical prowess.

Chef: Duncan McKay
Food Style: Modern, Traditional

Harajuku Kitchen
10 Gillespie Place, EH10 4HS
0131 281 0526
harajukukitchen.co.uk
Closed: Monday

Named after an area of Tokyo, this bistro offers authentic Japanese dishes with a touch of panache in an informal café-like atmosphere of exposed stone, vibrant artworks and chunky wood tables and low-back chairs. Family run, the kitchen sends out exciting and authentic cooking, with some dishes passed down through three generations.

Chef: Nobuo Sasaki
Food Style: Japanese

Edinburgh *continued*

Hotel du Vin Edinburgh ⊚ ♨ NOTABLE WINE LIST

11 Bristo Place, EH1 1EZ
0131 247 4900
www.hotelduvin.com
Open: All year

Chef: Ross Edgar
Food Style: Classic French

The former city asylum is the setting for HdV's Edinburgh outpost. The setting is considerably more cheerful thanks to the group's trademark gentleman's-club look of well-worn leather seats and woody textures. There's a splendid tartan-clad whisky snug, plus a buzzy mezzanine bar overlooking the bistro.

Kanpai Sushi ⊚

8–10 Grindlay Street, EH3 9AS
0131 228 1602
www.kanpaisushiedinburgh.co.uk
Closed: Sunday, Monday, 25 December to 1 January

Set in a side street close to the Usher and Traverse Theaters, Kanpai Sushi is a small restaurant with a sushi bar. Place settings are simple with a small plate, chopsticks and a ceramic soy sauce kettle. Service is attentive, food coming from the kitchen or the sushi bar. Decor is minimal, so the food does the talking.

Chef: Max Wang
Food Style: Japanese

The Kitchin ⊚⊚⊚⊚⊚ ♨ NOTABLE WINE LIST

78 Commercial Quay, Leith, EH6 6LX
0131 555 1755
www.thekitchin.com
Closed: 23 December to 12 January

Chef: Tom Kitchin
Food Style: Modern Scottish,
French influences

A former whisky warehouse in the regenerated Leith docklands has been Tom Kitchin's address since 2006 and it immediately shot into the premier league of the top foodie destinations. The interior looks sharp in hues of teal blue and grey, with exposed stone walls, painted brick pillars and industrial girders, while Kitchin's 'From Nature to Plate' mantra is articulated through cooking that applies top-level refinement and technical skills to Scotland's finest materials. From the à la carte choose a starter of Isle of Barra razor clams, early season broad beans, Château Leoube olive oil and Oscietra caviar then where better than here to try the modern Scottish dish of Balcaskie Estate mutton, Free Company's farm neeps, potato terrine accompanied by turnip top salsa verde? An alternative might be roast Hopetoun Estate roe deer loin and braised haunch with variation of beetroot and Granny Smith apple. Vegetarians shouldn't be concerned though, their choices are just as tempting as in a starter of cauliflower velouté, St Andrews cheddar, apple, caper and summer truffle, followed by courgette and basil risotto, Laganory cheese with a tempura courgette flower. Desserts are also handled with awe-inspiring dexterity, as in the memorable lemon soufflé with Knockraich Farm crème frâiche sorbet.

La Favorita
325–331 Leith Walk, EH6 8SA
0131 554 2430
www.vittoriagroup.co.uk/lafavorita
Closed: 25 December

Chef: Jarek Splawski
Food Style: Modern Italian,
Mediterranean

Well-sourced Italian ingredients supply the wherewithal for the Vittoria group's Leith pizzeria. From its wood-fired ovens comes a compendious list of pizzas, as well as cured meat platters and an imaginative diversity of pasta dishes and risottos. The ambience is upbeat and casual, and there's a bargain weekday set-price lunch worth considering.

La Garrigue ⌖ ▮NOTABLE WINE LIST
31 Jeffrey Street, EH1 1DH
0131 557 3032
www.lagarrigue.co.uk
Closed: 25–26 December

Named for the wild, herb-scented scrubland in Provence and Languedoc in the south of France. Chef-patron Jean-Michel Gauffre has brought the region's honest rustic cooking to his smart neighbourhood restaurant in Edinburgh's old town. Born in the heartlands of cassoulet, his take on the hearty stew of belly pork, duck confit, Toulouse sausage and white beans is the real deal.

Chef: Peter Duck
Food Style: French, Mediterranean

l'escargot bleu ⌖
56 Broughton Street, EH1 3SA
0131 557 1600
www.lescargotbleu.co.uk
Closed: 1 week January, 1 week July

L'escargot bleu is indeed blue – on the outside at least, and snails are present and correct among les entrées. The bilingual menu deals in classic bistro dishes such as those snails, which come from Barra in the Outer Hebrides, and there's a Scottish flavour.

See advertisement on page 573

Chef: Fred Berkmiller
Food Style: French, Scottish

Edinburgh *continued*

The Little Chartroom ⬡⬡
30–31 Albert Place, EH6 5JD
0131 556 6600
www.thelittlechartroom.com
Closed: Monday, Tuesday, Wednesday,
25–26 December, First 2 weeks January

A tiny restaurant on Leith Walk, The Little Chartroom
is a tightly packed and lively place with open brickwork
and plain tables. The food is ultra-seasonal, with menus
changing daily and focused on the delights of the
Scottish larder. Stripped back dishes are full of flavour
and perfectly timed.

Chef: Roberta Hall-McCarron
Food Style: Modern Scottish

Locanda De Gusti ⬡⬡
102 Dalry Road, EH11 2DW
0131 346 8800
www.locandadegusti.com
Closed: First 2 weeks July, 1 week October,
25–26 December, 1 January, First week January

With its painted brickwork and all-round rustic appeal,
this inviting restaurant has more than a hint of an Italian
domestic kitchen about it. Translating loosely as 'inn
of taste', you'll certainly find heaps of flavour in the
kitchen's big-hearted cooking; top-drawer local produce
is boosted by ingredients shipped in from Italy to keep
it all authentic.

Chef: Rosario Sartore
Food Style: Italian, Mediterranean,
Seafood

NAVADHANYA ⬡⬡
32–34 Grindlay Street, EH3 9AP
0131 629 7868
www.navadhanya-scotland.co.uk
Closed: Monday, 24 December, 1 January

Navadhanya's Haymarket venue was always a popular
spot and this continues in their newer, larger and more
central premises on Grindlay Street. The modern Indian
food steers clear of the usual high street curry and
offers an inventive menu of regional dishes. Sunhari
Jhingha (chargrilled king prawns, mustard, cumin and
coriander chutney) is a strong way to start, perhaps
followed by slow-cooked Hyderabadi lamb shank.

Chef: Tharveskhan
Food Style: Modern Indian

l'escargot bleu

56 BROUGHTON STREET EDINBURGH EH1 3SA   WWW.LESCARGOTBLEU.CO.UK   0131 557 1600

Edinburgh *continued*

New Chapter ◉
18 Eyre Place, EH3 5EP
0131 556 0006
www.newchapterrestaurant.co.uk
Closed: 24–26 December

A godsend for the neighbourhood, this cheery venue
combines a laid-back demeanour with clean-cut,
contemporary looks, breezy service, and a kitchen that
produces unfussy, full-flavoured dishes with European
leanings. If you're after top value, the lunch menu is
a steal.

Chef: Maciek Szymik
Food Style: Scottish, European

NEW No11 Brasserie ◉
11 Brunswick Street, EH7 5JB
0131 557 6910
www.11brunswickst.co.uk
Closed: 25–26 December

No. 11 was built in 1822 and is part of a terrace of
Georgian townhouses not far from Royal Terrace. These
days it's a restaurant with rooms that makes the most
of its history and character, including high ceilings
and feature fireplaces. The kitchen offers imaginative
cooking that utilises locally sourced provenance to
good effect.

Chef: Stevie Gerrard
Food Style: Modern Scottish

Number One, The Balmoral ◉◉◉◉ ♦NOTABLE WINE LIST
1 Princes Street, EH2 2EQ
0131 557 6727
www.roccofortehotels.com
Open: All year

Chef: Mark Donald, Gary Robinson
Food Style: Modern Scottish

The Balmoral Hotel is a long-established luxurious Edinburgh landmark, with impressive
public areas, all marble and ornate plasterwork. The classy Number One dining room is
spacious, and the immaculately presented tables, beautiful dove grey banquettes with yellow
buttoned backs and matching cushions, and red-lacquered walls hung with contemporary
artworks provide a fitting backdrop for the extremely high-quality cooking and exemplary,
dedicated service. The food is without doubt some of the best and most consistent the city has
to offer. A great deal of thought and imagination is given to the dishes, which are as delightful
to look at they are to eat – a good example being a starter of smoked Exmoor sturgeon
with beetroot and Oscietra caviar, a real highlight. Main course roe deer from the Borders is
wonderfully tender, while a fascinating dessert features the textural contrasts of Jerusalem
artichoke, malt and caramelised yogurt.

Ondine Restaurant ⑳⑳ ♪NOTABLE WINE LIST
2 George IV Bridge, EH1 1AD
0131 226 1888
www.ondinerestaurant.co.uk
Open: All year

Chef: Roy Brett
Food Style: Seafood

Ondine has earned a loyal following on the city's culinary scene, and it's not hard to see why: just off the Royal Mile, on George IV Bridge, it's a contemporary space with an upbeat bustle and great views out over the old town. Sustainable seafood, prepared simply and with an eye on exciting global flavours, is the main draw.

One Square ⑳
Sheraton Grand Hotel & Spa,
1 Festival Square, EH3 9SR
0131 221 6422
www.onesquareedinburgh.co.uk
Open: All year

Chef: Craig Hart
Food Style: Modern Scottish

The views of Edinburgh Castle give a sense of place to this slick, modern dining option. The floor-to-ceiling windows add a cool, classy finish. The lunch and dinner menus have a sharp focus on Scotland's fine produce in their crowd-pleasing medley of modern ideas.

Restaurant Martin Wishart ⑳⑳⑳⑳ ♪NOTABLE WINE LIST
54 The Shore, Leith, EH6 6RA
0131 553 3557
www.restaurantmartinwishart.co.uk
Closed: 25–26 December, 1 January, 3 weeks January

Chef: Martin Wishart, Joe Taggart
Food Style: Modern French

Martin Wishart's recognition of Leith as an opportunity and a destination made him a bit of a trailblazer, and it's hard to imagine, as you look round this buzzy hive of restaurants and bars, that it hasn't always been this way. Understated and unpretentious on the outside, discreetly located on the cobbled quayside, the restaurant is cool, classical and elegant within. Pale wood and muted colours make sure your focus is where is should be – on the food. Menus change seasonally and include a vegetarian tasting option, and the style is classic French with clear Scottish influences. Dishes are thoroughly fresh and vibrant, with precise attention to detail in every option. The haggis bonbon that might kicks things off, then moves to starters like céviche of Gigha halibut with mango and passionfruit, while mains like roast loin of Borders roe deer, with braised gem lettuce, goats' cheese gnocchi, morels and Grand Veneur sauce are equally inspiring. There's an excellent wine list too.

Edinburgh *continued*

Rhubarb at Prestonfield 🏵🏵 🍷NOTABLE WINE LIST

Priestfield Road, EH16 5UT
0131 225 1333
www.prestonfield.com/dine/rhubarb
Open: All year

Chef: John McMahon
Food Style: Traditional British

One of the city's most visually impressive dining rooms, Rhubarb at Prestonfield is a real stunner. Classical preparations mix with contemporary ideas in a menu with broad appeal. Have a classic Scottish steak followed by tarte Tatin for two.

The Stockbridge Restaurant 🏵🏵

54 St Stephen Street, EH3 5AL
0131 226 6766
www.thestockbridgerestaurant.com
Closed: 24–26 December, First week January

Affluent Stockbridge has quite a concentration of restaurants and bars, this being one of the longer established. Access is down stone steps into, in their words, a 'decadent grotto'. Modern Scottish cooking reigns on the weekly changing fixed-price menu and on the rolling carte, typified by Gressingham duck breast with crisp duck confit, and grilled halibut with Scotch quail egg.

Chef: Jason Gallagher
Food Style: Modern, Classic, Scottish, British

See advertisement opposite

Timberyard 🏵🏵🏵 🍷NOTABLE WINE LIST
See pages 578-579

The Witchery by the Castle 🏵🏵 🍷NOTABLE WINE LIST

Castlehill, The Royal Mile, EH1 2NF
0131 225 5613
www.thewitchery.com
Closed: 25–26 December

Chef: Douglas Roberts
Food Style: Traditional Scottish

One of several historic buildings at the gates of Edinburgh Castle, the baroque, oak-panelled restaurant within this 16th-century merchant's house makes for an atmospheric dining experience. Built around traditional dishes and native produce, the assured cooking follows a contemporary and seasonal route with Scottish seafood getting a strong showing.

Ratho

The Bridge Inn at Ratho
27 Baird Road, EH28 8RA
0131 333 1320
www.bridgeinn.com
Closed: 25 December

Right by the Union Canal, with views over the
water from both garden and restaurant, The Bridge
Inn is the perfect spot for watching the passing
boats. If the canal-side action doesn't float your
boat, there are cask ales, regional whiskies and an
appealing menu.

Chef: Tyler King
Food Style: Modern British

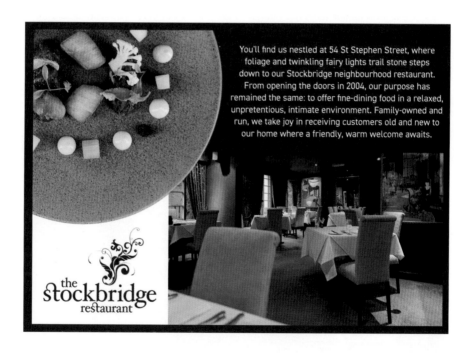

You'll find us nestled at 54 St Stephen Street, where foliage and twinkling fairy lights trail stone steps down to our Stockbridge neighbourhood restaurant. From opening the doors in 2004, our purpose has remained the same: to offer fine-dining food in a relaxed, unpretentious, intimate environment. Family-owned and run, we take joy in receiving customers old and new to our home where a friendly, warm welcome awaits.

the
stockbridge
restaurant

 NOTABLE WINE LIST

Timberyard

10 Lady Lawson Street, EH3 9DS
0131 221 1222
www.timberyard.co
Closed: 24–26 December, First week in January,
1 week in April, October

Chef: James Murray
Food Style: Modern British

Contemporary Scottish cooking in unique setting

First time visitors to Timberyard would be forgiven for thinking they'd arrived at the wrong place as they approach this modest venue. Concealed behind large red garage doors, this former warehouse (used for props and costume storage) just to the south of Edinburgh Castle, still gives the impression of a space used as a centuries old commercial concern rather than a space for high-level gastronomy. Inside, beyond the south-facing, suntrap yard, original brick walls, stripped wood floors and rusty panels keep things the industrial side of shabby chic but pots of edible flowers and herbs soon give the game away that this is a serious food operation.

This is very much a family run affair employing happy, welcoming staff who are clearly proud of the what's on offer here. The menu confirms this with a namecheck

for the local foragers and Scottish artisan breeders that keep the kitchen supplied with hyper-seasonal raw ingredients. The food is modern, bold and exciting, with intelligent flavour combinations, sound technique and precise presentation, all of which belies the tersely written menu descriptions.

A typical meal from the daily menu might start with wild garlic broth and St Andrews cheese, or sweetbread, burnt cream, chicory and beetroot. Making an appearance at the main course stage might be smoked eel, horseradish, wild leek and razor clams; hen of the woods, quince, sunflower seeds and alexanders; or monkfish, wild sea kale, Jersey Royals and horseradish.

Typical of the desserts are Amalfi lemon, yogurt and olive oil; blood orange Pavlova; and 'rhubarb and vanilla'. Timberyard's invention isn't confined to the food, just glance at the cocktail menu to find the likes of 'King's Jubilee' (nope,

not the 'Queen's Jubilee') – a concoction of rhubarb, maraschino, rye and wheat spirit, or 'Sazerac' – bramble, pastis, cider brandy and whisky.

> "The food is modern, bold and exciting, with intelligent flavour combinations, sound technique and precise presentation..."

Falkirk

Banknock

Glenskirlie House & Castle
Kilsyth Road, FK4 1UF
01324 840201
www.glenskirliehouse.com/dining
Closed: 26–27 December, 1–4 January

Chef: Richard M Leafe
Food Style: Modern British

A castle for the 21st century, Glenskirlie is a bright white pile, kitted out with a conical-roofed turret here, a little step-gabling there. The restaurant has a good ambience and a friendly and brisk service from the staff.

Fife

Anstruther

AA RESTAURANT OF THE YEAR FOR SCOTLAND 2022–23

The Cellar ⦿⦿⦿
24 East Green, KY10 3AA
01333 310378
www.thecellaranstruther.co.uk
Closed: 25–26 December, 1 January, 3 weeks January,
1 week May, 10 days September

Chef: Billy Boyter
Food Style: Modern British

The fishing harbour of Anstruther is a fitting location for chef Billy Boyter's restaurant housed in a 17th-century former smokehouse and cooperage just off the quayside. With beamed ceilings, stone walls and wood-burning stoves, the ambience is rustic and Boyter's inventive modern Scottish cooking sticks faithfully to the seasons on the nine-course tasting menu at dinner (six at lunch). Superb technique is evident in a pairing of smoked mussel, seaweed and lemon, which might lead on to heritage potato, Arbroath smokie and lovage. Well defined flavours continue with a dessert of set hay cream, apple and marigold.

What changes have you seen over the past few years?

A wonderful response to the hardships of Covid and Brexit –
the industry becoming more collegiate and collaborative.
The result is a focus on what really is essential to a restaurant.

AA Inspector

Elie

The Ship Inn 🏵
The Toft, KY9 1DT
01333 330246
www.shipinn.scot
Closed: 25 December

Not many pubs can boast a beachside beer garden and cricket matches played on the sand, but The Ship Inn is no ordinary tavern. Overlooking the briny, the first-floor restaurant sports a jaunty modern look involving bare tables and duck-egg-blue panelling and serves an unfussy roll-call of eclectic modern dishes, including splendid local seafood.

Chef: Mat Majer
Food Style: Modern, Seafood

Newport-on-Tay

The Newport Restaurant 🏵🏵
1 High Street, DD6 8AB
01382 541449
www.thenewportrestaurant.co.uk
Closed: 23–27 December, 1–9 January

There's not much better publicity than winning *MasterChef: The Professionals*, so 2014 winner Jamie Scott got off to a flyer when he opened his own restaurant. Cheerful and enthusiastic service and a breezy contemporary decor make for a relaxed dining experience, while pin-sharp contemporary cooking from Scott and his team make it a hot ticket.

Chef: Jamie Scott,
Anastasios Neofitos
Food Style: Modern Scottish

Peat Inn

The Peat Inn 🏵🏵🏵
KY15 5LH
01334 840206
www.thepeatinn.co.uk
Closed: 25–26 December, 1–10 January

Chef: Geoffrey Smeddle
Food Style: Modern British

This inn has been enough of a local landmark since the mid-18th century that the village in which it stands was named after it, rather than the other way round. It's a handsomely white-fronted, stone-built former coach-stop, the dining room decorated in sleek contemporary fashion with light woods, thick cloths and smart tableware. Geoffrey Smeddle has maintained the place in the upper ranks of Scottish gastronomy over an impressive stretch, and the modernist flourishes and precise presentations confer real character on the cooking. Begin with warm St Andrews Bay lobster with romesco sauce, cauliflower pannacotta (with perfect 'wobble') and sea herbs. For main, roast crown and smoked legs of Scottish partridge come with young parsnips, spiced Puy lentils and thyme and cider velouté. A mille feuille of lemon posset and blackberries with an intense lemongrass, chilli and ginger sorbet is beautifully made, with delicate pastry and great flavour.

St Andrews

The Grange Inn ⊛⊛
Grange Road, KY16 8LJ
01334 472675
thegrangeinn.com
Closed: Sunday, Monday, 25–26 December, 1 January

A lovely 17th-century converted farmhouse is the
setting for this delightful restaurant with panoramic
views looking out over St Andrews and the bay.
Chef-proprietor John Kelly has created a superb menu
finished with modern techniques and innovative
touches using the freshest of local produce available.
There's a warm and welcoming ambience throughout.

Chef: John Kelly
Food Style: Modern Scottish

NEW HAAR ⊛⊛⊛
1 Golf Place, KY16 9JA
01334 479281
www.haarrestaurant.com
Closed: Monday, Tuesday

Chef: Dean Banks
Food Style: Modern

Located just 50 metres from the oldest and most iconic golf course in the world, HAAR
is named after the cold sea fog that hits the east coast of mainland Britain. This is a cosy
restaurant designed and styled around the sea, with wood and exposed stone used to great
effect. An unwavering commitment to local provenance and sound technical skills produce
elegant global dishes. A fragrant and spicy Loch Etive trout with brown crab galangal curry
might lead to pink and tender Beech Ridge Farm duck, asparagus and black garlic. End with
strawberry, Thai basil and cardamom.

Playfair's Restaurant and Steakhouse ⊛
Ardgowan Hotel, 2 Playfair Terrace, North Street,
KY16 9HX
01334 472970
www.playfairsrestaurant.co.uk
Closed: Monday, Tuesday

Not far from the 18th green of St Andrew's Old Course,
Playfair's restaurant is a bustling and welcoming eatery,
with attentive service and a modern Scottish approach.
The restaurant is located under the reception, and
the configuration means that diners can often find
themselves eating close to drinkers using the bar.

Chef: Duncan McLachlan
Food Style: Steakhouse, Scottish

See advertisement opposite

Road Hole Restaurant ⊛⊛⊛
See pages 584-585 and advertisement on page 587

Rufflets St Andrews

Strathkinness Low Road, KY16 9TX
01334 460890
www.rufflets.co.uk/wine-dine
Closed: 4 January to 2 February

The creeper-covered turreted mansion has been in the same family since 1952, sitting in 10 acres of exquisite gardens. Its name refers to the 'rough flat lands' that once comprised the local landscape. The cooking is as modern as can be.

Chef: Scott Cameron
Food Style: Modern British, European

Road Hole Restaurant

Old Course Hotel, Golf Resort & Spa, KY16 9SP
01334 474371
www.oldcoursehotel.co.uk
Open: All year

Chef: Martin Hollis
Food Style: Modern, Steak, Seafood

Top quality Scottish cooking in St Andrews

There is no shortage of high quality places to stay on the Scottish golfing circuit, but for golf-mad gourmets only one will do: the Old Course Hotel overlooks the world-famous links at St Andrews and will certainly keep you fed and watered in grand style while basking in a spectacular location with views of West Sands beach and the majestic coastline. The grand old pile towers above the 17th hole, the 'Road Hole', so it seems only right that the main dining room here has been named after it. It's a civilised, upmarket spot with highly professional, genuinely engaged staff delivering perfectly pitched service, and an open kitchen providing an alternative theatre for those who have no interest in the stick-swinging action outside.

Given the setting, luxurious items come as no surprise – the modern Scottish menus are built on the finest produce from Scotland's larder, including some

classic local seafood and steak options. Open, perhaps with a well-balanced dish of smoked duck breast, confit duck leg presse, pickled mushrooms and berries, or if you want to experience the region's famous seafood, go for the hand-dived scallops, Stornoway black pudding crumb, sea buckthorn and vanilla gel with coconut foam.

When it comes to main course, Scottish seafood continues to catch the eye, perhaps with a perfectly cooked fillet of Gigha halibut teamed with langoustines, leeks, morels, tomato, tarragon hollandaise and a light shell sauce. Not that meat devotees are at all overlooked – lamb loin and sweetbread turns up with anchovy, asparagus, polenta, baby leeks, black garlic and thyme sauce.

When it comes to something sweet to finish, look no further than apple millefeuille with cinnamon croûton, caramel apples and green apple sorbet, although those in search of a savoury finale will opt for the board of Scottish cheeses.

See advertisement on page 587

"...a civilised, upmarket spot with highly professional, genuinely engaged staff delivering perfectly pitched service..."

St Andrews *continued*

St Andrews Bar & Grill 🏵️🏵️
Fairmont St Andrews, KY16 8PN
01334 837000
www.fairmont.com/standrews
Open: All year

A free shuttle bus takes you from the Fairmont to this
dining option in the clubhouse, but it is a lovely walk.
Spectacularly situated on a promontory overlooking
St Andrews Bay, the evening sees the seafood bar and
grill come into their own.

Chef: Ian Syme
Food Style: Scottish, Seafood

St Monans

Craig Millar @ 16 West End 🏵️🏵️ 🍷NOTABLE WINE LIST
16 West End, KY10 2BX
01333 730327
www.16westend.com
Closed: 12–26 October, 23–28 December,
1–18 January

Craig Millar@16 West End is an elegant, innovative
restaurant and bar that enjoys sweeping views of the
Firth of Forth and harbour at St Monans. The sea can
get dramatic but then so can the cooking, especially
the seafood, which was always going to be a big focus.
Don't forget to check out the outstanding top quality
wine list.

Chef: Craig Millar
Food Style: Modern Scottish

Glasgow

Glasgow

Brasserie 🏵️
ABode Glasgow, 129 Bath Street, G2 2SZ
0141 221 6789
www.abodeglasgow.co.uk
Open: All year

Food Style: Brasserie, Classic

The Brasserie at ABode Glasgow offers a stylishly designed brassiere with white brick-tiled wall
that goes back to the Victorian and Edwardian origins of the building. Bold feature walls break
up the starkness and critically placed black and white photography adds to the brassiere design
theme. The menu changes with the seasons plus there are dishes of the day.

OLD COURSE HOTEL
St ANDREWS
GOLF RESORT & SPA

A KOHLER EXPERIENCE

DISCOVER ST ANDREWS...
DISCOVER YOUR INNER FOODIE
AT THE OLD COURSE HOTEL

www.oldcoursehotel.co.uk | 01334 474371
reservations@oldcoursehotel.co.uk

Glasgow *continued*

Cail Bruich ◉◉◉ ▲NOTABLE WINE LIST

752 Great Western Road, G12 8QX
0141 334 6265
www.cailbruich.co.uk
Closed: 25–26 December, 1 January, 1 week January

Chef: Chris Charalambous,
Lorna McNee
Food Style: Modern Scottish

It isn't always necessary to head out into the Highlands in search of country cuisine. Here in Glasgow's swinging West End, the Charalambous brothers bring it to the city doorstep, in a modern bistro setting. The vegetarian dishes alone are inspired – Jerusalem artichoke, lettuce and Brinkburn goats' cheese, for mains perhaps. Elsewhere, stimulating combinations distinguish the seasonally changing menus, perhaps Loch Fyne scallop with smoked eel, sour cabbage and apple, and then lamb with sprouting broccoli, anchovies and black olives, or stone bass with langoustine, clementine and pumpkin. Speciality beers and a tempting list of imaginative cocktails supplement the commendable wine list.

Chez Mal Brasserie
Malmaison Glasgow, 278 West George Street, G2 4LL
0141 572 1001
www.malmaison.com
Open: All year

Chef: John Burns
Food Style: Modern French

The Glasgow Mal has made its home in a deconsecrated Greek Orthodox church. A mix of traditional and modern French brasserie cooking is the draw, with select breeds and cuts of thoroughbred beef the backbone. Soufflé du jour is worth a look at for dessert.

The Gannet
1155 Argyle Street, G3 8TB
0141 204 2081
www.thegannetgla.com
Closed: 25–26 December, 1–2 January

Chef: Peter McKenna, Ivan Stein
Food Style: Modern Scottish

Named after the seafaring bird with the robust appetite, The Gannet was created by a group of friends on a research trip to the Outer Hebrides. A showcase of Scotland's small artisan producers, foragers and farmers, this industrial-meets-rustic restaurant – all exposed brick, stone walls and stripped wood – offers daily changing four- and six-course menus. A typical meal might include West Coast crab teamed with squash and horseradish, which could lead on to Hereford beef, shallot, egg yolk with nut and seed granola. Things come to a close with a dark chocolate delice, white chocolate mousse and hazelnut.

The Hanoi Bike Shop
8 Ruthven Lane, G12 9BG
0141 334 7165
www.hanoibikeshop.co.uk
Closed: 25 December

Sister restaurant to the Ubiquitous Chip and Stravaigin, this colourful West End venture is set across two buzzing floors. The canteen-style vibe suits the authentic street food menu of dazzling Vietnamese flavours. The menu gives the original names of dishes followed by an English translation.

Chef: Jake Clark
Food Style: Vietnamese

See advertisement opposite

Glasgow *continued*

iasg ⬡

Kimpton Blythswood Square Hotel,
11 Blythswood Square, G2 4AD
0141 248 8888
www.iasgrestaurant.com
Closed: 26 December

Part of the Kimpton Blythswood Square Hotel, iasg
is a huge bright space with a central bar. The name is
pronounced 'ee-usk' and is Gaelic for 'fish'. There's a
definite brasserie feel, with turquoise tiling around the
bar, grey walls, modern art, and lots of polished brass.
Used to be the HQ of the Royal Scottish Automobile Club.

Chef: Sean Currie
Food Style: Seafood, Scottish

La Bonne Auberge ⬡

Holiday Inn Glasgow City Centre - Theatreland,
161 West Nile Street, G1 2RL
0141 352 8310
www.labonneauberge.co.uk
Open: All year

Chef: Gerry Sharkey
Food Style: French, Mediterranean

This ever-popular venue is kitted out in contemporary style with exposed brickwork, tiled and
wooden flooring and lamps on wooden tables, and has attentive and friendly staff. Meats,
including BBQ pork loin and rib-eye steaks, are cooked on the grill.

Number Sixteen ⬡⬡

16 Byres Road, G11 5JY
0141 339 2544
www.number16.co.uk
Closed: 25 December, 1–6 January

Set behind a tiny shopfront, Number Sixteen is split
over two levels. Inside are driftwood and bare wooden
tables with stripped wooden floors, and although it's a
small operation, the best is made of the available space
with banquette seating booths and individual chairs and
tables. The menu makes the most of what the Scottish
larder has to offer.

Chef: Paul Wallace
Food Style: Modern International

One Devonshire Gardens by Hotel du Vin 🏵🏵 🍷 NOTABLE WINE LIST

1 Devonshire Gardens, G12 0UX
0141 339 2001
www.hotelduvin.com
Open: All year

This supremely elegant Victorian terrace in the heart of Glasgow – with a long-standing foodie reputation to maintain – is the jewel in the crown of the Hotel du Vin group. The restaurant is an elegant setting for lunch and dinner where chef Gary Townsend has put his own contemporary European stamp on the kitchen's output bringing fresh, seasonal and locally sourced produce to the fore.

Chef: Gary Townsend
Food Style: Modern French

Opium 🏵

191 Hope Street, G2 2UL
0141 332 6668
www.opiumrestaurant.co.uk
Closed: 24–25 December, 1–2 January

A pin-sharp, contemporary-styled Asian-fusion restaurant in the heart of Glasgow. Big picture windows allow light to flood into a slick space where communal tables share the space with conventional seating. Kwan Yu Lee has honed an on-trend mix of classical and modern Asian fusion dishes.

Chef: Kwan Yu Lee
Food Style: Chinese, Oriental fusion

NEW The Prancing Stag 🏵

1A Ashwood Gardens, Jordanhill, G13 1NX
0141 959 9666
www.theprancingstag.co.uk
Closed: Monday, 25–26 December, 1–3 January

Whether you grab a table outside or in the restaurant itself, the family-run Prancing Stag showcases classic Scottish dishes with a global influence. Opposite the railway station and close to the stadium where Glasgow Warriors play, there's also a small bar area with plenty of wines by the glass.

Chef: Monique Paul
Food Style: Modern Scottish

Stravaigin

Think global, eat local

Our award-winning Scottish restaurant prides itself on using the most local produce to create a worldly culinary experience.

28 Gibson St
Glasgow
G12 8NX

Reservations:
+44 (0)141 334 2665

Glasgow *continued*

Shish Mahal 🏵️
60-68 Park Road, Kelvinbridge, G4 9JF
0141 339 8256
www.shishmahal.co.uk
Closed: 25 December

Set in Glasgow's vibrant west end, Shish Mahal is a large, spacious restaurant, with floor to ceiling windows so you can watch the world go by. The decor is cream with burnt brown tones and dark wooden flooring, while the brass ornamental touches create an authentic Indian setting. As you'd expect, the Indian cuisine is noteworthy.

Chef: Intsar Humayun
Food Style: Artisan, Indian, Pakistani

Stravaigin 🏵️
28 Gibson Street, Kelvinbridge, G12 8NX
0141 334 2665
www.stravaigin.co.uk
Closed: 25 December

In a busy West End street, this popular all-day bar/restaurant abides by its maxim "Think global, eat local". So, expect the unexpected, such as Peterhead monkfish cheek with red lentil dhal; sticky pork belly with rice noodles; and bay leaf and cardamom custard tart, as well as others from India, Korea, Mexico and elsewhere.

Chef: James MacRae
Food Style: Modern International, Scottish

See advertisement opposite

Ubiquitous Chip Restaurant 🏵️🏵️ 🍷NOTABLE WINE LIST
12 Ashton Lane, G12 8SJ
0141 334 5007
www.ubiquitouschip.co.uk
Closed: 25 December

Affectionately known by Glaswegians as The Chip, its long-held inspiration owes much to Scottish regional dishes. At least one – venison haggis – has been served here since opening day in 1971, but regardless of time served, there's Eyemouth crab, Barra scallops, Ayrshire chicken breast and Aberdeen Angus beef too.

Chef: Doug Lindsay
Food Style: Scottish

See advertisement opposite

Glasgow *continued*

AA WINE AWARD FOR SCOTLAND 2022-23

UNALOME by Graeme Cheevers 🏵🏵🏵   🍷 NOTABLE WINE LIST
36 Kelvingrove Street, G3 7RZ
0141 501 0553   Chef: Graeme Cheevers
www.unalomebygc.com   Food Style: Modern European
Closed: 25-27 December, 1-17 January

Occupying a prominent corner on Sauchiehall Street, UNALOME by Graeme Cheevers is close to all the action in the throbbing heart of Glasgow city centre, with the leafy West End and university nearby. Light and minimalist with muted greens, leather and wood furnishings, this classy restaurant has a noticeable buzz and staff are upbeat and efficient. Modern European cooking with the occasional global influence brings starters like veal sweetbreads, Wye Valley asparagus, pickled walnut and preserved lemon before fillet of sea bass, caramelised onion and vin jaune sauce. Finish with lemon verbena glazed strawberries, strawberry cream and vanilla ice cream.

Highland

Dornoch

Grant MacNicol at the Castle 🏵
Castle Street, IV25 3SD
01862 810216
www.dornochcastlehotel.com
Open: All year

Grant MacNicol's restaurant at Dornoch Castle is located though a low arched doorway and into a more modern extension where you'll find bistro style, wooden tables and muted colours for the decor. The windows along one side overlook the garden. Expect good seasonal cuisine with prime cuts more prevalent in the summer. There's also an impressive whisky bar serving from some 500 bottles.

Chef: Grant MacNicol
Food Style: Modern Scottish

Links House at Royal Dornoch 🏵🏵
Links House, Golf Road, IV25 3LW   Chef: Javier Santos
01862 810279   Food Style: Classic Scottish
www.linkshousedornoch.com
Closed: 25 December, 3 January to 25 March

Links House is part of the Royal Dornoch complex, and as you'd expect the focus tends to be on golf. Mara, the elegant restaurant has a view of the course and coast. The decor is both sumptuous and very smart, all blue, gold and copper brown. Decorations are a bit less golf, more fishing tackle and scenic paintings.

Fort Augustus

The Inch

Inchnacardoch Bay, PH32 4BL
01456 450900
www.inchhotel.com
Closed: 31 October to 31 March

Chef: Philip Carnegie
Food Style: Traditional Scottish

There are some incredible views of Loch Ness to be enjoyed from The Inch Country House Hotel, which was once a Victorian hunting lodge. The restaurant comes in two sections with charming character features such as plaster coving and wood panelling. The wildlife photos and tartan high-back chairs really add to the atmosphere.

Station Road

Loch Ness Side, PH32 4DU
01456 459250
www.thelovat.com
Closed: 2 January to 14 February

Chef: Sean Kelly
Food Style: Traditional Scottish

Situated in the small town of Fort Augustus on the edge of Loch Ness leading into the Caledonian Canal, Station Road is located in the luxury Lovat Hotel, so the surroundings are impressive to say the least. The kitchen, led by Sean Kelly, seeks to reflect these surroundings and does an outstanding job. Locally sourced seafood and other produce feature alongside foraged ingredients on an imaginative menu. You might choose a delicate pastry tart, topped with a disc of beetroot to start, and then move on to a Gigha halibut with mussels, shaved ribbons of courgette over crab, all elements were perfectly cooked. Finish with an Ecclefechan tart and vanilla ice cream – a perfect pastry base with the flavour of the fruit combining with treacle and dark muscovado sugar to make a wonderful end to the meal.

Fort William

Michel Roux Jr at Inverlochy Castle NOTABLE WINE LIST Rosettes Suspended

Torlundy, PH33 6SN
01397 702177
www.inverlochycastlehotel.com
Open: All year

Food Style: Modern French

The Rosette award for this establishment has been suspended due to a change of chef and reassessment will take place in due course.

This top-flight venue at Aberlochy, is the very epitome of a grand baronial castle set in a verdant valley at the foot of Ben Nevis. Views are spectacular, and there's a real sense of history and opulence in the richly decorated public spaces, with all the high ceilings, antiques and crystal chandeliers you could wish for. The restaurant is intimate and extremely formal in approach – gentlemen will need their jackets.

Glenfinnan

The Prince's House 🏵🏵
PH37 4LT
01397 722246
www.glenfinnan.co.uk
Closed: 25 December, October to March

Chef: Kieron Kelly
Food Style: Modern British

The Prince's House was originally a coaching inn constructed in the 17th century, while the Stage House Bistro and bar were built in the 1980s. It's all traditional Highland style with plenty of character. The bistro is bright and spacious, enjoying views of the nearby burn. Cooking is classic French with innovative and novel concept touches.

Grantown-on-Spey

Garden Restaurant 🏵
Grant Arms Hotel, 25–27 The Square, PH26 3HF
01479 872526
www.grantarmshotel.com
Open: All year

Chef: Steven Hart
Food Style: Modern Scottish

Conveniently located in the centre of town, the Grant Arms Hotel has retained much of the building's traditional 18th-century character. The Garden Restaurant is a large, elegant, traditional dining room with high ceilings and large windows. It's a very popular dining venue and offers hearty, straightforward cooking with no pretensions.

Invergarry

Glengarry Castle Hotel 🏵
PH35 4HW
01809 501254
www.glengarry.net
Open: All year

The Glengarry, overlooking Loch Oich, is a slice of Victorian Scottish baronial, built in the 1860s. Spotless white linen and quality glassware glow beneath the chandelier in the opulent dining room, where lightly modernised, traditional fare is the order of the day.

Chef: Romuald Denesle
Food Style: Scottish, International

Inverness

Bunchrew House Hotel ⊚⊚
Bunchrew, IV3 8TA
01463 234917
www.bunchrewhousehotel.com
Closed: 8–22 January

Bunchrew House is a magnificent 17th-century mansion, complete with turrets and a pink façade, on the water's edge of the Beauly Firth. There's a notable larder of ingredients on hand and the quality comes to the fore in the modern British cuisine. A very enjoyable experience.

Chef: Andrew McKelvie
Food Style: Modern British

Contrast Brasserie ⊚
Glenmoriston Town House Hotel, 20 Ness Bank, IV2 4SF
01463 223777
www.glenmoristontownhouse.com
Open: All year

Chef: Ian Chambers
Food Style: Pan-Asian

As Glenmoriston Town House Hotel's main restaurant, Contrast has a rather romantic air, thanks to low lighting and an evening pianist. Unsurprisingly, Scottish produce makes appearances, as in spiced North Uist scallops, and West Coast sea trout. Overall, though, the cooking is modern and international with Asian flavours getting a good look-in, so dishes of kimchi risotto and mugi miso monkfish also star.

Rocpool ⊚⊚
1 Ness Walk, IV3 5NE
01463 717274
www.rocpoolrestaurant.com
Closed: 24–26 December, 31 December to 3 January

On the banks of the River Ness, in the heart of town, Rocpool has a sharp contemporary design featuring lots of wood and natural tones. The team are young, friendly and smartly dressed, and the place has a real brasserie feel. The kitchen style is modern Scottish with an Italian influence, and it's always busy, so be sure to book.

Chef: George Sleet
Food Style: Modern European

Inverness *continued*

Rocpool Reserve Restaurant ◉◉
14 Culduthel Road, IV2 4AG
01463 240089
rocpool.com
Open: All year

Chef: Lee Pattie
Food Style: French, Scottish

Not far from the River Ness, Rocpool Reserve Restaurant has two sections. One is decorated in black, gold and red, with red chairs matching the pattern on the carpet. The other has a more oriental feel, all gold and framed pictograms. A vein of French classicism runs through the cooking that draws on the Scottish credentials for the produce.

Kilchoan

NEW Mingary Castle ◉◉
PH36 4LH
01972 614380
www.mingarycastle.co.uk
Closed: Monday, January to March

Mingary Castle is really quite an amazing place. It's essentially a modern restaurant with rooms that's been built inside the curtain walls of a ruined 13th-century coastal castle. The stunning restaurant showcases great technical skill making good use of the wonderful larder that the Ardnamurchan Peninsula has to offer. The Isle of Mull is just across the water.

Chef: Colin Nicholson
Food Style: Modern Scottish

Kingussie

The Cross ◉◉◉ 🍷 NOTABLE WINE LIST
Tweed Mill Brae, Ardbroilach Road, PH21 1LB
01540 661166
www.thecross.co.uk
Closed: 25 December, 2–31 January

Chef: David Skiggs
Food Style: Modern Scottish

Four acres of grounds in the Cairngorms National Park (look out for red squirrels) are the setting for this converted 19th-century tweed mill. There's a terrace by the river for drinks or dining in fine weather, while a mood of informal tranquillity reigns in the stylishly comfortable, beamed restaurant. You can expect modern, ingredients-led cooking and thoughtfully constructed dishes. The contrasting textures and colours of roast halibut with parmesan gnocchi, cauliflower, wild mushrooms, spinach and parmesan cream make for an effective main course, perhaps preceded by perfectly timed roast quail breast, a wonderfully delicate dish, with celeriac and apple adding bite.

Hickory Restaurant ✪
Golf View Hotel & Spa, Seabank Road, IV12 4HD
01667 452301
www.crerarhotels.com/golf-view-hotel-spa
Open: All year

Chef: Tommy McPherson
Food Style: Traditional, International

In case you get the impression there's only golf to look at, this hotel's seaside location looks out over the Moray Firth and dining at Hickory offers great views. The elegant conservatory restaurant features menus of locally-landed seafood and meat from local pedigree herds.

Russell's at Smiddy House ✪✪
Roy Bridge Road, PH34 4EU
01397 712335
www.smiddyhouse.com
Closed: Monday, November, 25–26 December, January

The AA has long recognised the well-presented Scottish cuisine served in this intimate, candlelit restaurant, once the village blacksmith's. Scottish produce is key. Menu highlights include Wester Ross salmon, Arisaig prawns, scallops from the Isle of Mull, Perthshire wood pigeon, Highland game, lamb and beef, pine nut-crusted monkfish and, of course, Scottish cheeses.

Chef: Glen Russell
Food Style: Modern Scottish

Kilcamb Lodge Hotel ✪✪✪ ⚑NOTABLE WINE LIST
See pages 600-601

Dining Room ✪✪
Glenmorangie House, Cadboll, By Fearn, IV20 1XP
01862 871671
www.theglenmorangiehouse.com
Closed: 2–27 January

The Glenmorangie Distillery, famous the world over for its whisky, is right by Glenmorangie House, which has a dining room with its own intimate, welcoming atmosphere. Dinner is served dinner-party style with all guests sitting around one large oval table. The kitchen uses local produce in modern cooking that shows skill as well as imagination.

Chef: John Wilson
Food Style: French, Scottish

Strontian

 **NOTABLE WINE LIST**

Kilcamb Lodge Hotel

PH36 4HY
01967 402257
www.kilcamblodge.co.uk
Closed: 1 January to 1 February

Chef: Gary Phillips
Food Style: Modern Scottish,
Seafood

Local seafood with loch views

Right on the shore of Loch Sunart, remote Kilcamb Lodge Hotel is set amongst 22 acres of private grounds and woodland on the beautiful Ardamurchan Peninsula, famous for its otters, red squirrels and eagles.

This historic house was one of the first stone buildings in the area and was used as military barracks around the time of the Jacobite uprising. It's now a comfortable and tranquil proprietor-run hotel where warm hospitality is assured, and views are guaranteed to wow first-time visitors or returning regulars.

The light and airy restaurant looks out across the grounds towards the loch and the one window table is highly prized. Traditional with floral curtains, fresh flowers at each table and candles in the evening, it's elegant and unfussy. The cooking is accomplished and utilises produce from the area, notably seafood

landed by *The Kirsty Ann*, a local boat that brings in fish and shellfish.

Start, perhaps, with a perfectly executed roast squash, lobster and crab risotto with crispy kale, an enjoyable dish with the sweetness of both the lobster and the crab being complemented by the flavour of the roast squash. Crispy kale and samphire add contrast of colour and texture. It's not only fish that impresses, as displayed by a pink and tender fillet and slow-cooked featherblade of Angus beef with a rich wild mushroom ragù. The long, slow cooking of the blade of beef provides plenty of flavour and chargrilled vegetables add texture and colour, as does a smooth and buttery pomme purée.

The well-presented, finely tuned dishes continue right through to dessert of triple-layered chocolate brownie served with a faultless salted caramel ice cream. The high cocoa content of the chocolate provides a wonderful bitterness, and the crunch of the mini meringue adds a textural contrast.

"The cooking is accomplished and utilises produce from the area, notably seafood..."

Thurso

Forss House Hotel 🌸🌸
Forss, KW14 7XY
01847 861201
www.forsshousehotel.co.uk
Closed: First 2 weeks January

You can't get much further away from urban bustle in the mainland British Isles than the northern Highlands, where this Georgian country-house hotel luxuriates in tranquillity below a waterfall on the River Forss, amid acres of woodland. Plenty of pedigree Highland produce is on parade.

Chef: Andrew Smith
Food Style: Modern Scottish

Torridon

The Torridon 1887 Restaurant 🌸🌸🌸 ⚑NOTABLE WINE LIST
Torridon, by Achnasheen, IV22 2EY
01445 791242
www.thetorridon.com/eat-drink/1887-restaurant
Closed: 2 January for 5 weeks

Chef: Paul Green
Food Style: Modern Scottish

Innovative Scottish cooking is the hallmark at The Torridon 1887 Restaurant, part of the Victorian Earl of Lovelace's turreted former shooting lodge. The drive to it requires a little determination, but its remoteness, wildness and scenery are worth it. This is a region where the surrounding land, lochs and the sea play a major role in the kitchen, with vegetables and herbs coming from the two-acre kitchen garden, meats and game from the estate, and shellfish and fish from Loch Torridon and beyond. The menu offers two choices per course, one of which might be Scrabster turbot with courgette and cider sauce.

Ullapool

NEW The Dipping Lugger 🌸🌸🌸
4 West Shore Street, IV26 2UR
01854 613344
www.thedippinglugger.com
Closed: Monday, Tuesday, Wednesday, 2–10 February, 3–9 July, 18–24 December

On the shore of Loch Broom, The Dipping Lugger is an 18th-century former manse transformed into a luxurious venue by local distillers. Unclothed marble tables and an open fire add to the charm, and Ullapool's famous seafood is a focus of the menu. Whether it's lunch or dinner, tasting menus are the way to go, the

Chef: David Smith
Food Style: Modern Scottish

choice changing with the seasons. Menu descriptions are terse, but a 'wild garlic' starter is a vibrantly coloured opener, the foraged ingredient paired with Jersey Royals. It might be followed by a perfectly timed piece of 'halibut', served with mushroom ravioli and asparagus.

Wick

Mackay's Hotel
Union Street, KW1 5ED
01955 602323
www.mackayshotel.co.uk
Closed: 24–25 December, 1–2 January

Chef: Ray McRitchie
Food Style: Modern Scottish

Mackay's is home to the No. 1 Bistro, a contemporary restaurant with a relaxed vibe. The kitchen makes good use of quality local ingredients, and there's a modernity to the output. There's a buzzy bar for real ales, cocktails and a terrific range of whiskies.

South Lanarkshire

Blantyre

Crossbasket Castle 🌸🌸🌸
Crossbasket Estate, Stoneymeadow Road, G72 9UE
01698 829461
www.crossbasketcastle.com
Open: All year

Chef: Michel Roux Jnr,
Jonathon Wright
Food Style: Classical French

A stunning country house hotel with roots dating back to the 16th-century, Crossbasket Castle is located just outside East Kilbride on the edge of the River Carron. The elegant dining room with its ornate gold leaf-decorated ceiling, crisp white linen tablecloths and flickering candles provides superb views of the garden. The French-inspired dishes combine classics with some innovative touches, as in a ballotine of chicken and goose liver with port, chestnut, blackberry, pear and pain d'epice. It might be followed by a super-fresh, pan-seared fillet of halibut with mussels, baby leeks, spinach and sauce Véronique.

East Lothian

Aberlady

Ducks Inn 🌸🌸
Main Street, EH32 0RE
01875 870682
www.ducks.co.uk
Closed: 25 December

Chef: Michal Mozdzen
Food Style: Modern British

Ducks Inn is a small restaurant with rooms with a bar-bistro and a main restaurant. With a number of world-class courses nearby, there's golfing memorabilia all around the bar area, although there's not so much in the dining areas. The whole operation is very comfortable and the cooking is based on local produce with both classic and modern influences.

Gullane

Greywalls and Chez Roux ❀❀
Muirfield, EH31 2EG
01620 842144
www.greywalls.co.uk
Open: All year

Chef: Ryan McCutcheon
Food Style: Modern French
Country

Golfers enjoy views of Muirfield's 9th and 18th holes from this elegant, Lutyens-designed country house hotel. Spread through four rooms, Chez Roux restaurant impresses and delights with Isle of Mull scallops and chicory; roast veal with sweetbreads; roast Loch Fyne salmon with fennel ravioli; and classic lemon tart with raspberry sorbet originally created by the late Albert Roux.

AA RESTAURANT WITH ROOMS OF THE YEAR FOR SCOTLAND 2022–23

The Stables at The Bonnie Badger ❀❀
Main Street, EH31 2AB
01620 621111
bonniebadger.com
Open: All year

Nestled between Gullane's golf courses and beaches, The Stables restaurant has become a coveted destination among guests and locals. It boasts a stylish Highlands-meet-Scandi interior and some seriously good comfort-food classics driven by the 'From Nature to Plate' philosophy of its founders. Soaring rafters and original sandstone walls create the setting.

Chef: Matthew Budge
Food Style: Modern Scottish

Midlothian

Loanhead

NEW The Radhuni ❀
93 Clerk Street, EH20 9RE
0131 440 3566
www.theradhuni.co.uk
Closed: Monday

Chef: Azad Miah
Food Style: Modern Indian,
Bangladeshi

Offering modern Indian and Bangladeshi cooking, The Radhuni has quite a loyal local following. It's also a bit of a TARDIS, much larger on the inside. The floors are wooden and there are feature walls and illuminated displays. Some outside seating is undercover on raised decking, with a water feature adding to the charm.

Moray

NEW Hearth at The Old Mill Inn Brodie 🏵
Brodie, IV36 2TD
01309 641605
www.oldmillinnspeyside.co.uk
Closed: 1–19 January

Hearth, situated on the ground floor of the Old Mill, has built a reputation over the last few years for creating unique interpretations of some classic Scottish dishes, inspired by the incredible larder and landscape of Moray. The weekly-changing menus are tailored around the seasons and enhanced by a carefully selected wine list. There's a private dining room available too.

Chef: Paul McKechnie
Food Style: Modern Scottish

See advertisement below

Perth & Kinross

Andrew Fairlie at Gleneagles 🌸🌸🌸🌸 ⚑NOTABLE WINE LIST
See pages 608-609

The Strathearn 🌸🌸
The Gleneagles Hotel, PH3 1NF
01764 694270
www.gleneagles.com
Open: All year

Chef: Jason Hardcastle
Food Style: French, Scottish

Set in 850 acres of glorious countryside, the dress code, trolleys and formal style of dining in the elegant art deco room may be a nod to The Strathearn's long past, but the Franco-Scottish cooking offers plenty of modern twists. Service is slick and nothing is too much trouble.

NEW The Glenturret Lalique Restaurant 🌸🌸🌸🌸
The Glenturret Distillery, The Hosh, Torreglen,
PH7 4HA
01764 656565
www.theglenturretrestaurant.com
Closed: 1–28 January, 1–11 May, 19 September to
12 October, 24–27 December

The Glenturret Lalique is part of a working distillery, and recent investment means it's full of luxury appointments, high gloss wood, stone tops and heavy carpets. The chandeliers are incredible, as is the whisky bar. Tableware is stunning, while service is

Chef: Mark Donald
Food Style: Modern European

formal, French, yet friendly. A daily-changing fixed menu displays highly skilled, precise, modern European cooking with a Scottish focus. Start with a remarkable tattie scone, autumn truffle, raw Wagyu beef and Baerii Platinum caviar, then move on to a langoustine, buttermilk and Daurenki Tsar Imperial caviar 'mini-taco'. Look out for the intriguing Kumquat Penicillin palate cleanser, and 'The Sweetie Box' dessert.

Dunkeld

Woodland Bistro
Atholl Street, PH8 0AR
01350 727322
www.royaldunkeld.co.uk
Open: All year

Food Style: Classic

Woodlands Bistro is one of two dining areas within The Royal Dunkeld Hotel, or three including the beer garden. Recognising its name, the bare-tabled space is designed to remind diners of woodland trails and the environment. Its classic dishes include pan-seared Scottish salmon fillet, sitting comfortably alongside the likes of vegetable moussaka.

Fortingall

Fortingall Hotel
PH15 2NQ
01887 830367
www.fortingall.com
Closed: January

Chef: David Dunn
Food Style: Modern Scottish

Fortingall, though tiny, is very much a tourist destination, and many end up at this Victorian country-house hotel. Dining takes place in two rooms, the main one done out in Arts and Crafts style, with a red carpet, open fire, paintings on the walls and tartan-effect curtains.

Grandtully

NEW The Grandtully Hotel by Ballintaggart
PH9 0PL
01887 447000
www.ballintaggart.com
Closed: 24–28 December, 8–18 January

This newly created hotel has modern food ideas to match. The menus are packed with outstanding local produce and the results are big, seasonal flavours – expect everything from sensational Scottish seafood to classic bistro dishes, paired beautifully with fine wines. There's a cookery school too.

Chef: Jordan Clark
Food Style: French, Scottish

 NOTABLE WINE LIST

Andrew Fairlie at Gleneagles

The Gleneagles Hotel, PH3 1NF
01764 694267
www.andrewfairlie.co.uk
Closed: 25–26 December, 3 weeks January

Chef: Stephen McLaughlin
Food Style: French, Scottish

France and Scotland in perfect culinary harmony

Andrew Fairlie's legacy is carried forward by head chef Stephen McLaughlin, whose passion for French cuisine runs deep. What is particularly striking is the pursuit of excellence that shines through in a team that delivers finely crafted, dazzlingly creative, contemporary French cuisine.

The five-star hotel and its three championship golf courses need little introduction and, after so many years at the top of the Scottish dining scene, neither does the restaurant. An independent business in the heart of the hotel, the lavish windowless dining room is a cossetting space, a shimmering haven with atmospheric lighting, deeply comfortable seating and original artworks. All is overseen by a passionate, knowledgeable team who instantly make you feel at ease and will seamlessly guide you through the menus and wine list. Choose between the à la carte or

eight-course dégustation menus and be prepared for high-intensity food from a team that puts in the hard graft to max out flavours.

The assured cooking is demonstrated in starters such as wild mushroom and truffle ravioli and pea velouté; or caramelised veal sweetbread, black garlic, red wine and bone marrow. Moving onto crown of Anjou squab, confit leg, pâté en croûte with port sauce; or roast fillet of turbot, surf clams, caviar and spiced verjus sauce. Showcasing the kitchen's undoubted capabilities is the Grand Marnier soufflé, honeyed citrus fruits and vanilla ice cream that makes a worthy finish to a very special meal.

The vegetarian dégustation and a là carte menus are just as luxurious and tempting. Try Jerusalem artichoke, secret garden cabbage, black garlic and baby leeks before a main dish of pea and broad bean pithivier, garden vegetables and brown butter sauce or sweet potato and Savoy cabbage, red rice and lime leaf and celeriac velouté.

"...a team that delivers finely crafted, dazzlingly creative, contemporary French cuisine."

Kinclaven

Ballathie House Hotel ❁❁
PH1 4QN
01250 883268
www.ballathiehousehotel.com
Open: All year

Chef: Scott Scorer
Food Style: Modern British

This turreted mansion overlooking the River Tay hosts a restaurant that impresses with its dedication to local ingredients. The dining room has a classical elegance. Traditional flavours combine with a moderated degree of invention to create dishes that seem entirely in keeping with the setting.

Meikleour

The Restaurant at the Meikleour Arms ❁
PH2 6EB
01250 883206
www.meikleourarms.co.uk
Open: All year

Food Style: French brasserie,
British Classics

The Restaurant at the Meikleour Arms has a large vaulted oak ceiling, with an exposed stone wall, flagstone flooring, bright decor and modern artwork. Game is very prominent and The Meikleour Arms has its own on-site butchery working with neighbouring smallholding farms and maturing meat in a traditional fashion.

Perth

63@Parklands ❁❁
Parklands Hotel, 2 St Leonards Bank, PH2 8EB
01738 622451
www.63atparklands.com
Closed: 25 December to 8 January

Chef: Graeme Pallister, John Taylor
Food Style: Modern European

Overlooking South Inch Park, this spacious hotel restaurant offers a good degree of dining comfort. A strong emphasis on seasonality and local produce steers the menu, which might present pigeon espice, burnt onion, honey and truffle ricotta followed by Highland red deer saddle and shoulder casserole with fermented barley and baked neeps purée.

63 Tay Street Restaurant ◎◎ ⁂NOTABLE WINE LIST
63 Tay Street, PH2 8NN
01738 441451
www.63taystreet.com
Closed: First 2 weeks July, 26 December to 12 January

Graeme Pallister's 63 Tay Street Restaurant occupies part of the ground floor of an imposing stone building. There's a red and grey modern colour scheme with tartan carpet adding a touch of luxury. 'Local, honest, simple' is the aim, although the kitchen adds a degree of complexity to the offering.

Chef: Graeme Pallister
Food Style: Modern Scottish

Deans Restaurant ◎◎
77–79 Kinnoull Street, PH1 5EZ
01738 643377
www.letseatperth.co.uk
Closed: 1 January, 2 weeks January, 2 weeks July

In the city centre, buzzy Deans and its Rose Lounge are ever popular. Here the kitchen turns out modern Scottish and other dishes, some declaring their origin up front, such as Shetland oysters with black pudding; Thai fragrant rice with pak choi and Marsala cream sauce; and Perthshire strawberries, elderflower liquor mousse and shortbread crumble.

Chef: Jamie Deans
Food Style: Modern Scottish

Murrayshall Country Estate ◎◎
New Scone, PH2 7PH
01738 551171
www.murrayshall.co.uk
Open: All year

The restaurant at Murrayshall County Estate has recently been refurbed, and it looks great. Contemporary decor, in a large open space with big windows looking onto the top of the golf course. Blue velvet chairs and banquettes add comfort, while the team offer a menu rich in Scottish ingredients. Cooking techniques combine contemporary and traditional elements.

Chef: Craig Jackson
Food Style: Modern British

Perth *continued*

The North Port Restaurant @@
8 North Port, PH1 5LU
01738 580867
www.thenorthport.co.uk
Closed: Sunday, Monday, 24–27 December,
1–5 January

This charming restaurant is full of Jacobean charm, with
dark oak panels, a spiral staircase, wooden floors and a
candle-filled fireplace. Staff are friendly, and the menus
focus on fresh Scottish produce from local suppliers,
with a slightly more sophisticated choice of dishes
available at dinner.

Chef: Andrew Moss
Food Style: Scottish

The Roost Restaurant & Grill @
Forgandenny Road, Bridge of Earn, PH2 9AZ
01738 812111
www.theroostrestaurant.co.uk
Closed: 11–25 July, 25 December to 9 January

Resembling a farmyard building, The Roost is smart as
can be inside, with crisply clad tables and a plethora
of pictures and mirrors. Thoroughbred Scottish
ingredients include some from the Roost's own kitchen
gardens and starters of sea trout tartare, pickled
vegetables and spiced Garibaldi set the scene.

Chef: Michael Wells
Food Style: Modern Scottish

Tabla @
173 South Street, PH2 8NY
01738 444630
www.tablarestaurant.co.uk
Closed: 25 December

At the Kumar family's central Perth eaterie the
ambience has more personality than many a formula
Indian restaurant, with exposed stone walls, full-drop
windows and a glass panel looking into the kitchen.
Indian music featuring the eponymous tabla drums
plays softly. A full listing of vegetarian dishes is
prominent on the menu.

Chef: Praveen Kumar
Food Style: Indian

Pitlochry

Fonab Castle Hotel & Spa ⊚⊚⊚

Foss Road, PH16 5ND
01796 470140
www.fonabcastlehotel.com
Open: All year

Chef: Rikki Preston
Food Style: Modern Scottish

Located on the edge of Loch Faskally, Fonab Castle is home to the fine dining Sandemans Restaurant. The castle is late Victorian, and was built for a member of the Sandeman port-shipping family. The seven-course taster menu offers an exciting programme of cutting-edge dishes, with appetisers and a pre-dessert filling in the gaps between main items. So, you could find the menu offering crab rillette with pickled cucumber and gazpacho, confit salmon with poached oyster, asparagus and caviar, or breast of Peking duck with confit leg with potato galette in a dashi stock. Unsurprisingly, considering the Sandeman connection, the wine list is excellent.

Knockendarroch Hotel Restaurant ⊚⊚

Higher Oakfield, PH16 5HT
01796 473473
www.knockendarroch.co.uk
Closed: mid December to mid February

A handsome sandstone house in a wooded setting, Knockendarroch has country-house comforts and a diminutive restaurant delivering daily-changing menus of classy modern Scottish food. It's very traditional within, with warming fires in the cooler months, ornate cornicing, chandeliers and the like, while hospitality is friendly and genuine.

Chef: Nick Imrie
Food Style: Modern Scottish

⊚⊚⊚ **Kilcamb Lodge Hotel**
Strontian, Highland
Page 600

⊚⊚⊚ **The Three Chimneys & The House Over-By**
Colbost, Isle of Skye
Page 621

⊚⊚⊚ **The Torridon 1887 Restaurant**
Torridon, Highland
Page 602

⊚⊚ **Duisdale House Hotel**
Isleornsay, Isle of Skye
Page 622

⊚⊚ **Moor of Rannoch Restaurant & Rooms**
Rannoch Station,
Perth & Kinross
Page 614

Best for remote location

Rannoch Station

Moor of Rannoch Restaurant & Rooms 🏵️🏵️
PH17 2QA
01882 633238
www.moorofrannoch.co.uk
Closed: Tuesday, Wednesday, 22 November to
8 February

You reach the Moor of Rannoch Restaurant via a
spectacular drive over the moor, which gives you the
chance to observe this ever-changing and spectacular
wilderness. The views from the restaurant are stunning.
Tables only have one setting, so guests can take their
time. Daily-changing menu focuses on the best
Scottish produce.

Chef: Stephanie Meikle
Food Style: Scottish

St Fillans

Lochview Restaurant 🏵️🏵️
On Loch Earn, PH6 2NF
01764 685320
www.achrayhouse.com
Closed: 10 January to 9 February

The Lochview Restaurant is wisely named, enjoying
a stunning 180-degree view of Loch Earn and the
mountains beyond. Inside it's cosy with leather
upholstery, bespoke wallpaper and recovered wooden
flooring. One part of the menu offers a contemporary
and adventurous tasting menu, while the other
concentrates on satisfyingly traditional quality dishes
like burgers, pie, salmon, and beef fillet Rossini.

Chef: David Racz
Food Style: Modern Scottish

Seasons View 🏵️
The Four Seasons, Hotel and Little Larder, A85,
Lochside, PH6 2NF
01764 685333
www.thefourseasonshotel.co.uk
Closed: 1–18 December, January, February

Chef: Ian Rainbird
Food Style: Modern International

On the edge of Loch Earn, sits The Four Seasons Hotel, and its restaurant, known as Seasons
View. As you'd expect, there are breathtaking views over the water and the wooded hills, and
these complement the modern menu which is built on spectacular Scottish ingredients.

Scottish Borders

1536 Restaurant ◉
Old Manse Road, EH45 8QW
01721 730395
www.baronycastle.com
Closed: First 2 weeks January

Part of the elegant and historic Barony Castle Hotel, 1536 Restaurant looks out onto the lovely gardens. It was the first place in the area to serve steak on a hot lava rock, so the diner can decide how well done they want it. If steak is the opposite of what you're after, there's a very decent vegan menu.

Chef: William Thomson, David Fulton
Food Style: Modern Scottish

The Capon Tree Town House ◉◉
61–63 High Street, TD8 6DQ
01835 869596
www.thecapontree.com
Closed: Sunday, Monday

The Capon Tree Town House restaurant with rooms is located in the heart of historic border town of Jedburgh. The husband and wife team give a hands-on feel to the whole operation. There is a small bar with an ever-growing collection of gins and a real passion for recommendations. The restaurant is compact and the dining experience is quite formal – expect visually impacting French cuisine involving local produce, some foraged from the surrounding areas. There's a great wine list for such a wee place and lots of good pairings with food.

Chef: Alasdair Wilkie
Food Style: French

Kelso

Ednam House Hotel ⑩
Bridge Street, TD5 7HT
01573 224168
www.ednamhouse.com
Open: All year

Located just off the town square and enjoying idyllic views of the Tweed, Ednam House is a lovely Georgian hotel full of character. The restaurant is set in the gardens, with windows on three sides offering great views of the grounds but more importantly, of the Tweed and Floors Castle beyond.

Chef: Steven Lyall
Food Style: Modern European

Peebles

Sutherland's Restaurant ⑩⑩
Cringletie, Edinburgh Road, EH45 8PL
01721 725750
www.cringletie.com
Closed: 2–22 January

Cringletie House is a stunning pink stone mansion, complete with conical turrets, and dates from the 1860s. The bright and airy Sutherland's Restaurant, with its stunning painted ceiling and impressive fireplace, is a welcoming setting for unpretentious seasonal dining, with a seven-course tasting menu available on Sunday evenings. Dishes make good use of produce from the hotel's walled garden where possible.

Chef: Iain Gourlay
Food Style: Modern British

Walkerburn

Windlestraw Rosettes Suspended
Galashiels Road, EH43 6AA
01896 870636
www.windlestraw.co.uk
Closed: mid December to mid February

Food Style: Modern Scottish, British

The Rosette award for this establishment has been suspended due to a change of chef and reassessment will take place in due course.
Located only 40 minutes from Edinburgh, in the rolling hills of the Scottish Border country, Windlestraw is a beautiful Edwardian Arts and Crafts villa set in two acres of grounds and lovingly restored by its present owners. Service is both personal and attentive in the oak panelled restaurant where contemporary Scottish menus are served.

Stirling

Callander

Roman Camp Country House Hotel ◉◉◉
See page 618

Dunblane

Cromlix and Chez Roux ◉◉◉ 🍷 NOTABLE WINE LIST
Kinbuck, FK15 9JT
01786 822125
www.cromlix.com
Open: All year

Chef: Darin Campbell
Food Style: Modern Scottish

Cromlix once belonged to the family of former Prime Minister Antony Eden, but the locals are rightfully rather prouder of the current owner, who plays a bit of tennis to quite a high level. Sir Andy Murray has chosen well and invested wisely, and his team have elevated the hotel to new heights. It can get very busy here, with diners keen to experience the superb wine list and modern Scottish cooking. A deceptively simple sounding salad of home cured Gressingham duck with Ibérico Bellota meats and celeriac rémoulade offers punchy flavours and textures. Follow that with an equally well balanced tronçon of halibut with root vegetables and sauce Grenobloise. Then warm dark chocolate fondant, salted caramel and clotted cream ice cream.

Stirling

Scholars Restaurant ◉
Spittal Street, FK8 1DU
01786 272727
www.stirlinghighlandhotel.co.uk
Open: All year

Chef: Mark Bain
Food Style: British, European

A grand Victorian property just down the hill from Stirling's historic castle, The Stirling Highland Hotel was built in the 1850s as a school. The eating takes place in three dining rooms of generous Victorian proportions. The menu takes a modern approach to familiar ideas.

Roman Camp Country House Hotel

FK17 8BG
01877 330003
www.romancamphotel.co.uk
Open: All year

Chef: Ian McNaught
Food Style: Modern French

Located just off the main street running through Callander, Roman Camp Country House Hotel edges onto the River Teith, which can be viewed from certain public areas. The house was built in 1625 as a hunting lodge for the Dukes of Perth before becoming a hotel and restaurant in 1939 and it retains plenty of character as well as lovely gardens. The restaurant is split into two rooms, both of a very good size, and tables are well appointed with linen cloths and tall flower vases. The abundant local produce of the region is used to good effect in the kitchen, which sticks to a modern remit with an unwavering eye on classic French technique. Perfectly timed hand-dived Orkney scallops are a good way to start, accompanied by blue cheese-topped king oyster mushroom and a surprising chocolate oil. Pink and tender Goosnargh duck breast and leg confit follows with rhubarb compôte and hispi cabbage slaw. To finish, try the passionfruit pannacotta with blackcurrant sorbet and Gariguette strawberries.

SCOTTISH ISLANDS

Isle of Mull

Craignure

Oran Na Mara 🏵

PA65 6BB

01680 812544

www.crerarhotels.com/isle-of-mull-hotel-spa

Open: All year

Food Style: Scottish, Seafood

Oran Na Mara means 'Song of the Sea' in Scottish Gaelic, but it's also the bistro belonging to the Isle of Mull Hotel and Spa, which overlooks Craignure Bay. Decor is natural wood, and stone table tops, some with green resin running through them. One wall is a wine display. Grills and seafood are specialities.

Tobermory

NEW The Galleon Bistro 🏵

PA75 6NT

01688 301117

www.thegalleontobermory.co.uk

Closed: Sunday, 25 December

Just off the seafront in picturesque Tobermory, The Galleon Bistro is an intimate restaurant with an open kitchen and a no-frills style down to the booths and paper napkins. The weekly menu sticks rigidly to the seasons and is backed up with local seafood specials showcasing prime Scottish produce.

Chef: Martin Cahill

Food Style: Modern Bistro

What is your advice for cooking great food?

Keep it simple, keep it fresh

AA Inspector

Isle of Skye

The Three Chimneys & The House Over-By ●●● ♣NOTABLE WINE LIST

IV55 8ZT
01470 511258
www.threechimneys.co.uk
Closed: 16 December to 16 January

Chef: Scott Davies
Food Style: Scottish,
Nordic Influence

An iconic pilgrimage for foodies over the past four decades, this remote whitewashed cottage restaurant continues to make its mark. A warren of small rooms with low ceilings, the restaurant's polished dark wood floors and tables are offset by exposed stone walls. Service from the friendly team is professional and fine-tuned. The food is firmly rooted in its island environment, particularly seafood from nearby waters. A meal could begin with Loch Dunvegan creel langoustine, lightly pickled mussels, Jerusalem artichoke and brown butter dressing, and be followed by Isle of Skye Vatten beef, asparagus, wild garlic and onion bhaji.

Edinbane Lodge ●●●●

IV51 9PW
01470 582217
www.edinbanelodge.co.uk
Open: All year

Chef: Calum Montgomery
Food Style: Modern Scottish

Once a historic hunting lodge, luxuriously renovated 16th-century Edinbane Lodge has an impressive stone fireplace in the elegant dining room with portraits of past owners. The seasonal tasting menus showcase the very best produce Skye has to offer and good technical skills combine with plenty of ambition in the kitchen for dishes that are big on flavour. A typical meal might begin with a rich BBQ celeriac crème brûlée, the glass-like top shattering to reveal a creamy caramelised celeriac purée with pieces of pickled and barbecued celeriac. Local seafood is of the highest quality and typified in a main of sparklingly fresh Kinlochbervie halibut with smoked seaweed butter sauce studded with cucumber for freshness. A beautifully simple dessert of dark chocolate ganache and biscuit with clean-flavoured sea buckthorn sorbet is a perfectly poised way to round things off. Knowledgable staff are happy to guide you through the comprehensive wine list.

Isleornsay

Duisdale House Hotel ⓐⓐ
Sleat, IV43 8QW
01471 833202
www.duisdale.com
Open: All year

Situated in the south of Skye, Duisdale House Hotel is a converted Victorian hunting lodge with amazing views. The restaurant has a subdued yet elegant style, leaving the scenery and the food to speak for themselves. Meals hit the mark, delivering a great balance of flavours. Expect modern cooking based on seasonal, regional ingredients that's beautifully presented.

Chef: Jason McKay
Food Style: Modern Scottish

Toravaig House Hotel ⓐⓐ
Knock Bay, Sleat, IV44 8RE
01471 820200
www.toravaig.com
Open: All year

Toravaig House Hotel is a small boutique property that enjoys enviable views over Knock Castle and the Sound of Sleat, while the interior is classy and stylish. The Iona restaurant is a smart candlelit space, offering up modern Scottish cuisine, in keeping with the majestic surroundings. Most of the produce comes from the island, including venison, lamb and seafood.

Chef: Jason McKay
Food Style: Modern Scottish

Stein

Loch Bay Restaurant ⓐⓐⓐ
Macleods Terrace, IV55 8GA
01470 592235
www.lochbay-restaurant.co.uk
Closed: January to February, First week August, reduced winter hours

Chef: Michael Smith
Food Style: Seafood, Traditional Scottish, French

Enjoying a magical setting in a row of 18th-century fishermen's cottages right by the loch shore, Loch Bay is a diminutive institution around these parts. Seating only 16 diners, its unpretentious decor of warm colours and gilt-framed mirrors convey a homely charm that belies the seriously accomplished food on offer. Chef Michael Smith's finely-honed skills, attention to detail and commitment to top-class Scottish ingredients deliver dishes of deceptive simplicity and integrity, showcased in the 'Skye Fruits de Mer' – a set menu of local shellfish and fish. The happy alliance of contemporary Scottish verve and classical French foundations shine from the nibble of crisp oatmeal oyster mignonette and first course of bay prawn and shrimp bisque with crab and Mull cheddar toastie through to a dessert of strawberry and iced whisky mac tart.

WALES

Isle of Anglesey

Beaumaris

Bishopsgate House Hotel ⊛
54 Castle Street, LL58 8BB
01248 810302
www.bishopsgatehotel.co.uk
Open: All year

The mint-green façade of Bishopsgate House stands out on its Georgian terrace and enjoys views toward Snowdonia across the Menai Strait. The intimate, low-ceilinged restaurant is full of old-world charm, and is popular with the local residents as well as visitors. Straightforward menus might feature roasted Welsh lamb rump with honey roast sweet potatoes.

Chef: Ian Sankey
Food Style: Traditional Welsh

Gaerwen

Gaerwen Arms ⊛⊛
Chapel Street, LL60 6DW
01248 421083
gaerwen-arms.co.uk/
Closed: 25–26 December

Well executed modern British dishes with well balanced flavours are the hallmarks at this friendly pub, just across the Menai Bridge from mainland Wales. The restaurant is modern in design with tartan-style carpeting and upholstered seating, and French-polished tables. When the weather demands it, expect a blazing fire in the main bar. Three miles away is famous 58-letter Llanfair PG sign.

Chef: Oli Thompson,
Andy Tabberner
Food Style: Modern British

Menai Bridge

Sosban & The Old Butcher's Restaurant ◎◎◎◎
Trinity House, 1 High Street, LL59 5EE
01248 208131
www.sosbanandtheoldbutchers.com
Closed: 25 December, 31 December, January

Chef: Stephen Stevens
Food Style: Modern

Dining at Sosban is a hot ticket, and definitely not your everyday restaurant experience. There is only room for 16 at any one time and it only happens three evenings and one lunch a week. But once you're inside you don't have to do much but give yourself over to the prodigiously talented Stephen Stevens, who will serve up his no-choice menu at a fixed time. Allow four hours from start to finish. The one-time butcher's shop on the high street has a rustic simplicity reflecting its former life. The procession of dishes displays amazing creativity, compelling visuals, and mightily impressive flavours. For example, reindeer moss is a stellar opening mouthful, rich with mushroom and fermented egg yolk. Duck with beetroot, anise, yogurt and mustard leaf is superb. Rhubarb and custard gets a reappraisal when a crisp rhubarb sphere is filled with duck egg custard and hits of rhubarb from poached and freeze-dried fruit. Complex, creative cuisine at its best and well worth the wait.

Bridgend

Bridgend

Leicesters Restaurant ◎◎
The Great House, 8 High Street, Laleston, CF32 0HP
01656 657644
**www.great-house-laleston.co.uk/
restaurant-in-bridgend**
Closed: 26 December

The 15th-century Great House, a Grade II listed building, is home to this restaurant that aims to provide an exquisite dining experience in welcoming and relaxed surroundings. Reflecting excellent Welsh cooking, expect bold, inventive food that's underpinned by a sense of quality and local sourcing.

Chef: Mathew Howells
Food Style: Modern Classic

Cardiff

Cardiff

Bully's ◉◉
5 Romilly Crescent, CF11 9NP
029 2022 1905
www.bullysrestaurant.co.uk
Closed: 25–26 December, 1 January

Bully's restaurant fills virtually every inch of its walls
with a quirky pot pourri of pictures, mirrors and other
retro paraphernalia. The kitchen may well rely on
Welsh providers for its materials but wears its Gallic
culinary allegiance on its sleeve in menus grounded in
the French repertoire, spiced with the odd foray into
global ideas.

Chef: Simmie Vedi
Food Style: French

NEW Heaneys ◉◉
6–10 Romilly Crescent, Pontcanna, CF11 9NR
02920 373009
www.heaneyscardiff.co.uk
Closed: 25 December

The outcome of a Kickstarter campaign, set in a row
of converted houses, Heaneys is a stylish, bustling
restaurant that offers a modern, relaxed atmosphere in
a neighbourhood setting. Menus range from full tasting
to a regular three course seasonal offering. Food is
fresh, simple and seasonal with some produce being
picked from the restaurant's own back garden.

Chef: Tommy Heaney
Food Style: Modern British,
Fish specialities

Park House Restaurant ◉◉ ♣NOTABLE WINE LIST
20 Park Place, CF10 3DQ
029 2022 4343
www.parkhouserestaurant.co.uk
Closed: 26–28 December, 1–4 January

Housed in a Gothic architectural extravagance, the
splendid panelled restaurant overlooks the gardens of
the National Museum of Wales. Do try the chocolate
platter involving a rich pavé and 'pulled' chocolate with
a peppermint macaroon and spearmint sorbet.

Chef: Thomas Martin
Food Style: Modern French

NEW Thomas by Tom Simmons ◉◉
3 & 5 Pontcanna Street, Pontcanna, CF11 9HQ
02921 167 800
thomas-pontcanna.co.uk
Closed: Sunday, Monday, Tuesday

A stylish restaurant tucked away in the Pontcanna district of Cardiff, eponymously named Thomas by Tom Simmons puts a classic French slant on high quality regional produce. The Pembrokeshire-born chef/owner is passionate about sourcing the best Welsh ingredients and the kitchen cooks the raw materials with due respect.

Chef: Tom Simmons
Food Style: Modern European

Carmarthenshire

Llansteffan

Mansion House Llansteffan ◉◉
Pantyrathro, SA33 5AJ
01267 241515
www.mansionhousellansteffan.co.uk.
Closed: Monday, Tuesday (November to January)

Mansion House Llansteffan is a compact yet perfectly formed Georgian building which has kept its architectural character and blended this seamlessly with a contemporary finish. Named after the Welsh word for 'estuary', Moryd Restaurant overlooks the gardens and the Towy Estuary beyond. Menus offer straightforward and well-rendered modern brasserie food.

Chef: Paul Owen
Food Style: Modern British

See advertisement on page 628

Nantgaredig

Y Polyn ◉◉ 🍷 NOTABLE WINE LIST
SA32 7LH
01267 290000
www.ypolyn.co.uk
Closed: 25 December, 1 January

This hospitable country pub is certainly more about dining than propping up the bar with a pint. Its owners win praise for hauling in the finest produce they can lay their hands on – salt marsh lamb and Welsh beef, for example – and transforming it into satisfyingly rustic lip-smacking dishes. The home-baked breads are fab too.

Chef: Susan Manson
Food Style: Classic European

MANSION HOUSE LLANSTEFFAN

Mansion House Llansteffan an award winning 5 star 2 AA rosette restaurant with rooms.
Set among Welsh farms in the gentle hills that slope down from the Cambrian Mountains to Carmarthen
In the 'Garden of Wales', this is the heart of the countryside, just 45 minute drive from Pembrokeshire,
Cardiganshire & Swansea. Carmarthen, with its historic castle, is just 5 miles up the road. And pretty
Llansteffan – a gem of a village – is practically a neighbour.
Serving breakfast, lunch and dinner in a handsome period dining room overlooking the gardens and the
estuary, Moryd Restaurant has two coveted AA Rosettes.
The food is fresh and contemporary with a strong local provenance and there is a choice of a Market Me
or an à la carte menu, both designed by head chef Paul Owen and his talented team.

eat   sleep   relax

www.mansionhousellansteffan.co.uk

Ceredigion

Eglwys Fach

Ynyshir Restaurant & Rooms 🌹🌹🌹🌹🌹 🍷 NOTABLE WINE LIST
SY20 8TA
01654 781209
www.ynyshir.co.uk
Closed: 2 weeks summer, 2 weeks Christmas and New Year, one week April, one week October

Chef: Gareth Ward
Food Style: Modern British

Deep within a 2,000-acre RSPB reserve, this country manor is one of the Principality's most treasured restaurants. The house and its lush green gardens are framed by the imposing Cambrian Mountains, and with chef-patron Gareth Ward at the helm, Ynyshir has been on the foodie trail for some time. The stylish dining room is darkly comfortable, with exposed stone walls, wooden furniture and sheepskins to soften the look. You get a view of what's going on in the busy no-shouting-zone kitchen as the dishes are constructed. Everyone who works here is passionate about what they do – Ward's delight in his food is clearly infectious. He's endlessly curious and the team do plenty of pickling, salting and fermenting, as well as preserving fruits, leaves and berries. Neither lunch nor dinner is a hurried affair – with literally dozens of courses, how could they be? – so expect at least a four-hour sitting. (There are rooms – and three tipis in the grounds – if you want to stay over.) Each of the six small tables is served by the chefs, who happily explain the genesis of the dishes, or what Gareth calls 'Alternative British Snap'. Using only brief descriptions, the menus signpost what's to come. There's a DJ, so this is not the place for a quiet meeting.

Tregaron

Y Talbot 🌹🌹
The Square, SY25 6JL
01974 298208
www.ytalbot.com
Closed: Monday, 25–26 December

Drovers of old began their long treks to the markets of the Midlands and London from Tregaron, no doubt first fortifying themselves in this part 17th-century inn. Through the pillared front doorway there's a bar one side and a restaurant on the other, with bilingual, wide-choice menus on offer.

Chef: Dafydd Watkin
Food Style: Modern British

Conwy

Abergele

Brasserie 1786 ◎◎

The Kinmel, St George's Road, LL22 9AS
01745 832014
www.thekinmel.co.uk
Open: All year

Brasserie 1786 is the main restaurant at the family-run, rurally located Kinmel. Recently refurbished, the plain dove grey decor has been further enhanced with striking modern art. Well-spaced tables also benefit from quality appointments. Staff are smartly uniformed, friendly and attentive, while the cooking is seasonal and plain speaking.

Chef: Patrick Haberland
Food Style: Modern British

Betws-y-Coed

Craig-y-Dderwen Riverside Hotel ◎

LL24 0AS
01690 710293
www.snowdoniahotel.com
Closed: 20–28 December, January

Built in the 1890s for an industrialist, the partly timbered house became a favourite bolt-hole for Sir Edward Elgar. A hotel since the 20s, it offers the full country-house package, complete with views of a riverside teeming with wildlife (do look out for the otters).

Food Style: Traditional, International

Colwyn Bay

Bryn Williams at Porth Eirias ◎◎

The Promenade, LL29 8HH
01492 533700
www.portheirias.com
Open: All year

Floor-to-ceiling windows offer sweeping views of Colwyn Bay, while exposed steelwork, pendant lights and industrial-chic create the feeling of a hip, big-city eatery. Diners can see right into the open kitchen where chefs turn local, seasonal ingredients into outstanding bistro-style food. Seafood takes up much of the menu but there's something for everyone.

Chef: David Parry
Food Style: British, Seafood

Conwy

Castle Hotel Conwy ⊛⊛
High Street, LL32 8DB
01492 582800
www.castlewales.co.uk
Closed: 25 December, 31 December

With its courtyard garden and stylish decor, Dawsons Restaurant & Bar offers modern British menus that deliver brasserie-style dishes and classic comfort options. Start with pan-seared king scallops, celeriac purée, black pudding and chorizo jam and follow it with fillet of sea bass, sweet potato fondant, buttered tenderstem broccoli and tomato pickle.

Chef: Leigh Marshall
Food Style: Modern British

NEW The Jackdaw ⊛⊛⊛
High Street, LL32 8DB
www.thejackdawconwy.co.uk
Closed: Monday, Tuesday, 25 September to 3 October, 25–29 December

Despite its faux-medieval appearance, The Jackdaw is housed in a 1930s building that was once a cinema. A dark staircase leads to the whitewashed first-floor restaurant where the style is simple with a touch of Scandinavian cool via hanging bunches of dry herbs and flowers, and chairs covered with sheepskins. Well-balanced dishes showcase seasonal raw materials

Chef: Nick Rudge
Food Style: Welsh

and a meal could start with wild garlic velouté, confit potato and barbecued leek before a main course of perfectly timed Welsh beef sirloin, barbecued king oyster mushroom and cubes of fruity bara brith bread to soak up those delicious juices.

Signatures Restaurant ⊛⊛
Aberconwy Resort & Spa, Aberconwy Park, LL32 8GA
01492 583513
www.darwinescapes.co.uk/parks/aberconwy-resort-spa/signatures-restaurant
Closed: Monday, Tuesday

The seaside holiday park location is a little left-field, but Signatures is well worth tracking down for its inspired modern cooking. An open kitchen adds to the buzz, and menus are full of modern accents, so prepare yourself for the likes of home-made black pudding and smoked bacon and leek rösti enriched with a runny egg, and mustard dressing. There's plenty of craft and attention to detail throughout.

Chef: Jimmy Williams, Chris Owen, Matthew Hopwood
Food Style: Modern British

Deganwy

Quay Hotel & Spa 🏵
Deganwy Quay, LL31 9DJ
01492 564100
www.quayhotel.co.uk
Open: All year

Chef: Ian Watson
Food Style: Modern European

Beautifully located on the Conwy estuary, with views across the marina to the castle, this is a stylish, modern boutique hotel. The smart Grill Room offers a relatively informal setting for straightforward European cooking. Locally-landed fish and seafood feature on the menu.

Llandudno

Bodysgallen Hall and Spa 🏵🏵🏵 🍷NOTABLE WINE LIST
The Royal Welsh Way, LL30 1RS
01492 584466
www.bodysgallen.com
Closed: 24–26 December

Chef: Abdalla El Shershaby
Food Style: Modern, Traditional

Bodysgallen is a supremely elegant Stuart mansion in 200 acres of parkland. Inside, the sober oak panelling is softened by garden views through mullioned windows and by sympathetic, personable service. Balancing traditional and modern British modes has become an essential skill of today's aspirant chefs, and Abdalla El Shershaby possesses it in abundance, garnishing barbecued ox tongue to start with deconstructed piccalilli and a cauliflower cheese fritter. A main of slow-cooked saddle of Welsh lamb is accompanied by glazed Bodysgallen root vegetables and tenderstem broccoli, and you might draw things to a conclusion with a soft and yielding cereal milk pannacotta with apricot sorbet and Mirabelle plum compôte.

Dunoon Hotel 🏵🏵
Gloddaeth Street, LL30 2DW
01492 860787
www.dunoonhotel.co.uk
Closed: 23 December to 31 January

The restaurant here is full of old-world charm, with oak-panelled walls, brass fittings and chandeliers, flowers and linen napery on the tables and a cooking style that's more likely to reassure than to startle, the kitchen quite rightly keeping its customers happy.

Chef: Rob Kennish, Josh Hughes
Food Style: Modern British

Imperial Hotel
The Promenade, Vaughan Street, LL30 1AP
01492 877466
www.theimperial.co.uk
Open: All year

Chef: Leighton Thomas
Food Style: Modern,
Traditional British

The wedding-cake stucco façade of the Imperial is a landmark on Llandudno's seafront. On a balmy day, alfresco dining on the terrace with a splendid backdrop of the bay is on the cards. The kitchen turns out menus of classically-inflected modern cooking featuring a sound showing of fine Welsh produce.

St George's Hotel
The Promenade, LL30 2LG
01492 877544
www.stgeorgeswales.co.uk
Open: All year

Llandudno's prom is the place to be for splendid sunsets and sweeping views across the bay, and St George's Hotel sits centre stage. The place is a timeless slice of Victorian wedding-cake grandeur, with an irresistible terrace and floor-to-ceiling windows in the restaurant.

Chef: Barry Williams
Food Style: Modern,
Traditional, Welsh

Gwynedd

Abersoch

The Dining Room
4 High Street, LL53 7DY
01758 740709
www.thediningroomabersoch.co.uk
Closed: Sunday to Wednesday

In pole position among the buzzy bars and hip surfie shops of trendy Abersoch's main drag, this low-key bistro with a tea-shop frontage and mismatched chairs and tables is building a loyal fan base for its warm hospitality and confidently executed food.

Chef: Si Toft
Food Style: Welsh Bistro

Abersoch *continued*

Porth Tocyn Hotel @@ ♦NOTABLE WINE LIST

Bwlchtocyn, LL53 7BU
01758 713303
www.porthtocynhotel.co.uk
Closed: November, 2 weeks before Easter

The Fletcher-Brewer family converted a terrace of lead miners' cottages into the comfortable, relaxed and unstuffy place we see today. Inside are antique-filled lounges and a smart restaurant, with spectacular views over Cardigan Bay to Snowdonia. The menu's repertoire combines traditional values and more modern sensibilities.

Chef: Darren Shenton-Morris
Food Style: Modern British

Bala

Pale Hall Hotel & Restaurant @@@ ♦NOTABLE WINE LIST

Llandderfel, LL23 7PS
01678 530285
www.palehall.co.uk
Open: All year

Chef: Gareth Stevenson
Food Style: British, European

Surrounded by 14 acres of grounds, this handsome pile once played host to numerous high profile guests including Queen Victoria. After cocktails in the sumptuous lounge, head to the grand dining room with its high ceilings, ornate carved plasterwork and floor-to-ceiling windows overlooking the grounds. Although the kitchen displays a firm grasp of classical French cooking, there is a modern approach to the menu. Start with a bouillabaisse packed with saffron-hued potatoes, fennel and well-timed pieces of brill and hake. Move on to rump of Welsh Black beef with ox cheek pie, parsnip and bordelaise sauce.

Caernarfon

The Gunroom Restaurant @

Plas Dinas Country House, Bontnewydd, LL54 7YF
01286 830214
www.plasdinas.co.uk/dining
Closed: Sunday–Monday November to April,
24–26 December

Set in Plas Dinas Country House, the small country house that was once the home of Lord Snowdon, The Gunroom Restaurant still displays a number of Armstrong-Jones family portraits and memorabilia. The space is intimate to say the least, with covers for 20 at any one time. The menu changes monthly, is designed around the seasons and uses the freshest local Welsh produce.

Chef: Daniel ap Geraint
Food Style: Modern British

See advertisement opposite

Caernarfon *continued*

Ty Castell ⬡⬡
18 Stryd Fawr, LL55 1RN
01286 674937
www.tycastell.cymru
Closed: 24–26 December, 31 December to 1 January

Chef: Charly Vaughan
Food Style: Welsh Tapas

Close to Caernarfon Castle and occupying a notable 18th-century building, this contemporary restaurant looks far beyond Wales for its culinary inspiration. The interesting tapas-style menu has a global influence, from dishes like cured salmon, pink grapefruit, white radish and ponzu dressing to the teriyaki beef, braised onion and sautéed mushrooms.

Criccieth

Bron Eifion Country House Hotel ⬡
LL52 0SA
01766 522385
www.broneifion.co.uk
Open: All year

Chef: Marius Curelea
Food Style: Modern British, Welsh

Built in 1883, Bron Eifion Hotel is set in extensive grounds to the west of Criccieth, commanding impressive sea views. The Garden Room restaurant is a modern extension to the original building and is very light and airy with large windows. The food is modern with plenty of local produce. The 50-strong gin list shouldn't be overlooked.

Dolgellau

Penmaenuchaf Dolgellau ⬡⬡ 🍷 NOTABLE WINE LIST
Penmaenpool, LL40 1YB
01341 422129
www.penhall.co.uk
Open: All year

The greystone Victorian hall gives spectacular views to Cader Idris and the Mawddach Estuary. Within, oak floors, panels, artwork and fresh flowers give a real sense of age and quality. The menu pays homage to indigenous produce, and there's no lack of contemporary, creative flair.

Chef: Owen Vaughan
Food Style: Modern British

See advertisement opposite and on page 648

Llanberis

Padarn Brasserie ⬤
The Royal Victoria Hotel Snowdonia, LL55 4TY
01286 870253
www.theroyalvictoria.co.uk
Closed: 25 December, 31 December

Located in Snowdonia National Park, Padarn Brasserie
is a spacious first-floor room furnished in traditional
style with a verandah extension that benefits from
views of the village of Llanberis, lovely countryside
and Peris and Padarn lakes. Popular with walkers and
tourists as much as locals, the modern British menu
keeps things simple.

Chef: Aron Davies
Food Style: Modern British

PENMAENUCHAF
DOLGELLAU
PENMAENUCHAF.CO.UK

★★★★

Portmeirion

The Hotel Portmeirion ◉◉
Minffordd, LL48 6ET
01766 770000
www.portmeirion-village.com
Closed: 2 weeks November

Chef: Mark Threadgill
Food Style: Modern Welsh

The fantasy Italianate village, created by Sir Clough Williams-Ellis, was conceived around the ruin of what is now The Portmeirion Hotel. With breathtaking views across the estuary, the curved dining room with wood and chrome accents is designed on a yacht theme. Expect the fresh, lively, modern Welsh cooking to enhance the whole experience.

Monmouthshire

Abergavenny

Angel Hotel ◉
15 Cross Street, NP7 5EN
01873 857121
www.angelabergavenny.com
Closed: 25 December

Set in the heart of town, the Angel Hotel was a posting inn back in the early 19th century, and its Georgian façade and spacious interiors remain in fine shape today. A brasserie-style menu is offered in the Foxhunter Bar, and in the Oak Room restaurant with its vibrant colours and original art on display.

Chef: Wesley Hammond,
Paul Brown
Food Style: British, International

Restaurant 1861 ◉◉
Cross Ash, NP7 8PB
01873 821297
www.18-61.co.uk
Closed: 26 December to 13 January

Built as a pub in 1861, this place much, much later became Simon and Kate King's attractive, slightly isolated restaurant. A starter of ethically produced foie gras or dill-cured mackerel might be followed by a fricassée, either rose veal or woodland mushrooms; or fillet of hake or sea trout. Kate's dad grows most of the vegetables.

Chef: Simon King
Food Style: Modern British,
European

The Walnut Tree Inn ◉◉◉ ♦ NOTABLE WINE LIST
See pages 640-641 and advertisement opposite

THE WALNUT TREE

✼

The famous Michelin-starred restaurant located two miles east of
Abergavenny offers dishes based on Shaun Hill's personal taste paired
with sound cooking techniques and truly exceptional ingredients.
Open Wednesday to Saturday.

01873 852797
Llanddewi Skirrid, Abergavenny, NP7 8AW
www.thewalnuttreeinn.com

Abergavenny

 NOTABLE WINE LIST

The Walnut Tree Inn

Llanddewi Skirrid, NP7 8AW
01873 852797
www.thewalnuttreeinn.com
Closed: Sunday, Monday, Tuesday, 1 week at Christmas

Chef: Shaun Hill
Food Style: Modern Italian, French

Contemporary flavours in beautiful Welsh countryside

Firmly established on the gastronomic map since the 1960s, The Walnut Tree Inn, with its neatly clipped topiary and white-painted exterior, is the perfect place to relax and unwind. Set amid rolling fields a couple of miles east of the charming market town of Abergavenny, it's a beautiful location close to the English border, that certainly deserves further exploration – it's surrounded by the Brecon Beacons and is only 45 minutes from Cardiff.

The Walnut Tree has been home to Shaun Hill many years, and he continues to cook the food he himself likes to eat, which sounds so sensible it's hard to imagine a time when it was almost revolutionary to take such a comfortable, eclectic approach. Hill's strong classical background and five decades of experience at the top of the culinary tree give a reassuring foundation for contemporary interpretations of flavour

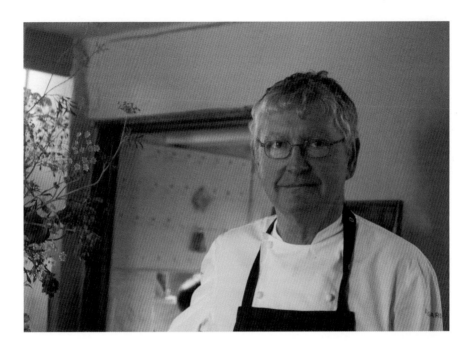

and texture which may appear simple but are conceived with extreme thoughtfulness and attention to detail.

The dining area is welcomingly informal and unpretentious with bare tables, bentwood chairs and striking modern art. The daily-changing menus reflect season and availability. The excellent value set lunch which might see you tucking into hake with a hazelnut crust, courgettes and brandade followed by gingered nectarine and blueberry pudding.

The à la carte offers more complex choices, so dinner might begin with lobster consommé with red mullet and scallop before a comforting dish of pork loin, belly and baked beans with sausages, or for a lighter option, Middle Eastern salads accompanied by lavash and labneh. Either pistachio and cherry tart with honey ice cream or gooseberry crème brûlée with a ginger cookie will bring things to a

close nicely. The wine list leans towards smaller winemakers, and, like the food, demonstrates the tastes and interests of Shaun and his team.

See advertisement on page 639

"...interpretations of flavour and texture which may appear simple but are conceived with extreme thoughtfulness and attention to detail."

Rockfield

The Stonemill & Steppes Farm Cottages ⑨⑨
NP25 5SW
01600 716273
www.thestonemill.co.uk
Closed: Monday, Tuesday, 25–26 December,
2 weeks in January

A beautifully converted barn in a 16th-century
mill complex provides an impressive setting for
accomplished cooking. It's a riot of beams and vaulted
ceilings, with chunky rustic tables around an ancient
stone cider press. The kitchen uses regional produce to
deliver simply presented, modern dishes.

Chef: Tom Redding
Food Style: Modern British

Usk

Newbridge on Usk ⑨⑨
Tredunnock, NP15 1LY
01633 451000
www.celtic-manor.com
Open: All year

Chef: Adam Whittle
Food Style: Traditional British

On a bend in the Usk, with river views, this restaurant with rooms is surrounded by well-tended
gardens. The property dates back 200 years, so you can expect the usual beams and fireplaces,
while the two-level restaurant has a rustic charm.

The Raglan Arms ⑨
Llandenny, NP15 1DL
01291 690800
www.raglanarms.co.uk

Chef: Peter Hulsmann
Food Style: Modern British

This unassuming property looking more like a private house is home to bistro-style cooking
and a friendly atmosphere. Log burners and scrubbed tables bring home the inn-like feel, and a
decked terrace allows diners to sit and enjoy the rural location.

Whitebrook

The Whitebrook ◉◉◉◉ ♨ NOTABLE WINE LIST

NP25 4TX
01600 860254
www.thewhitebrook.co.uk
Closed: 2 weeks in January

Chef: Chris Harrod
Food Style: Modern British, French

The lush Wye Valley setting of The Whitebrook is also the source of a good deal of the produce found on the menu, such is chef-patron Chris Harrod's passion for the food on his doorstep. This whitewashed former drovers' inn, now a comfortable restaurant with rooms, seems to fit organically into its environment, in a wonderfully secluded location very much off the beaten track. It's an unpretentious and relaxing setting for the vibrant, dynamic cooking. There is real vitality to each of the nine courses of the seasonally changing menu – with dishes often incorporating foraged and wild foods. Wye Valley asparagus cooked over pine embers is a delightfully elegant spring starter, served with hogweed, hedgerow pickings and Tintern mead sauce. Mains might include a superb dish of Ryeland lamb, making brilliant use of different cuts – loin, shoulder, belly and liver, accompanied by young leeks, chicken of the wood mushrooms, elephant garlic, turnips and orache. The wine list includes bottles from organic and biodynamic growers.

Newport

Newport

AA RESTAURANT OF THE YEAR FOR WALES 2022–23

Gem 42 ◉◉◉
See page 644

Rafters ◉

The Celtic Manor Resort, Coldra Woods, NP18 1HQ
01633 413000
www.celtic-manor.com
Open: All year

Chef: Mike Bates, Simon Crockford
Food Style: Welsh

There are views over the Ryder Cup course from Rafters, a classy grill restaurant within the Twenty Ten Clubhouse at the Celtic Manor Resort. Welsh ingredients take centre stage and there are locally reared, 21-day-aged steaks as the star attraction.

AA RESTAURANT OF THE YEAR FOR WALES 2022–23

Gem 42

42 Bridge Street, NP20 4NY
01633 287591
www.gem42.co.uk
Closed: Sunday, 25–26 December, Easter, Bank Holidays

Chef: Sergio Cinotti
Food Style: Modern Italian, French

Gem 42 is easy to miss but once inside this small and unassuming building, the exuberant Botticelli-style ceilings, crisply dressed tables with Murano glass ornaments soon transport you to the Mediterranean. The kitchen combines classical foundations and contemporary techniques to deliver entertaining medley textures and flavours in a number of tasting menus. The emphasis is on Italian ingredients and style but mixed with top quality local and seasonal produce. It's matched by an impressive wine selection with flights offered to match the dishes. Look out for starter of Scottish scallop wrapped around an egg yolk with wasabi vinaigrette, Oscietra caviar and black truffle. Then dive in to dry-aged Welsh Wagyu beef sirloin with butternut squash purée, salt baked beetroot, courgettes and an oyster emulsion, in potato purée and Matelote sauce. Smoked chocolate rum cremeux with cardamon gelato, pistachios and pain d'espice sable is one of the delicious desserts.

Steak on Six ◉◉
The Celtic Manor Resort, Coldra Woods, NP18 1HQ
01633 413000
www.celtic-manor.com/dining/restaurants/
steak-on-six
Open: All year

Chef: Michael Bates,
Simon Crockford
Food Style: Modern British

The 'Six' in question is the sixth floor of the upmarket, golf-centric Celtic Manor Resort, where this stylish, contemporary steakhouse looks out over Coldra Woods. When the culinary proposition is this straightforward, the quality of the raw materials is key, and the pedigree meat here proudly flies the flag for prime British protein expertly executed.

Pembrokeshire

Haverfordwest

Slebech Park Estate ◉◉
SA62 4AX
01437 752000
www.slebech.co.uk
Closed: Sunday to Thursday

The castellated, 18th-century Slebech manor house stands in 700 acres of parkland, part-bordered by the Eastern Cleddau River. Overlooking this so-called 'hidden waterway', the naturally lit modern restaurant is a big draw for its Little Haven picked crab and laverbread; roast halibut; 28-day, dry-aged Welsh beef fillet; and butternut squash and sweet potato pithivier.

Food Style: Modern, Classic

Narberth

AA WINE AWARD FOR WALES 2022–23

The Fernery ◉◉◉◉ 🍷 NOTABLE WINE LIST
See pages 646-647 and advertisement on page 648

St Davids

Blas Restaurant ◉◉◉
See page 649

Saundersfoot

Coast Restaurant ◉◉◉ 🍷 NOTABLE WINE LIST
See pages 650-651

AA WINE AWARD FOR WALES 2022–23

 NOTABLE WINE LIST

The Fernery

Grove, Molleston, SA67 8BX
01834 860915
www.thegrove-narberth.co.uk
Open: All year

Chef: Douglas Balish
Food Style: Modern British

Dynamic, contemporary dining in idyllic Pembrokeshire setting

The Grove is a beautiful 17th-century manor house, now a delightful boutique hotel with individually designed bedrooms, idyllically set in 26 acres of wonderful Pembrokeshire countryside. The atmosphere is relaxed and welcoming, and there are views of the Preseli Hills, as well as four acres of pretty gardens to explore, including a fine kitchen garden. This is where they grow a wide variety of

fruit, herbs and vegetables, much of which, along with plenty of local Welsh fare, will make an appearance on the menu.

Inside you'll find an elegant, intimate blend of traditional comforts and more modern touches, all very stylishly done, while The Fernery itself, with its calm, neutral decor and fern-inspired details, is an intimate and understated setting for Douglas Balish's dynamic, contemporary

food. Choose from a five or eight-course tasting menu, all courses with matching wine recommendations. You might begin with Grove Vegetables – a delightfully fresh combination of onion, celeriac, beetroot and turnip, all cooked beautifully, with a Hafod cheese cream and roasted kale and nettle velouté. Another choice might be an excellent Pembroke oyster, accompanied by crisp pickled cucumber, sea purslane and a well-judged sour cream and jalapeño foam, with caviar providing a touch of indulgence. Main course Anjou squab breast is perfectly timed – pink, tender and succulent, with a smooth walnut purée and flavours of cherry, celeriac and nasturtium. Beef fillet is accompanied by a delightfully crispy potato terrine, topped with chives and sour cream, the richness of braised oxtail contrasting with the freshness of Thai basil. Puddings show similar levels of intelligent precision – a good example pairs crisp layers of macadamia discs as a crunchy contrast to smooth mascarpone, with a perfect quenelle of deeply flavoured and refreshing rhubarb sorbet. This is a chef at the top of his game.

See advertisement on page 648

"...an intimate and understated setting for Douglas Balish's dynamic, contemporary food."

SEREN

A unique collection of Welsh hotels and restaurants by the sea

GROVE
NARBERTH
★★★★★

fernery
AT GROVE OF NARBERTH

BEACH HOUSE
OXWICH

coast
SAUNDERSFOOT

PENMAENUCHAF
DOLGELLAU
★★★★

serencollection.co.uk

St Davids

Blas Restaurant

Twr y Felin Hotel, Caerfai Road, SA62 6QT
01437 725555
www.twryfelinhotel.com
Open: All year

Chef: Sam Owen
Food Style: Modern British

Meaning 'Taste' in Welsh, Blas Restaurant is located in a former windmill dating back to 1806 which adds to the uniqueness of this venue. Part of the luxurious Twr y Felin Hotel, it's set in its own grounds and close to some great walks should you need to burn off a few calories after your lunch. Menus influenced by the seasons and locality means dishes using produce sourced predominantly from Pembrokeshire and Welsh suppliers, as well as foraged ingredients from the surrounding countryside and coast.

Mood lighting, bespoke handcrafted furniture and specially commissioned artworks contribute to the elegance of the dining room where a meal could kick off with curried crab, Jerusalem artichoke, pickled daikon and coriander before moving on to top quality venison saddle with soft creamed parsnip, pear and sprout leaf. To finish, try a well-presented baked custard tart, honey, orange and prune ice cream – the thin, crisp pastry containing a rich custard filling topped with honeycomb pieces.

Saundersfoot

 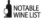 NOTABLE WINE LIST

Coast Restaurant

Coppet Hall Beach, SA69 9AJ
01834 810800
coastsaundersfoot.co.uk
Closed: Monday, Tuesday, 2 weeks January

Chef: Fred Clapperton
Food Style: Modern British,
Seafood

Local ingredients at the fore

A curved modern building right on the shoreline of the beach, Coast Restaurant boasts a stunning location. The split-level dining room looks across the bay and cleverly positioned mirrors ensure guests with their backs to the floor-to-ceiling windows can still see the sea views. A small bar area gives diners views from the kitchen pass and straight into the kitchen. There is a light, delicate style to the beautifully presented food, which utilises much fine local Welsh produce. This inevitably includes whatever the Pembrokeshire coastline offers on the day, whether it's oysters, fish, sea vegetables or herbs foraged from the beaches.

Start with an impeccably timed, deep-flavoured lamb breast with plump morel mushrooms and a vibrant salad, or maybe a pairing of smoked eel, charcoal and horseradish. You might move on to a wonderfully fresh fillet of pollock teamed

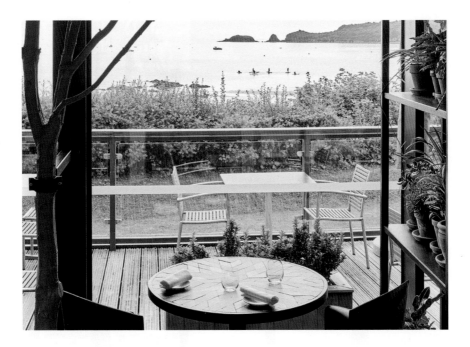

with coastal leaves, smooth cauliflower purée and a supporting cast of shrimps and crispy pieces of Black Bomber cheese.

Or, perhaps, a plate of short rib beef with brassicas and hen of the woods. To finish, try the refined dandelion root custard with pistachio ice cream and milk foam or maybe end with goats' yogurt, rhubarb and tonka bean.

The vegetarian set menu and tasting menu offers just as much choice, perhaps opening with duck egg, artichoke and morel before a main course of Savoy cabbage, kohlrabi and hen of the woods. Either way, there's also a fantastic Welsh cheese selection to round things off, and there's a carefully curated wine list showcasing progressive and sustainable producers from Europe and the New World, as well as more unusual places such as Japan. For those drinkers who want to keep the local theme going with the wines, there are even bottles from a vineyard in Monmouthshire.

See advertisement on page 648

"...beautifully presented food, which utilises much fine local Welsh produce."

Saundersfoot *continued*

St Brides Spa Hotel 🌸
St Brides Hill, SA69 9NH
01834 812304
www.stbridesspahotel.com
Open: All year

In a marvellous location overlooking Carmarthen Bay,
St Brides Spa Hotel has two main dining options, the
open-plan Cliff Restaurant and the more informal
Gallery, all with excellent sea views. The kitchen's
approach is modern British, with a heavy focus on
seafood, including fresh lobster straight from the tank.

Chef: Joshua Hughes
Food Style: Modern British

See advertisement below

St Brides Spa Hotel
Saundersfoot, Pembrokeshire
www.stbridesspahotel.com

AA RESTAURANT WITH ROOMS OF THE YEAR FOR WALES 2022–23

Crug Glâs Country House ⊛⊛
Abereiddy, SA62 6XX
01348 831302
www.crug-glas.co.uk
Closed: 24–28 December

Owners Janet and Perkin Evans have renovated 12th-century Crug Glâs using local materials to achieve smart modernity without trampling on the house's history. At the end of the day, kick off the walking boots and settle into the formal Georgian dining room for country-house cooking.

Chef: Ciappara-Brodie
Food Style: Modern British

Penally Abbey Hotel ⊛⊛
Penally Abbey Hotel, Penally, SA70 7PY
01834 843033
www.penally-abbey.com
Closed: January

Chef: Richard Browning
Food Style: Modern, Classic

Overlooking Carmarthen Bay, with the ruins of the 12th-century chapel still visible in the grounds, the fully restored 18th-century Penally Abbey has soothingly elegant interiors, where the pale colour scheme and delightful period details lend an air of quiet luxury. In the candlelit restaurant you can look forward to relaxed fine dining, with intensely flavoured, well-constructed dishes.

Trefloyne Manor ⊛
Trefloyne Lane, Penally, SA70 7RG
01834 842165
www.trefloyne.com
Closed: 25 December

This elegant manor house provides a relaxed country club setting in the heart of bustling Tenby. Accessed through a cosy bar area, the restaurant occupies a large glass-fronted orangery. The menu is supplemented with blackboard specials and a fish board, with classic British dishes.

Chef: Bogdan-Petru Dobre
Food Style: Classic British

Wolf's Castle

Wolfscastle Country Hotel ◉◉
SA62 5LZ
01437 741225
wolfscastle.com
Closed: 24–26 December

It's said that Welsh rebel leader Owain Glyndwr may be buried in the field alongside this old stone country hotel. Here, the principal restaurant offers unclothed tables and a menu of modern classics. Save room for chocolate fondant, served with salted caramel ice cream and orange jelly.

Chef: Roman Modrzynski
Food Style: Modern, Traditional

Powys

Brecon

Peterstone Court ◉
Llanhamlach, LD3 7YB
01874 665387
www.peterstone-court.com
Open: All year

Chef: Glyn Bridgeman
Food Style: Modern British, European

Peterstone Court is a gorgeous Georgian house set on the edge of the equally gorgeous Brecon Beacons, making it an ideal base for exploration. Despite its age, the place has a contemporary, classy feel that includes a swish bar and a spa. Best of all, there's great modern food in the Conservatory Restaurant.

Three Horseshoes Inn ◉◉
Groesffordd, LD3 7SN
01874665672
threehorseshoesgroesffordd.com
Closed: Monday (end October to Easter)

Just what you need to fuel a day in the great outdoors, this cosy pub is justifiably popular with hikers and bikers. The interior looks up to snuff with its original slate floors, heritage paint palette and modern sheen, while the food is buttressed by local suppliers – the lamb, for example, comes from the neighbouring farm.

Chef: Alex Parrett
Food Style: British

Hay-on-Wye

Old Black Lion Inn ✿
26 Lion Street, HR3 5AD
01497 820841
www.oldblacklion.co.uk
Closed: 25 December

Dating from the 17th century, the whitewashed inn
has bags of character, with beams, low ceilings and
stone fireplaces. You can eat in the bar or in the dining
room. The kitchen proudly sources all their meats from
organic farms in the foothills of Hay Bluff.

Chef: Mark Turton
Food Style: Modern British

Llanwddyn

Lake Vyrnwy Hotel & Spa ✿
Lake Vyrnwy, SY10 0LY
01691 870692
www.lakevyrnwy.com
Open: All year

Chef: Dan Furnival
Food Style: Modern British

Looking down the length of Lake Vyrnwy, while dining on good food, some grown on the
hotel estate itself, is a treat indeed. You might begin with goats' cheese, caramelised onion
and crystallised walnut tart, then follow with lamb loin, confit belly and dauphinoise potatoes,
finishing with banana, peanut butter, salted caramel and milk chocolate ice cream.

Llyswen

Llangoed Hall 🍷NOTABLE WINE LIST Rosettes Suspended
LD3 0YP
01874 754525
www.llangoedhall.co.uk
Open: All year

Food Style: Modern British

The Rosette award for this establishment has been suspended due to a change of chef and
reassessment will take place in due course.
An extensive kitchen garden and a smokehouse in the 17-acre grounds of this handsome
Edwardian mansion in the Wye Valley attest to the culinary focus at Llangoed. Originally
Jacobean, Clough Williams-Ellis (of Portmeirion fame) rebuilt the place in the early 20th century,
so expect luxurious lounges full of original features, fine furniture, and original artworks by
Whistler and Augustus John.

The Nags Head Inn ◉
Garthmyl, SY15 6RS
01686 640600
www.nagsheadgarthmyl.co.uk
Open: All year

Chef: Colin Clark
Food Style: Modern British

The Nags Head is a Grade II listed coaching inn, close to the Montgomery Canal and the River Severn. It's a pleasant spot for a nicely renovated country pub. The dining area is a richly decorated space opening onto a patio. Its high beamed ceiling, bookcases and pot plants really create a welcoming atmosphere.

Swansea

The Plough & Harrow ◉
88 Oldway, Murton, SA3 3DJ
01792 234459
www.ploughandharrowmurton.co.uk
Closed: Monday (except Bank Holidays)

In a lovely village not far from Swansea, The Plough & Harrow is an unassuming gastro pub with smart modern interiors; panelled walls and furniture painted in blues, creams and greys, a wood-burner, stacked logs and some bare stone walls. The menu features plenty of Welsh beef, lamb, cheese and even laverbread.

Chef: Nick Jones
Food Style: Modern European

Beach House Restaurant, Oxwich Beach ◉◉◉ ⌁NOTABLE WINE LIST
See pages 658-659 and advertisement on page 648

Hanson at the Chelsea Restaurant

17 St Mary Street, SA1 3LH
01792 464068
www.hansonatthechelsea.co.uk
Closed: Monday, Bank Holidays, 25–26 December

Andrew Hanson's unassuming-looking restaurant
resembles a classic modern bistro inside with clothed
tables pressed in cheek by jowl, blackboard menus
and small framed pictures against a delicate yellow
colour scheme. The cooking is an appealing mix of local
produce and French influences, with the emphasis on
fish and seafood, but not forgetting fine Welsh lamb.

Chef: Andrew Hanson
Food Style: Modern Welsh, French

How we assess for Rosettes

One Rosette

These restaurants will be
achieving standards that
stand out in their local
area, featuring:

- food prepared with care,
  understanding and skill

- good quality ingredients

- The same expectations
  apply to hotel restaurants
  where guests should be able
  to eat in with confidence
  and a sense of anticipation.

Two Rosettes

The best local restaurants,
which aim for and achieve:

- higher standards

- better consistency

- greater precision
  apparent in the cooking

- obvious attention
  to the selection of
  quality ingredients.

Three Rosettes

These are outstanding
restaurants that achieve
standards that demand
national recognition well
beyond their local area.
The cooking will be
underpinned by:

- the selection and
  sympathetic treatment
  of the highest quality
  ingredients

- timing, seasoning and
  the judgment of flavour
  combinations will be
  consistently excellent

- these virtues will tend to be
  supported by other elements
  such as intuitive service and
  a well-chosen wine list.

Four Rosettes

Among the top restaurants
in the UK where the cooking
demands national recognition.
These restaurants will exhibit:

- intense ambition

- a passion for excellence

- superb technical skills

- remarkable consistency

- an appreciation of
  culinary traditions combined
  with a passionate desire for
  further exploration
  and improvement.

Five Rosettes

The pinnacle, where the
cooking compares with the
best in the world.
These restaurants will have:

- highly individual voices

- exhibit breathtaking culinary
  skills and set the standards
  to which others aspire,
  yet few achieve.

Oxwich

 NOTABLE WINE LIST

Beach House Restaurant, Oxwich Beach

SA3 1LS
01792 278277
www.beachhouseoxwich.co.uk
Closed: 2nd and 3rd week January

Chef: Hywel Griffith
Food Style: Modern Welsh

Local seafood overlooking the bay

Literally on the beach, the coastal views from Beach House Restaurant towards famous Gower Peninsula landmark of Three Cliffs Bay are breathtaking whether your table is inside or on the sunny terrace. The stone-built building was originally used to store coal for the main house on Penrice Estate overlooking Oxwich Bay. Now thoroughly modernised with clean, modern lines, hues of maritime blue and cream, leather upholstery, stylish light fittings and floor-to-ceiling windows along the beach side, it's a spectacular setting for a restaurant. Outside, a glass partition separates diners on the decked seating area from the elements and there is driftwood effect throughout thanks to the abundance of wood.

Native Welshman head chef Hywel Griffith is passionate about produce from the Gower coast and that's reflected in his menu which often includes local meat and game as well as seafood and fish caught from the sea directly in front of the restaurant.

A typical meal might begin with a well-executed, creamy veal sweetbread with a hint of thyme on its seared exterior, served with asparagus spears and purée and slice of Morteau sausage. It might be followed by 'caught this morning' Oxwich Bay lobster cannelloni, braised vegetables, Lyonnaise potatoes and lemon thyme. The sweet lobster fills the delicate, thin pasta parcel and the braised julienne vegetables offer bite and texture. The Lyonnaise potatoes are scented with lemon and thyme and a rich lobster bisque finishes off a memorable dish with a real sense of place.

Puddings are a strength here – end the meal with a slice of light and wobbly egg custard tart, the richness tempered by poached rhubarb and a subtle blood orange ice cream. The extensive and intelligently arranged wine list offers a number of affordable options and there's a strong choice by the glass.

See advertisement on page 648

"...Hywel Griffith is passionate about produce from the Gower coast and that's reflected in his menu..."

Torfaen

Cwmbran

The Parkway Hotel & Spa ⚘⚘
Cwmbran Drive, NP44 3UW
01633 871199
www.parkwayhotelandspa.com
Open: All year

Chef: Clive Williams
Food Style: Modern European

Over seven acres of gardens surround the Parkway Hotel, making for a relaxing ambience, and Ravellos Restaurant is at the heart of it all. There's a strong emphasis on excellent Welsh produce, and the modern menus reveal sensibly balanced and confident dishes. There's also the option to try out the famous Parkway Carvery.

See advertisement opposite

Pontypool

The Lion ⚘
41 Broad Street, Blaenavon, NP4 9NH
01495 792516
www.thelionhotelblaenavon.co.uk
Open: All year

Chef: Jon Wellington
Food Style: Classic Welsh

At the heart of UNESCO World Heritage-recognised Blaenavon, The Lion has been revamped with a clean-lined modern look. Its relaxed dining room blends bare tables with neutral grey hues and light fittings that reference the bygone mining days. The food fits the bill, deploying excellent local ingredients in hearty, crowd-pleasing dishes.

Vale of Glamorgan

Hensol

Llanerch Vineyard ⚘⚘
CF72 8GG
01443 222716
www.llanerch-vineyard.co.uk
Closed: 25–26 December

Chef: Michael Hudson, Andy Aston
Food Style: Modern Welsh

Llanerch Vineyard is set on a working vineyard with countryside views beyond the vines. The Cariad Restaurant and Bistro is open for lunch, afternoon tea and dinner, with outdoor seating on the terrace in the warmer months. The style is modern British, using plenty of local Welsh produce. Obviously, Llanerch's wines appear on the wine list.

The Parkway Hotel and Spa

Cwmbran Drive
Cwmbran
NP44 3UW

Tel: 01633 871199

parkwayhotelandspa.com

Food...Just the way you like it

Located at the heart of the hotel, Ravellos is popular with both hotel residents
and guests who live in the surrounding area.

Our two AA Rosettes reflect the passion that our Kitchen Brigade puts into their food.
An outstanding à la carte menu that reflects the use of fresh, local produce.

We pride ourselves on the best Sunday lunch for miles, using only the best cuts of local meats.

For opening hours, please visit our website.

Llancarfan

The Fox & Hounds ◉
CF62 3AD
01446 781287
www.fandhllancarfan.co.uk
Open: All year

Chef: Jim Dobson
Food Style: Modern & Classic
British

Next to a stream in the heart of the pretty village of Llancarfan, The Fox & Hounds occupies a peaceful location next to the 15th-century St Cadoc's Church, but it's only 15 minutes from the M4. The restaurant offers pub classics.

Wrexham

Llanarmon Dyffryn Ceiriog

The Hand at Llanarmon ◉◉
Ceiriog Valley, LL20 7LD
01691 600666
www.thehandhotel.co.uk
Open: All year

All the usual suspects – beams, open fires, etc – are in this whitewashed country inn; the stuffed fox, however, is decidedly more unusual. The classic and modern pub food menu changes frequently, but old favourites, like slow-braised Welsh lamb shoulder, refuse to budge. Grilled Ceiriog trout is also one to try.

Chef: Grant Mulholland
Food Style: Classic British

Wrexham

NEW The Lemon Tree ◉
29 Rhosddu Road, LL11 2LP
01978 261211
www.thelemontree.org.uk
Closed: 25–30 December

At the heart of town lies The Lemon Tree, a renovated Victorian Gothic building that's made good use of its original features and woven them into its more modern designs. The restaurant is quite elegant but not at all formal, with separate tables, cosy booths and banquette seating. Menus feature French and Asian influenced food using locally sourced produce.

Chef: Ian Winqvist
Food Style: Modern British, Asian and French influences

NORTHERN IRELAND

County Antrim

Antrim

NEW Mill Race Restaurant ⚜
2 Islandreagh Drive, Dunadry, BT41 2HA
028 9443 4343
www.dunadry.com
Closed: 25 December

Previously the home of the 'High Kings of Ireland', then a paper mill and a linen mill, Dunadry Hotel is in a great location close to Antrim, set in mature gardens right by the Six Mile Water. The Mill Race Restaurant overlooks the river, making it the ideal venue for an appreciation of the team's Modern Irish cuisine.

Chef: Greg Ferguson
Food style: Modern Irish

Ballymena

NEW Fratelli Galgorm ⚜
136 Fenaghy Road, Galgorm, BT42 1EA
028 2588 1001
www.galgorm.com
Closed: Wednesday, Thursday

Chef: Michael Hartnett
Food style: Modern Italian

Fratelli Ristorante, Pizzeria & Bar is part of the Galgorm Manor hotel complex just outside Ballymena. The room is functionally elegant, with exposed beams, an open kitchen and a long bar, and it's no surprise to learn that the dining here has a particularly Italian direction. Expect traditional pizza and pasta dishes with a modern twist.

Galgorm ⚜⚜⚜ 🍷NOTABLE WINE LIST
See pages 666-667 and advertisement opposite

Bushmills

Bushmills Inn Hotel ⚜
9 Dunluce Road, BT57 8QG
028 2073 3000
www.bushmillsinn.com
Closed: 24 December

Located on the high street in this small distillery town, the Bushmills Inn Hotel dates back to the 17th century. With white-washed walls inside and out, exposed wood, an array of objet d'art and even a thatched roof inside the property, it's a fascinating place. The restaurant is very cosy and serves up some great modern Irish eating.

Chef: Gordon McGladdery
Food Style: Modern, Traditional

Ballymena

Galgorm

136 Fenaghy Road, Galgorm, BT42 1EA
028 2588 1001
www.galgorm.com
Open: All year (check daily opening times on website)

Chef: Israel Robb
Food Style: Modern Irish

Modern Irish cooking in historic house

Standing in 163 acres of private woodland and sweeping lawns beside the River Maine, this 19th-century mansion is just 30 minutes from Belfast. This luxurious resort offers a range of eating and drinking choices but if it's fine dining you're craving, look no further than The River Room.

A circular conservatory-style restaurant largely encased in glass, all window tables look out onto the river and a dramatic waterfall. Full tables with linen cloths and napkins are matched by professional skilled service.

There's no à la carte, just a modern Irish tasting menu, including a vegetarian version, and each dish showcases local artisan producers and seasonal ingredients sourced from carefully selected local suppliers as well as the resort's very own kitchen garden. After good sourdough and Irish butter, a meal could kick off with an attractively presented plate of subtly

cured loin of tuna with ponzu, sesame and cucumber. It might be followed by a rich and earthy dish of local venison, spelt, mushroom and Burgundy truffle or dry-aged beef, truffle, celeriac and tarragon.

When it comes to the main event, fish and meat dishes share the spotlight, whether it's a perfectly timed piece of halibut with spiced shellfish and sprout leaves or pink and tender Skeaghanore duck served with foie gras, walnut, fig and sherry vinegar.

To finish, a baked caramel tart with perfectly crisp and crunchy pastry is teamed with peanut, banana and miso ice cream. Mango parfait with yuzu, coconut and bergamot is another pleasing way to end a meal unless you tackle the Irish artisan cheeseboard, which is helpfully offered in different sizes with options of three, five, seven or nine cheeses.

A notable wine list offers plenty of interesting bottles and choices by the glass and there's also a wine flight on offer.

See advertisement on page 665

"...each dish showcases local artisan producers and seasonal ingredients sourced from carefully selected local suppliers..."

Newtownabbey

Sleepy Hollow
15 Kiln Road, BT36 4SU
028 9083 8672
www.sleepyhollowrestaurant.com
Closed: 25–29 December

It would take a jaded palate not to be thrilled by the hearty modern Irish cooking in this rustic restaurant. Locally-sourced artisan produce is at the heart of things, with meat and game supplied by neighbouring farms and estates, butchered in-house, and handled without fuss.

Chef: Paul Dalrymple,
Josh Crawford
Food Style: Modern Irish

Templepatrick

NEW The Rabbit Hotel & Retreat
882 Antrim Road, BT39 0AH
028 9443 2984
www.rabbithotel.com
Open: All year

With an open air spa and hot tubs as well as a quirky style all its own, the Rabbit Hotel and Retreat is just 20 minutes from Belfast. The restaurant is very popular, with its brick walls, rustic wooden floor and open kitchen, while the menu is brasserie style, offering plenty of steaks, seafood and international options.

Chef: Donna Hughes, Niall Sarhan
Food style: Modern Italian
American

Belfast

Belfast

NEW Berts Jazz Bar
The Merchant Hotel, 16 Skipper Street, BT1 2DZ
028 9026 2713
www.themerchanthotel.com/berts-jazz-bar
Open: All year

Ulster's only dedicated jazz bar, Bert's certainly comes up with the goods. If it's jazz you want, you'll get it seven days a week, in an intimate restaurant that was once part of the HQ of Ulster Bank. Dining is French bistro style with a regularly changing, seasonal menu.

Chef: Michael Weber
Food style: French

Deanes EIPIC ⊛⊛⊛
See page 670

Fitzwilliam Hotel Belfast ⊛
1–3 Victoria Street, BT2 7BQ
028 9044 2080
www.fitzwilliamhotelbelfast.com
Open: All year

Next door to the newly restored Grand Opera House, the swish Fitzwilliam Hotel makes a fine city-centre base. Decked out in warm, contemporary colours and local artwork, the elegant restaurant features both sharing tables for groups, and more intimate booths. As for the food, expect steak, venison, salmon, duck, hake, pizzas and paninis, with a pre-theatre menu for opera-goers.

Chef: Dean Butler
Food Style: Modern

See advertisement below

Belfast

Deanes EIPIC

28–40 Howard Street, BT1 6PF
028 9033 1134
www.deaneseipic.com
Closed: 1 January, 1 week Easter, 2 weeks July, 25-26 December

Chef: Alex Greene, Michael Deane
Food Style: Modern European

In the heart of central Belfast, refined and peaceful Deanes EIPIC is accessed via a bustling bistro and fish restaurant overseen by the same owner. A slate floor and palate of grey, black and white adds to the sleek, contemporary look with minimalist artwork but linen-clad tables and sumptuous seating adds a more formal elegance. Service from knowledgeable staff is also well-drilled, with dishes described in detail when served. Contemporary European cooking using local ingredients displays strong technique and flavours are well defined and clean.

Start with extremely fresh scallops seared to achieve the correct caramelisation and served with fresh peas and broad beans finished with leek oil, sea herbs and a light, foamy shellfish bisque. Continue with a tender, crisp-skinned honey and soy-glazed breast of lamb topped with black garlic crumb, the richness balanced with miso purée, charred hispi cabbage and pomme purée. End your meal with a crisp and buttery strawberry tartlet with smooth meadowsweet ice cream and a flurry of micro basil leaves.

The Merchant Hotel 🌸🌸 ⬧NOTABLE WINE LIST

16 Skipper Street, Cathedral Quarter, BT1 2DZ
028 9023 4888
www.themerchanthotel.com
Open: All year

If you want definitions of the 'wow' factor, The Merchant Hotel may be the place to provide one. The former headquarters of the Ulster Bank, it has huge ornate vaulted ceilings, and the opulent hall where the restaurant lives is basically fit for a palace. The team provide excellent and friendly service, and the kitchen's output is innovative and seasonal.

Chef: Kevin Sharkey
Food Style: Modern Classic

OX 🌸🌸🌸

1 Oxford Street, BT1 3LA
028 9031 4121
www.oxbelfast.com
Closed: 25 December, 1 week April, 2 weeks July

Chef: Stephen Toman
Food Style: Modern Irish

Right by the Beacon of Hope statue on the Lagan waterfront, OX is a pared-down space with board floors, teal colour scheme and a mezzanine level with extra tables. Friendly staff are ready with explanations of the tasting menus, which deal in top notch regional produce cooked with innovative flair. Although the menu descriptions are short and to the point, the resulting dishes are works of art and won't disappoint. So, for lunch you might choose 'mussels, bisque, turnip, buckwheat' followed by 'Mourne lamb, artichoke, bone marrow, burnt leek'. The attention to detail as in the hand-churned Cuinneog butter with the sourdough, inspires confidence.

Seahorse Restaurant 🌸

Hastings Grand Central Hotel, Bedford Street, BT2 7FF
028 9023 1066
www.grandcentralhotelbelfast.com
Open: All year

Chef: Damian Tumilty
Food Style: Modern

The hotel's main dining room is built to impress with its high ceilings, soaring walls of glass and sleek art deco-inspired lines. Caramel leather banquettes, plush fabrics and marble-topped tables add further to the allure, while the modern cooking scores a hit for its local ingredients handled with finesse, style and imagination.

What are the most common misconceptions you face?

That we ask for a specific (traditional) style; that service plays
a part in the award when assessing for AA Rosettes.

AA Inspector

County Down

Newtownards

Balloo House

1 Comber Road, Killinchy, BT23 6PA
028 9754 1210
www.balloohouse.com
Closed: 25 December

Balloo House is a charming country pub and restaurant just two miles from the shores of Strangford Lough. Downstairs is country pub style, with open fires, exposed brick, natural daylight and lots of objet d'art. Staff are friendly, helpful and very attentive. A more formal restaurant is open on a Saturday night upstairs.

Chef: Andrew Provan
Food Style: Modern Irish

See advertisement below

BALLOO
HOUSE

1 Comber Road
Killinchy
BT23 6PA

ballooinns.com

028 97541210

County Fermanagh

Lough Erne Resort 🌸🌸🌸
Belleek Road, BT93 7ED
028 6632 3230
www.lougherneresort.com
Open: All year

Chef: Noel McMeel
Food Style: Modern, Traditional

With spa treatments, exemplary golf facilities and views of the Fermanagh Lakelands, Lough Erne is one of the jewels of north west Ireland. Of the dining options, the pick is the Catalina restaurant, named after the seaplanes once stationed on the lough. Views over the 18th hole make for a beautiful setting to enjoy creative dishes such as a deep-flavoured roast artichoke and kale tart with sea buckthorn and caramelised hazelnuts. It might lead on to pan-fried chicken breast, roasted cauliflower, potatoes, truffle, sea lettuce and chicken jus. End with lemon verbena pannacotta, white chocolate and blackberry sorbet.

Manor House Country Hotel 🌸
Killadeas, BT94 1NY
028 6862 2200
www.manorhousecountryhotel.com
Open: All year

The colonel who rebuilt this old manor in the 1860s brought craftsmen over from Italy to spruce up the interior. The fine-dining action takes place in the Belleek Restaurant, housed in a conservatory extension that gets the very best of the view of the lough.

Chef: Ryan McMillan
Food Style: Irish, European

How do you keep yourself under the radar?

By adopting plenty of aliases, have 'reasons' to be in the area – perhaps looking at a property or undertaking consultancy work down the road.

AA Inspector

County Londonderry Derry

Londonderry Derry

Browns Bonds Hill ⊛
1 Bonds Hill, Waterside, BT47 6DW
028 7134 5180
www.brownsrestaurant.com
Closed: Sunday, Monday, 25–26 December

Situated on the edge of the city centre by Lough Foyle, Browns has built a local following for over 10 years. Get in the mood with some bubbly in the champagne lounge, then head for one of the white linen-swathed tables in the sleek, contemporary dining room. The kitchen turns out an appealing roll call of modern Irish ideas, with fish and seafood strong suits.

Chef: Ian Orr
Food Style: Modern Irish

Maghera

Ardtara Country House ⊛⊛
8 Gorteade Road, BT46 5SA
028 7964 4490
www.ardtara.com
Closed: 24–26 December

Once the home of a wealthy flax mill owner, Ardtara is a traditional country house located in rolling countryside. The main dining room has a mural of hunting scenes around the top of the wall, while the large skylight makes the room nice and bright. Modern Irish cooking uses locally sourced produce with some picked from the kitchen gardens.

Chef: Ian Orr
Food Style: Modern Irish

GIBRALTAR

Gibraltar

The Rock ⊛⊛
Europa Road, GX11 1AA
00 350 200 73000
www.rockhotelgibraltar.com
Open: All year

The Rock is something of an iconic hotel in Gibraltar, located on the lower part of the slope of the rock, to the front offering views of Gibraltar Port, Spain and across to Africa. The restaurant is split into two, with a white marbled interior inside, and a covered terrace outside.

Chef: Alfred Rodriguez
Food Style: Modern Mediterranean

Sunborn Yacht Hotel ⊛⊛
Ocean Village, GX11 1AA
00 350 2001 6000
www.sunbornyacht.com/gibraltar
Open: All year

Chef: Kilian Garcia
Food Style: Mediterranean

Permanently moored in Gibraltar's Ocean Village Marina, the Sunborn is a luxury liner that serves as an impressive floating hotel. There are two dining options – one fine dining, the other more relaxed. Tables offer good views over the marina and into Spain. Cuisine is a fusion of North African and Mediterranean.

❝

What excites you most in your work?

Being surprised by something or someone.
The simple pleasure of tasting something truly delicious.

AA Inspector

Index of Restaurants

This index shows restaurants in numerical name and alphabetical order, followed by their page number in the guide.